THE PROPERTIES OF
GLASS SURFACES

THE
PROPERTIES OF
GLASS SURFACES

L. HOLLAND *F.Inst.P.*

Head of Surface Physics Research Division
Edwards High Vacuum Ltd. Visiting Senior Lecturer
Brunel College of Advanced Technology

Wiley

1964

CHAPMAN and HALL

LONDON

First published in 1964 by
Chapman & Hall Ltd
11 New Fetter Lane, London E.C.4
© L. Holland 1964
Made and printed in Great Britain
by William Clowes and Sons, Limited
London and Beccles
Catalogue No. 4/748

*To Jenny, John and Peter
for waiting—sometimes quietly*

PREFACE

Glass is used for many purposes in both industry and research where a knowledge of the physical and chemical properties of its surface is essential. A number of texts are available on glass but these are chiefly concerned with its bulk properties, uses and working, *e.g.* Morey's *The Properties of Glass*, Shand's *Glass Engineering Handbook*, Volf's *Technical Glasses*, Twyman's *Prism and Lens Making* and Kitaigorodski's *Technologie Des Glases*. However, to obtain a coherent appreciation of the surface properties of glass, one must read a formidable number of papers appearing in journals of widely differing interests.

Glass has been a valuable material in the development of experimental science and yet many scientists do not stop to consider that the word 'glass' applied to a working material covers a vast range of different compositions and properties. Even if interest is limited to silicate glasses, as it is here, one must still consider an enormous number of industrial glasses. One commonly finds that physics texts which discuss phenomena occurring in and on solids use glass as a practical example of a solid material. Thus 'glass' is closely linked with both the development and teaching of science and this is probably the reason why it is conceived by some as a single substance endowed with ideal properties! Perhaps, therefore, a student can be excused if he believes that the properties manifested by a particular glass will necessarily be the same for all glasses. Thus physicists studying the properties of solid surfaces will often specify the solid used as 'glass' as if one was concerned with only a *structural state* of matter rather than a *real substance* – one of many thousands of possible oxide formulations.

It could reasonably be asked why the writer, who is not actively engaged in the glass field, undertook to produce the work presented here on the surface properties of glass? His explanation is that his interest in the subject was aroused whilst studying the influence of glass substrates on the properties of superimposed films and determining the sorption characteristics of glass in vacuum. The work presented here is an attempt to generalize and combine his experience with those of others. The subject matter has been chosen to be of maximum value to those concerned with the *use* of the glass surface. The effects of both the mode of preparation and the history of the glass surface on its properties have been considered.

Care has been taken not to separate artificially surface properties from related bulk characteristics and the latter have been discussed where considered essential. Thus electrical conduction in glass is usually ionic and although the conductivity of the surface layer may be enhanced by moisture adsorption the mode of conduction requires consideration of the bulk characteristics. Likewise the desorption and absorption of gases by glass depend upon the intimately linked processes of adsorption and diffusion in the solid. The mechanical strength of glass can be greatly influenced by its surface condition but detailed discussion of this topic was considered outside the scope both of the work and of the author. However, a review has been made of the literature on the nature of surface scratches and indentations because this is of importance in understanding how optically smooth surfaces are produced.

To determine the surface properties of a solid one must obviously have a clean surface, but after cleaning glass the chemical composition of the surface may differ considerably from that of the underlying material. Likewise, the composition of a glass surface is influenced by thermal treatment and atmospheric exposure. The chapter on producing 'clean' surfaces should, therefore, be read in conjunction with that on surface chemistry so that the influence of chemical attack on the nature of the so-called 'clean' surface can be better appreciated. Such an inter-relation, often between diverse topics, has constantly been made evident to the writer in the course of writing the book. Thus, to mention another example, the chapter on the optical working of glass will be better understood when the sections dealing with the frictional and chemical properties have also been read.

Glass is widely employed in contact with other solids where the nature and strength of the interfacial bonds are important. Thus glass is used:

(*i*) in contact with metals for insulating electrodes,

(*ii*) as a support for thin films, *e.g.* mirror coatings, optical interference filters and transparent electrically conducting coatings, and

(*iii*) combined with organic materials in laminated and reinforced plastics.

General information on these topics can already be found in Partridge's *Glass to Metal Seals*, the writer's *Vacuum Deposition of Thin Films* and in reference books on plastic materials. However, the nature of the adhesive forces and their dependence on the types of material in contact with glass are considered here.

It will be appreciated that the range of topics chosen cannot all be within the direct experience of a single person, although they are considered essential for completeness of the work. Thus, to safeguard the reader, the writer has invited criticism by pre-publishing reviews on the surface chemistry of glass and the wetting and frictional properties of glass in the journals *Glass Industry* and *Glass*; thanks are due to the editors of these journals for their co-operation. The writer is grateful to Dr M. E. Nordberg of the Research and Development Division of Corning Glass Works for reading and commenting on the chapter on surface chemistry and corrosion of glass. The book remains, however, the writer's work and responsibility.

Acknowledgements are made to the numerous journals from which figures have been reproduced and particularly to the *British Journal of Applied Physics* and *Vacuum* in which the writer had published much of the material on clean glass surfaces presented in Chapter 6.

The writer particularly thanks his wife D. E. Holland and secretary Mrs A. Colwell for their assistance in preparing the manuscript and Mr A. J. Duthie for help in preparing the drawings.

L. H.

CONTENTS

PLATES

Introduction to Theories on the Composition and Structure of Glass

This work is concerned with the properties of glass surfaces but first it is essential to define what is meant by 'glass' in terms of both molecular structure and chemical composition. The *glasslike* or *vitreous* state is believed to be that of a solid with the molecular disorder of a liquid frozen in its structure. Those fused inorganic compounds which we are generally accustomed to term 'glasses' are not the only substances which can exist in the vitreous state. Certain organic compounds, such as sugars, may also form glasses. However, the interest of this work is limited to glasses based on fused inorganic oxides of which silica† is usually the principal component.

The chemical composition and structure of glass will obviously influence its surface properties and both are considered here. However, space only permits a brief discussion of these topics and the reader will find more complete accounts in the references quoted in the text and in the works by Jones (1956), Kitaigorodski (1957), Mackenzie (1960), Morey (1954), Stanworth (1950), Stevels (1948) and Volf (1961).

The first real advance in the theory of the glass structure was due to Zachariasen who proposed the random network theory, *i.e.* a structure lacking symmetry and periodicity in contrast with the crystalline state. Many workers refused to completely accept this theory and continued to postulate an earlier idea that glass was comprised of micro-crystals joined by amorphous zones. Glasses exist which are opalescent or translucent due to the presence of either small crystalline zones in the glass (*e.g.* fluoride crystals precipitated in silicate glasses) or separate phases of different chemical

---

† The terms *fused silica* or *silica glass* should not be confused with the term *quartz* which is a crystalline modification of silica. The name *quartz glass* implies a *silica glass* which is made by fusing quartz but it is often used loosely for *fused silica*. The term *quartz* is sometimes used incorrectly for *fused silica* making it necessary to further define *quartz* as *crystalline quartz*!

1

composition (*e.g.* acid leachable glasses based on the sodium borosilicates); the latter type of glass can be considered an emulsion. However, real differences arose about the structure of optically clear glasses based on mixed oxides. Adherents of the Zachariasen theory held that the silica in such glasses formed polymer chains with branches and cross-linkages, whilst the remaining oxide components were statistically distributed in holes in the molecular structure. Some workers, principally Russian, either continued to believe in the crystallite theory or contended that glass was not a single solution but contained microscopic domains of different composition to the bulk, *i.e.* glass consisted of more than one phase with each phase being related to definite stoichiometric compositions. X-ray structural analysis tended to confirm the former hypothesis whereas certain glasses exhibited physical or chemical properties indicating either the presence of crystallites or chemical heterogeneities.

In recent years the problem has been partly resolved by the use of electron microscopy which has indicated a phase-like structure in certain optically transparent glasses. That some glasses show phase separation does not confirm the crystallite theory. Thus liquids which are immiscible will form emulsions when mixed but the random structure of a liquid is retained by each phase. On the Zachariasen theory glass resembles a super-cooled liquid.

Perhaps one of the faults in the development of a theory of glass structure has been the attempt to fit every possible oxide mixture into a single Zachariasen frame of reference. For example, certain sodium borosilicates form optically clear glasses and it has been contended that the boron cations with their threefold co-ordination substantially replace silicon cations with their fourfold co-ordination. On this basis one then only has a single type of structure. However, both silica and boric oxide taken separately are capable of forming glasses, and one would expect them to show phase separation in oxide mixtures because this would represent a lower energy level. In fact, droplets of separate phases can be detected in an optically clear glass by electron microscopy and such droplets grow with heat treatment. Such a stoichiometric ordering may be the first step before devitrification occurs in any mixed oxide glass.

The theory of the glass structure has been developed in recent years by Stevels, who has shown that many of the physical properties of glass depend on the ratio of the number of oxygen anions to cations in the polymer network because these determine the average length of the polymer chain.

We shall now consider some of the foregoing theories in greater detail.

RANDOM NETWORK THEORY

Glass appears to have many of the features of a normal solid, such as strength hardness, etc., but further examination shows that it has an extended melting range and X-ray structural analysis indicates a molecular structure akin to that of a liquid at low temperature.

Zachariasen (1932) proposed that the atomic or molecular arrangement in the glasslike state is an extended network which lacks symmetry and periodicity. He laid down a number of simple rules relating the way the oxygen anions and the cations must link together for an oxide to exist in the glassy state. Briefly, the glass forming cations (*e.g.* B^{3+}, Si^{4+}, P^{5+}) are surrounded by polyhedra of oxygen ions in the form of triangles or tetrahedra. The oxygen ions are of two kinds, viz. *bridging oxygen ions*, each of which link two polyhedra, and *non-bridging oxygen ions*, each of which belongs to only one polyhedron. Obviously such a system would produce a polymer structure with long chains cross-linked at intervals. In such a structure there are regions of unbalanced negative charge where the oxygen ions are non-bridging. Cations of low positive charge and large size (Na^+, K^+, Ca^{2+}) may exist in holes between the oxygen polyhedra where they compensate the excess negative charge of the non-bridging oxygen ions.

Thus in a typical sodium silicate glass the silicon cations are surrounded by oxygen tetrahedrons; some of the oxygen ions are bonded between two silicon ions and some to only one silicon ion. The sodium ions are held in various holes in the Si—O network and surrounded on the average by six oxygen atoms.

Some cations of large charge and small size may isomorphically substitute silicon ions in the structural network of the glass. Oxides forming the basis of a glass are known as *network formers* and those which are soluble in the network are termed *network modifiers*. Some oxides cannot easily be classified in this way and are termed *intermediates*. Warren (1933, 1937), using X-ray structural analysis, has probably done most to establish Zachariasen's views on the structure of glass. A two-dimensional representation of their proposed chain-like structure of glass is shown in the figure (*a*).

More recently Sun (1947) has advanced a theory that glasses are only formed from those oxides in which the bond strength between the oxygen and cation reaches a certain minimum value. Oxides with lower bond strength may act as network modifiers or intermediates but not network formers. The bond strength ($M \leftrightarrow O$) of all glass formers is greater than 80 Kcal per Avogadro-bond, that of intermediates 60 to 80, and that of the modifiers below 60; the transition is continuous and the classifications arbitary.

GLASS FORMING OXIDES

There is still incomplete information on the capacity of all the known oxides to form glasses. However, summarizing the data collected by Stanworth (1950) it has been established that glasses can be formed from B_2O_3, SiO_2, GeO_2, P_2O_5, As_2O_5, As_2O_3, Sb_2O_3 whilst the oxides V_2O_5, ZrO_2 and Bi_2O_3 are possible glass formers. Oxides of Ti, Zn, Pb, Al, Th and Be do not apparently form glasses but one or other of them may be included in glass to promote certain properties such as low electrical conductivity, chemical durability, high refractive index, etc. Oxides of many other elements may act as network modifiers but do not form glasses, *e.g.* those of Sc, La, Y, Sn, Ga, In, Mg, Li, Ba, Ca, Sr, Cd, Na, K, Rb, Hg and Cs. These oxide groups are based on the results of experimental studies and are divided roughly according to the rules laid down by Zachariasen and by Sun.

DEPENDENCE OF STRUCTURE ON TEMPERATURE

Stevels (1948) considers that the glass state arises during cooling of the liquid from increasing formation of bonds, which raises the viscosity and decreases the mobility of the individual particles. These changes correspond to an increasing degree of ordering in the liquid. Crystallization would necessitate a total regrouping of the particles, requiring a partial destruction of the bonds which have been formed and the construction of new ones. However, the mobility of the particles is too low and with further decrease of temperature the vitreous state is reached. Only by very slow cooling or annealing can the grouping of the atoms give rise in some cases to crystallization.

An example of the foregoing behaviour may be demonstrated with the element selenium. Thus, rapid cooling of liquid selenium produces an amorphous modification, whereas slow cooling or annealing at a given temperature may produce an ordered structure or partly developed crystallites in an amorphous material.

It is generally believed that in the vitreous state the energy required to break one of the chemical bonds holding the glass-forming network together is different for each individual link, but for the majority of bonds of the same type the energy values do not differ greatly from a certain average value; also that these energy values do not differ greatly from those in the corresponding crystalline solid; or, in other words, the free energy of the solid glass cannot appreciably exceed that of the crystalline phase because the tendency of glasses to crystallize is small. Glass systems are known where the free energy is less than that of the crystalline

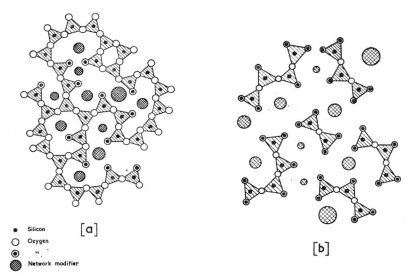

Silicon

Oxygen

"

Network modifier

[a]

[b]

TWO-DIMENSIONAL REPRESENTATION OF A GLASS NETWORK
(*After the model of Zachariasen and Warren*).

state, when judged from the vapour pressure. Apparently the formation of long chains by polymerization can lower the vapour pressure compared with that of the crystalline state. Thus the vapour pressure of phosphorus pentoxide, a typical glass former, decreases rapidly on heating above 250°c as a result of polymerization. Here we have an example of a substance which is more stable in the glass-like state than in the crystalline although the reverse is generally true.

The difference between the free energies of the crystalline and vitreous states is not the sole factor determining in which condition the substance will exist. Thus, the failure for molten glass to crystallize on solidification is due to the potential energy barrier being higher than the thermal energy (kT) of the atoms at normal temperature. However, if glass is held at an elevated temperature or cooled slowly, then devitrification can occur. Weyl (1958) makes the interesting observation that since attainment of the vitreous state depends upon the rate of cooling and this is limited by the quantity of substance being quenched, some easily crystallized substances can only be obtained as glasses in small quantities. Weyl gives the example of sodium metasilicate which can only be obtained in the vitreous state in small pieces.

Surface devitrification. When glasses are heated to induce crystallization the devitrification usually starts at the surface. Tabata (1927) noted that crystal growth could be promoted if the surface of a polished flint glass was scratched before heat treatment. Atoms on corners of scratches have greater free energy than those in the interior and thus require to gain less energy to move into the lower energy state of an ordered structure.

EFFECTS OF DENSITY OF BRIDGING OXYGEN IONS

Stevels (1946, 1948, 1960–61) has developed Zachariasen's theory giving attention to the effect of the number of bridging oxygen ions per polyhedra on the structure and properties of a given glass. He introduces for his theoretical analysis the following four quantities:

X = average number of non-bridging O^{2-}-ions per polyhedron,
Y = average number of bridging O^{2-}-ions per polyhedron,
Z = average total number of O^{2-}-ions per polyhedron,
R = ratio of total number of O^{2-}-ions to total number of network formers.

The following relations between these quantities can be solved by counting the ions:

$$Z = X + Y$$
$$R = X + \tfrac{1}{2}Y$$

Thus, for fused silica (SiO_2), $Z = 4$ and $R = 2$ so that $X = 0$ and $Y = 4$. Let us consider a glass made from $Na_2O \cdot SiO_2$, then $X = 2$

and $Y = 2$ and the average number of bridging oxygen ions have decreased by the inclusion of the soda. Generally the spatial coherence of the network is smaller the less the value of Y. This is shown by changes in physical properties. Thus, as Y decreases, there is an increase both in the coefficient of thermal expansion and in electrical conductivity and a decrease in viscosity. Stevels has shown that glasses with the same value of Y but with completely different chemical composition have almost the same physical properties (see, for example, Table 0.1).

Table 0.1

Effect of Y, the average number of bridging oxygen ions per polyhedron, on the 'melting temperature' (temperature at which the viscosity reaches the value 10^2 poise) and on the expansion coefficient a of various glasses
(After Stevels, 1960–61)

Composition	Y	'Melting temp.' $^\circ C$	$a \times 10^7$
$Na_2O.2SiO_2$	3	1250	146
P_2O_5	3	1300	140
$Na_2O.SiO_2$	2	1050	220
$Na_2O.P_2O_5$	2	1100	220

When Y is equal to 3 then some of the polyhedra can only be bound to their surroundings by two points of contact. Thus, raising Y above 3 will have a marked effect on the network stiffness and consequent physical properties. Stevels' theory is not always simple to apply. Thus he contends that certain cations (*e.g.* Co^{2+}, Ni^{2+}, Pb^{2+}, Ca^{2+} and Ba^{2+}) can exist *in* and *between* the oxygen polyhedra, their distribution depending on the glass composition and formation conditions. Where such glass *intermediates* are present it is not usually possible to determine R exactly.

A high metal oxide content does not always produce a low Y. When small amounts of metal oxide are fused with boron oxide the oxygen of the metal oxide does not become a non-bridging ion. The oxygen is taken into the network by the conversion of oxygen triangles into oxygen tetrahedra which consists entirely of bridging oxygen ions. Thus, initially raising the metal oxide content of pure borate glasses raises Y and strengthens the network. When the metal oxide concentration reaches a certain level the tetrahedra to triangle ratio attains a maximum value and non-bridging ions are formed so that Y decreases. These changes in Y are related to changes in the physical properties.

Invert glasses. When Y is smaller than 2 the tetrahedrons in a silicate glass have at most two points of contact. Spatial coherence by crosslinking is then not possible and the structure is formed by chains. In practice it is difficult to produce glasses in which $Y < 2$ because in a system such as $Na_2O . SiO_2$ devitrification occurs when the Na_2O content exceeds 50 mol %. However, if metal ions of different size and charge are present, crystallization is hampered and low values of Y can be obtained. The consequent glasses have been termed *invert* and a two-dimensional representation is shown in the figure (*b*). They have been studied in detail by Trap and Stevels (1959).

CRYSTALLITES AND PHASE SEPARATION IN GLASS

The principal theories of the composition and structure of glass have been briefly described at the beginning of this review. Having dealt above with the random network theory we shall now consider the evidence for domains of varying composition within certain optically clear glasses and microscopic crystallites in glasses generally.

Phase separation. Glasses consisting of several different substances (such as oxide glasses) cannot generally be designated by chemical formulae, *i.e.* in contrast to crystalline material in which the composition of a unit cell defines the chemical composition. However, it has been by no means certain that phase separation does not occur on a microscopic scale, because of the inability of certain oxides to readily form compounds or solutions with silica.

Two-phase separation in *certain* oxide systems has been known for some time, because the effects of phase separation have been easily observed optically. Thus, immiscible oxide systems form droplets of one phase immersed in another and the finely divided phase scatters incident light, producing an opalescent body. An example of a two-phase separation is found in the $CaO—SiO_2$ system when the CaO content is less than 28%. The melt then consists of two immiscible liquids at temperatures below 1700°c. On the other hand, the borate or silicate glasses with the oxides of the monovalent ions of lithium, sodium or potassium do not appear to be immiscible. This has been explained as follows: each silicon atom in the random silica network can bond more easily to four oxygen atoms if additional oxygen atoms are provided by an added oxide.

The bonds between Na—O, Li—O or K—O are weak compared to that between Ca—O. Thus, in the competition between the silicon and calcium cation for the extra oxygen, the calcium atom is able to retain its oxygen. At high concentrations of calcium oxide each calcium ion can be surrounded by the proper number of oxygen ions and a single solution is formed.

Phase separation may exist in certain glasses but not be detectable optically by light scattering or by optical microscopy because the dimensions of the droplets of the separated phase are negligible compared with the wavelength of light. It is now known from electron microscopy studies that there are several glass compositions which exhibit optical clarity, but which form domains of differing composition. The domains in an opalescent glass are about 0·1 to 0·5 μ in size, whereas in certain optically clear glasses domains have been detected down to the limits of electron microscopy replica techniques, *i.e.* about 30 Å.

Flint glass with a high lead oxide content, such as is used for optical purposes, is an example of a two-phase system observable only by electron microscopy. Vogel (1959) found domains suspended in the structure of a 60 mol % PbO 40 mol % SiO_2 glass, as shown in Plate 1, which he considered were rich in silica. Vogel believes that the silica in dense lead oxide glasses forms separate droplets which 'swim' in lead oxide when the glass begins to melt. He contends that it is the separate existence of the silica in this temperature region which is responsible for the viscosity and surface tension of the melt being almost independent of the silica content. Berger (1932) early formed the opinion that dense lead and barium oxide glasses had a colloidal structure. According to Vogel, when the foregoing glasses are molten they have a reddish translucence, becoming optically transparent near the transformation point.

There has been much conjecture about the structure of glasses based on the sodium borosilicates. Certain compositions in this system are opalescent because of phase separation whereas others are optically clear but may become opalescent when heat treated. Volf (1961) has discussed these glasses extensively. Skatulla *et al.* (1958) have found, as shown in Plate 2, that phase separation occurs even in an optically clear glass and that droplet separation is enhanced by heat treatment.

Sastry and Hummel (1959) have investigated glasses based on the system Li_2O—B_2O_3—SiO_2. Melts of such oxides, depending on their composition, cool to form opalescent or transparent bodies.

Clear glasses of certain compositions can be made opalescent by heat treatment. Sastry and Hummel found that the opalescent glasses contained spherical droplets of one phase in a matrix. Some of the clear glasses also showed phase separation with irregular channels and spheres of 100 Å or less in size. Electron diffraction studies by reflection from the surface indicated that the phases were not crystalline.

Evaporated thin film replicas of platinum and carbon taken from fracture surfaces of soda-lime glass broken *in vacuo* show by electron microscopy that the glass has a granular or micellar surface structure (Navez and Sella, 1960*a*). The domains in normal commercial plate glass are about 100 Å in size and in *float* glass about 50 Å. Electron micrographs prepared by direct electron transmission through thin foils taken from blown glass bubbles show a granular structure with domains ranging from 100 to 200 Å in size (Navez and Sella, 1960*b*). The domains are believed to be silica rich zones. Zarzycki and Mezard (1962) have confirmed the micellar structure of soda-lime glass by drawing glass fibres in argon within an electron microscope before examination. Exposure of a fibre to the atmosphere weakened the electron microscope image of the micellar structure as the fibre surface became hydrated. Evidence was also obtained that domains or 'micelles' existed in fused silica which became crystallization nuclei of cristobalite after prolonged heat treatment.

Crystallite theory. Morey (1954) has thoroughly reviewed the early literature advancing the crystallite theory and showed that the extensive crystalline order claimed by several workers has not been confirmed by X-ray analysis. However, many Russian workers do not agree with the view that glass is a completely disordered solid and interesting papers on this topic are given in two conference reports published by the Academy of Sciences, U.S.S.R. (1953, 1959). Details of most of the Russian work referred to in this section will be found in these conference reports.

Lebedev studied certain physical properties of glass, notably refractive index changes which occurred during heat treatment, and in 1921 expressed the view that glass contained ordered zones of crystallites. Lebedev has recently contended that there are crystallites in the structure of glass of about 10 Å in size, *i.e.* for a cubic crystallite, 3–4 atoms in a cube edge. The crystallites are probably of irregular form and contain distortions in their lattice. Thus, in Lebedev's opinion, glass may contain both amorphous and ordered zones which are linked by an intermediate formation and he proposed the term 'amorphous-crystallite' to designate the structure.

When one is considering crystalline structure on such a minute scale it is difficult to see where the concept of an irregular network and short range order actually begin to differ. Certainly those who hold to one or other theory are unable to assign definite limits for either the extent of the order or disorder because of the difficulties in making structural analysis in zones as small as 10 Å. Further, the dimensions of the crystallites could only refer to their breadth as the silica may form polymer-like chains.

Porai-Koshits has shown how the earlier views of the crystallite school have undergone marked change. Thus, at one time, they had an exaggerated estimate of the part of the glass volume occupied by crystallites which were considered regions of perfect order in a disordered matrix. For example, Randal *et al.* (1931) thought that in vitreous silica there was some 80% of cristobalite. However, the modern view of this school is of small regions of maximum order in the general spatial network, the ordered zones not being sharply defined at their boundaries. Porai-Koshits states that X-ray structural analysis of simple glasses has conclusively demonstrated the absence of large regions of heterogeneity of any kind – microcrystals, two-dimensional crystalline formations, 'phases', etc. At the same time *X-ray structural analysis is incapable at present of proving or disproving the existence of crystallites of* 15–20 Å *or smaller the presence of which is implied by certain physical properties of glass.*

Porai-Koshits (1959) has developed these views in a later article implying the presence of ordered zones within the foregoing dimensions. The presence of such ordered domains could be the outcome of a random distribution of bridging and non-bridging oxygen ions. Thus in a glass with $Y = 3$ there will be tetrahedra with four and two bridging ions as well as with three since Y is an average value. It would appear that we have the paradox that small scale ordering can arise from a random distribution. This is what must occur in a liquid except that the localized zones of high order are constantly forming and breaking down, whereas in glass they are spatially fixed at normal temperature. However, glass must be considered as a special case of a *super*-cooled liquid because, unlike, for example, water cooled below its freezing point, it lacks sufficient energy to break existing bonds and spontaneously crystallize. Douglas (1961) in reviewing the Russian conference reports mentioned above discusses the crystallite theory and develops the counter-view that the glass structure has a liquid-like configuration which is invariant with temperature, invariant meaning that the function describing the configuration would not change with temperature apart from a change of the scale of length due to thermal expansion.

Trap and Stevels (1960) believe that *invert* glasses containing titanium dioxide have crystallites of titania in their structure.

THE GLASS SURFACE

If the structure of glass lacked symmetry and periodicity in contrast with the crystalline state then a new surface created by fracture would possess in its outer layer a statistical distribution of the constituent atoms. Thus, any chemical or physical process (*e.g.* corrosion, gas sorption) occurring at the surface at specific atomic sites would proceed almost uniformly over the surface. In fact it is now known that certain glasses may contain microscopic domains varying in size from 0·01 to 0·1 μ. Such domains undoubtedly represent regions of differing chemical composition. Further, structural ordering may occur over a few unit cells, producing what have been termed crystallites. Under these conditions many processes occurring at a freshly created glass surface may be concentrated in certain zones. For example, if water was adsorbed to such a surface maximum adsorption would occur in the domains containing the most hygroscopic oxides and monolayer adsorption would not extend to any regions which were hydrophobic. When such a surface was wetted the resultant contact angle would be an average value for the surface regions of different composition. Silicate glasses containing large quantities of lead oxide can under certain conditions manifest a large contact angle for water. These lead oxide glasses appear to be formed of silica rich domains in a lead oxide matrix.

In the above discussion it is assumed that variation in composition within a glass does not arise from poor mixing of the melt, whereas in practice this may occur. Great trouble is taken with optical glasses to ensure thorough mixing but certain glasses, *e.g.* soda-lime, may show marked variation in soda content within and at the surfaces of the same body. Further, in the production of soda-lime glass it is possible for grains of sand to escape the melting reaction as shown by Leger *et al.* (1962)

The composition of the surface layers may differ from that of the bulk material, depending on the thermal and chemical treatment to which the glass has been submitted. For example, heat treatment may cause alkali components to diffuse to the surface or evaporate rapidly, lowering their surface concentration; chemical corrosion may selectively remove material from the surface or deposit reaction products. There is evidence, however, that a modified surface layer remains in a glasslike state. Thus, Antal and Weber (1953) found by electron diffraction that the annealed surface of soda-lime glass consisted of silicon and oxygen atoms in a random network, as in fused silica, with the alkali atoms absent from the surface for a depth equal to that examined (< 10 Å). The porous films which form on weathered glass are non-crystalline silica.

Physical studies of glass surfaces are often made on chemically cleaned surfaces. Acid attack of glass will leach out the basic oxides, leaving behind a silica enriched layer so that glasses of markedly varying composition tend to have the same surface composition after acid cleaning.

References

Academy of Sciences U.S.S.R., 1953, 1959, *The Structure of Glass*.
Vol. 1: Proceedings of a Conference on the Structure of Glass, Leningrad, November 1953.
Vol. 2: Proceedings of the Third All-union Conference on the Glassy State, Leningrad, November 1959.
English translation published by Consultants Bureau, New York, and Chapman Hall, Ltd., London.
Antal, J. J., and Weber, A. H., 1953, *Phys. Rev.*, **89**, 900.
Berger, A., 1932, *Kolloid-Beih.*, **36**, 1.
Douglas, R. W., 1961, *Phys. Chem. Glasses*, **2**, 132.
Jones, G. O., 1956, *Glass*, Methuen and Co. Ltd., London.
Kitaigorodski, I. I., Editor, 1957, *Technologie Des Glases* (translated from Russian), VEB Verlag Technik, Berlin.
Leger, L., Bray, J., and Plumat, E., 1962, *Advances in Glass Technology*, p. 175, Plenum Press Inc., New York.
Mackenzie, J. D., 1960, *Modern Aspects of the Vitreous State*, Vol. 1, Butterworths, London.
Morey, G. W., 1954, *The Properties of Glass*, Rheinhold Publishing Co., New York.
Navez, M., and Sella, C., 1960a, *C.R.S. Acad. Sci.*, **250**, 4325.
Navez, M., and Sella, C., 1960b. *C.R.S. Acad. Sci.*, **251**, 529.
Porai-Koshits, E. A., 1959, *Glastechn. Ber.*, **32**, 450.
Randal, J. T., Rooksby, H. P., and Cooper, B. S., 1931, *J. Soc. Glass Technol.*, **15**, 54.
Sastry, B. S. R., and Hummel, F. A., 1959, *J. Amer. ceram. Soc.*, **42**, 81.
Skatulla, W., Vogel, W., and Wessel, H., 1958, *Silikattechnik*, **9**, 51; 323.
Stanworth, J. E., 1950, *Physical Properties of Glass*, Clarendon Press, Oxford.

Stevels, J. M., 1946, *Philips tech. Rev.*, **8**, 231.

Stevels, J. M., 1948, *Progress in the Theory of the Physical Properties of Glass*, Elsevier Publishing Co., London.

Stevels, J. M., 1960–61, *Philips tech. Rev.*, **22**, 300.

Sun, K.-H., 1947, *J. Amer. ceram. Soc.*, **30**, 277.

Tabata, K., 1927, *J. Amer. ceram. Soc.*, **10**, 6.

Trap, H. J. L., and Stevels, J. M., 1959, 5th Inter. Conf. on Glass, *Glastechn. Ber.*, **32K**, VI, 31.

Trap, H. J. L., and Stevels, J. M., 1960, *Phys. Chem. Glasses*, **1**, 107.

Vogel, W., 1959, *Silikattechnik*, **10**, 241.

Volf, M. B., 1961, *Technical Glasses*, Sir Isaac Pitman and Sons Ltd., London.

Warren, B. E., 1933, *Z. Krist.*, **86**, 349.

Warren, B. E., 1937, *J. appl. Phys.*, **8**, 645.

Weyl, W. A., 1958, 'A New Approach to the Chemistry of the Solid State and its Application to Problems in the Field of Silicate Industries', Report issued by College of Mineral Industries, Pennsylvania; also published in *Silicates Industriels* (1958).

Zachariasen, W. H., 1932, *J. Amer. chem. Soc.*, **54**, 3841.

Zarzycki, J., and Mezard, R., 1962, *Phys. Chem. Glasses*, **3**, 163.

CHAPTER 1

The Nature of Optically Worked Surfaces

It would be impracticable to start a work on the properties of glass surfaces without first considering the influence of the method of shaping or working a glass object on the composition and structure of the surface layers. When glass has been subjected to heat treatment sufficient to melt the bulk or outer layers then the surface can be expected to be as smooth as that of a liquid, *i.e.* before corrosive agents in the atmosphere begin rapidly to attack the surface-developing fissures and porous material. The composition of the surface layer on a flame polished or cast object will depend on the extent to which the more volatile elements have evaporated and been replaced by diffusion from the bulk material. One of the most common methods of forming surfaces on glass is by optical working, but it is not so easy in this case to formulate generalizations about either the surface finish or the composition of the outer layers. Much of the subject matter of this book is related to the properties of optically worked surfaces and this chapter is devoted to their nature and mode of production. However incomplete our knowledge in this field the discussion here may at least have the value of indicating useful fields of work, and showing how, apart from pioneer work by Beilby, French and Preston in this country some thirty to fifty years ago, modern work on the polishing of glass has been done mainly by Russian and German workers (that is, unless industrial research work exists which has never been published†).

Both the nature and the topography of surfaces on optically worked glass depend on the mechanism of the polishing process. However, the mode by which ground glass surfaces are smoothed by polishing with finely divided metal oxides on cloth and pitch polishers has been the subject of conjecture for at least three hundred years and modern research work has not yet produced a

---

† The British Scientific Instrument Research Association have carried out work in glass polishing and their reports may be available to some readers.

qualitative and generally accepted theory of the process. Complex processes that have successfully evolved as arts have invariably been the last to receive the attention of applied science and nowhere is this more true than in the ancient craft of glass working which has brought into being a large optical and plate glass industry.

A concise review of both the technical and scientific aspects of polishing glass has been made by Oesterly (1957) and Cornish (1961). The practical aspects of the working of optical glass has been described by Twyman (1952) and the working of plate glass by Scholes (1952).

1. HISTORICAL

After glass has been roughly brought to the required shape by grinding the irregular surface is smoothed and Hooke (1665) in his *Micrographia* reasoned that a polished glass surface was made up of an infinite number of small broken surfaces '. . . since Putte or even the most curious powder that can be made use of to polish such a body must consist of little hard rough particles and each must cut its way and consequently leave some kind of gutter or furrows behind it. . . .' Newton (1695) in his *Opticks* had a similar view and believed that the surface finish was limited by the size of the polishing particles. He said, 'The smaller the particles of the substances are, the smaller will be the scratches by which they continually fret and wear away the glass until it be polished, but be they never so small, they can never wear away the glass no otherwise than by grating and scratching it and breaking the protuberances'. Rayleigh (1892) also thought that polishing consisted of wearing down the ground surface to the level of the deepest pits.

In contradiction to these Beilby (1903, 1921) believed that the surface of an article flowed during polishing so that crevices in the surface were filled with the smeared material. Thus he contended that an amorphous layer of silica was formed on quartz during polishing. Preston (1930) found that chemical reactions occurred between the polishing agent and the finely divided glass removed during polishing and this gave rise to the theory that chemical reactions at the glass surface were part of the polishing process. Grebenshchikov (1931) advanced the theory that the water used on the lap could react with the glass and form silica gel so that the glass was easily removed by the polisher where it projected above the common level.

There are many different theories of how the polishing of glass occurs but they can be roughly classified as follows:

(*i*) *Wear theory* It is held that asperities on the ground glass surface are worn down by the polishing agent, *i.e.* mechanically removed from the surface. Thus in its simplest conception polishing is viewed as an extension of the grinding process.

(*ii*) *Flow theory* It is claimed that the asperities plastically flow into surface cavities under the load of the polishing particles or melt due to frictional heat developed by the polishing.

(*iii*) *Chemical theory* It is considered that the glass surface chemically reacts with the polishing medium in such a way as to aid the removal or smoothing of the asperities.

The latter two theories have resulted in much attention being given to the mechanical properties of glass, such as plastic flow, and the surface chemistry of glass, *e.g.* the influence of the pH value of the polishing fluid on surface attack. An appreciation of the optical working problem can only be obtained from a knowledge of these subjects and the reader should study the Appendix to this chapter and Chapter 3 where they are fully discussed. None of the above theories of polishing can explain the polishing mechanism under all of the wide variety of conditions which can be chosen by an operator. After studying the relevant literature the writer is convinced that one or other of the proposed mechanisms may be dominant depending on the polishing conditions, and that during optical working the conditions may change so that different effects occur at different times. Rarely are the conditions thoroughly defined in reports of polishing studies and often the kind of glass used is not specified! Also, only recently has sufficient information become available on the physical and chemical properties of glass which would begin to permit the development of a unified theory of polishing. Observation of the polished surface by electron microscopy has greatly aided the study of fine surface detail and helped to elucidate polishing mechanisms.

2. THE GRINDING PROCESS

Surface splintering. Before discussing in detail the various theories of the polishing of glass it is necessary to be clear on the way glass is removed when it is initially shaped by grinding with, say, loose

2

abrasive grains on discs of iron or brass. The grinding medium used in the optical industry is usually silicon carbide or electro-corundum.† Both substances have a relative hardness between 9–10 on the Mohs scale, *i.e.* comparable to that of diamond, whilst glass has a scratch hardness of 4·5–6·5 and quartz a value of 7. Rayleigh (1892) observed that grinding consisted of breaking out small fragments of glass. French (1917) drew attention to the fact that abrasives such as *Carborundum* or corundum did not *cut* glass, but set up shearing strains in glass so that it was splintered away; diamond powder in a metal bonded tool should remove glass in a similar way. A simplified representation of the process is shown in Fig. 1.1. The grinding tool presses down on the abrasive grains so

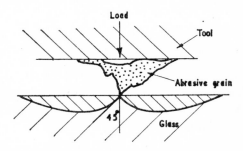

FIG. 1.1 SURFACE FRACTURING OF GLASS DURING GRINDING (*After French*, 1917).

that the load is communicated to the glass over a limited number of centres. Also, when the tool and glass are in relative motion the abrasive grains repeatedly turn over and become wedged against the sides of the asperities which are broken away. Thus the abrasive action is not lost by the grain losing a cutting edge, but to it changing shape so that limited regions of high loading are not produced. Water circulation is used to distribute the particles evenly and to prevent undue rise in surface temperature. Kroener (1953) contends that if the glass temperature rises the glass plastically deforms under the abrasive particles and cannot be easily removed by splintering. If too much water is present air may be excluded from between the tool and the glass so that the load reaches atmospheric

---

† Electro-corundum contains 60–70% aluminium oxide in addition to iron, silicon and titanium oxides. Material with an Al_2O_3-content of 99% is referred to as corundum. Technical silicon carbide SiC (Carborundum) has a purity of about 98%.

pressure. French found that the weight of glass removed during grinding using emery, Carborundum or sand was directly proportional to the weight on the tool or the relative speed between the tool and the glass.

Willott (1950) found that 'grinding hardness' determined in terms of volume change under specified grinding conditions did not give values agreeing with hardness ratings obtained from indentation tests.

Grinding flaws. Preston (1921) has studied the grinding of glass and found that the ground surface is not merely one of hills and hollows

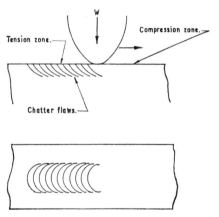

FIG. 1.2 CHATTER FLAWS PRODUCED IN THE WAKE OF A HARD ABRADING OBJECT, AS OBSERVED BY PRESTON.

but possesses flaws and fissures penetrating into the glass. He contended that the surface became covered with 'chatter' flaws in the tracks of the grinding particles in a similar way to the marring produced by a hard metal point scratching the surface. The flaws may arise from the glass breaking under the combined effect of the load on the grinding particles and the additional tensile stress in the surface due to their frictional pull. The flaws assume the form shown in Fig. 1.2.

When a polished surface is reground the tracks of the grinding particles must cross one another several times before the flaws are sufficiently connected for material to be removed from the surface. A ground or 'grey' surface is always flawed and material is removed immediately grinding is recommenced. The difference between a grey and polished surface makes it appear as if the polished surface resists grinding, *i.e.* is covered by a tough skin. The outer layer on a polished glass may differ from the bulk material but the slowness for grinding to take effect is due to the time required for the surface to become covered by a network of fissures such as can be seen in Plate 3.

Surface stress. Twyman (1905) noted that the surface of ground glass is under a compressive stress. Preston studied this effect and attributed it to particles of glass, etc., entering the fissures in the surface and forcing the glass apart. Such an effect produces a tension in the bulk glass just below the worked layer and a compensating compression in the unworked layer. A glass plate which has

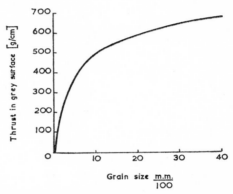

FIG. 1.3   DEPENDENCE OF THRUST OF GREY SURFACE ON GRAIN SIZE OF THE ABRASIVE (*After Dalladay*, 1921–22).

been ground on one surface tends to bow but when both faces are ground the bowing disappears. However, the glass will now be internally under a uniform tensile stress, due to the balanced compression stresses in the surfaces.

Dalladay (1921) studied the stresses produced in a hard crown glass when one face was ground with loose abrasive. He noted that a glass strip of some 3 mm thickness ground on one face with Carborundum appeared to be stressed as if it were being subjected to bending combined with extension, *i.e.* the neutral axis was straight and nearer the polished than the grey surface; that part of the strip adjacent to the grey surface was in tension and the other in compression. Dalladay measured the compression stress by determining the bending moment required to balance the thrust in the grey layer. He found that the thrust increased with the size of the abrasive grain as shown in Fig. 1.3. There was apparently no discontinuity in the results when the grain size was decreased by going from Carborundum to corundum and finally to emery. May (1949) used grinding particles of the following sizes 5, 12, 30, 65, 150, 350 and 600 microns and found that the compressive stress rose sharply when the particle size was increased to 65 μ, but above 350 μ the stress did not increase; the effect was reversible.

When a galvanometer mirror of 25 mm diameter and a radius of curvature of 1 m was reduced by Dalladay to a thickness of 0·5 mm at the centre by grinding to a fine grey the radius fell to 85 cm. Polishing the back of the mirror restored the mirror to its original curvature.

Levengood (1957) has studied the effect of grinding one side of glass fibres and found that they were bowed, with the ground surface convex. Glass fibres etched on one side did not bow to a measurable degree and this showed that the bowing did not arise from the grinding removing an existing stressed layer.

Milling flaws. It is shown in a later section that grinding marks reappear when a polished surface is etched with acids, but Jones (1946) observed that diamond milling marks reappeared even on fine ground surfaces after acid etching. These milling flaws could not be detected in the fine ground surface before etching when the surface was examined with a polarizing microscope ($\times 560$). A layer of about 5×10^{-4} in. was removed by the acid when exposing the flaws which either had been bridged over by grinding or were vertical to the surface and in optical contact. When two polished glass surfaces were placed in contact and ground the junction disappeared and only became visible as a fine line after etching.

Jones milled several glass slabs, then ground their surfaces to form a taper and polished them. When the specimens were etched it was possible to determine the point at which traces of milling marks were just visible and from a knowledge of the amount of glass removed from the wedge the depth of a milling flaw could be assessed – this was 0·005 in. The different thicknesses of the worked and etched layers in relation to the flaw depth are shown in Fig. 1.4. Glass which was milled with a Norton metal bonded diamond wheel containing 400-grit diamond had a measurable specular reflection and a minimum amount of polishing was necessary to prevent any traces of milling marks reappearing on etching. With a

200-grit wheel some 0·002 in. had to be polished off to remove all milling traces on etching.

When glass specimens were heated to 575°c, *i.e.* within 50°c of the softening point, the number of flaws exposed by etching were reduced because the cracks were in contact and welded together. Some cracks would be kept open by particles of glass wedged in the fracture.

A milled surface which had been polished to remove a layer 0·002 in. thick was more smooth when etched than the same surface after grinding and polishing to remove 0·0012 in. and 0·0008 in.

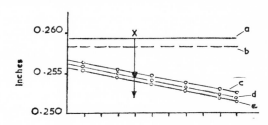

Fig. 1.4   Use of wedge to determine depth of milling flaws, (*a*) original surface, (*b*) milled, (*c*) ground, (*d*) polished and (*e*) etched. *X* is the point where a milling mark was detected on etching (*After Jones*, 1946).

respectively. Jones believed the polishing in the second case was insufficient to remove the effects of grinding.

3. PRACTICAL ASPECTS OF GLASS POLISHING

After grinding, the glass surface is polished, using a fine grain powder on a metal tool with a soft surface material, *e.g.* pitch, cloth, felt and paper. The latter have at least one property in common of tending to entrain the polishing particles in their working surfaces.

Felt is used in the continuous polishing of plate glass but where precision of surface contour is required pitch polishers are generally used. A layer of pitch about ⅜ in. thick is applied to a metal tool with the pitch divided by channels into squares of equal area. The desired profile is obtained on the polisher by pressing it when warm against a master surface using a glycerol–water lubricant to prevent sticking. The polishing medium is applied as a paste mixed with water. Water is used as a lubricant and after each application is allowed to dry by the frictional heat developed during polishing before more paste is applied. The channels in the pitch permit local concentrations of the polishing medium to be removed and thus ensure a uniform distribution of the particles over the lap surface. The polishing operation may be carried out by hand with a fixed or rotating tool. Polishing machines are arranged so that the path of the polisher over the glass can be adjusted to obtain a given surface profile. Also the load on the polishing tool and relative speed between glass and polisher can be controlled.

Typical polishing materials are rouge,† cerium oxide, zirconium oxide and putty powder, but other oxides, such as those of manganese and titanium also act as polishing agents. Twyman has given the size of the grains used in grinding and polishing as follows:

Roughing	200–400 μ
Trueing	50–100 μ
Polishing	6–12 μ

The grain size must not unduly vary in a given sample otherwise the surface being polished will be covered with scratches and sleeks. The hardness of the grains also seems to be important. Thus the polishing powders are heat treated before use and this can affect the crystalline condition and particle size of the powder. Kroener and Werner (1956) found that the optimum temperature for rouge heat treated in the range 750°–900°c was 850°c. Extra fine rouge has a grain size of 2–3 μ. Ray (1949) found that spent rouge had particles with more rounded corners than fresh rouge and their size had been reduced to about a $\frac{1}{4}$ μ.

4. POLISHING AND SURFACE WEAR

Work of Rayleigh. As is shown in the next chapter a ground surface need only be smoothed to a certain degree for it to specularly reflect incident light. Thus a surface which negligibly scatters light need not be smooth on an atomic scale. With this in mind Rayleigh (1892) believed that polishing consisted of wearing down surface asperities to the depth of the grinding pits. He quoted Herschel as saying that . . . 'a surface artificially polished must bear somewhat of the same kind of relation to the surface of a liquid, or a crystal,

---

† Rouge is mainly α-Fe_2O_3 formed by calcination of ferrous sulphate, carbonate or hydroxide in air. When heated above 600°c the rouge particles become resistant to acid attack and the tint and particle size depend on the calcination temperature.

that a ploughed field does to the most delicately polished mirror, the work of human hands'. Rayleigh found that in polishing a ground surface the level was reduced from six to ten wavelengths. He reasoned that the polishing action could not be the same as that of grinding because one used a softer tool, *i.e.* pitch or cloth instead of iron, which yields during the polishing. He believed that the asperities were ground away almost molecularly.

THOMSON PLANING THEORY

Thomson (1922) contended that surface flow did not occur during polishing and that surface prominences were removed by a self regulated planing action of the polishing medium and tool. He

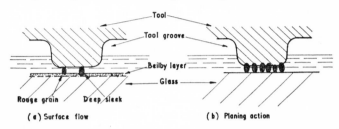

FIG. 1.5   EARLY CONCEPTIONS OF THE POLISHING ACTION BASED ON THE THEORIES OF (*a*) FRENCH AND (*b*) THOMSON.

stated that the particles which do the cutting in polishing are all *automatically adjusted* to cut the *same depth* during any stroke. This is possible because 'the yielding nature of the pitch surface not only ensures this, but makes it a necessary consequence, for any particle of rouge riding higher than another is at once depressed to the proper level by sinking into the pitch surface'. Thus the innumerable cutting edges of all the particles reach a common level, as shown in Fig. 1.5, and their continuously changing paths over the glass result in the production of an optically smooth surface.

Thomson produced a fair polish on a glass specimen, using a soft metal tool charged with fine Carborundum. It is of interest to note here that a glass surface polished with dry Carborundum on felt may have a different refractive index to the bulk and this can be accounted for by localized melting, as shown in the next chapter. Thomson further observed that the scratches or *sleeks* produced on glass during polishing had smooth sides and not fractured faces as occurred in grinding. He did not appreciate that smooth scratch marks were evidence of plastic flow during cutting as is discussed on p. 35. Scratch marks of sufficient size to be easily visible with a low power microscope would normally be of the fracture type. Preston (1921–22) reported that the kind of 'chatter' tracks produced during polishing showed that the polishing particles had slid over the surface and not rolled.

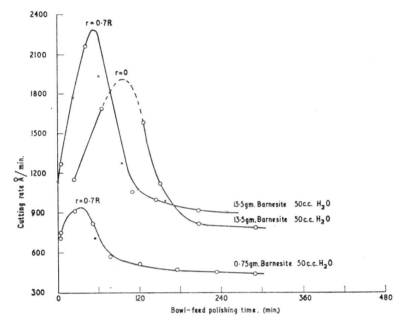

FIG. 1.6   CUTTING RATE CURVES OF A PITCH LAP (*After Koehler*, 1955). INTERFEROMETRIC MEASUREMENTS WERE MADE OF THE CHANGING DEPTH OF A SURFACE PIT AT RADIAL DISTANCES r ON A 2-IN. DIAMETER GLASS DISC.

Koehler (1953) has studied the polishing of glass using multiple beam interferometry for determining surface topography as decribed in Chapter 2. Koehler's work is of great value in assessing the optical smoothness of a polished surface but it cannot be considered sufficiently complete to confirm the Thomson planing theory as the only basis of polishing as he suggests. The rate of removing glass during polishing with *Barnesite*† was measured by determining the change in depth of a surface pit and it was found

---

† Trade name of Lindsay Chemical Co. (U.S.A.) for a mixture of cerium oxide and other rare earth oxides.

that the cutting rate initially rose to a maximum and then fell to almost a constant value (see Fig. 1.6). The constant cutting rate was attributed to the polishing medium embedded in the polisher, and the maximum rate to loose particles which worked themselves to the centre of the lap and then into the lap grooves.

When glass was polished with Barnesite on pitch the interference fringes shown in Plate 13 were obtained. Such fringes are contour lines of the region between the reference flat and the polished surface. The interferogram in Plate 13 was made using the cleavage face of topaz (assumed to be atomically smooth) as the reference plate parallel with an optical flat which had been polished with barnesite for 450 min. The fringes shown in Plate 14 were formed using two glass surfaces polished with Barnesite for 20 min and the enlarged profile drawing is the resultant roughness of the two glasses. Koehler states that examination of the region of an irregularity shows that the cusps in the surface profile are contour lines of cones with conchoidal sides and not contour lines of ridges. He believed that the general form of the surface profile agreed with that to be expected if the polishing grains had embedded themselves in the polisher and planed the surface in a random manner and to a uniform depth. In fact he stated, 'If one could obtain a collection of cones with conchoidal sides, mean height less than 60 Å, average deviation from the mean about one-third the mean, and bases less than 0·01 mm diameter, and then place them as close together as possible with their bases on a super-smooth surface, then one would have a model of a polished glass-surface'.

Koehler (1955) also studied the polishing of glass using Barnesite on a polyethylene lap. He found that when the lap was washed clean after use and subsequently used with water only it would not polish whereas a pitch polisher treated in the same way continued to show signs of polishing. He assumed that the polyethylene deformed only during use and entrained the polishing grains so that the planing action of the grains resembled that obtained with a pitch polisher. Polyethylene, unlike pitch, is chemically inert and it is shown in the section on the chemistry of polishing that the lap material may promote chemical reactions at the glass surface. However, as is often the case with results obtained in this field, there are several possible reasons why polyethylene does not polish glass with water alone. Thus one could argue that the softening temperature of polyethylene $\simeq 120°$c) is so low that frictional heating results in the lap flowing but not the glass asperities.

RADIOACTIVE TEST FOR SURFACE FLOW

Smith and Hooley (1953) have investigated whether glass flows when polished by using glass containing radioactive uranium fused to non-uranium glass and polishing across the fused boundary from the active to the inactive side. Two glass compositions were tested viz: silicate glass – 56% SiO_2; 14% Na_2O; 30% PbO and a phosphate glass – 67% P_2O_5; 4% Al_2O_3; 10% CaO; 19% BaO. The active glasses contained 5% U_3O_8.

After grinding the fused slabs were polished under a load of 300 g/cm^2 with a revolving disc which was covered with felt and steadily supplied with a water slurry of rouge or ceric oxide. Careful measurement of the surface radioactivity showed no surface flow at a distance of 0·2 cm from the boundary. Surface flow could also not be detected at a distance of 0·02 cm from the boundary of the silicate glass polished with ceric oxide. The sensitivity of the method was such that an active layer above 4 Å thick would have been detected.

The silicate and phosphate glasses were polished with rouge and ceric oxide for 20 min wet and then 10 min dry. Again no flow could be detected at a distance of 0·2 mm from the boundary, although in this experiment the surface temperature must have risen considerably.

The foregoing results do not preclude the possibility of glass flowing from a peak into an adjacent valley or fissure which is some 10 μ in width. It is shown on p. 31 that fissures less than 0·1 μ width can be bridged by polishing.

Smith and Hooley also polished silicate and phosphate glasses with neutron activated ceric oxide to find out whether the polishing medium became fused to the glass. Some surface radioactivity was present during the early stages of polishing but this was due to accumulation of the active material in cracks and fissures in the glass surface. Continuous polishing reduced the surface activity to a level corresponding to 4×10^{-8} g/cm^2 of ceric oxide. Such a low activity could also be due to the ceric oxide being contained in pits in the surface. The softening temperature of glass is well below the melting point of ceric oxide (1950°c) and thus the glass could flow without the ceric oxide being smeared over or dissolved within its surface. As shown on p. 96 there is evidence that the polishing medium can unite with the surface when silica is polished. If the surface material can be heated to the melting point then with silica the temperature attained would be nearer to the melting points of the normal polishing materials.

ELECTRON DIFFRACTION STUDY OF POLISHED QUARTZ

Finch, Lewis and Webb (1953) examined the surface of a quartz single crystal using a special high-voltage diffraction camera operating at 150 kV. With such an apparatus it was possible to work in reflection at a small glancing angle of 10′ with a mean depth of penetration of the electron beam below the surface of one or two atom layers. The single crystal of quartz was polished, using alumina and water on Selvyt cloth. At high voltages diffuse haloes characteristic of amorphous silica were present in the diffraction picture as well as the pattern due to the quartz single crystal. A check was made to ensure that the haloes were not due to hydrocarbon contaminants condensed on the specimen under electron bombardment, as can occur in a kinetic vacuum system. The amorphous silica film was estimated to be about 5 Å thick. Finch *et al.* did not apparently study the polishing of quartz under intense frictional conditions such as are outlined in the previous sections. Also it is doubtful whether one can use such polishing conditions with quartz without the uneven heating causing fracture. Thus this result cannot be taken as evidence that the disturbed layer on polished silica or glass must also be of such limited thickness.

However, as shown above, there is evidence that surface flow is not an essential requirement in the polishing of glass, but there is a great difference between the production of a smooth surface for laboratory study and the polishing of glass free from sleeks, as carried out by skilled workers under production conditions. When one considers the mode of polishing advocated by operators it appears that surface flow is an essential final step in the procedure as shown in the following sections.

5. POLISHING AND SURFACE FLOW

Work of Beilby. Study of Beilby's early work on polishing more than repays the time, if only to admire the way in which he developed his theory of surface flow from careful observation of polished surfaces using optical microscopy. *Beilby* (1903) *was apparently the first to observe that glass flowed during polishing.* He saw with a microscope that 'when a glass is furrowed by fine emery and then polished across the furrows appearances of flow similar to that seen in metals can be detected'. Beilby believed that the outer layers on polished materials were melted during polishing under frictional heat producing a viscous liquid which flowed over the surface and under surface tension forces formed a smooth surface. A polish layer is identifiable on metal surfaces because its crystalline structure differs from that of the underlying metal but a layer which has flowed on glass would be as structureless as the solid substance. However, a flowed layer may be identifiable on glass if, for example, it was under strain due to rapid cooling after formation and as will be shown there is evidence for this.

Work of French. A study of the polishing of glass was made by French (1917, 1921) who assumed that a Beilby layer was formed on glass during polishing. French emphasizes that in optical polishing it is customary finally to dry up the water so that the rouge is worked into the grooves of the polishing tool. The glazed pitch surface then comes into actual contact with the surface and all the minute furrows and sleeks produced in the surface are levelled down and filled in. French states that with one forward and backward stroke by hand over a length of 15 cm a transverse sleek having a width of 2λ can be filled in. He showed that in the final polishing rouge is not essential, because a glass surface could be polished on a new pitch lap with water alone. Thus French believed that the polishing process was made up of the following events : (1) frictional heat produced by polisher caused flow; (2) the rouge ploughed grooves or sleeks in the flowed layer; (3) as a result of combined action of the foregoing the irregular surface was reduced below the deepest pits; (4) to obliterate sleeks the water was allowed to dry up and the grains of rouge worked themselves into the grooves in the tool whose surface then came into direct contact with the glass and (5) the sleeks were filled in as the surface material flowed from the projections into the valleys.

FRICTIONAL HEATING AND SURFACE FLOW

It is not difficult to see how the surface temperature may rise during the polishing of glass if we consider the following example given by Macaulay (1926).

'If glass consisted wholly of silica there would be approximately 9×10^{14} molecules per unit area, each of mass 9×10^{-23} g. Taking the specific heat of glass as 0·16, initial temperature 20°c, melting-point 1100°c, and assuming a latent heat of fusion of 100 calories per gram, the heat required to melt a single layer of molecules of one square centimetre area would be 900 ergs.'

Now Beilby gives a pressure of 4 lb/in² (280 g/cm²) as sufficient to produce surface flow with rouge polishing. Taking a coefficient of 0·3, the work done against friction when this force is overcome through one centimetre is 83 000 ergs. As one stroke of a polisher will polish only a small proportion of the one square centimetre area considered, there will be available in the ordinary polishing procedure frictional energy of amount many hundreds of times that required to melt one layer of glass molecules.

At first sight it might be thought that any great rise in the temperature of the surface molecules would be prevented by the loss of heat due to conduction, etc. But this is to suppose that conduction would take place across plane interfaces. Is it not more reasonable to consider the heat as being produced at *points* of contact? If these were mathematical points, the temperature at the point would be infinite. . . .'

Later Macaulay (1931) gave evidence of the rise in interfacial temperature during glass polishing by showing that polishing powders made of either PbO_2 or $CaCO_3$ were converted during working to PbO and CaO respectively.

Bowden and Hughes (1937) made extensive studies of the formation of the Beilby layer and propounded the principle that 'If the polisher melts or softens at a *lower* temperature than the solid, it will melt and flow first and will have comparatively little effect on the solid. Experiment shows that this is the case. Surface flow, polish and the formation of the Beilby layer readily occurs on metals, crystals and glasses *provided the melting-point of the polisher is higher than that of the solid.*'

These workers observed with a microscope that when polished with oxamide (m.p. 417°c) the asperities on the surface of lead glass (soft., temperature 469°c) flowed readily, whereas those on soda glass (soft., temperature 600°c) flowed a little, on Pyrex (soft., temperature 815°c) to a negligible extent and on silica (m.p. 1610°c) not at all. The surface material on silica and all of the foregoing glasses flowed readily to form a polish layer when chromic oxide, stannic oxide, zinc oxide or ferric oxide was used as the polisher.

Schulz (1953) has also found that the larger the difference in the melting-points of the work and the polishing medium the greater is the efficiency of the polishing process. It is possible to polish glass on pitch or felt with only water, so the melting-point relation cannot apply under all conditions.

If surface flow occurs then it must be restricted in its effectiveness for filling in hollows, as shown by the following example. French silvered a ground surface before polishing but traces of the metal layer could not be traced within the polished surface and this suggests that the asperities must have been removed down to the base of the pits.

There can be no doubt of the ability of glass to flow and bridge over surface cracks and sleeks providing they are of limited width, as shown by Levengood and Fowler (1957). A glass plate was deliberately fractured and a crack normal to the surface was closed by lateral pressure. Compressed fracture regions of about 300 Å width and 3 mm depth were selected and polished with a felt polisher charged with rouge. The polisher motion was transverse to the direction of the fracture. When the laterally compressed glass was breathed on, the water droplets condensed in such a way as to expose the presence of the unpolished fracture as shown in Plate 4, but the fracture was not visible after the glass had been polished. Deep cracks less than a $\lambda/4$ wide could be bridged over by this method. Weathering the glass in the atmosphere or etching the surface with acid re-exposed the fracture. When these results are compared with those of Smith and Hooley (see p. 27), who failed to detect surface flow over distances of 20 μ, it appears that the upper limit of flow is about 0·1 μ.

EFFECT OF TEMPERATURE AND PRESSURE

Remmer (1951) has stated that polishing is essentially a thermal-plastic process so that it is rendered more easy by heating the glass. His experiments were made at temperatures up to 450°c and he observed that polishing occurred by plastic flow alone without removal of the glass if the initial temperature was high. Rawstron (1958) found that a lens polished under heavy pressure and at a high temperature could be brought to a polish with less loss of weight and thickness than one which was polished cold and with light pressure. He contends that in the first case glass flows into and fills the pits in the ground surface and in the second it is necessary to remove materials almost down to the level of the deepest pit. *Rawstron believes that the reason why some workers have not detected flow of the surface layer is that their polishing tests have been made at low pressures.*

The heat energy developed per unit area by the frictional drag of a polisher is dependent on the load applied per unit area and the nature of the polishing medium. When water is used with the polishing tool it does not act as a boundary lubricant for the glass but rather raises the coefficient of friction of the mating surfaces, because it tends to take into solution any adsorbed lubricating films and to react chemically with the glass.

The temperature rise in the surface layers of the glass will depend on the topography of the surface. However for a given surface roughness and polishing combination one would expect there to be a minimum load above which softening of the surface layers would be sufficient for flow.

The effect of moisture and pressure during polishing were known to Newton as is shown by his practical instruction on polishing speculum.

'. . . The Polish I used was in this manner. I had two round Copper Plates, each six Inches in Diameter, the one convex, the other concave, ground very true to one another. On the convex I ground the Object-Metal or Concave which was to be polish'd,' till it had taken the Figure of the Convex and was ready for a Polish. Then I pitched over the convex very thinly, by dropping melted Pitch upon it, and warming it to keep the Pitch soft, whilst I ground it with the concave Copper wetted to make it spread eavenly all over the convex. Thus by working it well I made it as thin as a Groat, and after the convex was cold I ground it again to give it as true a Figure as I could. Then I took Putty which I had made very fine by washing it from all its grosser Particles, and laying a little of this upon the Pitch, I ground it upon the Pitch with the concave Copper, till it had done making a Noise; and then upon the Pitch I ground the Object-Metal with a brisk motion, for about two or three Minutes of time, leaning hard upon it. Then I put fresh Putty upon the Pitch, and ground it again till it had done making a noise, and afterwards ground the Object-Metal upon it as before. And this Work I repeated till the Metal was polished, grinding it the last time with all my strength for a good while together, and frequently breathing upon the Pitch, to keep it moist without laying on any more fresh Putty. The Object-Metal was two Inches broad, and about one third part of an Inch thick, to keep it from bending. I had two of these Metals, and when I had polished them both, I tried which was best, and ground the other again, to see if I could make it better than that which I kept. And thus by many Trials I learn'd the way of polishing, till I made those two reflecting Perspectives I spake of above. For this Art of polishing will be better learn'd by repeated Practice than by my Description. Before I ground the Object-Metal on the Pitch, I always ground the Putty on it with the concave Copper, till it had done making a noise, because if the Particles of the Putty were not by this means made to stick fast in the Pitch, they would by rolling up and down grate and fret the Object-Metal and fill it full of little holes. . . .'

However, for polishing glass Newton warned against using undue pressure because the glass may bend or be scratched thus

'. . . An Object-glass of a fourteen Foot Telescope, made by an Artificer at *London*, I once mended considerably, by grinding it on Pitch with Putty, and leaning very easily on it in the grinding, lest the Putty should scratch it. . . . For by such violent pressure, Glasses are apt to bend a little in the grinding, and such bending will certainly spoil their Figure.'

Surface temperature and crazing. Ray (1949) states that old lenses sometimes show hairline cracks in the surface which can be as much as 30 wavelengths deep. Such cracks have been observed on old telescope lenses in different parts of the world and it is thought that seasonal changes in temperature might have caused them. Similar cracks could be produced by heating lenses to 100–120°c and subsequently chilling them on a cold metal plate. If the lenses had a surface layer which had chemically changed during polishing then this layer could crack due to fatigue when the glass subsequently expanded and contracted.

Rawstron (1958) claims that surface crazing due to rapid temperature change can be identified from polishing marks by the fact that each craze line intersects another, whereas polishing lines are independent of one another and are related to the relative motion of the glass and polisher.

STRESSES IN POLISHED GLASS

A *grey* surface may be under a compressive stress which changes to a tensile stress when polished (May 1949). Levengood (1957) polished one side of glass fibres made of soda-lime-silica glass and measured the amount of bow caused by the polishing developing a surface stress. The glass was flame heated and drawn into fibres less than 0·5 mm diameter. The fibre was cemented to a flat glass and polished on the outer surface with a $\frac{1}{2}$ in. dia. felt wheel soaked in a rouge slurry. The wheel rotated at 20 000 rev/min under an applied load of some 50 g with the axis of the wheel perpendicular to the long axis of the fibre. A layer of about 1000 Å thick was removed from the glass in 1 min. The glass fibre was removed from the plate and the depth of the bow d measured with the fibre laying against a straight edge. From the relationship for a uniformly loaded rod or fibre it could be shown that the surface stress S was given by

$$S = EC/R$$

where E is the modulus of elasticity (taken here as 10^7 lb/in^2), C the distance from the neutral axis to the fibre surface, *i.e.* the fibre radius, and R is the radius of curvature of the bow. When d is small compared with R then $R = r^2/2d$ where r is half the length of the chord formed by the arc of the fibre. The bow measurements on three polished samples of different length and diameter are shown in Table 1.1. In every case the bow corresponded to a tensile stress in the polished surface.

Table 1.1

Bow measurements and stresses in various polished fibres
(*After Levengood, 1957*)

Fibre diameter mm	Amount of bow d or Sagitta† mm	Calculated surface stress, S lb/in²
0·27	5·0	988
0·43	2·0	785
0·43	0·5	365
0·22	3·8(1.2–750°c)	2500

† Measured normal to the straight edge.

When the fibres were heat treated the bow began to diminish at 200°c and stopped at 430°c with one-third of the bow remaining. Fibres suspended vertically and heated up to 705°c still retained a degree of bowing, as shown in Table 1.1, whilst a flame bent fibre of the same diameter became completely straight at 630°c. The retention of bowing at high temperatures by worked fibres suggested that the polish layer had a high softening point and it was found that the polish layers raised the softening point of the fibres by 4·5°c. On the other hand, the softening points of drawn fibres was reduced by over 5°c after being soaked in water for 72 days. It was believed that the surface layer on polished fibres was silica gel, whereas that on water immersed glass was silica hydrate. The silica gel was presumed to lose its water at low baking temperatures and form a silica-rich layer of higher softening temperature than the silica hydrate layer. A more likely explanation is that silica gel is formed on both treated fibres but that produced in water lacks continuity whereas that on the polished glass surface is coherent because it is sintered or melted by frictional heat.

When oxides of silicon (*e.g.* SiO) are evaporated on to glass in vacuum to form silica layers the coatings are under a compressive stress if they absorb oxygen and water vapour during condensation. It is of interest to note that Holland *et al.* (1960) found that the compressive stress could be removed from such films by annealing above a *critical* temperature of 200°c. Polish films are under a tensile stress, probably because the surface material momentarily reaches a high temperature during working and then cools and contracts on the colder substrate. However, the minimum temperature required to permit structural changes to remove the stress from both types of film is the same, *i.e.* about 200°c. At this temperature sodium and hydrogen ions readily migrate in glass.

6. SMOOTH POLISHING TRACKS

It has been shown in a previous section that glass is shaped during grinding by particles being splintered out of the surface. However, when the load on an abrading particle decreases, the surface track obtained may change from the splinter type to a smooth track because the glass has flowed. Beilby (1903) was probably the first to observe that scratch marks on glass showed evidence of surface flow and believed this was due to frictional heating producing a liquified surface. Many years later Klemm and Smekal (1941) using an interference microscope obtained more definite evidence of smooth sided tracks. They also observed that glass flowed from one track into another where the scratch marks intersected. After a study of the hardness properties of glass they concluded that the smooth track was due to plastic flow. Koenig (1951) produced electron micrographs of glass surfaces which showed that scratches produced under light loads were smooth due to surface flow.

It is essential to have a knowledge of the mechanical properties of glass before one can appreciate how the various types of surface track are formed on glass and the reader will find a more full discussion of this subject in the appendix to this chapter. He may be surprised to learn there that glass exhibits plastic properties. Bridgeman and Simon (1953) found that glass was plastically deformed when subjected to a pressure above about 500 kg/mm². Glass will break under a tensile stress of about 3–9 kg/mm. whereas the yield point determined by hardness testing is as high as 200 kg/mm². The reason why glass breaks easily in tension without showing plastic deformation is because it is weakened by surface flaws. When a hard pointed article is pressed into a glass surface the glass under the indenter is in tension and providing the indenter is small (*i.e.* does not bridge too many surface flaws) and the load is not excessive then the glass will plastically flow and form a ridge at the edge of the indenter.

SMEKAL–THOMSON THEORY

Smekal (1950) has stated that the polishing of glass is principally due to the polishing medium producing a network of tracks within which the glass has plastically flowed. He found that glass could be polished with a grinding material providing that the load on the

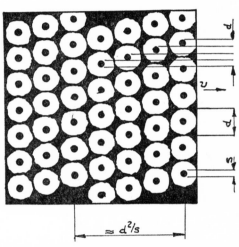

FIG. 1.7 SIMPLE MODEL OF PARTICLE DISTRIBUTION ASSUMED IN THE PRODUCTION OF SMOOTH SURFACE BY PLASTIC FLOW OF THE ABRASIVE TRACKS (*After Brueche and Poppa*, 1956c).

tool was not excessive, *i.e.* was insufficient to produce chatter flaws or splintered tracks. Brueche and Poppa (1957a, b) found that glass could be polished with dry rouge or diamond paste, but electron micrographs of the surfaces showed numerous smooth tracks, whereas normally polished surfaces showed no such defects. Smekal's theory of polishing is really the Thomson Planing theory, described on p. 24, extended to take account of plastic flow. It cannot explain the polishing process under all conditions, because, as previously stated, French observed that glass could be smoothed with water on a pitch tool without a polishing medium. Also, Joos (1957) found that scratch marks formed under a given load in vacuum, *i.e.* on dry glass, were splintered but were smooth on glass exposed to the atmosphere presumably because of the presence of silica gel. These aspects are discussed in the next section.

Brueche and Poppa (1955*a*, *b*) have made an extensive study of the polished glass surface using electron microscopy and have confirmed Klemm and Smekal's observation of plastic flow within surface scratches. The production of smooth surface tracks is strikingly shown in Plate 5a which is of a group of parallel surface marks. Plate 5b shows the transfer of material from one scratch into another where they intersect and Plate 5c shows the onset of 'chatter' flaws when the load on the abrader is increased.

Arising from their observations Brueche and Poppa (1955*a*) considered that surface flow penetrated only a small part of the depth of the ground surface and it was necessary to work down to the base of the depressions before finally smoothing with a plastically flowed layer. They give the following example of how the final smooth surface could be produced.

The polishing load is usually about 150 g/cm^2, whereas for glass to undergo plastic flow a pressure of about 50.10^6 g/cm^2 is required. Thus, if the glass in the tracks of the particles of the polishing medium plastically flows, the particles must only contact the glass over an area of 150 g/50.10^6 g/cm$^2 = 3.10^{-6}$ cm^2. The particles in the polishing powder (70% zirconium oxide, 30% cerium oxide) used by Brueche and Poppa were about 250 mμ in size so that the area per grain was about $\frac{1}{16}.10^{-6}$ mm^2 and the surface density of a closely packed layer of grains about 16.10^6 grains/mm.^{2} For plastic flow each grain must only touch the glass with some 3.10^{-6} part of its projected area so that the width of a track would be given by $\sqrt{\frac{3}{16}.10^{-12} \text{ mm}^2} \simeq 0.5.10^{-6}$ mm. Smooth tracks are then obtained with widths and depths of less than 1 millimicron at a distance of 250 mμ apart. Brueche and Poppa note that the finest groove which can be observed by electron microscopy is about 10 mμ in width.

Assuming that the polishing tracks are parallel, due to the motion of the polisher, and the polishing particles are uniformly distributed as shown in Fig. 1.9 so that each smooth track produced is only traversed once before the whole of the surface is disturbed, then one may estimate the time taken for the parallel marks to merge. Thus, for a track width $s = 1$ mμ and a spacing $d = 250$ mμ between two tracks formed by adjacent grains, some 250 grains must pass between the tracks to obtain complete plastic flow and this would require the passage of 250 rows of particles, *i.e.* a polishing stroke of $d^2/s \simeq 60$ μ. Assuming a polishing velocity of 6 cm/sec the time taken to completely cover the surface with smooth tracks would be one thousandth of a second. Brueche and Poppa (1956c) have developed a more exact equation for the polishing time to completely cover the surface with tracks, taking into account the random distribution of the particles but the time obtained still remains of the order of 10^{-3} sec.

If the surface is to be smoothed by the tracks plastically flowing and merging then the glass must remain plastic for some 10^{-3} sec after the load on the individual polishing particles is removed. It is shown in the appendix to this chapter that glass which has been plastically deformed also shows delayed elastic properties so that the tracks may become less pronounced with time.

Many workers have found that glass can be more easily polished at high temperature when the yield point of the glass would be lowered and plastic flow enhanced. Heat energy is of course generated by friction and high loading and a sharp body moving rapidly over a glass surface (*e.g.* the sharp edge of a rapidly rotating metal disc) will produce glass streamers which have been melted and thrown out by the abrader.

Whatever the mechanism of surface flow it would appear that the polish layer does not play a large part in filling in grinding cavities. Thus Brueche and Poppa (1956a, 1957a) found that electron micrographs of plate glass polished with rouge on felt (or zirconium oxide on pitch) showed that the initial stages of polishing consisted in wearing away the surface down to the bottom of the grinding pits as shown in Plate 6. Only in the last stages of polishing was there evidence that the small grinding cavities remaining in the surface were filled with a smeared layer of glass. Brueche (1956) and Brueche and Poppa (1956b) have reviewed the work of their school on the smoothing of glass by plastic flow. In a later series of papers they have modified their original opinion because they found (1957b) that a *grey* glass surface could be polished with diamond powder (1 μ) on Perlon cloth (chemically inert base), but grinding cracks in the surface were not filled in as occurred when glass was polished with rouge on felt or pitch with water.

7. CHEMICAL THEORY OF POLISHING

History

The polishing of glass involves the use of chemically active materials and it is not surprising that attention has been given to the part played by chemical reactions in the smoothing of the glass surface. Preston (1930) apparently first reported the occurrence of chemical reactions during glass working. He considered that hydrogen was released during the grinding of glass when using a cast iron tool because dislodged iron particles reacted with the circulating water thus

$$Fe + 2H_2O \rightarrow Fe(OH)_2 + H_2$$

He also considered the chemical reactions occurring when plate glass was polished with rouge on felt. Rouge is nominally ferric oxide (Fe_2O_3) but it usually contains ferro–ferric oxide (Fe_3O_4) and often some sulphate.† Preston found that in the plate glass industry the sulphate was deliberately retained and was termed 'acid'. The rouge was mixed with water and adjusted both with respect to 'density' (rouge content) and for 'strength' (sulphate content). Preston states that it is commonly held in the industry that the sulphate content is of vital importance because the polishing depends more on the acid than on the rouge. This is unusual because other industries that polish glass, such as the optical and spectacle industries use no sulphate and go to some trouble to wash out all soluble salts from rouge. Preston observed that during polishing the ferrous sulphate reacted with glass to produce sodium sulphate and silica gel. The silica gel gradually bound the polishing medium together to form a hard cake, whilst iron hydroxides and silica tended to block the polishing felt.

Hampton (1930) analysed the rouge cakes produced during polishing a soda-lime glass (72·68% SiO_2; 12·95% CaO; 13·17% Na_2O) with a rouge containing 91·85% Fe_2O_3 and 5·9% $Fe_2(SO_4)_3$. The rouge cake contained: 1·18% Na_2SiO_3; 1·03% Na_2SO_4; 14·56% $CaSO_4$; 0·92% $Ca(OH)_2$; 10·08% SiO_2 hydrated; 1·54% FeO; 5·45% Fe_2O_3; 25·7% $Fe_2(OH)_6$; 6·9% SiO_2 anhydrous plus tracer impurities found in original glass.

Hess (1923) claimed in an early patent that the effectiveness of polishing rouge could be increased by using a high basic ferric sulphate ($Fe_2(SO_4)_3$) content with as minute as possible proportion of ferrous sulphate ($FeSO_4$). A suitable product could be obtained by calcining copperas at a higher temperature than that previously used. Precipitated crystals of ferrous sulphate were believed to give

---

† For example, rouge prepared by calcining *copperas* ($FeSO_4 . 7H_2O$).

rise to polishing faults, whereas an optimum amount ($\simeq 20\%$) of the basic ferric sulphate increased the 'plasticity' of the rouge–water slurry and increased the surface friction giving rise to a more rapid polishing effect. Minakov (1954) has reported that hydrated zinc sulphate ($ZnSO_4.7H_2O$) enhances the polishing speed of rouge.

It is not difficult to understand why the optical industry finds sulphates in rouge undesirable although they are used by the plate glass industry. Plate glass is a sodium calcium silicate which has a high resistance to chemical attack compared to that of the glasses generally used in the optical industry. Thus, crown glasses containing a high proportion of barium oxide, or flint glasses with a high proportion of lead oxide, can be easily tarnished in the atmosphere. When such glasses are exposed to sulphur dioxide they form sulphides and sulphates on their surfaces and these can often be removed by water leaving a surface layer of low refractive index. In fact sulphur compounds were used in the early attempt to form low reflecting layers on optical glasses (see p. 99). In view of this the presence of sulphur in the polishing medium used with optical glasses would appear to be generally bad since it would accelerate staining and impair the polish.

INFLUENCE OF IRON SULPHATE

Kroener and Werner (1956) have studied the effect of adding ferrous sulphate ($FeSO_4$) to a polishing rouge suspension. Their method of determining the efficiency of a polishing medium was complex and we shall consider it first in detail. For measurement purposes they used a set of standard glasses which had been polished for different periods with a selected rouge. The test glasses, cut from plate, were finely ground and polished with different slurries. At stages during the polishing the test glass was matched to that standard glass which showed a similar surface finish in a Busch surface tester. The comparison method was subjective and not entirely reliable, but it was used because of its simplicity. The polishing effectiveness of a medium, termed the 'quality factor', was expressed as the ratio of the polishing time of the chosen standard glass to the polishing time of the test glass, *i.e.* a quality factor above one indicated a superior polishing medium.

The glasses were polished with felt under a pressure of 35 g/cm² with a spindle speed of 180 rev/min. The slurry (244 g of rouge in

1·5 litres of water) was held in a bowl around the rotating glass where it was stirred continuously and thrown on to the glass by deflecting vanes. Shown in Fig. 1.8 are the quality factors measured at different temperatures and with different polishing solutions based on α-Fe_2O_3. The results show that α-Fe_2O_3 by itself is more effective at 30°c than 60°c. Kroener and Werner believe that the reduced performance at the high temperature is due to the polishing medium smoothing the surface by plastic flow, whereas what is required in the initial stages of polishing is to cut away surface protuberances, *i.e.* the polishing medium should first function as a post-grinding material.

When ferrous sulphate was added to the rouge solution its polishing efficiency was raised almost throughout its polishing life. Generally the most effective solution was one containing 5·4 g of $FeSO_4$ operated at a temperature of 40°c. The pH of the sulphate modified rouge suspensions varied from 4·5 with 3·4 g of $FeSO_4$ to 4·3 with 7·4 g of $FeSO_4$ and was therefore almost constant. When HCl and H_2SO_4 were added to the rouge/ ferrous sulphate slurries the pH was reduced from 4·4 to 3·86 and 3·31 respectively. The polishing effectiveness was generally reduced by the acid, particularly with the sulphuric acid addition. It would appear from the foregoing results that the polishing action depends on an interaction of two processes, viz. surface wear (mechanical removal of asperities) and surface smearing (chemical attack of surface and deposition of dissolved glass products). However, more work is required before a reliable interpretation of Kroener and Werner's results can be given.

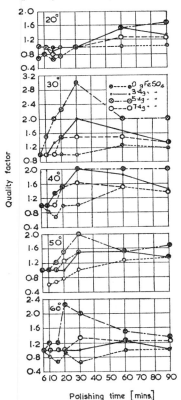

Polishing time [mins.]

FIG. 1.8 INFLUENCE OF THE TEMPERATURE AND THE ADDITION OF FERROUS SULPHATE ON THE POLISHING EFFICIENCY OF α-Fe_2O_3 ON FELT (*After Kroener and Werner*, 1956).

Formation of silica gel

It is shown in Chapter 3 that the chemical attack of a glass surface and the preferential dissolution of the glass components depend on the pH value of the solution. Thus acid solutions tend to leach out metal oxides from glass surfaces leaving the more inert silica component behind and with the chemically resistant glasses (*e.g.* soda-lime silicate) the silica outer layer forms a barrier to further attack. Other glasses, such as barium crown and flints, may show a high rate of attack and silica growth in almost neutral solutions. With these glasses the silica may remain on the glass in a porous state or become detached from the surface and be redeposited as its concentration grows in the liquid. In either case the silica layer is likely to be in the form of a gel which can be easily removed or smeared over the surface. Glasses which are exposed to alkali solutions tend to be uniformly dissolved at a constant rate.

Russian workers (Grebenshchikov, 1931, 1935; Kachalov, 1946) advanced the theory that silica gel was formed on a glass surface during polishing and that this layer was continuously removed by the cutting action of the particles of the polishing medium, which were embedded in the polisher. Such an effect could not explain the polishing of quartz or silica which do not form silica gel on their surfaces when chemically attacked.

The pH of a polishing slurry rises during the polishing of an alkali silicate glass. Anderson and Fowkes (1957) found that the pH of a neutral slurry rose to about 9·5 when polishing spectacle crown with cerium oxide or zirconium oxide powders. When the pH of the slurry was controlled the polishing rate was most efficient with alkaline solutions with a pH of about 9·5. With strongly acid slurries (pH < 3) the polishing rate fell rapidly and the glass surface was pitted.

Chemical activity of polishing tools. Interesting work on the role of silica gel in polishing has been done by Kaller (1956*a*), who found that pitch and felt polishers could be used for smoothing glass with water alone; he was apparently unaware of a similar observation by French discussed on p. 29. Kaller made a thorough investigation of the effect and believed that the 'activity' of the polisher in the smoothing process arose from the presence of carboxyl groups in the resinic acids in the pitch and the carboxyl and amino groups of high molecular weight proteins in the wool fibre of the felt. Kaller made the interesting discovery that vegetable fibres such as those of cotton or cellulose did not promote polishing when used with water and attributed their 'inertness' to the absence of acids or basic components in the molecules.

Kaller (1956*b*) measured the reduction in the thickness of glass specimens when polished with distilled water with pitch and felt under various loads and his results are given in Fig. 1.9 (*a*) and (*b*). The glass was worked at a constant temperature of 25°c with the tool rotating at 84 rev/min and 59 strokes/min. The specimens were

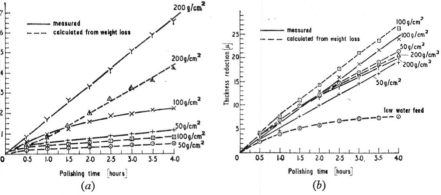

(*a*)   (*b*)

Fig. 1.9   Reduction in thickness of optical glass SK16 when polishing without a metal oxide powder but with (*a*) a pitch tool and water and (*b*) felt and water (*After Kaller*, 1956*b*).

SK16 glass † (30·4% SiO_2; 15·9% B_2O_3; 0·5% Na_2O; 48·6% BaO; 1·6% Al_2O_3) 10 mm thick and 50 mm diameter. The reduction in glass thickness during polishing was measured directly by an optical method and calculated from the loss in the specimen weight. The results show that for the pitch polisher (Fig. 1.9(*a*)) the measured reduction in glass thickness greatly exceeds that found from the weight loss and it was believed that the polishing tended to smear the asperities into the surface cavities thereby producing a greater thickness change than weight loss. Reverse results were obtained with a felt polisher, *i.e.* the directly measured thickness reduction was less than the values calculated from the weight loss and this was attributed to the fibres of the felt deforming to fit the surface undulations and removing material from the interior of

† The composition of the actual glasses studied was not reported by Kaller and the data given here were obtained elsewhere.

cavities, without unduly changing the general height of the surface peaks. Micrographs of the felt polished surface showed that it had a wavy surface which persisted even after prolonged polishing. The felt polisher removed glass very much faster than a pitch polisher under a similar load, but when the water feed to the glass surface was reduced the rate of wear determined from the weight loss was lowered because silica gel produced on the glass was not dissolved in the water.

One can criticize Kaller's explanation for the differences between the measured and calculated thickness reductions, because he did not take into account the true area of the surface being smoothed when determining the thickness reduction from the weight loss.

Thus, for a completely smooth plane surface, the weight loss W would give a thickness reduction $t = W/A\rho$ where A is the plane surface area and ρ the density. Now if an increasing fraction of the surface was smoothed as would occur during polishing a *grey* surface on pitch then t would be equal to $W/\bar{F}A\rho$, where $\bar{F}$ is the mean fraction smoothed during polishing. Clearly this would raise the calculated thickness and tend to decrease the difference from the measured value. Likewise, if the felt polisher smoothed out the grinding pits then $\bar{F}$ would be greater than 1, and allowing for this would tend to reduce the calculated thickness towards the measured values shown in Fig. 1.9(*b*). This subject is again discussed in the next section in relation to surface flow. It is sufficient to remark here that there is some uncertainty about the meaning of the differences between the curves in Fig. 1.9 although there can be no doubt about the chemical effect of the polishing tool and the water in wearing the glass surface. The reader will be interested to know that it is shown in Chapter 7 that when glass is rubbed on glass in certain liquids such as water, alcohols and primary amines glass is removed from the interface in a gel like state.

Cornish (1960) has polished ground discs of ophthalmic crown glass on a felt lap operated at 150 rev/min under a pressure of 29 g/cm². With a water/ceria slurry glass was removed at a uniform rate after an initial period and electron microscopy showed that a continuous polish surface was obtained. When the water was replaced by a hydrophobic oil the glass was removed at a negligible rate after initial smoothing of the grey surface. A continuous polish surface was not obtained and electron microscopy showed that the smoothed surface was covered with chain-like flaws which remained unfilled with glass. A paraffin/ceria slurry removed glass at a third of the rate of a water/ceria slurry and did not produce a continuous polish surface. Oil and paraffin reduce the polishing friction as well as prevent silica gel production at the glass surface.

EFFECTS OF DIFFERENT POLISHING MATERIALS

Kaller (1956b, 1959) has measured the reduction in the weight of various glass specimens as a function of the polishing time for different loads and polishing materials continuously fed to the polisher. Values of the thickness reduction calculated from the

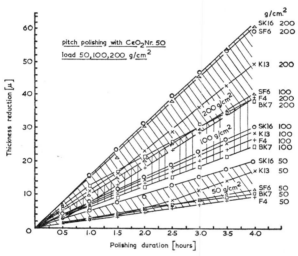

FIG. 1.10   DEPENDENCE OF THE SURFACE WEAR OF THE OPTICAL GLASSES SK16, BK7, K13, F4, AND SF6 ON THE POLISHING DURATION WHEN USING A NEW PITCH TOOL AND CERIUM DIOXIDE (No. 50) (*After Kaller*, 1959).

weight loss and assuming a completely smooth surface are given in Fig. 1.10 for glasses SK16, BK7, K13, F4 and SF6 polished with cerium dioxide (No. 50) on a new pitch tool. The samples were initially finely ground and the weight loss measured at half-hour intervals during polishing. The results show that the weight loss (or calculated thickness reduction) is directly proportional to the polishing time. It is shown in Fig. 1.6 that the rate of surface wear may rise and decrease with time when measurements are limited to the central regions of a glass and the polishing material is not continually fed.

Kaller confirmed that the use of a felt polisher in place of a pitch polisher gave a slightly faster rate of wear with a given polishing medium. The glasses tested showed a different order of wear when polished on felt instead of pitch.

The rate of surface wear for the various glasses tested is plotted in Fig. 1.11 as a function of the polishing load. These curves show that the rate of wear increases less rapidly when the load is above about 100 g/cm².

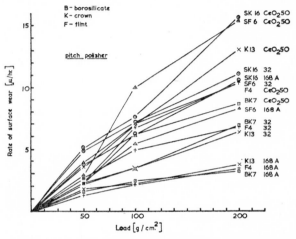

Fig. 1.11 Dependence of the rate of surface wear of the optical glasses SK16, BK7, K13, F4, and SF6 on the load when using different polishing materials (*After Kaller*, 1959).

Kaller has advanced a novel theory derived from solid state physics to explain the effect of a polishing medium. He contends that the role of a polishing medium is to supply a material with a high chemical activity and not to mechanically cut the surface, as is usually believed. Polishing materials are submitted to heat treatment before use and Kaller believes that this fulfils the purpose of producing particles with a large number of internal defects in their crystalline structure. He also argues that when the polishing particles are comminuted during polishing this creates smaller crystallites with the internal faults (positive or negative holes) now appearing at the surface together with those generated at fracture edges, etc. If the particles are fractured as they pass over the glass then the high chemical forces exhibited at defective sites can result in anions or cations of the glass adhering to the particle and being removed from the surface.

Kaller (1959) states that if soft † particles of a polishing medium are heat treated to improve their hardness at a very high temperature then the faults are removed and the particles lose their polishing power. The particles must be heat treated to produce a structure that will permit them to be broken up at a usable rate and not spontaneously which would wastefully dissipate their chemical binding forces in the polishing fluid rather than at the worked surface. Kaller attributes the greater polishing efficiency of cerium dioxide compared with α-Fe_2O_3 to the CeO_2-crystallites being harder and fracturing at a more economic rate and also to the attractive forces at defective sites in the CeO_2-surface being greater. The lattice energy for α-Fe_2O_3 was found to be -3860 cal/mol so that the energy per mol for the FeO-bond was about -965 cal. The lattice energy for CeO_2 was -2626 cal/mol giving a CeO-bond energy of -1313 cal/mol.

There is really no direct experimental evidence for or against Kaller's theory of the role of the polishing medium. However, it is known that metal oxides will adhere to glass because the glass, and presumably the metal oxide, attempt to extend their structure with atoms in the adjacent materials. Frictional adhesion between clean surfaces resulting in material being torn from either of the contacting bodies is an established fact, and enhancement of such an effect by creating deficient sites in the surfaces of the contacting solids would also seem reasonable. It is shown in a later chapter on friction that water does not lubricate glass but rather tends to remove adsorbed compounds from the surface by taking them into solution. Thus the rubbing friction between a metal oxide and glass in the presence of water would be very high, even supposing the water was chemically inert.

Croissant (1960) has found that when a pointed *cassiterite* (SnO_2) crystal is drawn over a glass disc at the rate of 1–3 cm/sec under a load of about 5–80 g ($\simeq 500$ kg/cm^2) crystals of $CaSnO_3$ are formed in the path of the scratch. The $CaSnO_3$ crystals were detected by micro-electron diffraction technique and their formation attributed to the combination of pressure and frictional heating.

---

† By 'soft' he probably means an easily fractured particle rather than an easily deformed particle.

INFLUENCE OF THE GLASS COMPOSITION ON SURFACE FLOW

The glass (SK16) used by Kaller in his studies of polishing with water on a polishing tool alone was a *dense barium crown* which had a low silica content and would be easily attacked chemically. Thus the tendency to fill in grinding pits during polishing found by Kaller could have been a *special* characteristic of this glass, because of the ease with which it would break down to form silica gel. The rate at which the surface is worn using a polishing medium is related to the chemical resistance of the different types of glass. Thus, in Fig. 1.11 the SK16 again generally shows the highest rate of wear together with SF6 which is a *very heavy silicate flint* with an exceptionally high lead oxide content (71%). The least rate of wear is shown with the higher silica content glasses, *i.e.* a *borosilicate crown* (BK7) and a *silica flint* (F4).

Poppa (1957) studied by electron microscopy the polishing of plate glass and the dense barium crown (SK16) as used by Kaller. Poppa used conditions as near as possible to those employed in industry, *i.e.* a rouge suspension with a specific gravity of 1·1 fed at a rate of 2 litres/h with a polishing velocity of 75 cm/sec and a load of 56 g/cm². He found that grinding cavities were partially filled in by smeared glass when polishing SK16, but with plate glass the smoothing action predominantly consisted of wearing the surface asperities down to the base of the grinding pits. Similarly it was found that high lead oxide and boron oxide glasses did not show smearing effects. So we are left with the conclusion that filling of grinding pits by surface flow or silica gel is not normally an important process in polishing glass, although the surface layers may be removed by chemical as well as by mechanical processes.

Using plate glass polished as specified above Poppa measured from micrographs the fraction F of the surface area of the glass that had been smoothed before and after polishing for a fixed time interval. He also determined the change in depth Δt of the grinding pits during the same time. The specimen had a total area $A = 16\cdot1$ cm² and the weight loss could be found from

$$G_{\text{cal}} = \rho \bar{F} \Delta t,$$

where ρ was the glass density. Thus during a polishing period the smoothed areas increased from 0·43 to 0·83A giving a mean figure of $\bar{F} = 0\cdot63A$ whilst Δt equalled 3·3 μ which gave a calculated weight change of $G_{\text{cal}} = 8\cdot5$ mg, compared with a measured change of 8·65 mg. If allowance had not been made for the fraction of the total area smoothed (*i.e.* F had been taken as 1) then the calculated weight change would have been 13·5 mg and when compared with the measured weight change this would have given the false impression that some 6 mg of glass had been smeared over the surface. The limitation of surface flow on polished glass can be seen in Plate 7, which shows a sharply outlined rough zone on an otherwise glazed surface.

RECONCILING THE CHEMICAL AND SURFACE FLOW THEORIES

The apparently contradictory theories of Kaller on the chemical basis of polishing and Brueche and Poppa on the thermal-plastic polishing mechanism can be reconciled if one considers that they are applicable or are important at different stages in the smoothing process. Brueche, Kaller and Poppa (1959) have appreciated this and issued a joint statement on the following lines.

(1) The basic processes in every polishing action are firstly the wearing away of the asperities remaining after grinding and secondly the formation of polish layers from polishing products on those surface regions where polishing has occurred.

(2) The wearing down of the 'mountainous' surface is the primary process which creates the gel material for smearing over the surface. During the wearing down stage the smearing process is unimportant because the accumulation of material within surface cavities is small.

(3) The degree to which material is deposited in the surface cavities depends both on the polishing conditions as well as the particular stage the polishing process has reached. When polishing under normal conditions, as in the optical or plate glass industry, the filling of surface cavities with polishing products is not an effective part of the process because the surface is worn much faster than such products can accumulate.

(4) During final polishing the smearing action of the products have an important role. They form a surface deposit layer which smooths out the surface roughness. The thickness of this deposit layer formed under normal polishing conditions was estimated from electron micrographs to be about 0·1 μ. Kaller believed that a layer ten times this thickness could be deposited and smeared over surface cavities.

4

8. ACID ETCHING WORKED SURFACES

Many workers have noted that polished glass surfaces become covered with a regular pattern of scratch marks when etched with acids and concluded that the tracks exposed were scratches which had been filled in by glass which had flowed during the working. However, etch patterns can be interpreted in so many ways that they cannot be taken as proof of surface flow under all conditions. We shall, however, consider some of the effects which have been observed.

Ground glass is initially dissolved many times faster than polished glass by hydrofluoric acid, but Preston (1921–22) found that after a few minutes the dissolution rate declined to the constant rate of a polished surface. The initially fast dissolution of a *grey* surface must arise from its large surface area and the presence of surface cracks and stresses.

Beilby (1907) believed that an underlying structure in fire polished glass was exposed by acid etching the surface layer which had thermally flowed. In a later work Beilby (1921) reported that W. D. Haigh had made scratch marks on glass and quartz and after removing them by polishing made them reappear by etching in hydrofluoric acid.

For specular reflection of light of wavelength λ from a glass surface it is shown in Chapter 2 that the height of the asperities on a surface must not exceed about $\lambda/16$, *i.e.* about 240 Å for blue light. Thus the production of a polished surface which scatters visible light to a negligible degree does not prove that the surface is completely free from disorder. It is well known that the surface of a solid is etched more rapidly in regions of molecular disorder; for example, at the edges of scratches. Thus there must always be some uncertainty whether the effect of etching polished glass is not merely enlargement of the remnants of the original scratch design. Moreover, electron microscope pictures of the most finely polished glass always show traces of scratches or sleeks in the background.

Rayleigh (1892) noted that a polished glass etched with hydrofluoric acid showed a pattern of scratch marks. He presumed that the scratches invisible to the naked eye were developed by the etchant. Thus fine lines ruled by a knife edge became visible when the glass was etched. Rayleigh found that ground surfaces were uniformly eaten away by the acid and thus, if one considers an ideal scratch, with perpendicular sides and a flat base, then this should not change in depth but should be broadened by the etching. Holland and Turner (1936) observed that scratches made with a gramophone needle which were invisible to the eye ($0.07\ \mu$ wide) became visible on etching in dilute hydrofluoric acid. A scratch mark made by a metal rod may not remove glass from the surface, but chatter flaws, which become visible on etching, are produced in the glass.

Schultz (1940) found evidence of cracks which had been filled in or covered over when different glasses were polished with rouge. Studying a glass (type SK16) he found that after etching in an acetic acid N/10 solution the cracks exposed had an exceptional depth of 0.2 mm. The glass studied was a very dense barium crown with poor chemical resistance and it has already been shown in the

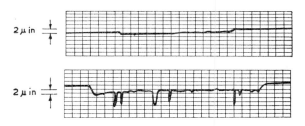

Two depths of etching [2 & 5 micro-inches] on polished specimens

FIG. 1.12 SURFACE FINISH MEASURED WITH A 'TALYSURF' OF A POLISHED GLASS SPECIMEN AFTER ETCHING TO DIFFERENT DEPTHS (*a*) 2 MICRO-IN. (*b*) 5 MICRO-IN. (*After Rawstron*, 1958)

previous section that pronounced smearing of glass products does occur on its surface. However, it is difficult to believe that cracks of this depth could be filled and it is more likely that the etching removed a flawed zone under the scratch; SK16 is a brittle glass.

Rawstron (1958) found that the etch patterns on polished glass treated with hydrofluoric acid showed scratch marks which were in the same directions as the motion of the polishing medium (see Plate 8). He employed a 'Talysurf' instrument which had a stylus for exploring the surface topography and observed that a glass could be etched to a depth of 2 micro-inches ($0.05\ \mu$) before scratches of 5 micro-inches ($0.12\ \mu$) were uncovered as shown in Fig. 1.12. The 'Talysurf' uses a stylus and does not give lateral magnification so it is uncertain whether the scratches exposed had been fully closed. Plate 9 is a photograph of a heavy scratch which has been filled in by the polishing, then exposed by the etching and the procedure repeated. Rawstron notes that it does not matter how long the polishing continues etching always shows scratch lines below a skin with the surface marks following the polishing motion. He states: 'When a good contact is established between polisher and lens, the drag of the polisher disturbs the surface layer to a depth of 4–6 micro-inches (0·1–0·15 μ). This thin layer may be considered as a highly viscous liquid, the viscosity increasing with depth until a level below the surface is reached at which the glass remains undisturbed. The layer is of extreme thinness, both in relation to the total amount of glass removed during polishing which may range

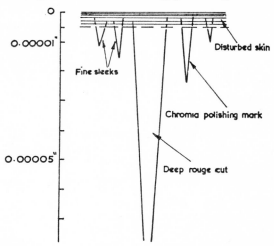

FIG. 1.13 SUGGESTED REPRESENTATION OF FINAL STAGE IN POLISHING PROCESS (*After Rawstron*, 1958).

from 0·0003 in. to 0·001 in. (7·5–25 μ) and also in relation to the rouge scratch marks which may extend to 0·0001 in. (2·5 μ) in depth. When a hard particle of rouge (or other polishing powder) is moved across the lens, this penetrates the glass below the disturbed surface layer producing an abrasion, which, however, is rapidly filled in by the viscous surface material (flowed into it by the drag of the polisher). The scratches lose their identity in the moving layer of glass, and are only revealed when the skin is fully penetrated by the etching fluid (the flowed material probably being different physically and chemically from the undisturbed glass)'.

Rawstron's representation of the final stage in the polishing process is given in Fig. 1.13.

Kaller (1957) states that polishing materials tend to contain small particles of sand which produce tracks several microns wide and chatter marks in the surface being smoothed. Thus, in 100 g of high purity rouge of 'analytical' quality, there were up to 10 000 sand particles of between 5–50 microns in size. Kaller found that tracks were exposed by etching which were not initially visible by electron microscopy. He contended that the exposed surface defects had been smeared over with silica gel formed by a chemical reaction at the surface. If the surface defects are filled with silica it is difficult to see why they are readily exposed by acid etching, because pure silica is not easily disolved by acids.

Brueche, Peter and Poppa (1958) studied the acid etching of polished glass and found that smooth surface tracks ($< 1\ \mu$ wide) were broadened as shown in Plate 10. On the other hand, heavier or splintered tracks became much deeper when etched. Thus a scratch mark of one micron depth as measured by interferometry appeared to be 30 μ deep when the glass was etched. Brueche *et al.* contended that there was a zone under the scratch mark in which the glass was under stress and that the etching had removed this disturbed region. It has already been shown that cracks in ground surfaces extend well below the worked surface and minute flaws may also penetrate the surface under polishing scratches.

Thus we have two contrary interpretations of the origin of tracks exposed by etching polished glass. The exposed scratches could be tracks of rouge particles that have been filled in by glass which has flowed or by glass products formed in the slurry. On the other hand, the etch marks could develop in disturbed regions that have remained after the scratched outer layers have been worn away. On the basis of the latter explanation, the exposed tracks shown in Fig. 1.12 would indicate regions of stressed or flawed glass that had been covered over by a smooth polish layer 0·05 μ deep.

9. FINAL ANALYSIS OF THE POLISHING PROCESS

After reading this chapter the reader will rightly conclude that a quantitative analysis of the polishing of glass by surface working is not yet possible, but that a qualitative analysis is possible, providing account is taken of the nature of the glass, the polishing conditions chosen and the changes which can occur during working. From such an analysis it is also possible to specify broadly the nature and finish of the worked surface at a particular stage in the working or at the end of the operation. The type of surface produced at each stage in the working is represented in Fig. 1.14 and the related smoothing processes are summarized as follows:

    (1) *Grinding.* Glass is removed during grinding because the load on the abrasive particles exceeds that for fracturing the surface. Circulating water is used to distribute the abrasive and

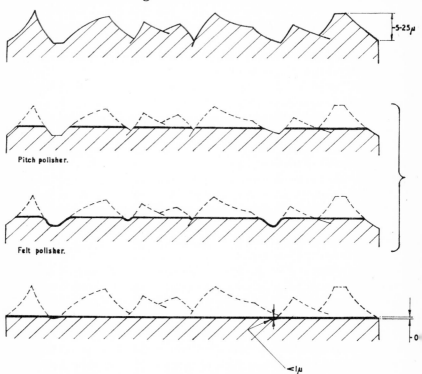

FIG. 1.14   Most probable representation of the polishing process based on work reviewed here.

to keep the glass cool; glass fractures more easily at lower temperatures. The fractures are conchoidal cracks or incomplete cracks (chatter flaws) which link together to produce glass fragments. Particles of glass and abrasive become wedged in surface cracks, producing a compressive stress. Progressively grinding with smaller size particles reduces the surface roughness and decreases the depth of the incomplete cracks. The cavities on a fine *grey* surface before polishing are several microns deep with chatter flaws and strained regions further extending into the surface.

(2) *Initial polishing.* A *grey* surface is initially smoothed by a metal oxide/water slurry on pitch or felt by the rough surface being worn down almost to the bottom of the surface cavities. The particles of the polishing medium cut into the asperities and mainly form smooth-sided furrows because the load on the individual particles is usually sufficient only to obtain plastic flow. Silica gel produced by a reaction between the glass and the polishing materials will smear and glaze the surfaces of the smoothed zones but it does not effectively help in erasing the grinding pits because the gel formed from worn glass only accumulates slowly in the surface cavities. When a felt tool is used the fibres deform and smooth the interiors of the cavities producing a smooth but wavy surface. A *grey* surface can be polished with a dry abrasive under a light pressure but this produces an unsmeared surface, with grinding cracks remaining in the smoothed glass. It is likely that glass is removed during polishing by frictional adhesion to the polishing particles.

(3) *Final polishing.* Smearing and glazing normally occur on the worked regions of the asperities as they are worn down. However, the final stage of polishing may be deliberately adjusted to increase the smearing effect and enhance the polish. Thus the surface flow may be increased by operation at a high polishing pressure ($\simeq 1$ kg/cm^2) and spindle speed to promote frictional heating or under certain chemical conditions to promote the production of silica gel which is smeared over the surface. Thus in fine optical polishing the rouge may be worked out of the tool and the water allowed to dry up. In the latter operation glass products may rise in concentration in the water and be rapidly deposited on the surface or the silica gel formed on the surface made to flow by the rise in frictional heating. The polish layer usually differs in chemical composition from the bulk glass and is predominantly silica. Schroeder (1949) has found from a study of the resistance to chemical attack of polished glass that the thickness of the surface layer on different specimens was as follows:

Soda-lime glass (plate) felt polished $- 0 \cdot 01$ μ
Soda-lime glass (plate) pitch polished $- 0 \cdot 03$ μ
Borosilicate crown (BK7) pitch polished $- 0 \cdot 3$ μ

The polish layer is probably thicker on glass smoothed on a pitch tool and is known to vary with the resistance of the glass to chemical attack. The polish layer thicknesses quoted above are in reasonable agreement with the estimates of different workers reported in this chapter which range from 0·05 to 0·1 μ for various glasses polished on felt or pitch. The polish layer may also flow and bridge surface cracks of up to 0·1 μ in width.

References

Anderson, D. G., and Fowkes, A. J., 1957, *The Influence of Variations in pH on the Polishing Efficiencies of Cerium Oxide and Zirconium Oxide*, Brit. Scient. Instrum. Res. Assoc., Report R.176D.

Beilby, G. T., 1903, *Proc. roy. Soc., A*, **72**, 218; 226.

Beilby, G. T., 1907, *Trans. opt. Soc.*, **9**, 22.

Beilby, G. T., 1921, *Aggregation and Flow of Solids*, Macmillan and Co. Ltd., London.

Bowden, F. P., and Hughes, T. P., 1937, *Proc. roy. Soc., A*, **160**, 575.

Bridgman, P. W., and Simon, I., 1953, *J. appl. Phys.*, **24**, 405.

Brueche, E., 1956, *Sprechsaal Keram. Glas. Email*, **89**, 191.

Brueche, E., Kaller, A., and Poppa, H., 1959, *Silikattechnik*, **10**, 213.

Brueche, E., Peter, K., and Poppa, H., 1958, *Glastechn, Ber.*, **31**, 341.

Brueche, E., and Poppa, H., 1955*a*, *Glastechn. Ber.*, **28**, 232.

Brueche, E., and Poppa, H., 1955*b*, *Silikattechnik*, **6**, 378.

Brueche, E., and Poppa, H. 1956*a*, *Glastechn. Ber.*, **29**, 183.

Brueche, E., and Poppa, H., 1956*b*, *J. Soc. Glass Technol.*, **40**, 513T.

Brueche, E., and Poppa, H., 1956*c*, *Z. angew. Phys.*, **8**, 486.

Brueche, E., and Poppa, H., 1957*a*, *Glastechn. Ber.*, **30**, 163.

Brueche, E., and Poppa, H., 1957*b*, *Silikattechnik*, **8**, 516.

Cornish, D. C., 1960, *Chemical Effects in the Polishing of Glass*, Brit. Scient. Instrum. Res. Assoc., Report R.259.

Cornish, D. C., 1961, *The Mechanism of Glass Polishing*, Brit. Scient. Instrum. Res. Assoc., Report R.267.

Croissant, O., 1960, *C.R.S. Acad. Sci.*, **251**, 742.

Dallayday, A. J., 1921–22, *Trans. opt. Soc.*, **23**, 170.

Finch, G. I., Lewis, H. C., and Webb, D. P. D., 1953, *Proc. phys. Soc., B* **66**, 949.

French, J. W., 1917, *Trans. opt. Soc.*, **18**, 8.

French, J. W., 1921, *Opt. Sci. Instrum. Maker*, **62**, 253.

Grebenshchikov, I. V., 1931, *Keram. i Steklo*, **7**, 36.

Grebenshchikov, I. V., 1935, *The Role of Chemistry in the Polishing Process*, Socialist Construction and Science, No. 2, 22.

Hampton, W. M., 1930, *J. Soc. Glass Technol.*, **14**, 133.

Hess, P. J., 1923, U.S. Pat. 1 446 181.

Holland, A. J., and Turner, W. E. S., 1936, *J. Soc. Glass Technol.*, **20**, 279.

Holland, L., Putner, T., and Ball, R., 1960, *Brit. J. appl. Phys.*, **11**, 167.

Jones, F. S., 1946, *J. Amer. ceram. Soc.*, **29**, 108.
Joos, P., 1957, *Z. angew. Phys.*, **9**, 556.
Kachalov, N. M., 1946, *Foundations of the Grinding and Polishing of Glass*, Academy of Sciences, U.S.S.R., Press, Moscow–Leningrad.
Kaller, A., 1956a, *Naturwiss.*, **43**, 156.
Kaller, A., 1956b, *Silikattechnik*, **7**, 380.
Kaller, A., 1957, *Jenaer Jahrbuch*, p. 145, VEB., Carl Zeiss, Jena.
Kaller, A., 1959, *Jenaer Jahrbuch*, p. 181, VEB., Carl Zeiss, Jena.
Klemm, W., and Smekal, A., 1941, *Naturwiss.*, **29**, 688; 710
Koehler, W. F., 1953, *J. opt. Soc. Amer.*, **43**, 743.
Koehler, W. F., 1955, *J. opt. Soc. Amer.*, **45**, 1015.
Koenig, H., 1951, *Glastechn. Ber.*, **24**, 167.
Kroener, G., 1953, *Glastechn. Ber.*, **26**, 300.
Kroener, G., and Werner, M., 1956, *Glastechn. Ber.*, **29**, 471.
Levengood, W. C., 1957, *J. Soc. Glass Technol.*, **41**, 289T.
Levengood, W. C., and Fowler, W. E., 1957, *J. Amer. ceram. Soc.*, **40**, 31.
Macaulay, J. M., 1926, *Nature*, **118**, 339.
Macaulay, J. M., 1931, *J. roy. Tech. Coll. Glasg.*, **2**, 378.
Madelung, E., 1942, *Naturwiss.*, **30**, 223.
May, E., 1949, *Glastechn. Ber.*, **22**, 301.
Minakov, A. G., et al., 1954, *Steklo i Keram.*, **11**, 23.
Newton, I, 1695, *Opticks* (4th Ed. 1730, republished by Dover Publications Inc. 1952).
Oesterley, H. M. T., 1957, Nov., 'The Theoretical and Technical Aspects of Glass Polishing,' British Scientific Instrument Research Association, Report No. M29.
Poppa, H., 1957, *Glastechn. Ber.*, **30**, 387.
Preston, F. W., 1921–22, *Trans. opt. Soc.*, **23**, 141.
Preston, F. W., 1930, *J. Soc. Glass Technol.*, **14**, 127.
Rawstron, G. O., 1958, *J. Soc. Glass Technol.*, **42** 253T–260T.
Ray, K., 1949, *J. opt. Soc. Amer.*, **39**, 92.
Rayleigh, Lord, J. W. S. (1892–1901), *Scientific Papers*, vol. **4**, pp. 54, 74, 542, University Press, Cambridge, 1903.
Remmer, K., 1951, 'The Polishing of Glass at High Temperature and the Effect of Boundary Films', Braunschweig, *Phil. Diss.*, V.5.5; Abst. *Glastechn. Ber.*, **25**, 1952, 422.
Scholes, S. R., 1952, *Modern Glass Practice*, Industrial Publ., Inc., Chicago.
Schroeder, H., 1949, *Glastechn. Ber.*, **22**, 424.
Schulz, H., 1940, *Glastechn. Ber.*, **18**, 158.
Smekal, A., 1950, *Glastechn. Ber.*, **23**, 362.
Smith, J. C., and Hooley, J. G., 1953, Feb–March, *Canad. J. Technol.*, **31**, 37.
Thomson, E., 1922, *J. opt. Soc. Amer., Rev. sci. Instrum.*, **6**, 843.
Twyman, F., 1905, *Proc. opt. Conv.*, 78.
Twyman, F., 1952, *Prism and Lens Making*, 2nd Ed., Hilger and Watts Ltd., London.
Willott, W. H., 1950, *J. Soc. Glass Technol.*, **34**, 77T.

APPENDIX TO CHAPTER 1

PLASTIC FLOW AND SURFACE MARKS

Having discussed theories of glass polishing and their supporting experimental evidence we shall consider those mechanical properties of glass which are of importance in the production of optically polished surfaces.

PLASTIC FLOW A TRANSITION STATE

Bridgman and Simon (1953) have studied the effects of very high pressures on glass and their results are of interest here. They state that up to pressures of some 10 000 atm. most glasses behave in a perfectly elastic manner. However, when the pressure is raised near to 100 000 atm or beyond, glasses begin to exhibit signs of plastic flow, strain hardening and permanent changes in their properties. One would expect substances without mechanical flaws to show perfect volume elasticity, but Bridgman and Simon found that silica and silicate glasses showed a rise in density above a threshold pressure. Vitreous boric oxide collapsed gradually at the lowest pressure and underwent plastic flow and strain hardening. X-ray analysis showed that the Si—O and B—O bond distances were approximately unchanged by the pressure and the rise in density was attributed to folding or bending of the chains in the glass network structure. Thus, glasses treated at high pressure assumed their normal density when annealed.

When the sodium content in a sodium silicate glass was increased the glass showed less change in its density but a rise in its permanent deformation and change of state. In fact a 31% soda-glass behaved more like a plastic than a brittle solid, as shown in Table 1.2. It

Table 1.2
Effect of high pressure on glass
(*After Bridgman and Simon, 1953*)

Molar percentage Na_2O	Pressure $(10^3$ atm.$)$	Relative increase in density $(\Delta\rho/\rho)\%$	Relative decrease in thickness $(-\Delta t/t)\%$
10	136	8·7	16
23	109	3·5	12
31	138	0·7	25

Specimens were thin discs 5–8 mm dia. and 0·15–0·25 mm thick.

is believed that the presence of the sodium ions in the silica structure hampers the bending of the network, but makes it easier to break the Si—O bond. Undoubtedly, raising the temperature of a glass, as occurs during polishing, would lower the pressure at which plastic flow starts.

HARDNESS TESTING

Yield point. When a hardened ball or cone is pressed into a glass surface under a high load the glass is fractured. However, if a diamond pyramid, as used in hardness testing, is lightly pressed into a glass surface an indentation is observed as the glass deforms (Klemm and Smekal, 1941; Taylor, 1950; Ainsworth, 1954).

Klemm and Smekal found that a lightly loaded diamond of square pyramid shape (slope 22°) did not produce the radial cracks observed at high loadings. However, microscopic examination of the diamond impression showed circular cracks inside the indentation concentric with its centre. Examination in polarized light indicated the presence of stressed layers and etching in hydrofluoric acid exposed the concentric cracks. By these means impressions were studied down to a depth of $0.5~\mu$ produced with a diamond pyramid under a 10 g load. Fractures within the indentation could still be discerned. Klemm and Smekal also observed that smooth scratch marks could be made on glass due to plastic flow and contended that for pit depths smaller than $0.5~\mu$ one is in a region of plastic flow. They observed, however, that in forming a smooth scratch the load is not the only important factor because frictional heating modifies the properties of the glass.

Taylor (1950) has shown that the glass displaced by a diamond micro-indenter in a Vickers' hardness machine flowed to form a raised ridge at the edge of the indentation. Taylor found that flow occurred immediately the indenter made contact with the surface and the flow ceased when the pyramid reached a depth dependent on the load. However, the indentation formed had a 'pin-cushion' shape, which could be attributed to elastic restoration in the least stressed regions, *i.e.* at the middle of the sides of the square pyramid. Shown in Plate 11 is an electron micrograph of a diamond indentation in glass prepared by Professor E. Brueche.

In the discussion following Taylor's paper Bastick suggested that energy arising from the penetration of the diamond pyramid under load would be dissipated as heat at the point of application. He considered that there might be a correlation between the hardness measured with a diamond pyramid and the softening temperature of glass. Bastick claimed that a roughly linear relation existed between the pyramid hardness number and the softening temperature at which the viscosity equalled 10^{11} poises.

Douglas (1958) reasoned that as the viscosity of glass varies rapidly with temperature then presumably the process is an activated one, involving energy barriers to motion. He deduced from theories of the viscosity of glass that a very high stress could reduce the viscosity in a similar way to a rise in temperature. He calculated that significant reduction in viscosity could occur when the applied stress reached a critical value which was about one-tenth of the theoretical strength of glass. (The usual estimate for the theoretical ultimate tensile strength of glass is about 10^{11} dynes/cm^2, whereas the yield stress deduced from hardness measurements, as described below, is about 2.10^{10} dynes/cm^2.)

Douglas stated that to observe flow in indented glass it was necessary to have a system in which the glass would not suffer brittle fracture before stresses very near to the theoretical breaking strength were applied. Under these conditions, he said, '... flow will continue until the area of contact between diamond and glass has increased sufficiently to reduce the shear stresses to such a magnitude that the viscosity returns to its normal value and no further flow takes place'.

Nature of indenter. It is usual to measure the hardness of materials either with a steel ball under a given loading or with a four-sided pyramid made of diamond. Hardness is assessed by measuring the diameter of the circle of contact and the diagonal length of the square impression of the diamond pyramid. When the hardness is tested with a steel ball it is more difficult to measure the diameter of the impression in the glass than the diagonal of the more sharply defined indentation of a four-sided pyramid. Some workers have therefore increased the pressure on a ball indenter until the glass surface fractured and have taken this limiting pressure as a measure of the hardness of the surface.

It is well known that small specimens of glass can usually stand a higher stress than large ones and that the observed strengths of both specimens are lower than that expected from theory. These affects were attributed by Griffith (1920), and many others since, to the presence of fine surface flaws of a few microns in length which lowered the breaking strength. From statistical treatment of variations in observed strengths Fisher and Holloman (1947) estimated the frequency of occurrence of such flaws as about one thousand per square centimetre of glass surface. It would therefore be expected that a glass surface would fracture less easily, *i.e.* the breaking stress would increase, as the size of the indenter used in hardness testing decreased, because flaws are less likely to be found in the indented region.

Powell and Preston (1945) pressed steel balls of different sizes into glass specimens and measured the load required for fracture. Pressing a ball into glass produces a radial stress which at the surface of the glass is a tensile stress reaching its maximum value at the edge of the contact area. Thus, an annular region of tension surrounds the contact circle and because, at failure, a crack develops at right angles to the radial tension the crack is roughly circular in form. Powell and Preston found that a steel ball of $1\frac{1}{4}$ in. diameter pressing into polished plate glass produced fracture under a load of 377 lb giving a maximum tension in the annular zone of 41 000 lb/in². Reducing the ball diameter to $\frac{1}{8}$ in. gave a load for fracture of 54·5 lb and a maximum radial tension of 100 000 lb/in². When a steel ball of 0·02 in. diameter was pressed into Fourcault window glass the load for fracture was 18·2 lb and the maximum radial tension 235 000 lb/in². The Fourcault window glass appeared to have a greater breaking stress than polished plate. Powell and Preston inferred that their results could be compared to the high breaking stresses measured in tension for glass fibres pulled quickly from hot glass and containing a minimum of surface flaws. Tillet (1956) found that the stress required to break Pilkington plate glass increased as the diameter of a steel ball indenter decreased.

Douglas (1958) advanced the opinion that with a spherical indenter flow was not likely to occur before fracture because of the way the stress was distributed in the glass. Levengood and Vong (1959) have examined the impressions made in glass with a hardened steel ball. They used a penetration of about 0·1 μ and claimed that this was a fractureless zone. When the load was applied for a short time the impression gradually disappeared due to delayed elasticity. It appeared that the permanent impression formed after prolonged application of load arose from flow.

D.P.H. number. Hardness is often assessed in terms of the Diamond Pyramid Hardness number (D.P.H.) which has the units of a stress, *i.e.* the applied load divided by the total area of contact. If the angle between opposite faces of a square pyramid indenter is θ then the total surface area of an impression made by the pyramid will be $D^2/2 \sin (\theta/2)$ where D is the length of the base diagonal. Hence the D.P.H. number is equal to

$$\frac{2P \sin (\theta/2)}{D^2}$$

where P is the applied load. If a Vickers pyramid is used with $\theta = 136°$ then the Vickers hardness number is

$$\frac{2P \sin 68°}{D^2}$$

The effective force acting on the glass surface at the surface of contact of a Vickers pyramid may be resolved into two components, one parallel to, and the other perpendicular to, the contact surface. The stress perpendicular to the contact surface is compressive and is equal in magnitude to D.P.H. $\sin 68° = $ D.P.H./1·08. An effective tensile stress acts in the plane of the contact surface of the indentation which is given by D.P.H. $\cos 68° = $ D.P.H./2·68.

When the indenter is under load it sinks into the test material and by increasing the area of contact reduces the stress. Ainsworth (1954) contends that the important stress is the tensile one acting parallel to the side of the indentation. When the indenter sinks into the glass under a given load the area of contact increases until this stress is reduced to the value Y, given by the D.P.H. divided by 2·68. Thus, at tensile stresses higher than Y, the glass is plastic and flow takes place until the stress is reduced to Y; at lower stresses the material is elastic and no flow occurs. *It is shown further on that delayed elastic effects can occur which resemble flow.*

Ainsworth (1954) measured the diagonal length of the Vickers diamond impressions in different glasses and showed that D^2 was a linear function of the load P (Fig. 1.15). At loads above about 100 g cracks appeared in the glass around the indentation.

Ainsworth's simple treatment of stresses produced by an indenter permitted him to estimate the yield point of glass Y from the relation D.P.H. $\simeq 2·7 Y$. A similar relation has been experimentally found in the hardness testing of metals (Tabor, 1948). Thus the relation *hardness* $= c Y$ was found to hold for a ball indenter with the constant c having a value of 2·8–2·9 and for a diamond pyramid $c \simeq 2·9$–3.

Using $c = 2.7$ Ainsworth estimated the yield point of plate glass as 202 kg/mm², whereas a breaking strength of about 7 kg/mm² is normally measured for large specimens.

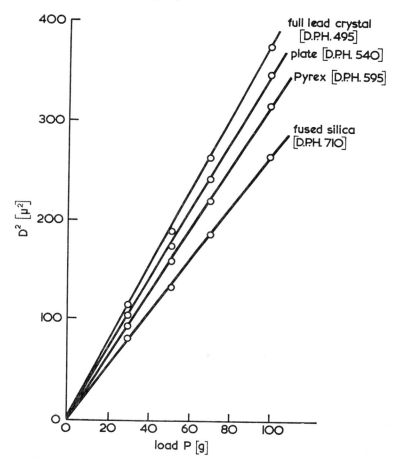

FIG. 1.15   DEPENDENCE OF THE SQUARE OF THE DIAGONAL LENGTH D WITH LOAD FOR FUSED SILICA, PYREX, PLATE AND FULL-LEAD CRYSTAL GLASSES (*After Ainsworth*, 1954).

Effect of surface layer. The pyramid indenter used in these experiments had a depth of penetration in plate glass of about 2·5 μ for a 100 g load and about 0·75 μ for a 10 g load. Thus, if the glass was covered with a layer of different structure or composition to the bulk glass, this could have influenced the hardness measurement.

Ainsworth considered a case where plate glass was covered with a surface layer of different hardness to the base. The measured hardness number would then be given by the relation

$$\text{D.P.H.} = \frac{(100 - x)H_1 + xH_2}{100}$$

where H_1 and H_2 are the D.P.H. numbers of the bulk glass and surface layer respectively, x is the percentage area of the sides of the pyramidal indentation occupied by the surface layer. It was shown that a 200 Å thick film of solid silica on plate glass would only raise the measured hardness by about 4% when using a 10 g load on a diamond pyramid. The silica layer on weathered glass is porous and this would lower the D.P.H. value. Hardness testing of optically polished, freshly fractured and fire polished surfaces of plate glass showed a tendency for the hardness number to increase in the order given, but the increase (from 540 to 547 kg/mm^2) was too near the possible experimental error to be conclusive. It is shown further on that Brueche and Schimmel have estimated the hardness of a weathered layer on a soda-lime glass after measuring the dimensions of smooth scratch marks made with a diamond. Professor Brueche has also sent the writer an electron micrograph of a pyramid indentation in the weathered surface of soda-lime plate glass, which clearly shows that as flow occurred the porous surface skin cracked exposing the underlying solid glass.

Delayed elasticity. Levengood and Vong (1959) have studied the indentations made in the fire polished surface of soda-lime glass (0·086 in. thick) by a hardened steel ball of $\frac{1}{8}$ in. dia. when using loads under the limit required for fracture ($< 3·4 \times 10^{10}$ dynes/cm^2). In this region of loading the indentations were found to recover with time. Levengood and Vong observed that the indentation depth d (in microns) decreased with time t after removal of the load and followed a relationship of the kind

$$\log d = -m \log t + K$$

where m and K were constants. The rate of recovery or slope m was greater the smaller the loading period. Shown in Fig. 1.16 is a typical recovery curve of an indentation which had been formed by loading the steel ball with 30 kg for 96 h. The influence of the loading time on the rate of recovery of an indentation is shown in

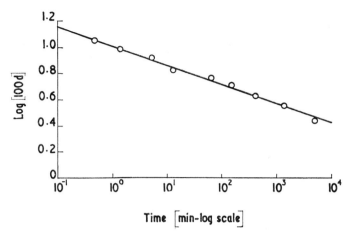

FIG. 1.16 TYPICAL RECOVERY CURVE FOR INDENTATION (*After Levengood and Vong*, 1959).

Fig. 1.17; the glasses were indented for different periods with a 30 kg load on the steel ball.

An interesting deformation effect occurred when particles of rouge were placed between the steel ball and a clean glass surface.

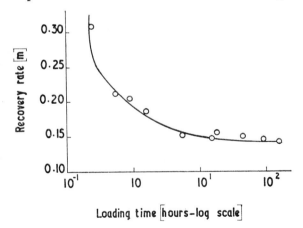

FIG. 1.17 EFFECT OF LOADING TIME ON THE RATE OF RECOVERY OF INDENTATIONS (*After Levengood and Vong*, 1959).

A ½-in. dia. steel ball was held under an average pressure of $3 \cdot 8 . 10^5$ lb/in² for 21 h. After removal of the load it was observed

5

that groups of rouge particles filled the centre of the indentation showing the localized deformation of the glass. The particles were adherent to the glass and not easily removed.

Effect of heat treatment. Diehl and Schulze (1957) have noted that the shape and depth of an impression in glass from a Vickers' hardness tester changes if the glass is heated after testing. They observed that the depth of an indentation in a Schott-glass FK6 decreased

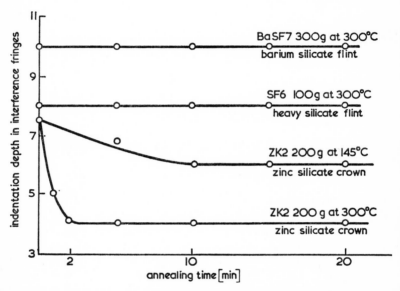

FIG. 1.18 CHANGE IN DEPTH OF VICKERS HARDNESS INDENTATION IN DIFFERENT SCHOTT GLASSES AS A FUNCTION OF TEMPERATURE AND TIME (*After Diehl and Schulze, 1957*).

when the glass was heated by a glow discharge during aluminizing in vacuum. Shown in Plate 12 are the interferograms of three Vickers' impressions in FK6 glass. They were produced (*a*) under a load of 300 g at room temperature and subsequently heated (*b*) to 130°c for 30 min and (*c*) to 300°c for 15 min. When the impressions were first made there was an elastic restoration of the glass so that the depth was only 50% of the penetration of the diamond. On heating the impression was further reduced and for the FK6 glass the indentation volume was finally only 6% of its original value.

All types of glass do not behave in the same way. Thus hardness indentations in brittle glasses, which showed cracks about the impression, were not unduly affected by subsequent heating. This can be seen from Fig. 1.18 which shows the change in the depth of Vickers' impressions in various glasses when held at different temperatures as a function of time. Indentations in the glass types SF6, BaSF7, and in some special lead phosphate and lead borate glasses did not change in depth when heated. Silica and Schott-glasses ZK2, ZK5, ZK7, FK3, K10 and BK7 all showed changes in the hardness impression when heated. Thus glasses with heavy cations do not show the thermo-elastic effect, whereas silica and glasses with low co-ordination number exhibit it strongly.

Bridgman and Simon (1953) found that the glass density may rise by as much as 17% under high pressure and resume normal density on heating. Diehl and Schulze therefore conclude that a change takes place in the density of the glass under the Vickers' pyramid. Thus, brittle glasses undergo fracture and deformation when indented, whereas the less brittle glasses on indentation show both elasticity and a change in density which is only released by heating.

This result, taken with that of Levengood and Vong considered above, indicates that an activation energy is required to release the molecules in the glass from the structural form assumed under compression. Thus, at a given temperature, the faults locked in the structure decay exponentially and every rise in temperature releases those faults with the higher energy barrier.

It has been shown in this section that the characteristics of an indentation produced in glass by a hardened steel ball or diamond pyramid depend on the glass composition, applied load and time of application, and the temperature. The glass displaced from micro-indentations that are substantially free from large fractures may exhibit elasticity, delayed elasticity, strain hardening or density rise (removed by annealing), and permanent flow. Undoubtedly further work on relating these phenomena to different types of glass and shapes of indenter would be worthwhile.

SMOOTH AND FRACTURED TRACKS

Considerable attention has been given to the nature of the scratch marks produced when glass is abraded by hard materials. Apart from the information it has given on the frictional behaviour of glass it has also led to a better understanding of both the way surface cracks develop when glass is cut and the processes occurring during optical working, *i.e.* grinding and polishing.

Beilby (1907, 1921) appears to be the first to observe that very fine scratch marks made by a hard point rubbed on glass show traces of flow and not the conchoidal fracturing along the path of the stylus which is characteristic of heavier abrasions. Beilby identifies two principal types of mark on a glass surface when it is rubbed by a hard point : he states that 'A *scratch* is caused by the splintering of the glass along the track over which the hard body has moved. A *furrow* is ploughed when the hard body is so formed and guided that its points lay hold of a layer only a few molecules in depth. A certain amount of glass is shaved off, but the perfectly smooth coating of the groove which is left shows that the surface layer has passed through the mobile or liquid condition. A cleft results when a wedge-like point is drawn along the surface. The entry and passage of the thicker part of the wedge may result in furrowing or splintering at the outer surface. . . .'

It is not generally appreciated that the load on a hard stylus drawn across a glass surface determines not only its penetration but also the nature of the track. When a hard pointed rod is lightly pressed into glass the glass deforms or flows producing a raised rim at the edge of the indenter. As the load is increased a stage is reached where the tensile stress in the glass at the edge of the indenter reaches the yield point and a ring crack appears. The yield strength of glass is usually lowered by surface flaws which localize the applied tension. When the indenter is of small cross-section the indented region will embrace a small number of flaws and the yield strength will approach that of the perfect solid.

If a loaded rod is rubbed over the surface of a glass then, because of the frictional force, there will be a tensile stress behind the rod and a compressive stress in front as shown in Fig. 1.19. The tensile stress acting in the surface as a result of the static loading will be added to that due to the frictional force. Thus, a statically loaded indenter which does not cause failure may produce failure under frictional movement. However, when the indenter is in motion sufficient frictional heat may be produced to raise the temperature of the indenter thereby aiding plastic flow of the glass. When glass is optically worked a layer may be formed on the surface under mechanical strain, whereas weathered glass may be covered with a layer of porous silica; these surface coatings will behave differently when scratched.

From the foregoing it is now obvious that the nature of a scratch mark on an abraded glass will depend in a complex manner on the size and shape of the indenter, the applied load, the frictional energy produced, the thermal conductivities of glass and abrader and the state of the glass surface layers. When a soft metal is rubbed on glass the metal usually yields leaving a metallic trace on the glass, but the glass surface under the metal may be fractured.

We shall now consider the experimental evidence for the fore-

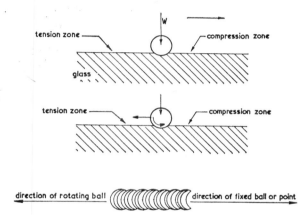

FIG. 1.19   STRESSES IN A GLASS SURFACE ABRADED BY A ROUNDED ROD OR ROLLING BALL WITH RESULTANT CHATTER MARK.

going statements. Shown in Plate 5 are a group of electron micrographs which show plastic flow and transverse cracks in surface scratches produced under different loads.

HIGH PRESSURE TRACKS

French (1917) studied the effect of drawing a loaded gramophone needle over a glass surface and noted it formed conchoidal cracks. He did not observe this type of surface cracking on the smooth surfaces of crystals, but it occurred on the surface of mechanically polished quartz. French also observed that the fracturing of the surfaces of glass became less pronounced in the order: mechanically polished; fire polished; glazed fractured surface. Preston (1921–22) observed that when a hardened metal ball was rubbed on a glass surface under a moderate load, conchoidal fractures could be found in the rear of the ball which were incomplete flaws penetrating the glass surface. When a ball was pushed over a surface it could not produce a track of less than a certain critical width, which was practically the same as the diameter of the initial flaw-circle formed when the ball was statically loaded.

When a loaded ball was rolled over the surface the resulting chatter marks resembled that produced by a fixed ball, but the concave sides of the chatter mark faced the direction from which the ball came instead of facing the rear.

LOW PRESSURE TRACKS

Plastic deformation. Klemm and Smekal (1941) scratched a polished glass (type SF2) with a lightly loaded point and found that the glass was not fractured in the scratch mark. They used a diamond and sapphire and steel needles and obtained the same result. Examination of the scratch marks with an interference microscope showed that the disturbed glass in the scratches had flowed without fracturing. In fact when two scratch marks were made at right angles the glass in the first track flowed to form the bed of the second. Such effects were obtained with a steel gramophone needle under a load of 300 g producing scratch marks of 0.3μ depth and 0.5μ width. Klemm and Smekal found similar types of surface flow when scratching with a hard point the surfaces of freshly fractured glass, synthetic sapphire crystals, fused silica and quartz. A second investigation by Loos *et al.* (1941), using phase contrast microscopy, showed fine marks within the main track of a gramophone needle. These fine scratch marks showed signs of flow where a second scratch crossed their path at right angles. Examples of smooth furrows can be seen in Plate 5(*a*) and (*b*).

Klemm and Smekal examined the impression made in glass (type FK3) by a diamond in a micro-hardness testing machine. They found that the diamond did not splinter the surface if lightly loaded. The diamond was a four-sided pyramid with an angle of 136° between opposite faces. The indentations showed surface cracks and tears when the load was 10 g and the corresponding impression 0.5μ deep. With smaller penetration depths and loads fractureless impressions were formed and these corresponded to the conditions existing when smooth scratch marks were produced as described above.

Taylor (1949) noted that when the pyramidal diamond of a

micro-hardness tester was drawn across borosilicate crown and extra dense flint glasses under a load of 50 g it formed smooth tracks of 12·3 and 14·6 μ width respectively. A raised rim was produced at the sides of the track. A load of 100 g produced visible fracture.

Frictional heating. Madelung (1942) drew attention to the fact that the production of smooth scratch marks on glass may be assisted by frictional heating. Thus the frictional force is given by $Mg = \mu_k mg$, where M is the weight necessary to maintain movement in a rider under a load m and μ_k is the coefficient of kinetic friction. The rate of producing heat energy when the rider moves with a constant velocity v is the force on the rider times the rate of displacement divided by J the mechanical equivalent of heat, viz.

$$\frac{\mu_k mgv}{J} \text{ cal/sec}$$

The frictional properties of glass are discussed in Chapter 7.

Marx, Klemm and Smekal (1943) studied abrasion tracks by electron microscopy and observed that flaw free tracks were produced with a weakly loaded steel needle. They believed that smooth tracks were produced by plastic deformation which was aided by the frictional heating during the abrading.

Thus we have the position that a hardened point under a small load can produce a smooth-sided scratch on glass requiring microscopic observation to be seen, whereas a scratch made under a high load splinters the glass.

Effect of water sorption. Glass surfaces may be covered with surface layers which strongly influence the type of scratch marks obtained. Thus Joos (1957) found that microscope slides (15% Na_2O; 9% CaO; 76% SiO_2) which were scratched under light loads by a diamond in vacuum ($< 10^{-7}$ torr) developed splinter type tracks after being vacuum degassed at 500°c. When water vapour at a pressure of 1 torr was admitted to the vacuum chamber the scratch marks gradually developed smooth tracks over a period of 30 min. The smooth tracks were attributed to the glass plastically flowing as the adsorbed water formed silica gel.

Aged and polished surface layers. Rawstron (1958) etched part of a polished glass surface and then scratched the surface with a hardened steel stylus. The etched zones appeared to be more easily marked than the polished surface as shown in Plate 8.

Taylor (1949) could find no difference in plastically formed tracks of 12·3 μ width made by a diamond on borosilicate crown glass which had been optically polished, flame polished and newly fractured. Brueche and Schimmel (1954, 1955) found that aged microscope slides when scratched with a diamond behaved as if they were covered with a soft surface layer. Using a diamond in the form of a three-sided pyramid with an angle of 100° between the inclined planes they made micro-grooves on a variety of glasses. The grooves were in the region of plastic flow and explored the glass surface to a depth of 3 μ. A soda-lime microscope slide some ten years old had a surface film of 600 Å thick with about a quarter of the hardness of the substrate glass.

SUMMARY

We may conclude from the foregoing that glass may undergo plastic flow permitting the production of smooth surface tracks. Further, that plastic flow within surface tracks will be enhanced if the glass temperature is raised by frictional heating or if the glass is of a kind which adsorbs water forming a silica gel outer layer. When such porous outer layers are dehydrated they become brittle.

References for Appendix to Chapter 1

Ainsworth, L., 1954, *J. Soc. Glass Technol.*, **38**, 479, 501, 536T.
Beilby, G. T., 1907, *Trans. opt. Soc.*, **9**, 22.
Beilby, G. T., 1921, *Aggregation and Flow of Solids*, Macmillan & Co., Ltd., London.
Bridgman, P. W., and Simon, I., 1953, *J. appl. Phys.*, **24**, 405.
Brueche, E., and Schimmel, G., 1954, *Glastechn. Ber.*, **27**, 239.
Brueche, E., and Schimmel, G., 1955, *Z. angew. Phys.*, **7**, 378.
Diehl, W., and Schulze, R., 1957, *Z. angew. Phys.*, **9**, 251.
Douglas, R. W., 1958, *Trans. Soc. Glass Technol.*, **42**, 145.
Fisher, J. C., and Holloman, J. H., 1947, *Metals Technol.*, **14**, T.P. 2218.
French, J. W., 1917, *Trans. opt. Soc.*, **18**, 8.
Griffith, A. A., 1920, *Phil. Trans. roy. Soc. A*, **221**, 163.
Joos, P., 1957, *Z. angew. Phys.*, **9**, 556.
Klemm, W., and Smekal, A., 1941, *Naturwiss.*, **29**, 688; 710.
Levengood, W. C., and Vong, T. S., 1959, *J. opt. Soc. Amer.*, **49**, 61.
Loos, W., Klemm, W., and Smekal, A., 1941, *Naturwiss.*, **29**, 769.
Madelung, E., 1942, *Naturwiss.*, **30**, 223.
Marx, Th., Klemm, W., and Smekal, A., 1943, *Naturwiss.*, **31**, 143.

Powell, H. E., and Preston, F. W., 1945, *J. Amer. ceram. Soc.*, **28**, 145.
Rawstron, G. O., 1958, *J. Soc. Glass Technol.*, **42**, 253.
Tabor, D., 1948, *Proc. roy. Soc.*, *A*, **192**, 247.
Taylor, E. W., 1949, *Nature, Lond.*, **163**, 323.
Taylor, E. W., 1950, *J. Soc. Glass Technol.*, **34**, 69T.
Tillett, J. P. A., 1956, *Proc. phys. Soc.*, *B*, **69**, 47.

CHAPTER 2

Optical Properties of Glass Surfaces

*There is no Glass or Speculum how well soever polished, but,
besides the Light which it refracts or reflects regularly, scatters
every way irregularly a faint Light, by means of which the
polish'd Surface, when illuminated in a dark room by a beam
of the Sun's Light, may be easily seen in all positions of the Eye.*†

1. INTRODUCTION

We are concerned here with the optical properties of glass,
giving particular attention to the fact that glass is used in optical
instruments both for reflecting and refracting elements. The
optical assessment of surface finish is also discussed in this section,
because such studies not only show the nature of polished glass
surfaces but also provide information on the usefulness of worked
specimens, *e.g.* as interferometer plates. It must be stressed that
we are concerned here with the optical assessment of surface *topography* and not the *figure* or *profile*, which is of importance when
shaping glass to a desired form. Also the discussion of optical
theory is limited and serves merely as an introduction to the discussion of surface properties and measurement techniques.

2. REFLECTION AND TRANSMISSION WITH SMOOTH AND ROUGH SURFACES

CONDITIONS FOR REGULAR REFLECTION AND TRANSMISSION

Glass surfaces are usually polished because they must regularly
reflect and not scatter incident light. However, because light
behaves as a periodic disturbance in space the reflecting surface
need only be 'smooth' in keeping with its optical task. In fact, if
the visual response of the eye occurred in the far infra-red, polishing

---

† Part IV, *The Second Book of Opticks*, Sir Isaac Newton.

of ground glass surfaces would not be necessary. Thus, if one considers a surface covered by prominences of height h above the general surface plane as shown in Fig. 2.1(a), then the path dif-

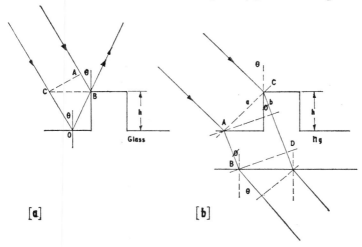

[a]   [b]

Fig. 2.1 The effect of surface prominences on regular reflection and transmission of a parallel light beam. The dashed lines show position of wave fronts and the optical path difference between the waves for (a) is $COB - AB$ and for (b) $N_g(CD - AB)$.

ference Δ between the reflected plane waves which strike the surface at an incidence angle θ is

$$COB - AB = \frac{2h}{\cos \theta} - CB \sin \theta$$

and since $CB = COB \sin \theta$ we have

$$\Delta = \frac{2h}{\cos \theta} - COB \sin^2 \theta$$

and, substituting for COB

$$\Delta = \frac{2h - 2h \sin^2 \theta}{\cos \theta}$$

from which we obtain

$$\Delta = 2h \cos \theta$$

To obtain a specular reflection from a surface the optical path difference between the reflected waves $\Delta = p\lambda$ should not exceed about an eighth of a wavelength, so that at normal incidence h should not be higher than $\lambda/16$, which is about 250 Å for blue light. A number of deductions can be made from this simple treatment:

(*i*) Light scattering first occurs at the shortest wavelengths as h is increased. Thus a partly polished surface may diffusely reflect blue light.

(*ii*) A surface which diffusely reflects in one wavelength region will specularly reflect in a longer wavelength region. This was demonstrated by Rayleigh (1893) who showed how a ground glass surface reflected infra-red light almost as well as a polished surface.

(*iii*) A diffusely reflecting surface can become specularly reflecting as the angle of incidence is increased with regular reflection initially occurring for red light.

In the above discussion it has been assumed that the shape and height of the surface irregularities do not affect the value of the specular reflection R at given values of $2h \cos \theta$ and wavelength. It also follows from the relation $p\lambda = 2h \cos \theta$ that with constant R the term $h \cos \theta$ should be a linear function of wavelength. Knowles Middleton and Wyszecki (1957) have investigated these two hypotheses at incidence angles between 80°–89°. They found that using ground glass surfaces with a 'Talysurf' roughness measurement of 0·75–8·25 μ the relation between R and $h \cos \theta$ measured at $\lambda = $ 4230 Å was independent of the surface roughness for values of $h \cos \theta$ up to 0·08 μ; the relation was almost independent of the degree of roughness for $h \cos \theta$ up to 0·14 μ. Using constant values of $R = 40\%$, they found that $h \cos \theta$ was a linear function of λ in the measured wavelength range 4000–7000 Å. From the foregoing results p was found by the writer to equal $\frac{1}{10}$ when $R = 40\%$.

Bennett and Porteus (1961) have applied a theory developed for the reflection of radar waves from rough water surfaces to the reflection of light from ground and polished surfaces. The theory was based on the assumption that the reflector was a conductor and Bennett and Porteus used glass specimens coated with evaporated aluminium films. They found that for $p = 0·01$ the specular reflection was reduced by 1% for green light. Irregularities of 20 to 50Å in height can be expected on optically polished surfaces.

Now we shall consider the effect of surface prominencies on the transmitted wave as shown in Fig. 2.1(*b*). A wavefront incident normally on the surface will first strike the upper face of a prominence and traverse an optical path hn_g where n_g is the refractive index of the glass, whilst the wave in air travels a distance h. Thus the optical path difference between the waves entering the body of the glass when $n_g = 1.5$ is $1.5h - h$ or $h/2$. Thus, for regular reflection at normal incidence we have $2h = p\lambda$ and for regular transmission $h/2 = p\lambda$, so that for the path difference between the waves passing into the glass to equal that between reflected waves the surface prominences must be four times higher.[†] If the irregular surface is covered with a liquid with a refractive index n_m near to that of the glass the optical path difference at normal incidence will decrease and be given by $h(n_g - n_m)$.

Rayleigh (1893) has observed that a finely ground glass surface gives a well defined transmitted image but that there is a great loss of light by irregular reflection from such a surface.

When a plane wave strikes an irregular surface at an angle of incidence θ as shown in Fig. 2.1(b), then the refracted ray CD travels an optical distance $n_g b$ further than AB.

Since $AC = a$

$$a = \frac{h}{\cos(90 - \theta)} \quad \text{and} \quad a = \frac{b}{\sin(\theta - \phi)}$$

then

$$b = \frac{\sin(\theta - \phi)}{\sin \theta} \cdot h \tag{1}$$

From the addition theorem we have

$$\frac{\sin(\theta - \phi)}{\sin \theta} = \cos \phi - \frac{\sin \phi}{\tan \theta} \tag{2}$$

Also

$$\cos \phi = \sqrt{1 - \sin^2 \phi}$$

and from Snell's law

$$\sin \phi = \frac{\sin \theta}{n_g}$$

[†] Newton in his *First Book of Opticks* commented on the difference between the effects of surface irregularities on the reflected and transmitted rays thus: 'And by reason of these Inequalities, Objects appeared indistinct in this Instrument. For the Errors of reflected Rays caused by any Inequality of the Glass, are about six times greater than the Errors of refracted Rays caused by the like Inequalities.'

from which can be obtained

$$\frac{\sin(\theta-\phi)}{\sin\theta}=\frac{1}{n_g}(\sqrt{n_g^2-\sin^2\theta}-\cos\theta)$$

Now the optical path difference between the rays is

$$p\lambda=n_g b$$

so that from (1) above the optical path difference in terms of the height of the irregularity is

$$p\lambda=h(\sqrt{n_g^2-\sin^2\theta}-\cos\theta) \qquad (3)$$

so that for normal incidence $\theta=0$

$$p\lambda=h(n_g-1)$$

as already shown above. If the path difference between the transmitted waves due to a surface irregularity is about $\lambda/8$, as considered above for reflection, then $p=\frac{1}{8}$ and

$$h=\frac{1}{8}\frac{\lambda}{\sqrt{n_g^2-\sin^2\theta}-\cos\theta}$$

Formula (3) shows that the irregularity has more effect as the angle of incidence increases. Thus, for the path difference between the waves in the transmitted beam not to exceed $\lambda/8$, with $n_g=1.5$ and $\lambda=4000$ Å, the value of h must not exceed 1000 Å at $\theta=0$ and 435 Å at $\theta=90°$.

Brandt (1938) has measured the light intensity in transmission for glass surfaces at different stages of optical working and his results are shown in Fig. 2.2. The intensity of the transmitted light was measured over a small range of angles with the incident light normal to the worked surface. Brandt has also measured the depth of grinding pits in sectioned surfaces prepared for polishing with different types of grinding material. With ground surfaces showing fairly good images in transmitted light the average grinding depth was equivalent to an optical path difference of $\frac{4}{15}\lambda$ for normal incidence. If this path difference is now inserted in equation (3) one obtains,

$$h=\frac{4}{15}\frac{\lambda}{\sqrt{n_g^2-\sin^2\theta}-\cos\theta}$$

From this one can approximately find the average height or depth of the surface disorder by determining the wavelength and the incidence angle at which regular transmission commences.

Ehrenberg (1949) observed that the imperfections in the surfaces of bent optical flats used for focusing X-rays gave rise to scattered light (X-rays) in the region of the focus. Experiments with diffraction gratings prepared by evaporating thin gold strips ($\simeq 5$ Å thick) on to worked optical flats indicated that the existing surface irregularities did not exceed 10 Å high. When the X-rays from a narrow slit were reflected from a plane glass surface it was observed that the surface irregularities produced a striated image. This was attributed to the individual surface undulations having a focusing effect. The striations could have been formed by a surface consisting

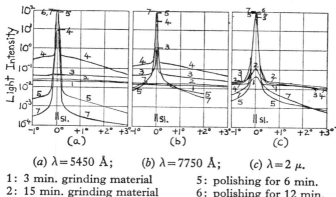

(a) $\lambda = 5450$ Å;   (b) $\lambda = 7750$ Å;   (c) $\lambda = 2\ \mu$.

1: 3 min. grinding material   5: polishing for 6 min.
2: 15 min. grinding material   6: polishing for 12 min.
3: American grinding material   7: polishing for 29 min.
4: French grinding material

FIG. 2.2 TRANSMISSION OF GLASS BK7 WHEN WORKED WITH VARIOUS MATERIALS AND MEASURED AS A FUNCTION OF SCATTERING ANGLE AND AT DIFFERENT WAVELENGTHS (*After Brandt*, 1938).

of hills and valleys of about 10 Å height and 1 mm width. This value for the height of surface disorders on polished glass surfaces is lower than that determined by optical interferometry discussed on p. 119.

REFLECTION FROM TRANSPARENT AND ABSORBING MEDIA

When light is incident on a boundary between two media of different optical properties reflection and refraction of the light occur. If the boundary is smooth and makes a sharp transition between two uniform media then the reflectance and transmittance of the substance in the path of the light will depend on the refractive indices of the adjacent media. If the substance is light-absorbing the optical properties will also depend on its extinction coefficient at the wavelength of the incident radiation.

Apart from its obvious importance in applied optics the measurement of the reflectance and transmittance of glass as a function of wavelength plays a useful part in studies of the structure of glass. Also, information on the nature of the molecular bonds and the molecular species present can be derived from such spectral response curves. Optically worked and aged glass surfaces are usually covered with surface films of different optical properties to the bulk material and comparison of the reflectance of a given surface with that derived from bulk properties can indicate the presence of transition layers. The properties of ideal boundaries are well enumerated in optical textbooks and we shall principally concentrate on dealing with the properties of real surfaces.

Dependence on incident angle. When radiation is incident on a transparent medium the amplitudes of the reflected and refracted rays depend upon the relative refractive indices of the two media, the angle of incidence and the state of the polarization of the incident vibrations. Thus the phases and amplitudes of the reflected components r_s and r_p, *i.e.* perpendicular to and in the plane of incidence, of the electric vector are given by:

$$r_s = E_s \frac{\sin(\phi - \theta)}{\sin(\phi + \theta)} \tag{1}$$

$$r_p = E_p \frac{\tan(\phi - \theta)}{\tan(\phi + \theta)} \tag{2}$$

Where E_s and E_p are the electric amplitudes of the incident vibration and θ and ϕ are the incident and refracted angles which for glass in a medium with an index n_0 is given by $n_g/n_0 = \sin\theta/\sin\phi$.

The intensity of each component in the reflected beam is found by squaring its amplitude, and the intensity of each transmitted component for incident radiation of unit intensity is given by $\mathbf{T}_s = 1 - r_s^2$ and $\mathbf{T}_p = 1 - r_p^2$.

Perpendicular incidence. When the radiation is at normal incidence the amplitude and phase of the reflected wave is given by

$$r = E \frac{n_0 - n_g}{n_0 + n_g} \tag{3}$$

when the radiation is incident in air $n_0 = 1$.

The intensity of the reflected light is given by

$$r^2 = \mathbf{IR} = \mathbf{I}\left(\frac{n_0 - n_g}{n_0 + n_g}\right)^2 \tag{4}$$

where $\mathbf{I}$ is the intensity of the incident light and $\mathbf{R}$ is the reflectance of the surface given by the ratio of the reflected to the incident intensities.

Absorbing medium. The reflectance of an absorbing medium at normal incidence is given by

$$\mathbf{R} = \frac{(n-1)^2 + n^2k^2}{(n+1)^2 + n^2k^2}, \tag{5}$$

where n and k are the refractive index and extinction coefficient respectively measured at the wavelength of the incident vibration. The amplitude of the wave transmitted in the absorbing media decreases in the ratio $1 : \exp(-2\pi nlk/\lambda)$, where l is the distance traversed.

In the region of an absorption band resulting from a structural vibration the values of n and k change rapidly with wavelength. When one approaches an absorption band from the short wavelength side n passes through unity to a minimum and then within the band rises to a maximum and on the long wavelength side falls again. The reflectance falls to zero at the wavelength for which n equals 1 and rises to a maximum slightly on the shorter wavelength side of the absorption maximum.

INFRA-RED REFLECTANCE OF FRESH AND AGED SURFACES

Shown in Figs 2.3, 2.4 and 2.5 are the reflectance of a series of typical glasses for the wavelength intervals 4–15 μ as measured by Jellyman and Procter (1955). The characteristic peak reflectances of fused silica (8·9 μ) and of fused boron oxide (7·8 μ) still tend to show themselves at slightly displaced wavelengths in the borosilicate and soda-lime glasses.

Pfund (1946) established the presence of a SiO_2-layer on a chemically attacked surface by measuring the infra-red reflectance of the glass. Shown in Fig. 2.6 is the reflectance of a fresh glass surface ($n_g = 1·52$) and a normally aged glass surface compared with

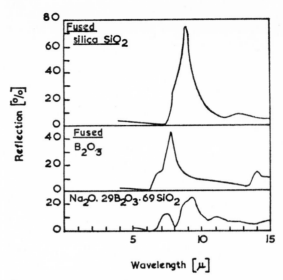

FIG. 2.3 SPECTRAL REFLECTION OF SILICA, BORON OXIDE AND SODIUM BOROSILICATE GLASSES (*After Jellyman and Procter*, 1955).

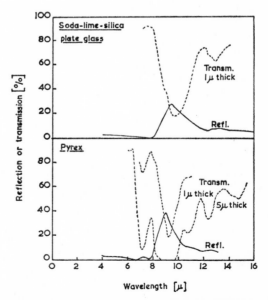

FIG. 2.4 SPECTRAL REFLECTION AND TRANSMISSION CURVES FOR PLATE GLASS AND PYREX (*After Jellyman and Procter*, 1955).

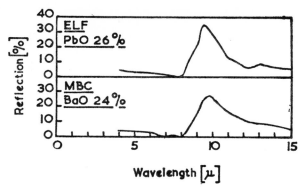

FIG. 2.5 SPECTRAL REFLECTION OF COMMERCIAL OPTICAL GLASSES ELF – EXTRA LIGHT FLINT; MBC – MEDIUM BARIUM CROWN (*After Jellyman and Procter*, 1955).

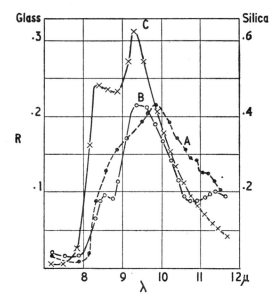

FIG. 2.6 OPTICAL EVIDENCE FOR SILICA SURFACE LAYER ON AGED GLASS $n_g = 1.52$ (*After Pfund* 1946). THE REFLECTION CURVES ARE FOR A – A FRESH GLASS SURFACE; B – NORMALLY AGED GLASS SURFACE; C – SILICA.

fused silica. Similar curves to that of the aged glass were obtained with glass 100 years old and with glass which had been exposed to the combustion products of a bunsen burner. Pfund (1946) also measured the infra-red reflectance of glass which had been attacked by hydrofluoric acid vapours to produce a low index layer ($n_g \simeq 1\cdot3$).

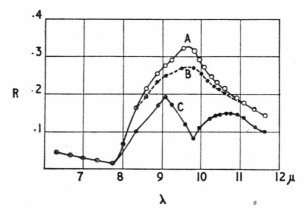

FIG. 2.7 REFLECTION CURVES FOR BARE GLASS A ($n_g = 1\cdot52$) WITH ACID PRODUCED SURFACE FILMS OF DIFFERENT OPTICAL THICKNESS ($n_f t$) $B - 1300$ Å AND $C - 6500$ Å (*After Pfund*, 1946).

Fig. 2.7 shows the spectral characteristics of such glass with surface layers of 1300 and 6500 Å optical thickness.

3. REFRACTIVE INDEX AND THICKNESS OF SURFACE FILMS

There are several ways of measuring the refractive index of glass but the particular result obtained may depend on the method used. Thus the index of aged glass is apparently lower than the bulk value when it is determined from the *Brewster angle* (*i.e.* tan $\theta = n_g/n_0$) but the index of the same glass does not differ greatly from that of the bulk when it is measured with a *refractometer* because the immersion liquid fills the pores in the surface film. On the other hand, a physically dense and high index surface may form on silica when polished under certain conditions and this can be detected when using an immersion liquid with an index comparable to that of the solid. Measurement of refractive index by the *minimum deviation* method gives a value for the solid glass unaffected by the presence of surface layers. Changes in the condition of glass surfaces may produce layers of approximately uniform index or transition zones in which the index changes slowly from the surface to the bulk value; layers produced by corrosion can often be treated as regions of uniform index.

BREWSTER ANGLE METHODS

Pfund's method. Pfund (1941) has shown that the refractive index of a substance cannot be accurately found from the Brewster angle

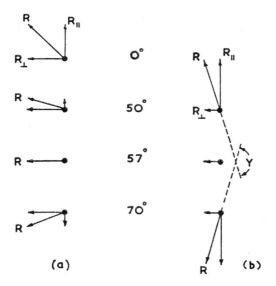

FIG. 2.8   DETERMINATION OF BREWSTER ANGLE (*After Pfund,* 1941). (*a*) *R* REPRESENTS THE RESULTANT AND AZIMUTH OF THE RESTORED PLANE-POLARIZED LIGHT REFLECTED FROM GLASS AT DIFFERENT ANGLES OF INCIDENCE; (*b*) THE ANGLE γ REPRESENTS THE LARGE CHANGE IN THE AZIMUTH OF THE RESTORED PLANE-POLARIZED LIGHT WHEN THE INCIDENT POLARIZED LIGHT MAKES ONLY A SMALL ANGLE WITH THE PLANE OF INCIDENCE.

because the azimuth of the restored plane polarized light undergoes small angular rotation for a large change in the incidence angle between 50° and 70° (see Fig. 2.8(*a*)). The angular change in the azimuth can be greatly increased by allowing the incident plane polarized light to vibrate in a direction which makes an angle of only a few degrees with the plane of incidence as in Fig. 2.8(*b*).

Using this technique Pfund was able to measure the index of plate glass ($n_g = 1\cdot515$) with an accuracy of $\pm\,0\cdot0015$. The existence of surface films produced a large change in the apparent refractive index. Pfund measured the Brewster angle of aged glass but, as he himself stated, no importance must be attached to the numerical values of n_g obtained except that they indicated the presence of surface films. Thus a Brewster angle determination of the index of a 40-year-old prism of dense flint glass gave an apparent index of 1·549 which rose to 1·784 when the glass was reground and polished. Shown in Table 2.1 are the apparent indices of fresh and

Table 2.1

Refractive indices of fresh and aged glasses
determined by various techniques
(*After Pfund, 1941*)

Material		Refractive Indices, *n*			Comments
	Side	Minimum deviation	Abbe Refr.	Brewsterian	
Dense flint prism	Aged		?	1·549	Surface films showed faint interference colours
		1·783			
	Fresh		too high	1·784	
Medium flint prism	Aged		1·612	1·548	No visible surface film
		1·613			
	Fresh		1·612	1·616	
Jamin Infr. plate	Aged		1·479	1·492	No visible surface film
		—			
	Fresh		1·516	1·518	

aged glasses using various measuring techniques. The use of Pfund's method for detecting an adsorbed film of water on glass is described in Chapter 4.

MEASUREMENT BY ABELÈS' METHOD OF THE REFRACTIVE INDEX
OF A SURFACE LAYER

Abelès (1950) has described a method of measuring the index of a supported dielectric by which the Brewster angle of the film is determined. The method has been applied to coatings deposited on glass by vacuum techniques but does not appear to have been used for finding the index of surface films on chemically corroded glass.

Abelès' method is based on the fact that for light polarized in the plane of incidence the reflectance ($r_{p\bullet}^2$) of a film of index n_f on a glass of index n_g is the same as that of the unfilmed glass (r_p^2) when $\tan \theta = n_f/n_0$. Thus, as shown in Fig. 2.9, when the parallel component of the electric vector E_p strikes the film at the Brewster angle it is reflected from the film/solid boundary but no reflection or multiple reflection occurs when the wave crosses the film/air boundary; the reflected wave strikes the film/air boundary at the Brewster angle $\tan \phi_1 = n_0/n_f$. Refraction of the wave in the film results in the incidence angle ϕ_1 at the inner boundary rising and

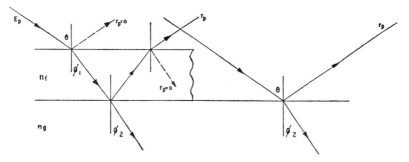

FIG. 2.9 ABELÈS'S METHOD OF MEASURING THE REFRACTIVE INDEX OF A TRANSPARENT FILM ON GLASS.

this compensates for the change in the relative indices at the boundary so that the reflectance of the filmed glass is equal to that of the unfilmed glass. This can be seen from equation (2) on p. 80 and since $r_{p\bullet}^2 = r_p^2$ we have

$$r_p^2 = E_p \frac{\tan^2(\phi_2 - \theta)}{\tan^2(\phi_2 + \theta)} = E_p \frac{\tan^2(\phi_2 - \phi_1)}{\tan^2(\phi_2 + \phi_1)}$$

Consider, for example, a glass of $n_g = 1\cdot5$, covered with a film which by the foregoing method gives a Brewster angle of $54°$ so that $n_f = 1\cdot37$. The angles of refraction ϕ_1 and ϕ_2 would then be $36°$ and $33°$ respectively and for $E_p = 1$ these give $r_p = -0\cdot02$ so that the reflectance (r_p^2) of the filmed and unfilmed surfaces is $0\cdot04\%$. Provided the index of the film does not differ too greatly from that of the base ($\pm 0\cdot3$) n_f can be determined with an accuracy of $\pm 0\cdot002$.

Measurements may be made using a spectrometer with a monochromatic light source. The light source is projected on to a pinhole at the focus of the collimator and the test glass is mounted on the prism table. A sheet of Polaroid is placed anywhere between the collimating lens and telescope objective. The telescope eyepiece must be removed so that the telescope is focused on the specimen when the visual brightness match is made and replaced for focusing on the pinhole for angular measurements. Traub and Osterberg (1957) have described an instrument which simplifies the tracking of the reflected beam and avoids the need for alternate focusing. Accurate measurements may be made by determining r_p^2 and $r_{p\bullet}^2$ individually as a function of incidence angle using a photocell and then from a pair of overlapping curves finding the angle at which the reflectances are equal.

DETERMINATION OF THICKNESS AND INDEX FROM INTERFERENCE MAXIMA AND MINIMA

The refractive index and thickness of interference films formed on chemically corroded glass may be studied by a number of

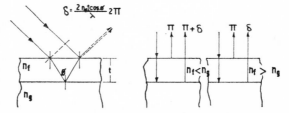

FIG. 2.10   PHASE RETARDATION BETWEEN TWO INTERFERING BEAMS REFLECTED FROM A TRANSPARENT SURFACE LAYER ON GLASS.

techniques. Invariably the optical theory used treats the surface layer as non-dispersive and of uniform index. Such theory has been well developed for vacuum deposited films and for complete accounts of the optics of thin films the reader should consult Mayer (1950) and Heavens (1955). We are concerned here with films whose thickness is generally less than a wavelength of light.

Maxima and minima. When white light is reflected from a glass specimen with a surface layer of different refractive index from the bulk and analysed with a spectroscope interference maximum and minimum can be observed. (If the film is very thick alternate maxima and minima generally termed channelled spectra can be observed.) The optical path difference between two interfering beams in a surface layer is $2n_f t \cos \phi$, as shown in Fig. 2.10 and a maximum occurs when the path difference is a multiple of a wave-length and $n_f < n_g$. Now let λ be the wavelength of a maximum for incidence angle θ, and λ_* be the wavelength of the maximum for incidence angle θ_*. Then

$$2n_f t \cos \phi = m\lambda$$

$$2n_f t \cos \phi_* = m\lambda_*$$

where m is the order of interference. When the film is of higher index than the base only one beam, that incident on the air/film boundary, undergoes a phase change of π on reflection so that inter-ference maxima occur when the phase difference is $m(\lambda/2)$ and m is an odd integer; in either case we obtain

$$\cos \phi/\cos \phi_* = \lambda/\lambda_* \tag{1}$$

From Snell's law it can be shown that

$$\cos^2 \phi = 1 - \frac{\sin^2 \theta}{n_f^2}$$

and substituting for $\cos \phi$ and $\cos \phi_*$ in (1) we obtain

$$n_f = \left(\frac{\lambda_*^2 \sin^2 \theta - \lambda^2 \sin^2 \theta_*}{\lambda_*^2 - \lambda^2}\right)^{1/2} \tag{2}$$

This expression is also applicable if λ and λ_* correspond to a minimum in the observed spectrum.

The reflectance of a thin transparent film on glass is given by

$$\mathbf{R} = \frac{r_1^2 + 2r_1 r_2 \cos \delta + r_2^2}{1 + 2r_1 r_2 \cos \delta + r_1^2 r_2^2} \tag{3}$$

where $\delta = 2\pi(2n_f t \cos \phi/\lambda)$, and r_1 and r_2 are the amplitudes of the reflections from the film boundaries which are given in terms of their respective states of polarization, r_s and r_p, by the Fresnel equations (1) and (2) on p. 80. From the above equation we obtain

$$\cos \left(\frac{4\pi n_f t \cos \phi}{\lambda}\right) = \frac{r_1^2 + r_2^2 - \mathbf{R}(1 + r_1^2 r_2^2)}{2r_1 r_2(\mathbf{R} - 1)} \tag{4}$$

so that if the index of the film and bulk glass and the reflectance $\mathbf{R}$ at a given incidence angle θ are known t can be found.

If the Fresnel coefficients are small, as occurs when the index of the film approaches that of the bulk glass, the effect of multiple reflections within the layer can be neglected and we obtain for the reflectance

$$\mathbf{R} = r_1^2 + 2r_1 r_2 \cos \delta + r_2^2$$

If **R** is measured at normal incidence the Fresnel equations for r_1 and r_2 are greatly simplified and t can be more easily calculated. When the surface film is a low index layer of $\lambda/4$ thick the reflectance at the wavelength of the minimum is approximately $\mathbf{R} = r_1^2 - 2r_1r_2 + r_2^2$. Derivation of **R** from measurement at normal incidence of the transmittance **T**, where $\mathbf{R} = 1 - \mathbf{T} - \mathbf{A}$, is usually difficult because the percentage change in reflectance due to the presence of an aged film on a glass represents a much smaller amount when expressed as a percentage of the transmission. Also, the absorption **A** must be carefully measured because with some glasses (such as plate) this can amount to as much as 2% and be comparable to the reflectance of a low index layer. If one measures the reflectance directly using a photocell and light source an incidence angle of up to 10° can usually be used before the reflectance varies considerably from that at $\theta = 0$.

Determination of Thickness and Index by Polarimetric Method

When polarized light is incident on a boundary between two media of different refractive index it should always be reflected as plane polarized light. In practice this is seldom so, because the ideal boundary rarely exists. Thus, if light incident on glass is polarized at an angle of 45° with the plane of incidence, then the reflected light is invariably elliptically polarized, as shown further on, for both optically and flame polished surfaces. The phase difference between the reflected components polarized in and perpendicular to the plane of incidence is designated Δ and if a phase difference equal and opposite to this is introduced between the vibrations plane polarized light is again obtained. The angle between the plane of the vibration and the normal to the plane of incidence for the restored plane polarized light is designated ψ.† By measuring Δ and ψ it is possible to find the index and thickness of surface films (Fig. 2.12a).

Alternatively, one may convert elliptically polarized light to plane polarized light with a quarter-wave plate whose axis is parallel to the major axis of the elliptical vibration. An estimate of the

---

† There is much variation in the designation of the azimuth, here we define ψ as $\tan^{-1}(R_p/R_s)$ because this agrees with the values given in the polarimetric tables prepared by Vašiček. Many writers define ψ as $\tan^{-1}(R_s/R_p)$.

properties of a surface film can then be made by measuring, as shown in Fig. 2.12b, the angle χ of the major axis of the ellipse and the angle γ of the restored plane vibration. Well known relations exist between the foregoing measurable quantities, viz., $\cos 2\psi = \cos 2\gamma \cos 2\chi$ and $\tan 2\chi = \tan 2\psi \cos \varDelta$ (Vašiček, 1960).

Drude (1891) derived approximate equations relating the changes in the values of ψ and $\varDelta$ when a film is present on a surface to the thickness and index of the film for the case $t \ll \lambda$. It is not possible to enter into a complete treatment of polarimetric theory here, but Vašiček (1947a) has written an interesting paper on the polarimetric method of determining the refractive index and thickness of thin films on glass. Briefly his treatment is as follows. The reflection factors R_p and R_s for the amplitudes of the wave reflected from a thin transparent film on glass are given by

$$R_p \exp (i\varDelta_p) = \frac{r_p' + r_p'' \exp (-i\delta)}{1 + r_p' r_p'' \exp (-i\delta)} \tag{1}$$

$$R_s \exp (i\varDelta_s) = \frac{r_s' + r_s'' \exp (-i\delta)}{1 + r_s' r_s'' \exp (-i\delta)} \tag{2}$$

These expressions take into account multiple reflections within the film. $\varDelta_p$ and $\varDelta_s$ are the phase changes of the resultant amplitude factors R_p and R_s; r_p', r_s' and r_p'', r_s'' are the amplitude factors for the waves reflected from the air to film and film to glass boundaries respectively and are given by the Fresnel equations on p. 80, using the appropriate angles of incidence and refraction at each film boundary; δ is the optical retardation the reflected wave suffers by traversing the film given by $2n_f t \cos \phi \, 2\pi/\lambda$, where ϕ is the incidence angle in the film and n_f is the film index.

The quantities determined by the polarimetric method are the azimuth ψ of the restored plane of polarization given by

$$\tan \psi = \frac{R_p}{R_s}$$

and the phase difference $\varDelta = \varDelta_p - \varDelta_s$. Dividing equation (1) by (2) above we obtain an expression equivalent to $\tan \psi e^{i\varDelta}$, *i.e.* $\tan \psi$ $(\cos \varDelta + i \sin \varDelta)$.

Equating the real and imaginary parts on the two sides of the equation we finally obtain for the phase difference

$$\tan \varDelta = \frac{AB' + A'B}{AA' - BB'} \tag{3}$$

where

$$A = r_p'(1 + r_p''^2) + r_p''(1 + r_p'^2) \cos \delta,$$
$$A' = r_s'(1 + r_s''^2) + r_s''(1 + r_s'^2) \cos \delta,$$
$$B = -r_p''(1 - r_p'^2) \sin \delta,$$
$$B' = +r_s''(1 - r_s'^2) \sin \delta.$$

The azimuth is found by taking the ratio of equations (1) and (2) as before and multiplying the complex expression obtained by its complex conjugate tan $\psi e^{-i\Delta}$ which gives

$$\tan^2 \psi = \frac{(r_p'^2 + r_p''^2 + 2 r_p' r_p'' \cos \delta)(1 + r_s'^2 r_s''^2 + 2 r_s' r_s'' \cos \delta)}{(1 + r_p'^2 r_p''^2 + 2 r_p' r_p'' \cos \delta)(r_s'^2 + r_s''^2 + 2 r_s' r_s'' \cos \delta)} \quad (4)$$
$$= \mathbf{R_p}/\mathbf{R_s},$$

where $\mathbf{R_p}$ and $\mathbf{R_s}$ are the intensities of the reflected components.

It is not possible to put the equations for Δ and ψ in the explicit form required for finding the index n_f and the thickness t of a surface film, because the amplitude factors r' and r'' depend upon n_f and the optical path difference δ is related to $n_f t$.

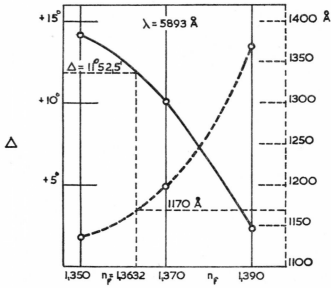

FIG. 2.11   DERIVATION OF THICKNESS AND INDEX OF A FILM ON GLASS FROM POLARIMETRIC MEASUREMENTS (*After Vašiček*, 1947a)

Vašiček (1947a) has obtained a solution using a graphical method. This is done by assuming that n_f falls within certain limits and using these restricted values calculating δ for corresponding observed values of ψ. By using the δ values in equation (3) above, possible values of Δ can be found. The computed values of Δ are plotted as a function of n_f and from the curve we can find the correct value of n_f corresponding to the observed value of Δ. One can also plot n_f versus possible values of t, the film thickness, which can be derived from the calculated values of δ and the assumed film indices. The film thickness can then be obtained from the index as shown in a typical example in Fig. 2.11. The computations for this example are based on an incidence angle of 70°, a glass with an index of 1·5687 and a film with an index between 1·35 and 1·39. The measured value of Δ was 11° 52–55' and this gives in Fig. 2.11 a film index of 1·3632 and a thickness of 1170 Å.

Vašiček (1947b) has calculated tables of values of ψ and Δ at $\lambda = 5893$ Å for films of different thickness and index on Schott glass BK7($n_g = 1·5163$). These tables can be used in the graphical interpolation method.

Table 2.2

Azimuth angle and phase difference for thin films on glass
(*After Vašiček, 1947b*)

t	$n_t = 1\cdot300$		$n = 1\cdot400$		$n_t = 1\cdot500$		$n_t = 1\cdot750$	
Å	ψ	Δ	ψ	Δ	ψ	Δ	ψ	Δ
10	5°19·0'	1°09·0'	5°19·0'	0°46·0'	5°19·0'	0°07·5'	—	—
50	5°21·5'	5°43·5'	5°20·5'	3°49·5'	5°19·0'	0°38·0'	5°18·5'	348°07·5'
100	5°28·5'	11°15·0'	5°25·5'	7°42·0'	5°20·0'	1°15·0'	5°16·5'	336°03·5'
200	5°56·0'	21°07·5'	5°44·5'	14°10·5'	5°22·5'	2°24·0'	5°10·0'	313°37·5'
300	6°38·5'	28°55·0'	6°14·0'	19°23·0'	5°27·0'	3°22·0'	5°02·0'	292°20·0'
400	7°33·0'	34°35·0'	6°52·0'	22°58·0'	5°33·0'	4°05·0'	4°54·0'	272°37·0'
500	8°39·5'	38°25·0'	7°37·0'	24°59·5'	5°39·5'	4°30·0'	4°48·0'	254°18·0'
600	9°55·0'	40°42·5'	8°26·0'	25°37·0'	5°46·5'	4°35·5'	4°43·5'	237°17·0'
700	11°20·5'	41°43·5'	9°19·0'	25°00·0'	5°54·0'	4°24·0'	4°40·5'	221°05·5'
800	12°56·0'	41°34·0'	10°11·5'	23°16·5'	6°00·5'	3°54·5'	4°38·5'	205°32·5'
900	14°43·0'	40°18·0'	11°03·5'	20°33·5'	6°06·0'	3°10·5'	4°37·5'	190°21·0'
1000	16°41·5'	37°45·5'	11°51·5'	16°57·0'	6°10·5'	2°14·5'	4°37·5'	175°18·5'
1100	18°50·5'	33°57·5'	12°31·5'	12°33·0'	6°13·0'	1°10·5'	—	—
1200	21°04·0'	28°31·5'	13°00·5'	7°33·0'	6°14·0'	0°05·5'	—	—
1300	23°10·5'	21°16·5'	13°15·0'	2°10·0'	6°13·5'	358°53·5'	—	—
1400	25°17·5'	12°17·5'	13°13·0'	356°40·0'	6°10·5'	357°49·0'	—	—
1500	25°35·0'	2°04·0'	12°55·5'	351°20·5'	6°06·5'	356°52·5'	—	—

$\theta = 60°$; $\lambda = 5893$ Å; $n_g = 1·5163$. When $n_t = 1$ or $t = 0$ then $\psi = 5°19'$ and $\Delta = 0$. If $n_t > n_g$, $t = 0$, $\Delta = 2\pi$.

Polarimetric apparatus. The general arrangement of the apparatus used for polarimetric measurements is shown in Fig. 2.12. It consists of a spectrometer with the glass specimen to be studied mounted on the table. The polarizer and analyser may be made of polaroid and fixed to rotating mounts capable of reading to one minute of arc. The light source S can either be a lamp suitably filtered (*e.g.* mercury or sodium) or a monochromator. When working at a specified wavelength a quarter-wave plate can be made from mica split along cleavage planes to give the required thickness

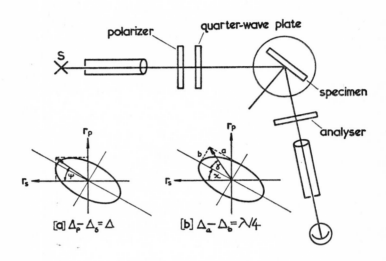

Fig. 2.12 Apparatus for polarimetric measurement. Inset drawings show restored plane waves after introducing equal but opposite phase retardation in the elliptic vibration.

at the operating wavelength. If measurements are to be made over a range of wavelengths then it is desirable to use a Soleil–Babinet compensator, which can also be adjusted to give the desired phase difference Δ.

The usual method of analysing the elliptically polarized light is as follows. The polarizer is set so that the plane of the polarized light is at 45° to the plane of incidence and the components of the vibration parallel and perpendicular to the plane of incidence are equal. The analyser is rotated until the transmitted intensity is a maximum, *i.e.* the principal plane of the analyser is parallel to the major axis of the elliptic vibration. If a quarter-wave plate is now inserted for the analyser with its axis parallel to the major axis of the elliptic vibration then the vibration components will be brought into phase as plane polarized light. The plane of the polarized light will be rotated through an angle with respect to the major elliptical axis given by $\pm \tan \gamma = b/a$, where a and b are the major and minor components of the elliptic vibration. The angle γ is usually known as the ellipticity of the polarized light.

The elliptic vibration can also be converted to a plane wave with a compensator of variable phase set with its axis parallel to the plane of incidence. The azimuth ψ (defined on p. 91) is the angle between the plane of the vibration and the normal to the plane of incidence. If the polarizer is adjusted so that the azimuth of the incident polarized light is $+45°$ and $-45°$ then the azimuth of the restored plane polarized vibration will be rotated through $2\psi + \pi$ as shown in Fig. 2.12a.

It is shown further on that new or aged glass surfaces are never completely free from surface layers with different optical properties to the bulk material. The thinnest surface layer obtained by Vašiček (1947b) when polishing BK7 glass ($n_g = 1.516$) gave an ellipticity angle $\gamma = 2'$ corresponding to a thickness of 10–20 Å for a film index of about 1.47.

Properties of mechanically and fire polished surfaces

Mechanically polished surfaces. Lord Rayleigh (1937) accurately measured the reflectance of polished silica and glass using immersion liquids with refractive indices matched to that of the bulk material. Using the Fresnel formula $\mathbf{R} = [(n_g - n_0)/(n_g + n_0)]^2$ he determined the refractive index of the polished surface and found that under certain conditions the index was raised by the optical working. A surface with the reflectance of the bulk glass could be obtained by etching in hydrofluoric acid. Careful measurement with immersion liquids showed that the polishing had disturbed a layer on the glass surface. The reflection amplitude of the outer surface of this layer was much greater than that of the inner surface and the layer appeared to be mainly a transition region between the modified outer surface and the bulk silica. However, the fact that an inner reflecting boundary existed throws considerable doubt on any calculation of the surface index from the Fresnel equation.

The high index surface was produced when silica specimens were repolished, using rouge on a cloth polisher with the polisher either very wet or completely dry. When the polisher was damp the surface had the same index as the bulk. Thus, starting with a wet polisher, the reflectance of the silica specimens initially rose as a high index film was formed, and then fell as the polisher dried, and, finally, rose again as the polisher became completely dry. Lord Rayleigh weighed the specimens and found that surface material was not removed when the high index surface was being produced, *i.e.* with the wet or dry polisher, whereas material was removed when the surface with the bulk index was produced with the damp polisher.

According to Lord Rayleigh fine abrasives such as carborundum used dry on felt do not grind glass or silica although they do when wet. Further, dry carborundum was more efficient in increasing the reflection of a silica surface than rouge or putty powder.

The highly reflecting layer produced by these techniques on silica is unaffected by lapse of time, vigorous rubbing with a wet or dry cloth, by heating to redness with a blowpipe or by prolonged treatment with hot sulphuric or chromic acid. Lord Rayleigh observed that immersing a polished silica specimen in a 2% solution of hydrofluoric acid for a minute or two and then washing the surface and drying was sufficient to remove the high index layer without markedly impairing the surface.

Quartz did not show the large variations in reflection found with fused silica. However it cannot be as vigorously polished as silica because the heat of friction on a cloth or felt polishing wheel is liable to result in cracking.

The index of the outer layer formed on a series of silica specimens using a dry abrasive known as 'Abradum' was 1·61 or more. The thickness of the disturbed layer was determined by acid etching away the polished surface until the reflection had disappeared in an immersion liquid of equal index to the bulk silica. The depth of the erosion was then measured by interferometry and found to be about 340 Å. Lord Rayleigh (1937) stated that the high index of the surface made it impossible to identify it with any of the recognized modifications of silica.* Thus quartz has a mean refractive index of 1·55 and all other known modifications fall below 1·486 (cristobalite). Also, electron diffraction did not show the existence of a crystalline layer and Lord Rayleigh was unable to explain the phenomenon.

Adhesion and diffusion of polishing agent. There is, however, a simple explanation if one considers an interaction between the glass and the polishing agent. Lord Rayleigh was using exceptional conditions of surface treatment and the high frictional drag of the dry abrasive was bound to cause high surface temperatures. The abrasive used was of the silicon carbide type and several chemical reactions are possible at high interfacial temperatures. Thus the silicon carbide may have been oxidized, liberating free silicon which was dissolved by a molten layer on the silica, or a chemical reaction may have occurred directly between the silicon carbide and the silica. In either case a lower oxide of silicon, such as silicon monoxide, with an index greatly in excess of that of silica, could have formed. In fact such reactions are known to occur when silica is melted in silicon carbide crucibles. Also, evaporated films with the general formula SiO_x with x varying from 1 to 2 have been found to show the halo of SiO by electron diffraction.

Likewise the production of a high surface temperature when polishing with dry rouge could have resulted in iron oxide combining with the silica to form a high index glass. Thus one can evaporate mixtures of ferric oxide and silica *in vacuo* and form thin films with an index rising from 1·5 to 2 or more; such coatings on glass are hard and acid resistant (Holland 1956a).

Confirmation of this hypothesis would appear to be given by the fact that the surface index of a crown glass specimen treated with an abrasive on a dry polisher rose from 1·53 to a maximum value of about 1·55 which was less than that for polished fused silica. The crown glass would soften at a lower temperature than the silica and the chemical reaction or diffusion of metallic ions at the polishing interface would be less.

Using polarimetry technique Philpot (1931) found that polished surfaces on various glasses initially had, almost without exception, a surface layer of higher refractive index than the bulk glass. Some workers have contended that the ellipticity of light reflected from polished glass arises from mechanical stresses in the surface. If the polish layer was formed from pure silica gel then its index would be lower than that of the glass. However, the polish layer may be stressed if it is frictionally heated during polishing (see p. 33) or thermally contracts less than the base. All workers agree that aged polished glasses have surface indices equal to or less than the bulk values.

Fire polished surfaces. Bishop (1944) measured the refractive index of fire polished sheet glass. The samples were cut whilst the

7

glass was still hot from the drawing operation and placed immediately in a sealed box held at 30°c to prevent moisture condensing on the glass. Measurements of the index by the minimum deviation method showed practically no dependence on the surface condition. The glass surface was also studied using the polarimetric method as described on p. 90. The ellipticity of the light reflected at the Brewster angle was measured at $\lambda = 5600$ Å with a quarter-wave plate and analyser. A split field analyser was used, made from a

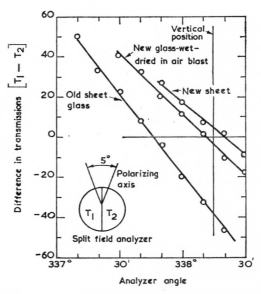

FIG. 2.13   DIFFERENCE IN LIGHT TRANSMISSION THROUGH TWO HALF FIELDS PLOTTED AGAINST ARBITRARY ANALYSER ANGLES, THE BALANCE POSITION IS WHERE THE CURVES CROSS THE ZERO AXIS (*After Bishop*, 1944).

piece of Polaroid of 40 mm diameter cut across the diameter at an angle of about $2\frac{1}{2}°$ with the polarizing axis and remounted with one piece turned over so that the axes were 5° apart. With this arrangement the quarter-wave plate was adjusted to compensate the elliptically polarized light and the analyser was then moved in 10 min steps and a series of photographs taken over 2° on either side of the visually balanced position. The difference in the transmission of the two halves of the analyser are plotted in Fig. 2.13 as a function of the analyser angle. The balance position is that where the curves cross the zero axis $\Delta T = 0$.

A number of measurements were made using the foregoing technique to determine the deviation from the *vertical* position of the analyser and the results were as follows:

(1) Five samples cut from stock sheet glass gave an average deviation of $+27 \cdot 9 \pm 0 \cdot 6$ min, with an index of $1 \cdot 514$ by the minimum deviation method and $1 \cdot 485$ by the Brewster angle method due to Pfund (see p. 85). (Pfund's method is valuable for detecting changes in surface index but the index of surface layers cannot be derived from the tangent of the Pfund angle.)

(2) Twelve samples of fresh sheet glass kept dry and warm gave a deviation of -7 min; the negative value indicated the presence of a layer of higher index than the glass, which by assuming it to be crystalline silica gave a film thickness of 39 Å.

(3) Four samples of newly made glass wetted with a spray of distilled water and then dried in a warm air blast for 24 h gave a deviation of $+2$ min. There was also a deviation of $+9$ min when water was retained on the surface which corresponded to a layer 15 Å thick.

(4) Four samples of new glass were given a light polishing with black rouge and then washed in distilled water and dried resulting in a deviation of -18 min, *i.e.* a change of -11 min from the new glass value. Measurement of the index by the Brewster angle method gave a value of $1 \cdot 519$ compared with the constant deviation value for the bulk of $1 \cdot 513$.

The raising of the index by polishing confirms the observations of Rayleigh (1937) discussed above. Calculations of film thickness based on the index obtained from the Pfund method of measuring the Brewster angle are bound to be in error as shown on p. 86. Thus Bishop (1944) obtained the extremely large thickness of 585 Å for the high index layer on the polished glass using the Brewster value. This value is nearly twice that measured by Rayleigh for silica polished under conditions which promoted the effect.

REDUCTION OF REFLECTION BY SURFACE FILMS

Taylor (1896) noted that the transmission of tarnished lenses was often higher in regions where the atmospheric corrosion had formed a coloured film on the lens surface. He proceeded to study the artificial production of tarnished films and found that they could be produced by immersing the glass in an aqueous solution of ammonia and hydrogen sulphide to which nitric acid had been added; the solution had to be acidic for film formation. Taylor (1904) later patented the chemical treatment of glass to increase its light transmittance and stated that dense barium crown and dense barium flint were the easiest to treat. Kollmorgen (1916) increased the transmissivity of flint and barium crown glasses by acid treatment and Amy (1927) treated glass with $(NH_4)_2SO_4$ to enhance the transmission. None of these early workers gave a satisfactory explanation of the optical effect of the tinted film which formed on chemically attacked glass. In fact it was not until the early 1930's, when workers began to increase the transmittance of glass by reducing its reflectance with superimposed films, that the behaviour of the chemically produced layers was properly explained. It was then appreciated that the anti-reflection film produced by chemical attack was usually a low index silica layer of *optical interference thickness* which remained on the surface after the other less resistant metal oxides had been leached from the glass.

Nicoll (1942) and Nicoll and Williams (1943) found that hydrofluoric acid vapour attacked certain constituents of glass more readily than others. If after exposure to hydrofluoric acid vapour the glass was washed then a 'skeleton' layer remained which could be used as a non-reflecting film. These workers showed that the surface film was amorphous silica with an index of 1·3. Vašiček (1940c) noted that the film formed by sulphuric acid on lead (flint) glass had an index of 1·46 which is almost identical with that of fused silica (1·458). Probably the high proportion of lead oxide present resulted in total destruction of the glass during the dissolution and redeposition of dissolved silica on the surface of attack. This and other effects of acids on different types of glass are discussed more fully in the next chapter.

To produce a uniform tarnish layer on glass the surface must be acid etched immediately after polishing, otherwise the erosion may be accentuated in areas where finger prints or the atmosphere has already produced local staining. Bugbee (1919) patented the chemical treatment of glass with hydrogen sulphide in ammonia added to a rouge solution to produce an anti-reflection layer during polishing. It is shown in Chapter 1 that when glasses are etched by acids polishing marks can be exposed. Thus to produce a uniform tarnish layer on a worked surface the polishing must be done with care.

It is of interest to note here that Blodgett (1939) deposited sequentially mono-layers of oriented long chain molecules on glass by a novel adsorption technique described in Chapter 7. The layers could be made sufficiently thick to demonstrate anti-reflection properties but because of their softness were of no practical interest.

Theory and modern technique. It is not intended to deal fully with the anti-reflection coating of glass here and a reader interested in the history of the technique and its modern application should consult Holland (1956a). We shall briefly consider the theoretical basis of anti-reflection films as a means to understanding the optical properties of chemically produced layers. When a transparent film is present on glass the optical path difference between the waves reflected from the two film boundaries is $2 n_f t \cos \phi$, as shown in Fig. 2.10, where n_f is the film index, t the thickness and ϕ the angle of refraction and reflection within the film. When the optical retardation is a half wavelength, *i.e.* the optical thickness of the film at normal incidence is $\lambda/4$, then the waves reflected from the film boundaries are out of phase. It can be shown that at a given wavelength the resultant amplitude of the interfering waves (taking into account multiple reflections) is reduced to zero at normal incidence when $n_f = \sqrt{n_g n_o}$, where n_g and n_o are the indices of the glass and surrounding medium (normally air) respectively. The transmitted waves are reinforced by the suppression of the reflected light. Light may be suppressed by films which are odd multiples of a quarter of a wavelength thick, *e.g.* $3\lambda/4$, $5\lambda/4$, etc., but a first-order film is the most effective in reducing the reflection over a range of wavelengths. It can be shown from equation (3) on p. 89 for the reflectance of a thin film on glass that when a low index film is a $\lambda/2$-thick and of *uniform* index the reflection at the maximum is the same as that of the unfilmed glass.

The reflectance of glass can be raised by depositing a film of a high index dielectric on its surface. When the film has an optical thickness of $\lambda/4$ the waves reflected from the two film boundaries at normal incidence reinforce because there is no reflection phase change at the inner film surface (see Fig. 2.10).

Anti-reflection films which are chemically produced lack durability because they are porous and they are no longer used for practical purposes. Following the early work of Strong (1936) who evaporated durable $\lambda/4$-films of calcium fluoride on to glass in vacuum, the modern technique is to evaporate the low index layer.

Magnesium fluoride is normally evaporated because the films have a fairly low index and when baked become exceptionally hard. In fact sensitive glasses which are easily attacked in the atmosphere can often be partially protected after optical working if they are immediately coated with magnesium fluoride.

The chemically produced layer is usually less effective optically than the vacuum deposited film. Thus Jacobs (1943) has stated that as a general rule the reflection from high index glasses ($\geqslant 1\cdot6$) is reduced by the chemical technique to about 20% of its original value and for low index glasses ($\simeq 1\cdot5$) reduced only to about 75% of its initial value. A single evaporated M_gF_2-film is very effective on high index glass ($\geqslant 1\cdot6$) and has a minimum reflection on low index glass ($\simeq 1\cdot5$) of about 25% of the uncoated value. Shown in Fig. 2·14 is the transmittance of evaporated and chemically prepared layers as a function of wavelength; the data for the chemically produced films is based on transmission values reported by Schroeder (1941).

There is evidence that the chemically produced films are not of uniform index, but such films must terminate internally with a well defined boundary, otherwise optical interference could not occur. Thus the curves in Fig. 2.14 for the chemically treated heavy crown glass ($n_g = 1\cdot59$) can be matched to calculated curves for $\lambda/4$-films having a mean index of 1·441 and thicknesses of 920 and 1170 Å.

One would expect that if the index of a porous silica film was to vary it would be lowest at the air/film boundary, *i.e.* the film would tend to be a transition layer between air and glass. However films of porous silica have been formed on plate glass in which silica has been deposited in the outer pores thereby forming a two-layer film or a transition layer with a higher index *at the air boundary*. Nicholl (1952) treated low index glass either with hydrofluoric acid vapours or a bath of fluosilicic acid containing silica. Using the latter treatment he found that when the surface layer was above $\lambda/2$ in thickness it had formed two zones. The zone next to the glass was porous with an index between 1·28 to 1·46 and the outer zone had the index of silica (1·46) because silica had been deposited in the porous glass from the solution.

Low index glass. The refractive index of magnesium fluoride is 1·38 and it does not efficiently reduce the reflection from glasses with an index below 1·6. No material has been found which can be evaporated to form absorption free and durable films with an index of about 1·23 suitable for coating low index glass ($n_g \simeq 1·5$).

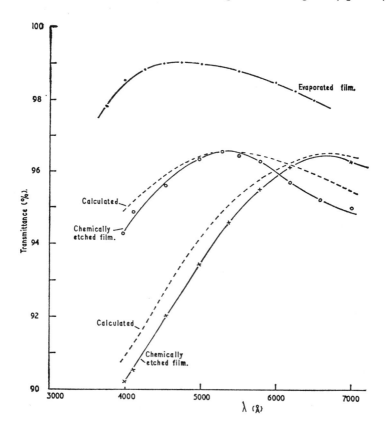

FIG. 2.14 TRANSMITTANCE OF GLASS WITH ANTI-REFLECTION FILM. CHEMICALLY TREATED GLASS $n_g = 1·59$ WITH TWO SURFACE LAYERS PREPARED BY SCHROEDER (1941) CORRESPONDING TO A MEAN INDEX OF 1·441 AND THICKNESSES OF 920 AND 1170 Å. EVAPORATED MgF_2-FILM ($n_f \simeq 1·38$) ON GLASS ($n_g = 1·625$).

Glass plate has been prepared commercially with a fine ground surface which is intended for use in instrument windows, etc. The irregular surface prevents a coherent reflected image being formed which would confuse the viewer's vision. A reasonable transmitted image can be obtained for the reason given in Section 1 of this chapter.

Several multi-layer interference systems, using high and low refractive index films, have been proposed for suppressing the reflectance of low index glass. Such interference systems are arranged so that the amplitudes of the light reflected from the various film boundaries sum to zero at one or more wavelengths in the visible region. This is achieved by controlling the optical thicknesses of the films so that the phase angle between the reflected components at a given wavelength results in a closed vector. However, the fact that one did not have to use a film with an index obeying the square root relation did not immediately simplify the practical problem of treating low index glass, because it proved equally difficult to prepare absorption-free films of high index materials. Thus, of the metal oxides with a high index, only the rare earth oxides and cerium oxide, which is the most notable, evaporate in vacuum without dissociation and produce absorption-free films. The rare earth oxides evaporate at very high temperatures and their rate of deposition is difficult to control.

Holland and Putner (1959) have devised a practical anti-reflection coating which is used effectively on glasses having an index from 1·5 to 1·6. The coating consists of a high index layer of bismuth oxide followed by a low index film of magnesium fluoride, the layers have an optical thickness of 0·049λ and 0·33λ respectively. The two films are prepared in sequence by a procedure developed by the writer (1956*b*) which consists of first sputtering bismuth in a glow discharge in oxygen, thereby producing a transparent oxide film, and afterwards evaporating the magnesium fluoride in high vacuum. When the films are baked at 300°c they are exceptionally hard. The reflectance of this type of two-layer system rises more steeply on the short wavelength side of the minimum value and to obtain the best overall response the reflection minimum must be made to occur at $\lambda = 5000$ Å and not at $\lambda = 5500$ Å as is usual with single layer films. In this way the reflectance of a low index glass can be reduced to zero at $\lambda = 5000$ Å and the reflectance kept below 0·5% throughout most of the visible spectrum. Although the plant cost for this technique is more than that for chemical methods its effectiveness makes it valuable when treating optical elements of low index and plate glass used for instrument windows, etc.

Shown in Fig. 2.15 are the reflectance values as a function of wavelength of a series of two-layer coatings with their reflectance minima set at different wavelengths. A full description of the method of treatment and optical control of the film thickness is given by Holland and Putner.

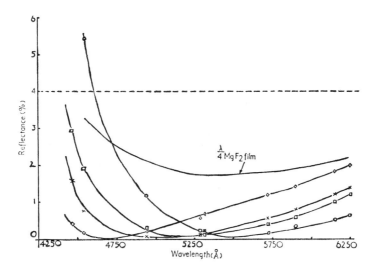

FIG. 2.15   REFLECTANCE OF TWO-LAYER ANTI-REFLECTION COATING (0·049 λ $Bi_2O_3/0·33\lambda MgF_2$) AS A FUNCTION OF WAVELENGTH ON GLASS ($n_g = 1·5$) WITH MINIMUM AT DIFFERENT WAVELENGTHS; CURVE OF SINGLE-LAYER MgF_2-FILM INCLUDED FOR COMPARISON. THE DOTTED LINE IS THE REFLECTANCE OF THE UNTREATED GLASS (*After Holland and Putner*, 1959).

Water adsorption. It has been shown that the surface layers which form on chemically attacked glass are porous and mainly silica in content. This layer may be weakened by water adsorption and thickened by water erosion of the underlying glass. It has been claimed that the silica layer may be rendered more durable and dense by sintering at high temperature.

The index of porous silica films will rise if they are filled with another substance *e.g.* grease or water. Coelingh (1939) used an optical method to determine the sorption of vapours by weathered glass. She noted that interference colours on the walls of a flask showed sharp changes as the temperature was varied. Coelingh attributed the colour changes to capillaries in the glass surface being filled or emptied of liquid. The changes in temperature produced changes in the relative pressure of the vapour. If the distribution of the pore sizes in the surface layer was discontinuous then capillaries of a given size would be suddenly emptied or filled when a certain relative pressure was reached and thereby produce a rapid change in the interference colour. Noting the relative pressure at which the colour changes one can find the capillary radius from the Kelvin equation

$$P_e = P_0 \exp\left(-\frac{2\gamma V \cos\theta}{rRT}\right)$$

where P_e is the equilibrium pressure, P_0 the vapour pressure, γ the surface tension, V the molar volume, θ the contact angle; R the gas constant, T the temperature in degK, and r the radius of the capillary in which adsorption occurs.

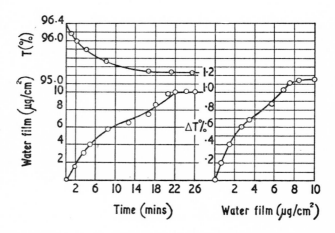

FIG. 2.16   THE EFFECT OF WATER VAPOUR ABSORPTION ON THE TRANSMISSION OF A GLASS WITH AN ACID PRODUCED AND DRIED ANTI-REFLECTION COATING (*After Schroeder*, 1941).

Schroeder (1941) studied the effect of moisture adsorption on the transmittance of an anti-reflection layer produced by chemical means. Shown in Fig. 2.16 is the influence of the water formation on the anti-reflection coating after the surface had been dried by baking at 150°c and then exposed in a wet atmosphere. It can be seen that the transmission of the glass falls as the weight of adsorbed moisture and the film index rise.

Surface stains. When glass is coated with evaporated interference films the presence of chemical stains may be exposed if they locally increase the optical thickness of the superimposed film. The wave reflected from the interface separating a low index film from a surface stain usually has a small amplitude because the indices of the films are similar and can therefore be neglected. The optical thickness of a $\lambda/4$-film varies from 1125–1625 Å when the film changes from straw to magenta in reflection colour corresponding to an interference minimum moving from the blue to the red end of the spectrum. Thus if a stain is present with a low index ($\simeq 1.3$) and of an optical thickness of, say, 250 Å then this will shift the reflection minimum of a superimposed anti-reflection film 1000 Å. If the glass has been coated with a magenta reflecting film (enhanced green transmission) the existence of such a stain would shift the transmission maximum to red and produce a blue–green reflection colour. Miyake (1957) has made a study of the effect of stains on anti-reflection films.

4. OPTICAL ASSESSMENT OF SURFACE FINISH

It is shown at the beginning of this chapter that an optically polished glass surface only needs to be smooth in keeping with its optical task. For general reflection or refraction purposes surface pits or prominences can be tolerated whose size is a small fraction (< 0.01) of the wavelength of the incident light. Surface disorders of small magnitude may however influence certain optical processes, for example the band-width of the pass-band of Fabry–Perot type interference filters is greatly influenced by irregularities in the opposed reflecting surfaces. For this and other reasons it is valuable to know the order of magnitude of the defects in glass surfaces.

Electron microscopy offers a useful method of studying the finish of glass surface, as shown in Chapter 1, because a large horizontal magnification can be obtained. The heights or depths of disorders in surface replicas may be laterally amplified using shadow-casting techniques, but this is of limited value with, say, partly worked glass surfaces, because the shadows of prominencies are projected on to an uneven plane. Also, electron microscopy is unable at present to resolve the surface structure of the finest polished surface. Optical techniques provide a way of detecting surface disorder if they introduce differences in the optical paths of reflected or transmitted waves. Thus, multiple beam interferometry, discussed at length below, provides vertical magnification of surface irregularities. Other optical methods have been used for studying surface disorder such as phase contrast microscopy (Cagnet *et al.* 1962) and schlieren techniques (Meyer-Arendt 1956), but these do not differentiate between optical path differences arising from either refractive index variations in the surface or departure from the geometrical plane.

Multiple beam interferometry

Optical interferometry is commonly used for determining the profile of optical elements and by a refinement of technique it is also possible to detect local disorders in optically worked surfaces. Thus interference fringes showing the contour of a surface can be sufficiently sharpened so that asperities and pits in the surface produce discernible displacements in the fringes. Interference fringes of high contrast are obtained if the reflectance of the surfaces being studied is increased by coating them with partially reflecting silver films evaporated in vacuum. This technique, used in the Fabry–Perot interferometer, has been primarily developed for the study of surfaces by Tolansky (1948) and his co-workers. The silver films deposited on the interferometer plates are aggregates of microcrystallites and thus are not themselves entirely free from surface disorder even when deposited on liquid smooth substrates. It has been shown that the size and density of the crystallites in silver films formed on surfaces under similar conditions depend on the nature of the surface material. Thus if the composition of a glass varied over the surface plane then the structure of the silver deposit would not necessarily be the same all over the surface, but at present there is no direct evidence for this.

Several multiple beam interference systems have been devised but there are certain common expressions relating the intensity of the transmitted light to the interferometer spacing and wavelength of the incident light. Thus when light of intensity $\mathbf{I}_0$ is incident at an angle θ on an interferometer with a pair of adjacent silvered surfaces with an air gap y the intensity of the transmitted light is given by

$$\mathbf{I} = \mathbf{I}_0 \left[\left(1 + \frac{\mathbf{A}}{\mathbf{T}} \right)^2 + \frac{4\mathbf{R}}{(1-\mathbf{R})^2} \sin^2 \left(\frac{\delta}{2} + \beta \right) \right]^{-1}$$

where $\delta = 2\pi(2y \cos \theta)/\lambda$ is the phase difference between successively reflected beams; $\mathbf{R} + \mathbf{T} + \mathbf{A} = 1$ and $\mathbf{R}$, $\mathbf{T}$ and $\mathbf{A}$ are the reflection, transmission and absorption coefficients respectively of the silver films measured in the direction air to silver boundary; β is the phase change for light reflected from the air to silver boundary.

From the foregoing can be derived the maximum and minimum of the transmission, that is

$$\left(\frac{I}{I_0}\right)_{max} = \left(1 + \frac{A}{T}\right)^{-2} \quad \text{and} \quad \left(\frac{I}{I_0}\right)_{min} = \left(\frac{T}{1+R}\right)^2$$

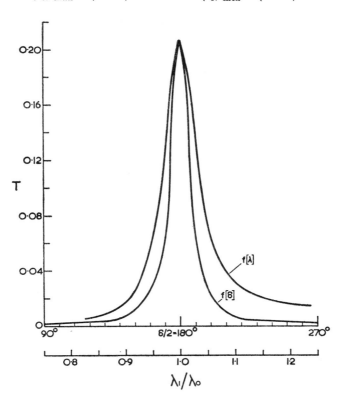

FIG. 2.17   VARIATION OF TRANSMITTED INTENSITY WITH SEPARATION FOR TWO PARALLEL PLATES COATED WITH SILVER FOR WHICH $R = 0.9$, $T = 0.045$

The relation between the transmitted intensity and the plate separation for the mercury green line 5461 Å has been plotted in Fig. 2.17, assuming the practical case of silver films with a transmittance of 0.045 and a reflectance of 0.9. The intensity distribution in Fig. 2.17 has also been related to the wavelength of the incident light for the case of a first order filter with uniform plate separation. The half-width of such a filter is approximately given by

$$\Delta\lambda_{1/2} = \frac{\lambda(1-\mathbf{R})}{m\pi\mathbf{R}^{1/2}}$$

where m is the interference order and $m\pi = \delta/2$.

These expressions will be referred to again in the discussion below.

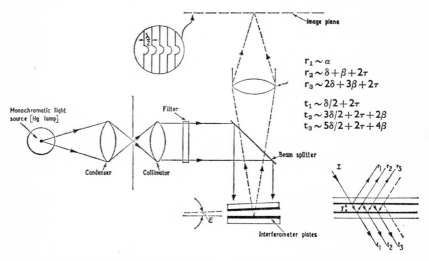

FIG. 2.18 APPARATUS FOR STUDYING SURFACE DISORDER USING FIZEAU FRINGES OF EQUAL THICKNESS. SHARP INTERFERENCE FRINGES ARE OBTAINED WHEN THE INTERFEROMETER PLATES ARE SILVERED.

Fizeau fringes. When a pair of glass plates are separated by a narrow wedge angle and illuminated at normal incidence by monochromatic light as in Fig. 2.18 then Fizeau fringes of equal thickness are formed. If the plates are coated with highly reflecting silver films with a small transmittance and viewed with a low-power microscope the fringes form bright fine lines against a dark background in transmission and dark fine lines against a bright background in reflection. The interference fringes tend to occur in transmission at points along the wedge where the phase difference between the reflected waves (including phase changes produced by reflection) is $2n\pi$ and in reflection where the phase difference is $(2n-1)\pi$. Pits or scratches in the surface planes of the glasses will produce displacements in the fringes as shown in Fig. 2.18. Thus the height or depth of a disorder can be found from the fraction of a fringe it occupies.

As the reflection coefficient of the silver films is increased the half-width of the fringes decrease, *i.e.* the fringes become sharper. However, with silver films raising the reflectance from, say, 80 to 90% increases the absorption from about 3·5 to 5·5% and this decreases the contrast or visibility of the fringes in terms of the quantity $(\mathbf{I}_{max} - \mathbf{I}_{min})$.

The contrast of reflected fringes is much greater than that of transmitted fringes and their half-width is smaller. For these reasons the reflected fringes are normally used for measurement purposes. Holden (1949) has shown that a slight rise in the absorption of a highly reflecting silver film $(\mathbf{R} = 90\%)$ greatly reduces the contrast factor of reflected fringes. To obtain efficient silver films the coatings must be evaporated in a good vacuum and used before their absorption rises due to deterioration in the atmosphere.

Two other matters are of importance when using reflected fringes: these are the effective increase in path difference due to the phase changes which the waves undergo on reflection or transmission through the silver films, and the effect of the wedge angle between the plates on the fringe symmetry.

Examination of the reflection of the waves in a parallel plate interferometer (Fig. 2.18), shows that the multiply reflected components in the transmitted beam suffer a phase retardation of $\delta + 2\beta$, every time they traverse the interferometer gap, where β is the phase change for reflection from air to silver. All waves undergo a phase change τ when passing through a silver film. The reflection phase change can be considered as an effective increase in the path difference between the plates, but as shown on p. 116, β is almost equal to π for high reflecting silver deposits. Holden (1949) has shown that with reflection fringes the beam reflected from the glass to silver boundary (*i.e.* r_1 in Fig. 2.18) undergoes a phase change α which introduces an out-of-balance component. Multiply reflected waves increase their phase difference with respect to r_2 by $\delta + 2\beta$ every time they traverse the interferometer. The out-of-balance component r_1 is responsible for producing asymmetrical fringes when $R > 15\%$ but when the plates are highly reflecting its effect on the summation of the interfering waves is negligible. Thus for $R > 85\%$ Holden found that the fringe asymmetry was not greater than that due to focusing defects and the wedge angle effect considered below.

When interference occurs in a wedge the path difference traversed by a multiply reflected wave successively rises as a consequence of the growing wedge spacing. For a parallel plate of gap y the phase difference of the nth beam due to the air gap is ny, but if the reflections occur in a wedge the phase difference in the nth beam at the point where the separation is also y will be less than ny. Brossel (1947) has shown that the phase of the nth beam with respect to the direct at a point where the air gap is y is closely given by

$$\phi_n = n\delta - \tfrac{4}{3}n^3y\epsilon^2 \cdot 2\pi/\lambda$$

where ϵ is the wedge angle. If $\tfrac{4}{3}n^3y\epsilon^2 = \lambda/2$ then the nth beam will oppose the direct. It is important to keep a small gap and wedge angle between the interferometer plates and minimize this effect which produces broader and asymmetrical fringes. The fringes must be viewed with a low-power microscope ($\times 50$) because, at high magnification, a large wedge angle is required to obtain a reasonable number of fringes in the field of view. The number of fringes per cm X is related to the wedge angle by $\epsilon = X\lambda/2$.

Kinosita (1953) has calculated the intensity distribution of a multiple-beam Fizeau fringe for a given set of conditions. Thus for silver reflecting films ($\mathbf{R} = 0\cdot9$ $\mathbf{T} = 0\cdot02$) and $\epsilon = 0\cdot01$ rad. (100 fringes/cm) the sixth order fringe ($m = 2y/\lambda$) was asymmetric with its maximum occurring at $m = 6\cdot01$. The maximum intensity of the fringe was 80% of that obtained with a parallel plate system as in Fig. 2.17.

DETERMINATION OF SURFACE IRREGULARITIES USING PARALLEL PLATE SYSTEM

Heavens (1951) studied the surface structure of glass specimens employing the method used by Tolansky and Wilcock (1946) for examining crystal surfaces. Two silvered glass specimens are placed *parallel* and close to one another. The intensity of monochromatic light transmitted by the system depends on the separation of the surfaces and passes through a sharp maximum for separations $m(\lambda/2)$, where m is an integer. Shown in Fig. 2.17 is the intensity distribution as a function of plate separation and, as can be seen, the intensity changes rapidly with the spacing in the region of half the peak intensity. The variation in intensity of the interferometer can be recorded on a photograph and its density determined. Then, by relating the density measured along a line to the curve in Fig.

2.17, the combined irregularities of the glass specimens can be found.

Heavens examined a pair of optical flats which over a diameter of 6 cm were claimed to be flat to within λ/20, and a pair of optical window glasses 2·2 cm × 1·1 cm which, over their area, were flat to within one or two wavelengths. Each photographic record covered a section of the specimens 4 mm in diameter. Two records were taken at each position on the flats with the separation adjusted to give slightly over and under half maximum intensity. In this way regions of low sensitivity on one photograph fell on the high sensitivity part of the second record. The resolving power of the microphotometer permitted irregularities to be detected over dis-

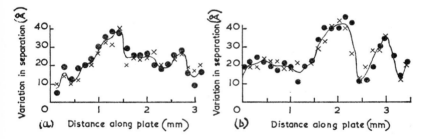

Fig. 2.19   Surface irregularities determined by multiple beam interferometry (*After Heavens*, 1951). (a) Two zeiss optical flats, (b) optical window glass matched against a zeiss flat.

tances along lines of the surfaces of about 30 μ. The results obtained for the two types of worked glass are shown in Fig. 2.19(a) and (b).

Fringes of equal chromatic order. If the interferometer used in the Fizeau system is illuminated with white light instead of monochromatic radiation, and the light reflected from the interference region projected on to the slit of a spectroscope, as in Fig. 2.20, then dark fringes can be observed in an otherwise continuous spectrum. When both silver films are transparent fringes may be observed in the transmitted light. These white light fringes have been termed by Tolansky *fringes of equal chromatic order*. The fringes are localized in the air gap between the specimen and reference plates and are in focus when the image of the plane of the gap is projected on to the slit of the spectroscope. Each fringe forms a contour line of a

8

region of the interference film whose area is equal to that of the spectroscope slit divided by the magnification of the projection lens L2. Fringes of equal chromatic order possess certain advantages over Fizeau fringes for measurement purposes. Thus, as the silvered surfaces are parallel, there is no fringe broadening due to a wedge effect (see p. 112) and the projection lens may be a high power microscope objective.

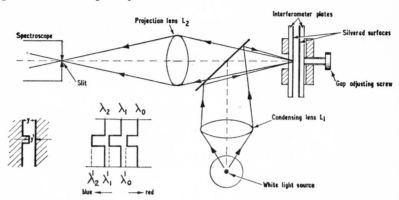

FIG. 2.20 APPARATUS FOR PRODUCING MULTIPLE BEAM FRINGES OF EQUAL CHROMATIC ORDER BY REFLECTION AND APPEARANCE OF FRINGES WITH AN IRREGULARITY ON ONE OF THE INTERFEROMETER PLATES.

The relation between one of the wavelengths λ at which a maximum in the *transmitted* light occurs and the geometric separation y of the reflecting surfaces for light at normal incidence is given by

$$m\lambda = 2y + \lambda\beta(\lambda)/\pi \tag{1}$$

where m is the fringe order and β is the phase change on reflection from a silver surface. It has already been shown for Fizeau fringes that there is an out-of-balance component with *reflected* fringes due to a reflection from the glass to silver boundary and this also applies to fringes of equal chromatic order. However, as with Fizeau fringes, the effect of this component can be neglected when highly reflecting silver films are used ($R > 85\%$). Reflection fringes have the highest contrast factor and are thus normally used for measuring surface defects.

Consider two successive fringes at λ_0 and λ_1 as in Fig. 2.20. The order number of the fringe at the longer wavelength λ_0 is one less than the order number, $m+1$, of the adjacent fringe at λ_1. Equation (1) above becomes

$$m\lambda_0 = 2y + 2x(\lambda_0) \tag{2}$$

$$(m+1)\lambda_1 = 2y + 2x(\lambda_1) \tag{3}$$

where the reflection phase shift β is expressed as a function of wavelength in terms of an equivalent path length $x = \lambda\beta(\lambda)/2\pi$. If now we consider a projection in the plane of one of the interferometer plates the separation in that region becomes y' displacing the adjacent fringes to λ_0' and λ_1'. The conditions for maximum are now

$$m\lambda_0' = 2y' + 2x(\lambda_0') \tag{4}$$

$$(m+1)\lambda_1' = 2y' + 2x(\lambda_1') \tag{5}$$

Following Koester (1958) the fringe order is given by

$$m = \frac{\lambda_1}{\lambda_0 - \lambda_1} + 2\frac{x(\lambda_0) - x(\lambda_1)}{\lambda_0 - \lambda_1} \tag{6}$$

and the height of the projection by

$$y - y' = (\lambda_0 - \lambda_0')\left[\frac{1}{2}\frac{\lambda_1}{\lambda_0 - \lambda_1} + \frac{x(\lambda_0) - x(\lambda_1)}{\lambda_0 - \lambda_1}\right] - [x(\lambda_0) - x(\lambda_0')] \tag{7}$$

It has been usual to derive an approximate and simple equation for the fringe displacement by assuming that x is either zero or does not change with wavelength, *i.e.* is equal to a constant optical length. Equations (6) and (7) then reduce to

$$m = \frac{\lambda_1}{\lambda_0 - \lambda_1} \tag{8}$$

$$y - y' = \tfrac{1}{2}(\lambda_0 - \lambda_0')\frac{\lambda_1}{\lambda_0 - \lambda_1} \tag{9}$$

Koehler (1953a) found that the reflection phase change between successively reflected waves was independent of wavelength in the measured range 4500–6300 Å providing the films had a reflectance above 60% and were freshly deposited. If the phase change is independent of wavelength then one can write for the equivalent path differences at λ_0, $x_0 = \lambda_0\beta/2\pi$ and at λ_1, $x_1 = \lambda_1\beta/2\pi$. When we substitute these for $x(\lambda)$ in equation (7) we obtain

$$y - y' = \tfrac{1}{2}(\lambda_0 - \lambda_0')\left[\frac{\lambda_1}{\lambda_0 - \lambda_1} + \frac{\beta}{\pi}\right] - \left[\frac{\beta}{2\pi}(\lambda_0 - \lambda_0')\right] \tag{10}$$

which reduces to the simple formula (9) above. The fringe order is given by

$$m = \frac{\lambda_1}{\lambda_0 - \lambda_1} + \frac{\beta}{\pi} \qquad (11)$$

Koehler found that β/π was between 0·9 and 1·0 for the visible region. If one uses the simple formula and takes the fringe order m to the nearest whole number then the elementary equation (8) gives an order of interference one less than that derived from equation (11) assuming $\beta/\pi = 1$. When $\beta/\pi = 0·9$ and $m = 2$ then $\lambda_1/(\lambda_0 - \lambda_1)$ $= 1·1$, whereas the measured value based on the simple theory would here have been taken as 1. The possible error in the measurement of a surface displacement due to β departing from π or being a function of λ becomes less as the fringe order is raised.

When both the test and reference plates are of similar roughness then the variation in the air gap y will be the result of the addition of the local disorders. Thus when polished surfaces are being examined there may be zones where pits and asperities on opposing plates combine to give a maximum or minimum air gap.

Experimental results. Koehler (1953b) has studied the fringes obtained with optically worked glass as the test plate and a cleavage face of Topaz as the reference plate. The optically worked glass had been polished with Barnesite for 450 min. Plate 13(b) shows a drawing of the surface contour of the glass derived from the interferogram in Plate 13(a). The surface contour of the glass was obtained by tracing over an enlargement of one of the fringes.

Shown in Plate 14(a) are the fringes formed between two glass surfaces which had been fine ground and polished with Barnesite for 20 min. The resultant fringes represent the combined roughness of both glasses as shown in Plate 14(b). The sharp peaks in the fringes corresponding to abrupt discontinuities in the polished surface are believed to be wide grinding cracks, because they disappear as polishing proceeds.

Plate 15 shows the fringes formed between two glass surfaces which had been fine-ground and polished for 330 min. In this case the bending of the fringes is attributed to a grinding pit.

When the surfaces of the test glasses were scanned the peaks of the cusps in the fringes rose to a maximum and diminished within a distance separating two cusps. It was concluded that the cusps were not cross-sections of furrows but the contour lines of cones with conchoidal sides. The cones had a mean height less than 60 Å and a base diameter less than 0·01 mm. Koehler believed that the surface contour obtained was evidence that flow had not occurred and the surface had been smoothed by the rouge particles having a uniform planing action, as discussed on p. 24. Thus the surface cones were produced by the repeated crossing of the planing tracks due to the relative motion of glass and pitch lap. Undoubtedly these interferograms substantiate the planing theory but they cannot be taken as evidence against possible surface flow. Such a surface finish could be obtained by the rouge particles producing smooth furrows which repeatedly cross one another. Thus surface flow may have occurred within the scratches as discussed on p. 36. Failure to obtain uniform surface flow could be due to the load on the polisher being insufficient either to generate frictional heat for overall thermal-plastic flow or to drive the rouge particles out of the space between lap and glass surface.

In a further paper Koehler and White (1955a) made an estimate of the combined effects of fringe order and the slope of the reflecting faces of the surface irregularities on the fringe fine structure. Mention has already been made in the discussion of Fizeau fringes of the effect of the wedge angle on the fringe symmetry and whilst this does not apply to fringes of equal chromatic order produced with plane parallel plates it does apply to deviations in the fringes arising from surface disorder. Koehler and White found that a cusp produced in a fringe formed by two polished glasses corresponded closely to the actual shape of the combined surface disorders, because the inclination of irregularities on polished glass to the general surface plane was small (10^{-3} radians).

Half-width determination. It is possible to study the effect of irregularities in glass surfaces on the half-width ($\Delta\lambda_{1/2}$) of the interference fringes. An expression relating $\Delta\lambda_{1/2}$, *i.e.* the band-width at half peak intensity, to the reflectance of the coatings on the interferometer plates and the interference order has been given on p. 110. There it is shown that $\Delta\lambda_{1/2}$ is inversely proportional to the interference order $m = 2y/\lambda_1$ where y is the plate spacing. If the interferometer plates have disordered surfaces these will combine to increase or decrease the spacing resulting in widening of the fringes. Koehler and White (1955b) have measured the half-widths of multiple-beam fringes of equal chromatic order and related them to surface roughness; typical fringes are shown in Plate 16. Shown in Fig. 2.21

are the calculated and measured half-widths of a fringe at $\lambda = 5350$ Å versus m when produced between two silvered polished glass plates. It can be seen that the experimental points in Fig. 2.21 can be represented by the linear equation

$$\Delta\lambda_{1/2} = (\Delta\lambda_{1/2})_0 + S(2/m)$$

where S exceeds the ideal value because of roughness of the interferometer surfaces. An independent measurement of the roughness can be made as follows. A cross-hair is placed along the

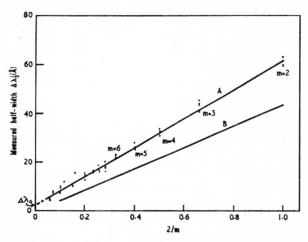

FIG. 2.21 A. MEASURED HALF-WIDTHS OF AN EQUAL CHROMATIC ORDER FRINGE OF DIFFERENT INTERFERENCE ORDERS AT $\lambda = 5350$ Å (*After Koehler and White*, 1955). B. HALF-WIDTHS CALCULATED FOR COMPLETELY SMOOTH INTERFEROMETER PLATES ASSUMING A REFLECTANCE OF 95%.

central part of a fringe and a second cross-hair is then placed so that it corresponds to given elevations above the general plane. The observer can then count along the fringe the number of irregularities with heights h greater than 10, 20, 30 Å, etc. By plotting a distribution curve one can derive the root-mean-square height h (rms). Using the same set of fringes employed for determining the half-width Koehler and White obtained a value of h (rms) = 68 Å compared with $S = 60$ Å. Measurement on some ten optical flats polished under similar conditions showed that h (rms) had an average value of $67\cdot5 \pm 0\cdot5$ Å compared with an average value for S of 60 ± 1 Å.

Table 2.3

Roughness of the combined glass surfaces determined from half-widths of inter-ference fringes after 5 hours of fresh-feed polishing with Barnesite, water and a pitch lap

(*After Koehler and White, 1955*)

Material of flats	h (rms) Å
Flint glass	154
Plate glass	68
Pyrex	51
Silica	36
Microscope slide (fire polished) †	56

† Measured on slides selected for flatness over an area 1 cm × 1 cm giving Fizeau fringes straight to within ¼ fringe.

Given in Table 2.3 are the h (rms) values for a range of polished glasses using pairs of specimen glasses. The specimens were $1 \times 1 \times 0.3$ cm and polished using the fresh feed method for 5 hours with Barnesite and water on a pitch lap; larger polishing periods did not improve the smoothness. The results show that the com-bined roughness decreases as the glass hardness increases. The roughness values are higher than those measured by Heavens (1951), (see p. 113), this may have been due to the continuous supply of polishing medium to the lap.

Fire polished slides. Scott *et al.* (1950) studied fringes of equal chromatic order and observed that with microscope slides the fringes were one quarter the width of those obtained with optical flats. This was attributed to the rolled or fire polished slides being smoother over distances of about 10 μ than flats which had been polished by an abrasive. Koehler and White (1955*b*) determined the combined roughness of microscope slides selected for overall flatness using Fizeau fringes described above. They found that the surface disorder was comparable to that of most optically worked glasses (see Table 2.3). Microscope slides are normally made from soda-lime glass and the state of the surface when measured would critically depend on the degree to which the surface had been eroded in the atmosphere.

References

Abelès, F., 1950, *J. Phys. Rad.*, **11**, 310.

Amy, P., 1927, *Rev. d'Opt.*, **6**, 305.

Bennett, H. E., and Porteus, J. O., 1961, *J. opt. Soc. Amer.*, **51**, 123.

Bishop, F. L., 1944, *J. Amer. ceram. Soc.*, **27**, 145.

Blodgett, K. B., 1939, *Phys. Rev.*, **55**, 391.

Brandt, H. M., 1938, *Glastechn. Ber.*, **16**, 123.

Brossel, J., 1947, *Proc. Phys. Soc.*, **59**, 224, 235.

Bugbee, L. W., 1919, U.S. Pat. No. 1,317,481.

Cagnet, M., Françon, M., and Thrierr, J. C., 1962, *Atlas of Optical Phenomena*, Springer-Verlag, Berlin.

Coelingh, M. B., 1939, *Kolloid-Zeit.*, **87**, 251.

Drude, P., 1891, *Wied. Ann.*, **43**, 126; *Lehrbuch der Optik* (Leipzig 1900); *The Theory of Optics* (Dover Publications, New York, 1959).

Ehrenberg, W., 1949, *J. opt. Soc. Amer.*, **39**, 746.

Heavens, O. S., 1951, *Proc. Phys. Soc.*, London, B, **64**, 419.

Heavens, O. S., 1955, *Optical Properties of Thin Solid Films*⌐Butterworths Scientific Publications, London.

Holden, J. 1949, *Proc. Phys. Soc.*, B, **62**, 405.

Holland, A. J., and Turner, W. E. S., 1941, *J. Soc. Glass Technol.*, **25**, 164.

Holland, L., 1956a, *Vacuum Deposition of Thin Films*, Chapman & Hall Ltd., London.

Holland, L., 1956b, *Nature*, **177**, 1229.

Holland, L., and Putner, T., 1959, *J. Sci. Instrum.*, **36**, 81.

Jacobs, D. H., 1943, *Fundamentals of Optical Engineering*, McGraw-Hill Book Company Inc., New York.

Jellyman, P. E., and Proctor, J. P., 1955, *J. Soc. Glass Technol.*, **39**, 173.

Kinosita, K., 1953, *J. Phys. Soc. Japan*, **8**, 219.

Koehler, W. F., 1953a, *J. opt. Soc. Amer.*, **43**, 738.

Koehler, W. F., 1953b, *J. opt. Soc. Amer.*, **43**, 743.

Koehler, W. F., and White, W. C., 1955a, *J. opt. Soc. Amer.*, **45**, 940.

Koehler, W. F., and White, W. C., 1955b, *J. opt. Soc. Amer.*, **45**, 1011.

Koester, C. J., 1958, *J. opt. Soc. Amer.*, **48**, 255.

Kollmorgen, F., 1916, *Trans. Illum. Engng. Soc.*, **11**, 220.

Knowles Middleton, W. E., and Wyszecki, G., 1957, *J. opt. Soc. Amer.*, **47**, 1020.

Mayer, H., 1950, *Physik Dünner Schichten*, 1st Ed., Wissenschaftliche Verlagsgesellschaft M.B.H. (Stuttgart).

Meyer-Arendt, J. R., 1956, *J. opt. Soc. Amer.*, **46**, 1090.

Miyake, K., 1957 Dec., *Science of Light*, Tokyo, **6**, 85.

Nicoll, F. H., 1942, *R.C.A. Rev.*, **6**, 287.

Nicoll, F. H., 1952, *J. opt. Soc. Amer.*, **42**, 241.

Nicoll, F. H., and Williams, F. E., 1943, *J. opt. Soc. Amer.*, **33**, 434.

Pfund, A. H., 1941, *J. opt. Soc. Amer.*, **31**, 679.

Pfund, A. H., 1946, *J. opt. Soc. Amer.*, **36**, 95.

Philpot, A. J., 1931, *A Study of Polished Glass Surfaces*, British Sci. Instrum. Res. Assoc., Rep. R. 74.

Rayleigh, Lord, J. W. S., 1892–1901, *Scientific Papers*, vol. 4, pp. 54, 74, 542, University Press (Cambridge, 1903).

Rayleigh, Lord, 1937, *Proc. roy. Soc.*, **160**, 507.
Schroeder, H., 1941, *Z. Tech. Phys.*, **22**, 38, 75.
Scott, G. D., McLauchlan, T. A., and Sennett, R. S., 1950, *J. appl. Phys.*, **21**, 843.
Strong, J., 1936, *J. opt. Soc. Amer.*, **26**, 73.
Taylor, H. D., 1896, *The Adjustment and Testing of Telescope Objectives*, 2nd Ed., T. Cooke and Sons, York, 1921.
Taylor, H. D., 1904 Dec., Brit. Pat. No. 29561.
Tolansky, S., 1948, *Multiple Beam Interferometry*, University Press, Oxford.
Tolansky, S., and Wilcock, W. L., 1946, *Nature, Lond.*, **157**, 583.
Traub, A. C., and Osterberg, H., 1957, *J. opt. Soc. Amer.*, **47**, 62.
Vašiček, A., 1947a, *J. opt. Soc. Amer.*, **37**, 145.
Vašiček, A., 1947b, *J. opt. Soc. Amer.*, **37**, 979.
Vašiček, A., 1940c, *Phys. Rev.*, **57**, 925.
Vašiček, A., 1960, *Optics of Thin Films*, North Holland Publishing Co., Amsterdam.

CHAPTER 3

Surface Chemistry and Corrosion of Glass

On the Changes produced by Electricity in Water.

The appearance of acid and alkaline matter in water acted on by a current of electricity, at the opposite electrified metallic surfaces was observed in the first chemical experiments made with the column of VOLTA. . . .

In cases when I had procured much soda, the glass at its point of contact with the wire seemed considerably corroded; and I was confirmed in my idea of referring the production of the alkali principally to this source, by finding that no fixed saline matter could be obtained, by electrifying distilled water in a single agate cup from two points of platina connected with the VOLTAIC battery.†

1. INTRODUCTION

Most silicate glasses in general use have a high resistance to corrosion and this has led many workers erroneously to treat glass as if it was an inert substance. Certain special types of optical glass are readily stained in the atmosphere or etched by very mild acids and with these the effects of corrosion are easily observed. However, even apparently chemically resistant glasses undergo localized attack and their surface composition may be completely different from that of the underlying material. Surface phenomena such as adsorption of gases, reflection of light, etc., may be critically influenced by chemical corrosion of the glass surface even though it is on a minute scale.

Much of the work on the chemical attack of glass has had the practical purpose of determining the durability of different compositions when exposed to corrosive conditions. Complete discussion and review of all the literature which has been published on the chemical durability of glass would occupy several volumes and require the labour of many specialists. Beattie (1952) has reported a list of some 250 references dealing with corrosion of glass surfaces and his bibliography is not complete. Morey (1954) and Shand

---

† Humphry Davy, *The Bakerian Lecture* on some chemical agencies of electricity (November, 1806).

(1958) have reviewed the literature on the chemical durability of glasses and discussed the formulation of corrosion resistant types.

Durability assessments made from accelerated laboratory tests have often proved to be as critically dependent on the conditions of testing as on the glass under examination. This is because the reactions at the attacked surface are invariably complex and strongly influenced by slight changes in the concentration and temperature of the corrosive agent. Other important factors are the form of the glass (*i.e.* powder or bulk) and whether the reaction products or decomposed glass become detached from the attacked surface during corrosion. Thus much of the work in this field is empirical and the published results cannot be generalized.

The prime aim in this work of discussing the chemical corrosion of glass is to enhance the reader's appreciation of related subjects such as the chemical cleaning of glass or processes influenced by chemical attack, *e.g.* optical working, gas sorption and optical properties. Consequently unnecessary discussion on durability assessment methods has been avoided and principal attention has been given to the mechanism of attack under specified conditions. Needless to say, in a field where specification of the experimental conditions is so important, the writer's review work has all too often been frustrated by incomplete reporting.

2. GENERAL CORROSION PROPERTIES

Glass articles may be exposed in normal use to the chemical attack of water, acid, alkali and salt solutions and gases and vapours in the atmosphere, *e.g.* water vapour, carbon dioxide, sulphur dioxide, etc. Corrosion may occur in one or a combination of several ways; thus the glass may

(*i*) react with the corrosive materials to form new compounds on the surface;

(*ii*) be preferentially dissolved leaving a leached surface layer or

(*iii*) be totally dissolved continuously exposing fresh glass.

Types of glass exist which contain components that can be completely leached out from the *bulk* material and these are discussed separately at the end of the chapter.

We shall commence by considering generally the nature and degree of attack of various liquids and gases on different types of glass and then consider the mechanism of attack in detail.

COMPARATIVE RESISTANCE OF POWDERED AND PLATE GLASSES

A common method of determining the chemical resistance of glasses is to measure the amount of alkali dissolved in a solution, and powdered glass is sometimes used to obtain a large surface area for accelerated corrosion. However, due to the nature of the surface attack and changes in the composition of the corrosive liquid the results obtained with powder specimens may not always be directly applicable to bulk materials. But if changes in the attacking solution are avoided during dissolution then the results obtained with a powered specimen must indicate the *intrinsic* resistance of the particular glass composition to chemical attack.

Some of the problems of the powder method will become obvious from the work of Taylor and Smith (1936), who made a study of the alkali dissolved in water, acid and alkali from the range of glasses given in Table 3.1. Tests were made with powdered glass (40 to 50-mesh screen, size 0·295 to 0·417 mm). The soda-lime sample had a weight of 10 g and a surface area of about 7000 cm². When using glasses of different density the sample weight was adjusted to maintain a constant area. The extraction solutions (50 c.c in volume) consisted of water, N/50 H_2SO_4, and N/50 NaOH. Shown in Fig. 3.1 are the amounts of Na_2O dissolved from the glasses at 25° and 95°c after 4 hours.

Table 3.1
Composition of glasses studied by Taylor and Smith (1936)

	Percentage composition					
	A	B	C	D	E	F
SiO_2	81	73	72	63	35	60
R_2O_3	2	1	1	1	—	3
Na_2O	4	17	13	7	—	8
K_2O	—	—	—	7	7	—
B_2O_3	13	—	—	—	—	29
CaO	—	5	9	—	—	—
MgO	—	3	5	—	—	—
PbO	—	—	—	22	58	—

It will be noted that the order of the alkali solubilities† are similar for water and alkali solutions but are different with acid

† The word *solubility* is used here in a general sense to mean dissolution ability and has no specific physical or chemical meaning.

solutions. The results must only be taken as generally indicative of the relative resistances of the glasses to alkali extraction. Thus, after 4 hours at 25°c in water, the soda-lime glass B liberated more alkali than the sodium borosilicate glass F, but after 72 hours glass F liberated the most.

If the rate of attack is limited by a diffusion process, *i.e.* by migration of either the corrosive agent into the glass or the soluble

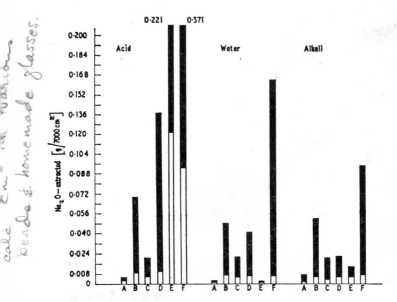

FIG. 3.1   ALKALI EXTRACTED FROM GLASS POWDERS AT 25°C (DOUBLE LINES) AND 90°C (SOLID BLACK) (*After Taylor and Smith*, 1936).

components to the glass surface, then the large area of attack of powdered material should result in them being leached faster than bulk glass. Shown in Table 3.2 is the *alkali extracted* from boro-silicate and soda-lime powder specimens with areas of 7000 cm² compared with the *weight lost* by plate glass specimens of 100 cm² area. The results show that the ratio of the material dissolved by acid to that dissolved by water is less than 1 for plate glass and greater than 1 for powder. The acid dissolves the alkali and basic oxides in the glasses at a greater rate than water and with plate glass the diffusion process slows down the attack. It is interesting to note that the ratio of the material dissolved by sodium hydroxide

Table 3.2

Comparative loss of material from two types of glass
in plate and powder form
(*After Taylor and Smith, 1936*)

	90°c – 4 h No. 1 powder method (g Na_2O/7000 cm²)			90°c – 100 h Loss-in-weight method (g glass/100 cm²)		
	N/50 H_2SO_4	Water	N/50 NaOH	N/50 H_2SO_4	Water	N/50 NaOH
Glass A	0·0047	0·0011	0·0062	0·00167	0·00184	0·0326
Ratio	4·27	1·0	5·64	0·9	1·0	18·6
Glass B	0·0594	0·0434	0·0401	0·00164	0·00502	0·0517
Ratio	1·36	1·0	0·92	0·33	1·0	10·5

solution to that dissolved by water is greater for the plate glass than for the powder. The reason for this is more fully discussed on p. 152, where it is shown that the rapid dissolution of silica from powdered glass in alkaline solutions reduces their rate of attack.

ATTACK BY WATER AND STEAM

General properties. Silica is almost insoluble in water except at high temperatures (> 250°c) and thus the attack of glass by water only occurs due to the existence of soluble components such as alkali. Simple alkali silicate glasses (*e.g.* sodium silicate) are fairly soluble, but the addition of lime and certain other oxides raises their water resistance. Dissolution of the alkali in glass will raise the alkalinity or pH value of the water so that other glass components will be attacked. When acid substances such as boric oxide are present in the glass they tend to be extracted and neutralize the alkali. Nordberg gives examples of the foregoing using powdered glass (40–60 mesh) specimens heated in water at 120°c for 1 h. With 10 g of glass in 100 c.c of water, soda-lime glass raised the pH of the water to above 11, whereas low expansion borosilicate glass (Corning 7740) increased it to only 8·5.

Shown in Table 3.3 is a classification, prepared by Nordberg, of different glass compositions according to their water resistance. Glasses marked excellent will normally be chemically resistant to water at temperatures under 100°c, whereas glasses classified fair to poor have limited application. The borosilicate sealing glasses have

Table 3.3

Water resistance of glasses
(*After Nordberg*)

Grading	Glass type	Corning glass number
Excellent	Silica	7940
	96% Silica	7900
	Durable borosilicate	7740, 7331, 7800
	Aluminosilicate	1710, 1720, 1723
	High lead	8870
Good	Soda lime	0080
	Alkali lead	0010, 0120
	Lead borosilicate	7720
	Borosilicate sealing	7052, 7055
Fair to poor	High alkali	——
	Borosilicate sealing	7040, 7050
	Calcium aluminate	——
	Phosphate	——
	Borate	——

more durable outer surfaces if the soda and boric oxide components evaporate during high temperature working.

Hubbard (1946) has studied the water absorption of glass powders prepared from optical and commercial glasses. He found that the water absorption was highest for the soda-lime glasses and least for chemical 'Pyrex', and optical glasses such as those of lead borate, dense flint, barium crown and borosilicate crown.

Morey and Bowen (1927) studied the effect of water on glass at temperatures of 300° and 550°c. They found that the soft crowns were badly decomposed at 300°c and completely decomposed at 550°c; in one case a hydrous glass was formed containing 2·6% of water. Raising the lead oxide content of flint glasses improved their durability and the extra-dense flints possessed a remarkable water resistance. (It is shown in Chapter 6 that extra-dense flint glass has a high contact angle to water and adsorbed lead ions can be made to reduce the wetting of glass.)

Taylor and Smith (1936), using the glass compositions given in Table 3.1, measured the weight of material extracted when distilled water was heated to 260°c in sealed glass tubes for 6 hours. The material extracted was measured by evaporating the water and weighing the residue. The results are given in Fig. 3.2. The high lead glass E showed the least attack at high temperatures and this was attributed to the presence of a protective film; silica was not found in the extracted material. However, when the glasses were tested under erosive conditions in the form of tubular condensers exposed to escaping steam for 100 hours, the lead glass E lost thirteen times as much glass as the borosilicate glass A! Borosilicate glasses are used for boiler gauges because of their durability and clarity after attack. However, even this glass finally becomes deeply

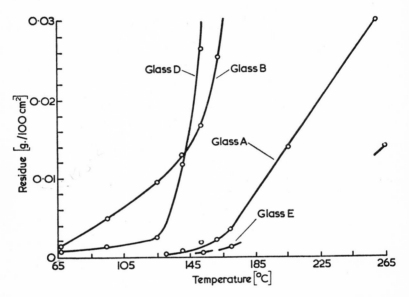

Fig. 3.2   Material removed at high temperatures from sealed glass tubes exposed to distilled water (*After Taylor and Smith,* 1936).

etched under erosive conditions and there is at present no satisfactory glass for this application.

Dissolution of alkali glasses. It has already been stated that water tends to dissolve the alkali in glass, resulting in a rise in the alkalinity of the water which then attacks the remaining glass more readily. The incorporation of lime or other oxides in simple alkali silicates makes them more durable in water and alkali solutions. The reactions which occur at the surface of alkali glasses exposed to water are complex. The water may be adsorbed by the surface to form a hydrated alkali silicate which dissociates by hydrolysis to form a silicic hydrate and free alkali held by the adsorbed water.

Carbon dioxide in the atmosphere may combine with the free alkali to form sodium carbonate.

Koenig, Loeffler and Lappe (1955) contend that if fresh soda-lime glass is leached so that the alkali and its products are removed from the surface then a silica sponge is produced on the surface which has a very high water content. Evidence for this was obtained

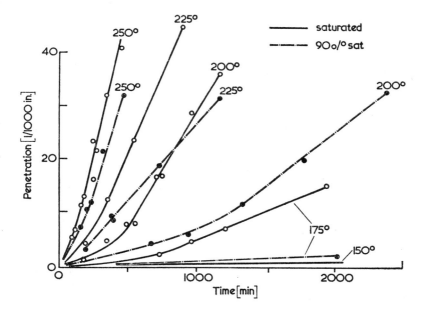

FIG. 3.3 CORROSION PENETRATION OF SODA LIME RODS IN SATURATED AND 90% SATURATED STEAM AT DIFFERENT TEMPERATURES AS A FUNCTION OF TIME (*After Charles, 1958*).

in vacuum experiments where very small changes in the water content of a surface could be detected. If the alkaline products remained on the surface during the water attack then these had a gelatizing effect on the formation of the silica, *i.e.* aided the coagulation of the silica so that its interior surface area was less.

Charles (1958) has studied the effect of saturated and unsaturated water vapour at high temperatures (150°–250°c) on soda-lime glass (lamp bulb Corning 0080). He found that the decomposed material formed a sharply defined layer on the glass and the depth of the decomposed zone could easily be measured on a sectioned specimen. Shown in Fig. 3.3 is the depth of penetration of the

9

decomposed layer measured as a function of time and at different temperatures. The attack of glass in liquid water was less than in steam because the corrosion products were diluted by the water.

Electron microscopy studies of attacked surfaces. Microscopy studies have established that surface films on weathered and attacked plate glass are of porous structure. Thus the film formed on aged plate (Libbey–Owens–Ford) was found by Brueche and Poppa (1957) to be penetrated by small craters of similar diameter to the layer thickness ($\simeq 0\cdot1$ μ). When the ageing was artificially accelerated the pores were some ten times larger in diameter than those on the normally aged glass and a central raised spike became visible at the base of the craters. After prolonged artificial weathering of plate glass Brueche and Poppa finally obtained a visible grey deposit with the fine structure shown in Plate 17(*a*). The glass has been scratched and the fragile outer layer has been removed to expose the bulk glass; the scratch is 4–5 μ wide and the film $< 0\cdot5$ μ thick.

Geilmann and Toelg (1955) have used polystyrene and cellulose nitrate surface replicas for studying the appearance of weathered glasses by optical microscopy. Complicated and beautiful patterns were observed on ancient glass vessels at magnifications of a few orders. The replicas were prepared by spreading a solution of the plastic in solvent over the clean glass surface and then stripping the cast film by immersion in water. Shown in Plate 17(*b*) is the replica taken from the fractured handle of a third-century Roman vessel.

ATTACK BY ALKALINE SOLUTIONS AND SODIUM

Silicate glasses are more rapidly attacked in alkaline solutions than in neutral or acid solutions because the alkali supplies hydroxyl ions for reaction with the silica network. Normally a protective layer does not form on silicate glasses attacked by alkaline solutions and the dissolution proceeds at a constant rate. A special alkali resistant glass (*e.g.* Corning 7280) has been produced which, it is claimed, contains material that forms an insoluble protective film on the surface, but this glass becomes opaque on severe attack. Given in Table 3.4 are the amounts of material lost as reported by Nordberg for a range of glasses, including a resistant type, when attacked by a 5% NaOH solution at 100°c for 6 hours.

Hubbard and Hamilton (1941) have measured by optical inter-

Table 3.4
Alkali durability of a range of glasses
(*After Nordberg*)

Corning glass	Glass type	6 h, 5% NaOH, 100°c, *Weight loss* (mg/cm²)
7900	96% silica	0·9
7740	Borosilicate	1·4
0080	Soda-lime – bulb	1·1
0010	Lead glass – electrical	1·6
7050	Borosilicate–tungsten sealing	3·9
8870	High lead	3·6
1710	Aluminosilicate	0·35
7280	Alkali resistant	0·09

ferometry the depth of glass removed from flat specimens (2 × 3 cm) immersed for different times in a 5% NaOH solution at $80 \pm 0·2°c$; the displacement between two fringes corresponded to 2900 Å. Shown in Fig. 3.4 are the results obtained for eight commercial glasses. When NaCl was added to a sodium hydroxide solution it increased its rate of attack.

Hubbard and Hamilton measured the attack of aqueous sodium hydroxide and aqueous potassium hydroxide on four glasses used for chemical ware. They used 0·1 and 1·0 N-solutions and found that the rate of attack was always higher for sodium hydroxide. The order of chemical resistance of the glasses was: Kimble N-51-A; Tamworth: Pyrex.

Sodium. Silicate glasses are generally attacked by sodium at temperatures above 200°c, as found by Fonda and Young (1934), and normal glasses cannot be used in the construction of sodium vapour discharge tubes. Philips Electrical (1934) have described a borate glass containing less than 10% of silica which can be used as a protective liner for normal glass. A typical composition was 6% SiO_2; 53% B_2O_3; 15% Al_2O_3; 10% CaO and 16% Na_2O. It has been claimed that a glass can be protected with an alkali fluoride/boric oxide mixture fused to its surface. Recently Wheeldon (1959) has shown that sodium diffuses into even special resistant glasses and rapid chemical attack occurs at 450°c.

Elyard and Rawson (1962) found that simple glasses of Na_2O–SiO_2 became more resistant to attack by sodium vapour at 350°c as the soda content was raised. When silica was attacked by sodium at 288°c between 1·1 and 1·7 sodium atoms combined with each SiO_2 group. The attack of both the sodium silicate and silica could be explained on thermodynamic grounds.

Detection of surface flaws. Andrade and Tsien (1937) observed that the attack of sodium vapour developed crack patterns on the

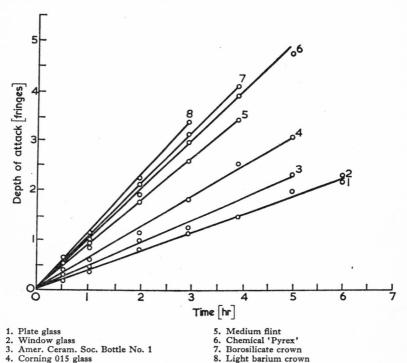

1. Plate glass
2. Window glass
3. Amer. Ceram. Soc. Bottle No. 1
4. Corning 015 glass

5. Medium flint
6. Chemical 'Pyrex'
7. Borosilicate crown
8. Light barium crown

FIG. 3.4   DEPTH OF SURFACE REMOVED FROM SERIES OF COMMERCIAL GLASSES EXPOSED TO 5% NaOH AT 80°c (*After Hubbard and Hamilton*, 1941).

surfaces of hard (low alkali) glasses held at elevated temperatures. The network nature of the surface cracks could not be attributed to the development of mechanical scratches. The inner walls of freshly drawn Pyrex tubes developed many more cracks when attacked after ageing. Griffith (1920) had postulated stress concentration at minute surface flaws in aged glass to explain its low yield strength and it was considered that the sodium treatment exposed such surface cracks. Gordon, Marsh and Parratt (1959) obtained by sodium vapour treatment crack patterns on fused silica and soda-lime slides. The crack pattern was affected by abrading the glass before treatment or applying a stress during treatment.

Ernsberger (1960, 1962) found that Pyrex (7740) plate glass treated at 400°c in sodium vapour only showed surface cracks after cooling to room temperature. After a lengthy study he concluded that the cracks produced by sodium vapour were fractures due to a tensile stress developed on cooling in a surface layer of changed chemical composition with a high thermal expansion. However, he reasoned that while differential thermal contraction supplied the stress the surface cracks must have occurred at the weakest sites, which he believed were remnants of large Griffith cracks which had not been healed during the high temperature vapour reaction.

If a crystal of lithium nitrate is melted on a soda-lime glass surface for a few minutes at 270°c the treated surface becomes covered with a network of cracks (Stewart and Young, 1935). The effect has been attributed to the treated glass shrinking at the surface as the smaller lithium ions replace those of sodium in the glass. Ernsberger observed that the lithium substituted glass may have a higher thermal expansion coefficient than the parent glass. He lowered the heat treatment temperature to 200°c by using a eutectic mixture of KNO_3 and $LiNO_3$. Few surface flaws are initially produced by the latter ion-exchange method but crack propagation is rapid when a treated glass is exposed to water vapour.

ATTACK BY ACID SOLUTIONS

Attack of silicate glasses by acids differs from that by water in that any alkali dissolved is neutralized by the acid; also the alkali and basic oxide components may be preferentially dissolved, leaving a silica surface layer which reduces the rate of attack with time. When the soluble oxides are present in major amounts the silica component may be insufficient to form even a porous surface layer and the glass will disintegrate. This may occur with certain optical glasses, *e.g.* high refractive index types containing a large quantity of lead oxide.

Soda-lime silicate (*e.g.* plate glass) and borosilicate (*e.g.* chemical 'Pyrex') form thin but highly protective films on their surface and the rate of attack by acids is low. Some optical glasses, such as dense barium crown, can be attacked rapidly by weak acids such as phosphoric, acetic and boric acid. Nitric acid forms salts of greater solubility than those of hydrochloric or sulphuric acid and has been used in preference for preparing anti-reflection films by acid attack. (The effect of acid etching on exposing strains and surface marks in optically worked surfaces is considered in Chapter 1.)

Given in Table 3.5 are the resistances of different glasses to acid attack (after Nordberg). Tests were made by measuring the weight

Table 3.5
Acid durability of a range of glasses
(After Nordberg)

Glass No.	Designation	Plate test 24 h 5% HCl 100°c Weight loss (mg/cm²)	Powder test 4 h N/50 H₂SO₄ 90°c (% Na₂O)
7900	96% Silica	0·0004	—
7740	Borosilicate – chemical	0·005	0·005
7280	Alkali resistant	0·01	0·05
0080	Soda-lime – bulb	0·01	0·08
0010	Lead glass – electrical	0·02	0·15
1720	Aluminosilicate	0·35	0·06
7050	Borosilicate–tungsten sealing	Leached	—
8870	High lead	Disintegrated	—

lost by plate samples in hydrochloric acid and the alkali leached from powders in sulphuric acid. It should be noted that all silicate glasses are attacked by hydrofluoric and hot phosphoric acids.

One type of borosilicate having a typical composition 75% SiO_2; 5% Na_2O; 20% B_2O_3 separates into phases one of which is rich in silica and the others rich in boric oxide and alkali. Phase segregation can be enhanced by heat treatment at 525°–650°c. The treated glasses can be readily leached by acids leaving a porous body mainly composed of silica. This is the method used for producing a glass with a high silica content† known as 'Vycor', originally described by Hood and Nordberg (1934). The leached glass is heat treated at 900°–1000°c and forms a dense transparent body. The special properties of these glasses when attacked by acids are discussed in a later section.

3. ION EXCHANGE AND SURFACE ALKALINITY

The foregoing discussion considered in a practical manner the resistance of glasses to attack by various substances and we shall

---

† Morey (1954) gives the composition of 'Vycor' products as 96·3% SiO_2; 2·9% B_2O_3; >0·02% Na_2O; >0·02% K_2O; 0·4% Al_2O_3.

now discuss the mechanisms by which the components in an attacked glass are replaced by ions of metals and other substances.

Ion exchange phenomena. It has been contended that Na^+ ions can be removed from glass in water by an ion exchange process in which H^+ ions diffuse into the glass to preserve the electrical neutrality as the Na^+ ions diffuse out. Before discussing this at length the literature on ion exchange in glasses will be considered. It was shown by Devaux and Aubel (1927) that a column of glass wool which had been rinsed with water would remove sufficient calcium ions from a calcium sulphate solution to form a monolayer on the glass. When the calcium-treated glass was exposed to a NaCl- or KCl-solution the calcium ions were released and the alkali ions adsorbed in their place. The glass could be made to adsorb reversibly cations of Ca, H, K, Na, NH_4 and quinine. Glass which had been treated for a prolonged period with acid afterwards absorbed calcium ions in depth.

Kraus and Darby (1922) studied the ion exchange between soda-lime silica glass and fused salts of Li, K, Cu, Pb, Zn and Ag and found that the cations could enter the glass and replace the sodium. However, with the exception of silver, the treated glasses cracked on cooling. The silver ion has almost the same radius as that of sodium, whereas the other ions have considerably different radii and it would appear that silver is the only substitutional ion which fits into the glass structure without producing strain. Kraus and Darby also investigated the replacement of sodium by silver from a fused $AgNO_3$ bath. The silver salt served as the anode with mercury as the cathode. They found that the sodium ions were the current carriers in the glass and could measure the depth of silver diffusion by microscopic examination of the sectioned glass. They obtained 70–80% replacement of Na^+ ions by Ag^+ ions. Kubaschewski (1936) made a similar experiment using metallic silver and obtained a 4% replacement of sodium. (It is well known that sodium ions from fused salts can be made to pass through glass under the action of an electrical field.)

Marboe and Weyl (1945) have considered the processes occurring in the chemical deposition of metal films on glass. They believed that the initial step in the production of a silver mirror was the replacement of Na^+ ions by Ag^+ ions, which acted as nuclei for the growth of a fine grain metal film. Thus glasses with a high sodium content are particularly suitable for silvering. Adherent copper films cannot be prepared on glass if Cu^{2+} ions are produced in the chemical reaction because the divalent ions do not easily replace the monovalent ions of sodium. Consequently there are no nuclei for subsequent adhesion of copper atoms and the copper precipitates to form coarse aggregated crystallites which grow as loose layers on the glass. Examples of this are films prepared from cupric chloride reacting with hydrogen and cupric tartrate-formaldehyde mixture. Copper mirrors can, however, be prepared from decomposition of cupric formate on glasses heated to 150–200°c and it is presumed that the thermal energy of the Cu^{2+} ions permit them to penetrate the glass surface. Copper films can also be formed from Cu^{+} ions obtained by reduction of cuprous oxide (Cu_2O). If a glass is initially exposed to an acidic solution of silver nitrate and washed with distilled water then the silver ions are exchanged for the sodium at the surface and act as condensation centres for forming a fine grain film from cupric copper ions (Cu^{2+}).

It will be of interest to note here that silver or copper films evaporated *in vacuo* are not adherent to glass substrates. Thus the films will form large aggregates of atoms if heated because ion exchange has not occurred to bind the metal atoms to the surface.

Metallic stains. Marboe and Weyl (1947) noted that wet glass brought into contact with iron or manganese acquired a brown stain. Contamination of glass by iron is rapid, the stain becoming visible 10 min after the glass and iron are brought together. The effect is galvanic in nature. The iron immersed in water liberates positive ferrous ions into solution leaving the metal with a negative charge. When the glass is in contact with the iron the negative charge is partially dissipated by electrical conduction in the glass surface. The negatively charged glass surface then attracts the positive metal ions from the solution. If a glass surface is not in contact with the immersed iron but acquires a negative charge from a platinum electrode connected to a battery the brown stain still appears.

Reaction of the iron cations with the hydroxyl groups adsorbed to the glass surface results in the formation of an insoluble ferric hydrosilicate.

Chemisorption of the positively charged iron can be prevented by adding to the solution positively charged ions such as Al^{3+} and Cr^{3+} which at high concentrations have a greater probability of being adsorbed by the glass. Marboe and Weyl found that the aluminium cations lost their protective influence with increasing NaOH-concentration in the solution. Thus, using a solution containing 0·5% by weight of $AlCl_3$, no detectable amount of aluminium was adsorbed when the concentration of NaOH exceeded 3%. The chemisorbed iron may be represented thus:

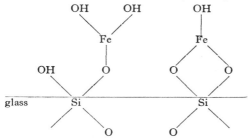

If the iron-treated glass was exposed to soap (sodium stearate or palmitate) the glass surface became water repellent as the soap molecules formed oriented layers on the glass. The chemisorbed iron atoms joined the polar group of the soap $(Fe—OOC.C_NH_{2N}.CH_3)$ to the glass with the water repellent methyl group outermost.

Alkali content and hydrogen diffusion. If the first stages of chemical attack of a glass containing alkali is a base exchange process in which H^+ ions replace Na^+ ions then the attack should be influenced by the alkali content of the glass surface. Of the basic oxides Na_2O has the greatest effect in lowering the surface tension of glass. Thus alkali ions will migrate to the glass surface and they are mobile enough for this to occur below the softening range. The alkali may, however, be depleted at the surface by evaporation of Na_2O at high temperature or by chemical reaction with furnace gases.

Williams and Weyl (1945) investigated methods of reducing the alkali content of soda-lime glass. They found that microscope slides heated in contact with kaolin at 150–200°c had the alkali removed in a similar way to that of acid attack. It was believed that Na^+ ions had diffused out of the glass and been replaced by H^+ ions. Glasses treated with kaolin at 500°–550°c were also dealkalized but unlike those treated at a lower temperature had become highly resistant to acid attack. It is possible that the H^+ ions in the 'hydrogen' glass formed by the ion-exchange process were removed from the glass at 500°–550°c in combination with oxygen, *i.e.* the glass was dehydrated and the structure of the leached layer compacted.

When alkali is removed from glass in water at high temperature the silica network may also be disrupted by OH^- ions released in the water by dissolved Na^+ ions. Charles (1958) has discussed this process and described it as follows:

'Two structures assume importance in the corrosion of soda-lime glass by water or water vapour. One of these is the silica network which is unending, and the other is the terminal structure which associates the alkali ions to the silica network. It has been observed that at moderate temperatures ($100°$–$300°c$) and in the presence of water vapour fused silica remains essentially unaltered for long periods of time whereas a glass containing alkali, which has the terminal alkali structures as well as the unending silica network, quickly undergoes severe decomposition. One concludes that the degradation of the glass structure is very much dependent on the terminal structures (as are most of the other properties of simple glasses) and writes the following equation describing the reaction between the terminal ends and water. Only the terminal end which associates Na^+ ion to the network is considered for in dissolution it is by far the most important.

$$[-\underset{|}{\overset{|}{Si}}-O-(Na)] + H_2O \rightarrow -\underset{|}{\overset{|}{Si}}OH + Na^+ + OH^- \qquad (1)$$

Equation (1) illustrates a typical hydrolysis reaction of the salt of a weak acid. An oxygen sodium bond near the interface is broken by the migration away of a Na^+ ion and the oxygen atom dissociates a water molecule to satisfy its force field with a hydrogen ion. A free hydroxyl ion is formed in the process and the second important step in glass dissolution may proceed.

$$[-\underset{|}{\overset{|}{Si}}-O-\underset{|}{\overset{|}{Si}}-] + OH^- \rightarrow -\underset{|}{\overset{|}{Si}}OH + -\underset{|}{\overset{|}{Si}}O^- \qquad (2)$$

In this step, which can proceed only if the first step has already been taken, the very strong Si—O—Si bond is broken such that one end of the break becomes a silanol end by proton transfer or hydroxyl ion attachment and the other produces an end structure capable of dissociating another water molecule, viz.

$$[-\underset{|}{\overset{|}{Si}}O^-] + H_2O \rightarrow -\underset{|}{\overset{|}{Si}}OH + OH^- \qquad (3)$$

This step is essentially the same as the first with the important difference that it could not occur unless steps 1 and 2 preceded it. One might be tempted to by-pass step 1 by writing,

$$[-\underset{|}{\overset{|}{Si}}-O-\underset{|}{\overset{|}{Si}}-] + H_2O \rightarrow 2[-\overset{|}{Si}OH] \qquad (4)$$

Such a reaction has little significance in glass dissolution as evidenced by the fact that fused quartz and quartz crystal are virtually insoluble in water at a neutral pH and moderate temperature.

One sees that after the first three reactions are completed excess hydroxyl ions are formed in equivalent amount to each Na^+ ion that is no longer associated with silica in the corrosion products. This increase in pH within the corrosion layer tends to make the glass dissolution process autocatalytic and acceleration occurs. From the curves in Fig. 3.3 it is apparent that acceleration does not occur indefinitely but the process approaches some limiting velocity. A limit to the pH build up in the corrosion products would be expected for as the pH increases the tendency to form silicate ions (with the consequent co-ordination increase of hydroxyl groups around silicon atoms) instead of hydrated silica increases and silicate ion formation removes free hydroxyl ions from the solution.'

Sulphur dioxide treatment. When glass is exposed to furnace gases it may develop a more chemically resistant surface. Thus Cousen and Peddle (1936) compared the water solubility of bottles annealed in open-fired and muffle lehrs and found that exposure to the furnace fumes greatly decreased their water solubility. Sulphur compounds are often present in the furnace gas and combine with the surface alkali to form sodium sulphate.

Keppeler (1930) obtained a patent for a process for improving the resistivity of the inner surface of bottles by dropping inside substances which produced reactive gases such as sulphur.

Coward and Turner (1938) studied the effect of sulphur dioxide on soda-lime silica glass and reported that the 'bloom' was sodium sulphate. The surface deposit formed was the same in 1% or 100% SO_2 and repeated treatment of the surface gave successively lower deposits.

During heat treatment the alkali flows to the surface under a concentration gradient and is removed by reaction with sulphur dioxide. The sulphuring process can therefore be used to produce a glass with a low alkali content at the surface.

Water vapour in the furnace gas may influence the dealkalizing process. Thus if H^+ ions did not diffuse into the glass to replace the Na^+ ions removed then the process would stop as the glass became electrically negative. Alternatively, the alkali may diffuse to the surface as Na_2O if the furnace gas is dry, but the dealkalizing process will then be much slower because of the lower diffusion constant of soda.

Williams and Weyl (1945) suggest that the formation of sodium sulphate on a glass surface follows one of the two following reactions

$$2Na^+ \text{-glass} + SO_2 + \tfrac{1}{2}O_2 + H_2O = 2H^+ \text{-glass} + Na_2SO_4$$

$$Na_2O + SO_2 + \tfrac{1}{2}O_2 = Na_2SO_4$$

The second reaction only becomes important at temperatures above 500°c when diffusion of Na^+ and O^{2-} to the surface predominates over the base exchange process.

Sendt (1962) reports that glass treated with sulphur dioxide is under a tensile stress after the $Na^+ \rightarrow H^+$ ion exchange. When the glass is heated above the transformation point the tensile stress becomes compressive as H_2O is removed.

Williams and Weyl found that practically all compounds which can combine with Na_2O at high temperature are suitable reagents for dealkalizing glass surfaces. Thus zirconium oxide (ZrO_2) which forms sodium zirconate was effective, whereas thorium oxide was ineffective because a corresponding thorium compound apparently did not exist.

Holland *et al.* (1957) found that titanium films on soda-lime silica glass reacted with the glass when heat treated in air at 400°c to produce titanium dioxide films; possibly a sodium titanate was formed at the film/glass interface. The reaction could be prevented by an Al_2O_3 or MgF_2-film previously deposited on the glass.

4. TIME LAWS OF SURFACE ATTACK

THEORETICAL CONSIDERATIONS

We shall now consider the relations which have been derived between the degree of attack of glass surfaces, the period of attack and the nature and temperature of the corrosive solution. When a leached layer is formed on glass due to selective removal of one or several of the glass components then this layer may impede the leaching process as its depth increases. Early workers (Keppeler and Thomas-Wezlow, 1933; Berger, 1936) showed that the dissolution of alkali from glasses exposed to water or acid followed a diffusion process, but it was not clear how the reaction occurred. Some believed that the leached layer was hydrated and a chemical reaction occurred in the glass interior which released soda.

Surface film. Lyle (1943) proposed that the solution of the soluble component (Na_2O) was controlled by the rate at which it could diffuse through the hydrated layer.† If we designate the concentration of leachable material as c_0 at the hydrated layer/glass interface and c_1 the concentration at the hydrated layer/liquid interface then the rate at which soluble material is transferred to the liquid from one surface of a glass specimen is

$$\frac{\mathrm{d}S}{\mathrm{d}t} = \frac{aD(c_0 - c_1)}{d} \tag{1}$$

where S is the mass of dissolved material, a is the surface area, D is the diffusion constant of the soluble material in the hydrated layer with the dimensions $l^2 t^{-1}$ and d is the thickness of the layer at time t. If the concentration of leached material c_1 at the outer surface is small compared with c_0 and not allowed to rise as the dissolution proceeds, because the liquid is stirred, then we may rewrite equation (1) as

$$\frac{\mathrm{d}S}{\mathrm{d}t} = \frac{aDc_0}{d} \tag{2}$$

The amount of soluble material lost by the glass at time t will be equal to the volume of the hydrated layer times the mean concentration of the diffusing material, *i.e.*

$$S = ad \frac{c_0}{2}$$

so that

$$d = \frac{2S}{ac_0} \tag{3}$$

Substituting this in equation (1) we have

$$\frac{\mathrm{d}S}{\mathrm{d}t} = \frac{D(ac_0)^2}{2S} \tag{4}$$

and integrating we obtain

$$S^2 = D(ac_0)^2 t + M \tag{5}$$

where M is a constant of integration assumed to be zero since at

---

† It is shown further on that alkali is probably removed from glass in water by an ion-exchange process involving the diffusion of Na^+ ions. However, the simple treatment initially made here would apply to the removal of other glass components through a leached layer of silica.

$t=0$, $S=0$. As $D(ac_0)^2/2$ is a constant we may replace this by a single constant K_1 and write

$$S^2 = 2K_1 t \tag{6}$$

The thickness of the hydrated layer d measured from the film surface ($c=0$) to the glass/film interface ($c=c_0$) can be found from equation (5) by substituting $dac_0/2$ for S which gives

$$d^2 = 4Dt \tag{7}$$

and this shows that the thickness of the layer at time t is dependent on the diffusion coefficient and not the concentration of the soluble material. This equation can be written in similar form to equation (6), *i.e.*

$$d^2 = 2K_2 t \tag{8}$$

Effect of temperature. The effect of temperature on the rate of attack when a surface layer is present depends on the nature of the flow process. There is ample evidence that the diffusion of alkali and basic oxides from glass is activated suggesting that diffusion occurs either through small pores or in a compact body. Under activation conditions

$$D = A\,e^{-E/RT} \tag{9}$$

where E is the activation energy and A a constant. In equations (6) and (8) above D is equal to $2K_1/(ac_0)^2$ and $2K_2$ respectively and since ac_0 is a constant we may rewrite equation (9) as

$$K_1 = A_1\,e^{-E/RT} \quad \text{and} \quad K_2 = A_2\,e^{-E/RT} \tag{10}$$

from which we obtain

$$\log_{10} K = -\frac{E}{2\cdot303RT} + C = -\frac{B}{T} + C \tag{11}$$

where $B = E/2\cdot303R$ and C is a constant.

Substituting for the constants in equations (6) and (9) we obtain

$$2\log S = \log t - \frac{B}{T} + C_1 \tag{12}$$

and

$$2\log d = \log t - \frac{B}{T} + C_2 \tag{13}$$

When glass is attacked by alkali the reaction proceeds at a constant rate $dS/dt = V_s$ and $dl/dt = V_0$, where l is the depth of surface removed. This process, as with many chemical reactions, is subject to an activation energy so that V_s or $V_0 = Ae^{-E/RT}$.

Sodium diffusion. The attack of alkali glasses by *water* has recently been attributed to an ion-exchange process in which hydrogen ions diffuse into the glass to maintain electrical neutrality as sodium ions diffuse out. It has been shown by Douglas and Isard (1949) that a parabolic law for the solution of alkali ($S \propto \sqrt{t}$) is still obtained when it is assumed that the reaction is controlled by the rate at which sodium ions diffuse to the glass surface. Such a process produces a 'hydrogen' glass in the attacked zone and the leached zone would not form a sharp boundary with the unattacked glass. If diffusion of the sodium ions is the rate controlling process then a solution must be obtained of Fick's law for a non-stationary state of flow, *i.e.*

$$\frac{\partial c}{\partial t} = D \frac{\partial^2 c}{\partial x^2}$$

where c is the concentration of sodium in the glass at a time t at a point x from the origin and D is the diffusion constant with the dimensions $l^2 . t^{-1}$. Solutions of this equation for bodies of various shape will be found in Barrer (1951), who has given the general equation for a semi-infinite solid where the medium extends from $x = 0$ to $x = \infty$, *i.e.*

$$c = \frac{1}{\sqrt{(\pi Dt)}} \int_0^\infty f(x') \exp\left[-\frac{(x-x')^2}{4Dt}\right] dx'$$

This general equation would be applicable to the diffusion of sodium from a glass into water where one surface ($x = 0$) of a thick specimen forms the interface with the liquid.

Thus if the initial uniform concentration c_0 falls instantaneously to zero at $x = 0$ and $t = 0$ then the quantity of alkali removed at $t = t_1$, is given by $S = 2c_0 \sqrt{\dfrac{Dt_1}{\pi}}$

When experiments are made to derive the relationship between dissolution and the period of attack allowance must be made for the alkali content of the glass initially being either higher at the surface (*e.g.* freshly melted glass) or lower (*e.g.* weathered glass).

Diffusion inct and porous la compayers. It is known that well-defined films of low refractive index showing optical interference colours can be formed on certain glasses by *acid treatment*. Further, such films when dry have a refractive index less than that of silica, indicating that they are porous. Of course, in this case, basic oxides as well as alkali are leached from the glass by the acid. The process of attack would then be complex and depend on a two-stage process in which the basic oxides are removed after the alkali has been leached and replaced by hydrogen. The sodium ions diffusing through the compact glass would subsequently have to pass through a porous and hydrated silica layer which remains as the basic oxides are removed.

Another example of a complex corrosion process is that of soda-lime glass attacked at high temperature by water or water vapour. The attacked glass forms a loose corrosion layer on its surface and Charles (1958) found that the activation energy of the attack corresponded to that for migration of sodium ions to the glass/corrosion layer interface. If the silica network in the alkali leached glass is broken down by the hydroxyl groups formed in the water by the dissolved sodium ions, then at equilibrium the rate of growth of the leached layer under diffusion conditions will equal its rate of disruption. Thus, once equilibrium is reached, the depth of attack becomes proportional to t, as shown in Fig. 3.3, because the sodium ions diffuse within a layer whose concentration gradient remains constant with time.

Dissolution of porous layer. It is shown further on p. 166 that porous silica films formed on glass in nearly neutral solutions also may be dissolved as the attack proceeds. The kinetics of this type of attack has not been dealt with elsewhere and we shall consider briefly the kind of process which could occur. In acid solutions the alkali is removed more rapidly from the glass than the basic oxides so that we can assume that the rate controlling process will be the diffusion of the basic ions through the porous silica layer. If the silica component is slowly dissolved† as the basic oxides are removed then the rate of film formation will be given by

---

† Since manuscript preparation a paper has appeared by Rana and Douglas (1961) which shows that the rate of reaction of alkali glass in pure water varies to a close approximation with the square root of time but finally the rate of reaction becomes constant. In the later stage the ratio of silica to alkali dissolved is similar to that of the glass.

$$\frac{dd}{dt} = \frac{K}{d} - V_g \tag{1}$$

where V_g is the rate of dissolution of the silica layer and d is its thickness. When the thickness of the porous film has reached a value d_L such that $K/d_L = V_g$ then $dd/dt = 0$ and the film will have a constant thickness as the attack proceeds. We can find the film thickness at a given time t during its growth from $d = 0$ to $d = d_L$ by rearranging equation (1)

$$\frac{dt}{dd} = \frac{d}{K - V_g d} \tag{2}$$

and integrating

$$t = \int \frac{d}{K - V_g d} \, dd + M$$

which from a table of standard integrals (Dwight, 1947) gives

$$t = \frac{K}{V_g^2} - \frac{d}{V_g} - \frac{K}{V_g^2} \log (K + V_g d) + M \tag{3}$$

when $t = 0$ then $d = 0$, so that

$$\frac{K}{V_g^2} - \frac{K}{V_g^2} \log K + M = 0 \tag{4}$$

and subtracting equation (4) from (3) we obtain

$$t = \frac{K}{V_g^2} \log K - \frac{d}{V_g} - \frac{K}{V_g^2} \log (K - V_g d)$$

$$t = \frac{K}{V_g^2} \log \frac{K}{K - V_g d} - \frac{d}{V_g} \tag{5}$$

Examples of the relations discussed in the preceding sections for the amount of material dissolved from an attacked glass or the growth of a surface layer as a function of the time of the attack are shown graphically in Fig. 3.5. The curves have been drawn assuming diffusion across a surface layer (*i.e.* s, $d \propto \sqrt{t}$) and correspond to the following cases: (*a*) growth of leached layer on a glass with initially uniform alkali dispersal, (*b*) growth of leached layer on fresh glass with high alkali content initially at the surface, (*c*) growth of leached layer on weathered glass *i.e.* with an initial leached layer and (*d*) erosion at a linear rate of the leached layer during its growth.

10

DETERMINATION OF DEGREE OF ATTACK

A common method of assessing the durability of optical glass (due to Mylius, 1907) is to determine the alkali released from fresh and aged glass surfaces. A glass of known surface area is immersed in a solution of iodeosine in ether for a known time, the alkali salt of the dye is dissolved in water and the amount of alkali determined colorimetrically by comparison with a standard solution.

Various other methods have been used for determining the degree of attack of a glass surface. Thus, the thickness of a leached

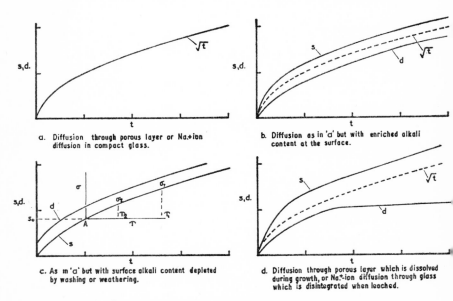

a. Diffusion through porous layer or Na+ion diffusion in compact glass.

b. Diffusion as in 'a' but with enriched alkali content at the surface.

c. As in 'a' but with surface alkali content depleted by washing or weathering.

d. Diffusion through porous layer which is dissolved during growth, or Na+-ion diffusion through glass which is disintegrated when leached.

FIG. 3.5   SURFACE FILMS AND THE PARABOLIC LAW OF FILM GROWTH.

layer can be measured by optical interferometry as described in Chapter 2 if the layer forms a sharply defined boundary with the bulk glass. Extensive attack may be determined by weight loss. Care must be taken when measuring either weight changes or optical thickness that the results are not affected by water sorbed by the leached layer.

It has been shown that the alkali and basic oxides are normally selectively removed from glass by the attack of acid and neutral solutions whilst the silica component resists attack. Thus, if one measures the amount of a particular component (*e.g.* alkali) dissolved in an attacking solution then this quantity will not be proportional to *the mass of glass* dissolved. Berger (1936) has contended that one should determine *the quantity of glass decomposed* based on the following considerations.

'If we understand an element of the glass to be the smallest atomic complex which reflects the structure of the glass as a whole (we may imagine the elementary cell of the X-ray photograph), a piece of glass will appear as a combination of a number of similar elements. The analytical composition of each element is given by the glass analysis. If now, through the action of water or acid from an element near the surface, the most loosely combined atoms are removed, the remainder will no longer be identical with the original glass, but will represent an element of more or less decomposed glass. Following the complete removal of a component from the element, we can then calculate the amount of decomposed glass z, from the quantity in solution m, and the original quantity from the glass analysis (M) by the relation $z = m \cdot 100/M$. Since, from a knowledge of the specific gravity ρ, this quantity can be expressed in volumetric form, we arrive, with reference to the unit of surface, at a linear or lamina thickness d as a comparable numerical figure for the durability.

Under the action of hydrofluoric acid or alkali all the glass components are usually dissolved. In this case the quantity of decomposed glass is equal to the loss in weight suffered by the glass. The relations for the resistance to other acids are less simple. With strongly basic glasses all components apart from the silica acid are generally found in solution. If then the loss in weight is measured after heating at 500°, in order to convert the hydrated silicic acid to the oxide SiO_2, this quantity divided by the sum of the percentage contents of all the components except silica gives the quantity of decomposed glass z. This quantity can also be determined indirectly.'

EFFECT OF WEATHERED FILMS

It has been shown above that a parabolic time law for film growth or dissolution is obtained irrespective of whether the dissolution rate is controlled by the passage of sodium ions or reaction products through a surface layer. We shall now deal with some early attempts to fit measured dissolution rates to the parabolic law for the growth of a surface layer or of the mass dissolved viz.,

$$S^2 = 2K_1 t \tag{1}$$

and

$$d^2 = 2K_2 t \tag{2}$$

where d is the *equivalent* thickness of decomposed glass i.e. glass denuded of one of its components, and its value will be less than that of d defined on p. 141 for a region of varying concentration.

It is assumed in the derivation of these equations that the film forms rapidly on the surface in the initial stage of attack, that the liquid is stirred to keep the concentration of the dissolved components at the attacked surface almost at zero and that the quantity of liquid is sufficient to prevent undue accumulation of glass dissolution products. The mass of glass decomposed per unit area is $z = S.100/aM$, where M is the percentage of the dissolved component in the bulk glass. From this we can obtain the thickness of the decomposed layer if the silica network remains intact.

$$d = \frac{S.100}{aM\rho} \tag{3}$$

where ρ is the density of the bulk glass. Inserting (3) in equation (2) we obtain

$$S^2 = 2K_2 \frac{a^2 M^2 \rho^2}{10\,000} t \tag{4}$$

where

$$K_2 = \frac{10\,000K_1}{a^2 M^2 \rho^2} \tag{5}$$

The constants K_1 and K_2 depend on the nature of the glass and attacking solution and the temperature of the system.

Aged glass surfaces are leached by washing and atmospheric attack and optically worked surfaces may have a surface film produced by the polishing. Thus the parabolic law may not start at $d = 0$ at $t = 0$ but at a shifted origin as in Fig. 3.5(c). Starting at a point A as origin we can measure the amount dissolved σ and the time τ. Thus $\sigma + S_0 = S$ at $\tau + t_0 = t$ and the parabolic law will be

$$(\sigma + S_0)^2 = 2K_1(\tau + t_0) \tag{6}$$

i.e.
$$\sigma^2 + S_0^2 + 2\sigma S_0 = 2K_1\tau + 2K_1 t_0$$

As $S_0^2 = 2K_1 t_0$ it follows that

$$\sigma^2 + 2\sigma S_0 = 2K_1\tau \tag{7}$$

which is a growth law with two constants. By choosing two times τ_1 and τ_2 at which the masses dissolved are σ_1 and σ_2 respectively we obtain for the constant of the resistance to attack

$$K_1 = \frac{1}{2} \frac{\sigma_1 - \sigma_2}{\tau_1/\sigma_1 - \tau_2/\sigma_2} \tag{8}$$

Keppeler and Thomas-Welzow (1933) calculated a constant for the resistance to attack using the simple expression

$$K_* = \frac{1}{2} \frac{\sigma_1^2 - \sigma_1^2}{\tau_1 - \tau_2}$$

However, it follows from equation (7) that

$$2K_1 = \frac{\sigma_1^2 - \sigma_2^2}{\tau_1 - \tau_2} + 2S_0 \frac{\sigma_1 - \sigma_2}{\tau_1 - \tau_2} \tag{9}$$

which shows that K_* tends to equal K_1 the smaller is S_0 and the larger is $(\sigma_1^2 - \sigma_2^2)$.

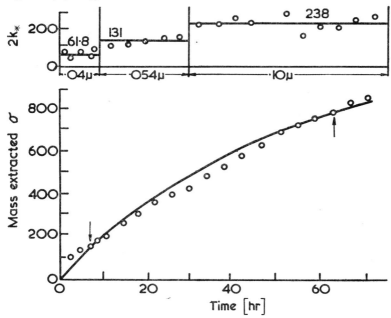

FIG. 3.6 EXTRACTION OF THURINGIAN FLASKS (*Keppeler and Thomas*, 1933), AND THE TWO CONSTANT PARABOLIC EQUATION (*Berger*, 1936). THE UPPER CURVE SHOWS HOW *constant* K_* CHANGES WITH FILM GROWTH AND THE ARROWS INDICATE VALUES CHOSEN FOR MATCHING THE TWO CONSTANTS LAW.

Using their equation Keppeler and Thomas-Welzow obtained values of K_* for a series of soda-lime silica glasses. Their results indicated that K_* was a function of t. The variation of K_* with duration of extraction time as determined by Keppeler for Na_2O leached from Thuringian flasks is shown in Fig. 3.6. Berger has calculated the constants K_1 and S_0 from the extraction results given in this graph. Using the values marked by arrows in Fig. 3.6, *i.e.* $\tau_1 = 62$ and $\tau_2 = 6$, $\sigma_1 = 800$ and $\sigma_2 = 160$, then from equations (8) and (9) one can obtain $K_3 = 8000$ and $S_0 = 220$. With these values the curve in Fig. 3.6 was calculated which is a fair match for the experimental points.

Berger (1936) found that the progress of attack by water or acids

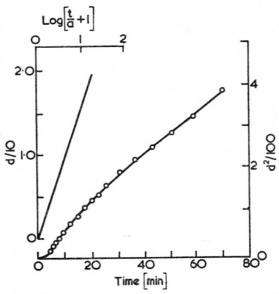

FIG. 3.7   TEST OF LOGARITHMIC AND PARABOLIC LAWS (*After Berger*, 1936).

of glasses of low alkali content but rich in alkaline earths was more accurately represented by the logarithmic law

$$S = L \log \left(\frac{t}{R} + 1 \right)$$

where S is the amount of material dissolved in time t and L and R are constants. Shown in Fig. 3.7 is the thickness d of an acid formed surface layer, measured by optical interferometry, plotted against the logarithmic time function. Also for comparison is a curve of the square of the film thickness as a function of time. The logarithmic law produces a straight curve and is therefore more closely obeyed than the parabolic relation. Allowance was not made in either case for an existing film before treatment, because the glass used was not noticeably attacked by water. The logarithmic law can be rewritten to allow for an initial deposit, *i.e.*

$$\sigma = L \log \left(\frac{\tau}{\alpha} + 1 \right)$$

where σ is the quantity dissolved after time τ and $\alpha = t_0 + R$. This expression could be used for more accurate curve matching than the two constant parabolic equation (7).

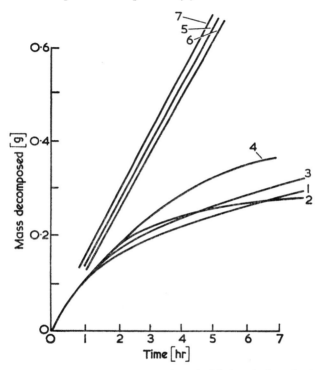

Curve 1. Without renewal
    2. Colorimetric determination of SiO_2
      1 c.c renewed per hour
    3. Colorimetric determination of SiO_2
      10 c.c renewed per hour
    4. Colorimetric determination of SiO_2
      10 c.c renewed every 20 mins

Curve 5. Colorimetric determination of SiO_2
      90 c.c renewed every $\frac{1}{2}$ hr
    6. Powder loss—90 c.c renewed every
      $\frac{1}{2}$ hr
    7. Quantitative determination of SiO_2
      90 c.c renewed every $\frac{1}{2}$ hr

FIG. 3.8   TREATMENT OF POWDER WITH AND WITHOUT RENEWAL OF THE
N/2-NaOH SOLUTION (*After Berger*, 1936)

Although the logarithmic law was found by Berger to more accurately fit an attack/time curve than the parabolic law it appears more difficult to theoretically justify since it is derived from the differential $dS/dt = L/(t+a)$ which implies a reduction in the rate of attack with time without linking this with a definite physical or chemical process. Also, Lyle (1943) found that the parabolic law and not the logarithmic law was applicable to the corrosion of bottle glass by water.

APPARENT PARABOLIC TIME LAW WITH ALKALINE SOLUTION

Berger (1936) found that the attack of powdered glass specimens by an alkaline solution was linear, providing the products of the corrosion were not allowed to accumulate in the solution. The tests were made using a glass powder with a surface area of about 1200 cm^2 in a stirred solution of 100 c.c $N/2$ NaOH at 93°c. The quantity of glass decomposed as measured by different techniques and a function of time is plotted in Fig. 3.8. The results show that using a corrosive solution without controlling its alkalinity results in an attack roughly following a parabolic time law, whereas continuously renewing the attacking liquid produces a linear relation. Independent tests were made with plate glass in alkaline solutions which were stirred to maintain a uniform concentration of alkali. The plate glass was attacked at a uniform rate which indicated that the progressive fall in the attacking rate occurring with powders could not be attributed to surface changes in the glass. It was established that silica and other glass components dissolved in the solution from the large area of eroded powder greatly reduced its attacking power.

Thus, the differential time law can be approximately modified to take account of the quantity of silica in unit volume of the attacking liquid and we obtain: $dS/dt = K/(r+s)$, where r and k are constants. This relation would give rise to a parabolic law but, unlike that considered in the previous section, the quantity s is not related to a surface film but to the presence of an inhibiting material in the attacking solution with $s \propto S$.

STUDIES OF THE EFFECT OF TEMPERATURE ON THE RATE OF ATTACK

It has been shown on p. 142 that the attack of a glass surface by a corrosive solution may follow the Arrhenius relation because diffusion through a surface layer during the acid attack of glass is activated or the chemical reaction occurring at the glass/liquid interface during alkali attack is activated. Experimental evidence for both of these processes has been obtained. The activation of the diffusion has been confirmed for the initial rate of attack ($t \to 0$) of acid on low resistant glasses (Berger, 1936), for the solution of alkali from bottle glasses immersed in water (Lyle, 1943). The activation of the chemical attack of a range of glasses by alkaline solutions has been reported by Hubbard and Hamilton (1941).

Irrespective of the attacking process the Arrhenius expression for the velocity of the attack in terms of the activation energy E (cal/g mol) and the absolute temperature T can be written

$$\log_{10} V = -\frac{E}{2 \cdot 303RT} + C = -\frac{B}{T} + C$$

where $B = E/2 \cdot 303R$, C is a constant, and R is the gas constant ($1 \cdot 9865$ cal_{15} deg^{-1} g mol^{-1}).

Alkali attack. Shown in Fig. 3.9 is the rate of attack as a function of $1/T$ of a series of glasses immersed in a 5% NaOH-solution. The surface attack was measured after 3 hours by optical interference. The key to the glasses tested is given in Table 3.6 together with the

Table 3.6

Glasses investigated by Hubbard and Hamilton (1941) in 5% NaOH solution with Arrhenius equation constants and activation energies

Glass	$-B$	C	E (kcal/g mol)
1 Plate Glass	3600	10·23	16·56
2 Window glass	3600	10·26	16·56
3 American Ceram. Soc. bottle No. 1	3960	11·38	18·22
4 Corning 015 glass	4280	12·37	19·69
5 Medium flint glass	3870	11·37	17·80
6 Chemical 'Pyrex'	4020	11·84	18·49
7 Borosilicate crown	3700	10·97	17·02
8 Light barium crown	3320	9·90	15·27

constants B and C calculated from the curves in Fig. 3.9. The writer has added values of E the activation energy. The curves in Fig. 3.9 have different slopes and Hubbard and Hamilton have warned *that it may not be correct to use observations made solely at high temperature as criteria of chemical durability at room temperature.*

Table 3.6 shows that E has an average value of about 17·5 kcal/g mol. Geffcken and Berger (1938) studied the attack of Na_2CO_3-solutions on borosilicate and other glasses and found that E was almost constant having a value of about 18·5 kcal/g mol.

Attack by water. Lyle (1943) examined the effect of temperature on the attack time law which from equation (11) on p. 142 can be written

$$\ni \log S = \log t - \frac{B}{T} + C$$

where $\ni = 2$ when the parabolic law is obeyed. Applying this relation to the alkali extracted from a series of bottle glasses he found that

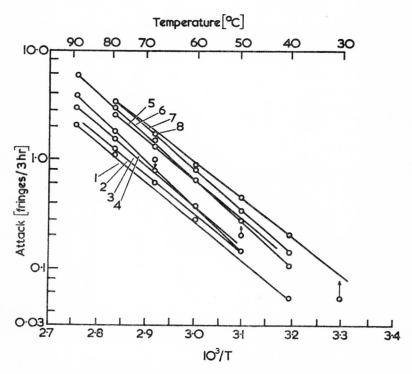

Fig. 3.9 RATE OF ATTACK OF A 5% NaOH SOLUTION ON A SERIES OF GLASSES PLOTTED AS A FUNCTION OF THE RECIPROCAL OF THE ABSOLUTE TEMPERATURE (*After Hubbard and Hamilton*, 1941)

over the temperature interval 20°–120°c $B = 5080$, $E = 23\cdot4$ kcal/g mol and $\ni \simeq 2$ but out of eleven samples there were two for which $\ni \simeq 1$ (this may have been due to some pretreatment of the glass as its history was not specified).

The attack of alkali glasses by water has been attributed to an ion-exchange process in which Na^+ ions are replaced by H^+ ions. Douglas and Isard (1949) found that the rate controlling process for attack by water was the diffusion of sodium ions to the glass surface and this was activated ($E = 18 \cdot 3$ kcal/g mol). A detailed examination is made of their work in a later section.

Attack by steam. Charles (1958) has measured the growth of a corrosion layer on soda-lime glass exposed to steam. He derived from the curves shown in Fig. 3.3 the *initial* rate of penetration as a function of temperature and found that the resultant activation energy for both saturated and 90% saturated vapour was equal to 20 ± 4 kcal/g mol. It has been suggested that the OH^- ions in the alkaline solution are adsorbed to the SiO_2 network and form an adsorption compound $Si—O—Si—OH^-$ which is released as SiOH when the $Si—O—Si$ network breaks with the supply of sufficient activation energy. Charles advances the view that the rate controlling process for the attack of soda-lime glass by steam is the diffusion of the Na^+-ion to the reaction surface. Thus, from volume resistivity data on soda-lime glass, he found that the activation energy for Na^+ diffusion was $19 \cdot 4$ kcal/g mol, which was of a similar order to the activation energy of the corrosion.

Acid attack. Jones and Homer (1941) have measured the times taken to form an anti-reflection coating for visible light on a series of optical glasses when treated with nitric acid at different temperatures. Their results are shown in Fig. 3.10 for light barium crown, borosilicate crown, barium flint, dense barium flint, extra dense flint and dense barium crown. The films were $\lambda/4$-thick which at $\lambda = 5000$ Å corresponds to an optical thickness of 1250 Å. From the efficiency of the films in suppressing the reflectivity it is apparent that they had a refractive index of about $1 \cdot 4$ so that their true thickness would be about 900 Å. This value has been used by the writer for calculating the rate of attack in Å/min given in Fig. 3.10. Soda-lime silicate (plate-glass) and borosilicate (chemical 'Pyrex') form in acid solutions thin protective films which grow too slowly to produce anti-reflection films and therefore cannot be examined by the foregoing method.

The strength of the acid solution used by Jones and Homer was not given and it is shown in Section 5 that the rate of attack of acid solutions with pH values varying between 1 to 7 can change

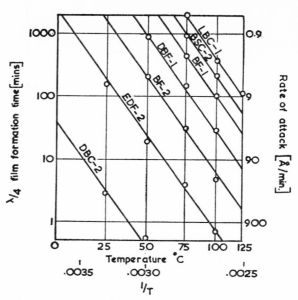

FIG. 3.10 TIME TO FORM A $\lambda/4$-FILM ON DIFFERENT OPTICAL GLASSES IN ACID SOLUTION AS A FUNCTION OF THE RECIPROCAL OF THE ABSOLUTE TEMPERATURE (*After Jones and Homer*, 1941).

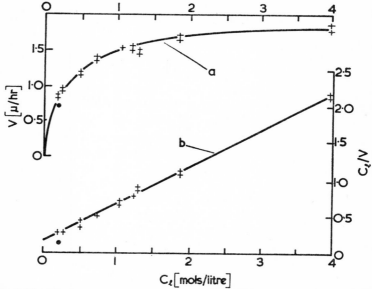

FIG. 3.11 EFFECT OF CONCENTRATION OF Na/CO_3-SOLUTION ON: (*a*) THE RATE OF ATTACK OF A BOROSILICATE GLASS PLATE AT $100°C$ AND (*b*) AGREEMENT WITH LANGMUIR ADSORPTION ISOTHERM (*After Geffcken and Berger*, 1938).

markedly and alter the order for the relative attack of a series of glasses.

A value of E has been roughly calculated from the curves in Fig. 3.10 and is about 17 kcal/g mol.

It is shown on p. 168 that a nearly neutral solution forming a surface layer has two activation energies, one corresponding to the production of the porous layer, the other to the complete dissolution of the glass. Undoubtedly more work must be done to unravel the mechanism of the corrosion of glass in acid before a complete physico–chemical interpretation of the significance of the activation energy of attack can be made.

Effect of solution concentration. Geffcken and Berger (1938) have studied the attack on glass of sodium carbonate solutions with different concentrations at 100°c. They measured the depth of surface removed by optical interferometry. Using a borosilicate crown glass and solutions with concentrations ranging between 0·2–4·0 N they found that with weak stirring of the solution the rate of surface removal remained constant with time. It would appear that all of the glass components were dissolved. When the concentration of the solution was raised the rate of attack rose until it reached a constant value as shown in Fig. 3.11(a). From this curve it can be deduced that as the concentration of the active material in the solution rises, the number of molecules or ions adsorbed on the glass surface, producing surface attack, tend to proportionally increase until they reach a saturated value. If V is the rate of surface removal and C_1 the concentration of the solution then Fig. 3.11(a) can be represented by a relation of the form

$$V = \frac{1}{\dfrac{a}{C_1} + b}$$

from which we obtain

$$\frac{C_1}{V} = a + bC_1$$

by plotting C_1/V as a function of C_1 we obtain the curve in Fig. 3.11(b) from which a and b can be derived. (It should be noted that the foregoing relation resembles the hyperbolic equation developed by Langmuir for the fraction of a surface covered by adsorbed gas in equilibrium with a gas at a given pressure.)

Ion-exchange Theory of the Attack of Alkali Glasses by Water

Certain glasses such as soda-lime silica and 'Pyrex' do not form anti-reflection films on their surfaces and are not disintegrated by distilled water or buffered solutions with pH values between 0·65–7 after 6 hours' exposure at temperatures of up to 80°c (Hubbard and Hamilton, 1941). However, alkali can be extracted from these glasses although their structure remains substantially unaffected.

Douglas and Isard believe that the alkali is removed from such glasses by the diffusion of sodium ions to the glass surface and the counter diffusion of H^+ ions into the glass to maintain electrical neutrality. Experiments were made with glass† tubes filled with distilled water and the alkali extracted measured by determining the electrical conductivity of the water. They found that below 50°c sodium carbonate was formed in the water by the leaching process because excess carbon dioxide was present, but above 50°c sodium hydroxide was formed. The extraction cell was calibrated with corresponding solutions. When the electrical conductivity of the extraction cell (proportional to alkali extracted) was plotted as a function of $\sqrt{t}$ a linear relation was obtained for temperatures between 20°–100°c as in Fig. 3.12*a*, *b*. When the curves were extrapolated to zero time they gave a variable intercept on the extraction axis. This was attributed to alkali being present on the surface of the fresh tubes, which was immediately released on water immersion. Thus washing a tube before testing at 30°c produced an extraction curve which passed through the origin.

If the sodium ions diffusing out of the glass leave a negative charge which is neutralized by the counter-diffusion of H^+ ions the process would involve a double diffusion, the mathematical treatment of which is complicated. Should the diffusion constant for one of the ions be much lower than the other then the process may be dealt with as one of simple diffusion, with a diffusion constant not very different from the lower one. Following Douglas and Isard and assuming that the diffusion of sodium ions is the rate controlling factor, then one can obtain an approximate value for the diffusion constant (D) of sodium ions at different temperatures from the electrical conductivity of the glass.

---

† Soda-lime X8 glass.

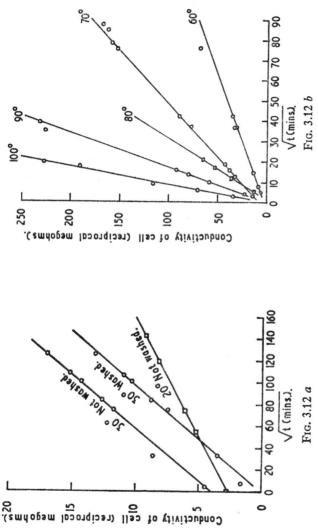

Fig. 3.12 WATER-LEACHING OF SODA-LIME SILICA GLASS AS A FUNCTION OF THE SQUARE ROOT OF THE TREATMENT TIME AND AT DIFFERENT TEMPERATURES (*After Douglas and Isard, 1949*).

159

The specific conductivity σ of an ionic conductor in which movement of the ions is opposed by a potential barrier of height E is approximately given by

$$\sigma = a^2 \gamma \frac{n\epsilon^2}{kT} e^{-E/kT} \qquad (1)$$

where n is the number of ions per cubic centimetre which can be found from the sodium content of the glass, a the average distance between the ions, γ the vibrational frequency, ϵ the charge on an ion, k the Boltzmann constant, and T the absolute temperature. The diffusion constant is given by

$$D = a^2 \gamma \, e^{-E/kT} \qquad (2)$$

Dividing (1) by (2) we obtain the Einstein relation between diffusion and electrical conductivity

$$\frac{\sigma}{D} = \frac{n\epsilon^2}{kT} \qquad (3)$$

The quantity of sodium removed from a glass in time t (after Barrer 1951) is for a semi-infinite solid

$$Q = \int_0^t D \left(\frac{\partial n}{\partial x} \right)_{x=0} dt$$

$$= \frac{2}{\sqrt{\pi}} n_0 \sqrt{Dt} \qquad (4)$$

which assumes that the initially uniform ion concentration n_0 instantaneously falls to zero at the surface ($x = 0$) at commencement of attack ($t = 0$) (see Barrer (1951)).

Combining (3) and (4) the value of $Q/\sqrt{t}$ deduced from the electrical conductivity is

$$\frac{Q}{\sqrt{t}} = \frac{2}{\sqrt{\pi}} n_0 \sqrt{\frac{\sigma kT}{n_0 \epsilon^2}} \qquad (5)$$

since $n = n_0$ in the electrical conduction measurements. Using a soda-lime silica glass with $16 \cdot 8\%$ of Na_2O equation (5) can be simplified to

$$\frac{Q}{\sqrt{t}} = \sqrt{\sigma T} \times 69 \cdot 92$$

where Q is in mg Na/100 cm^2; t in min; and σ in cm^{-1} Ω^{-1}. It can be seen from equations (2) and (4) that

$$\frac{Q}{\sqrt{t}} = \text{constant} \times \exp\left(-\frac{\frac{1}{2}E}{kT}\right) \qquad (6)$$

Shown in Fig. 3.13 are the sodium extraction values measured by Douglas and Isard at different temperatures plotted as $\log (Q/\sqrt{t})$

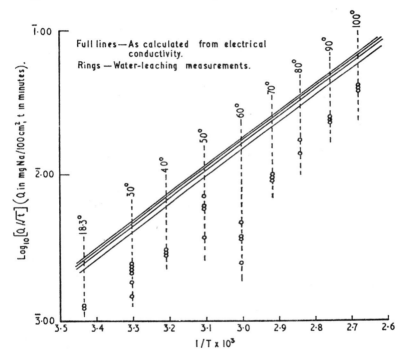

FIG. 3.13 EFFECT OF TEMPERATURE ON WATER-LEACHING OF SODA-LIME SILICA GLASS. (*After Douglas and Isard, 1949*).

as a function of $1/T$ with for comparison the calculated values of $\log (Q/\sqrt{t})$ derived from the electrical conductivity σ using equation (5). The curves have roughly the same slope and the activation energies are $E = 0.774$ eV (17·8 kcal/g mol) for the electrical conductivity and $E = 0.794$ eV (18·3 kcal/g mol) for water leaching. The latter value agrees with the values of E for soda-lime silicate glass given in the previous section. The fact that the values of E for

11

leaching and electrical conductivity are similar indicates that diffusion of sodium ions is the rate controlling process. The theory is based on several approximations and undue stress should not be placed on the constant factor of about 2 between the calculated and measured values of $Q/\sqrt{t}$. The measured values at 60°c are in error because an unknown mixture of hydroxide and carbonate existed in the extraction cell.

Recently Rana and Douglas (1961) have reinvestigated the reaction between glass and water and found a marked difference between the diffusion coefficient D_R determined for Na^+ ions leached from glass and the diffusion coefficient D_c derived from conductivity measurements. For the commercial X8 glass discussed above $D_R/D_c = \frac{1}{3}$ whereas for a similar soda-lime glass (15% Na_2O; 10% CaO; 75% SiO_2), the ratio was about 3. Small changes in alkali content or replacement of Na_2O by K_2O made enormous differences in the value of D_R/D_c which rose to several hundred or more indicating failure of the theory. Rana and Douglas believe the theory is at fault because there is no experimental evidence for assuming that D is independent of concentration and that all of the Na^+ ions participate in conduction or reaction.

Activation energy for sulphur dioxide treatment. Douglas and Isard (1949) treated soda-lime silicate glass with sulphur dioxide and confirmed by X-ray analysis that the deposit formed on the glass was pure anhydrous sodium sulphate. The amount of sodium sulphate formed on a treated surface was determined by washing off the deposit in doubly distilled water and measuring the electrical conductivity of the solution. Under nearly all conditions the amount of Na_2SO_4 deposited on the glass was found to increase in proportion to the square root of the time of treatment, as would be expected for a diffusion process. If a specimen was given repeated treatments and the deposit removed between treatments then the total mass of the deposit was still dependent on the total time of treatment, showing that the parabolic time law arose from diffusion *through the glass* and not through the sulphate layer. The parabolic time law was obeyed for treatment temperatures from 300° to 600°c with a 1% concentration of SO_2 in air. Adding water vapour to the SO_2/air mixture accelerated the rate at which sodium sulphate formed and the deposit mass was proportional to $\sqrt{t}$ as before.

When the sulphur dioxide content of the furnace atmosphere was reduced to 0·1 and 0·2% the initial growth of the Na_2SO_4-deposit was slow and tended to be proportional to t and not $\sqrt{t}$. However, after a period the parabolic law was obeyed and the developed curve has the same slope as that obtained with higher concentrations of sulphur dioxide. As shown earlier the parabolic time law is applicable *providing the surface reaction leading to removal of the sodium ions is not the rate controlling process, i.e.* it is assumed that the sodium concentration at the surface falls to zero immediately the reaction commences. Obviously if the concentration of the reactive gas in the furnace atmosphere is decreased a stage will come where the surface reaction is the limiting process; a similar effect occurs with liquids with a low concentration of reactive groups as discussed on p. 157. If the gas concentration was constant at the glass surface and the rate controlling process then the surface reaction would proceed at a uniform rate *i.e.* $Q \simeq t$. As the surface layer becomes denuded of sodium diffusion to the surface decreases until it becomes the rate controlling process and the $Q \simeq \sqrt{t}$ relation is obtained.

The activation energies for sulphur dioxide treatment under various conditions together with that for water leaching are given in Table 3.7.

Table 3.7

Activation energies for alkali removal from soda-lime silica glass
(*Based on work of Douglas and Isard, 1949*)

Process	(eV)	E (kcal/g mol)
Sulphuring below 600°c with H_2O-vapour present	0·55	12·7
Sulphuring without H_2O-vapour	2·6	59·9
Water leaching	0·794	18·3
Electrical conductivity	0·774	17·8

It is to be noted that the activation energy is higher when water vapour is absent from the furnace gas. Williams and Weyl (1945) have suggested that at high temperature Na_2O is removed from glass, not sodium ions. If the Na^+ ions were to diffuse to the surface and not be replaced by H^+ ions from water then electrical neutrality of the glass would not be maintained. Douglas and Isard believe that the high activation energy determined with the dry furnace gas is that for the negative oxygen ions which diffuse to the surface with the sodium ions.

Heat treatment of leached layer. It has been stated on p. 137 that treatment of soda-lime silica glass in contact with kaolin at high

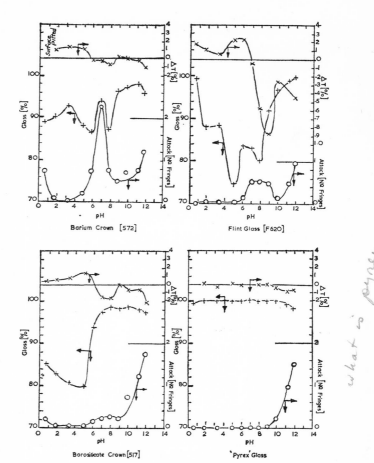

Measurements cover: specular surface gloss at 45°;
change in transmittance ΔT; and depth of attack in
terms of interference fringes.

FIG. 3.14   COMPARISON OF THE ATTACK ON VARIOUS GLASSES AFTER 6 HOURS
IN SOLUTIONS WITH DIFFERENT pH VALUES AT 80°C (*After Hubbard and
Rynders*, 1948).

temperature (500°C) produces a glass of exceptional chemical
resistance and similar results were obtained with sulphur dioxide
treatment at high temperature. Douglas and Isard believe that the
'hydrogen' glass formed during dealkalizing is dehydrated by the
H^+ ions combining with oxygen and diffusing out of the glass.
The water molecules so formed would be electrically neutral and their
diffusion would not be opposed as would that of H^+ ions. Douglas
and Isard prepared specimens of water leached glass and then baked

164

them at 400°c and found that the slope of the leaching curve $(Q/\sqrt{t} = K)$ was greatly reduced. Glass which had been treated with sulphur dioxide at 500°c also gave a greatly reduced alkali extraction rate in water at lower temperature. *The high temperature of treatment enables the leached surface layer to form a compact structure through which sodium ions diffuse with difficulty.*

5. GROWTH OF SURFACE FILMS

EFFECT OF pH VALUE ON ATTACK AND GLOSS

It is shown in Chapter 2 that the surface attack of glass may produce porous silica coatings of low refractive index and if these have an optical thickness of a quarter of a wavelength the surface reflection will be reduced and the transmittance increased. We shall consider here the work which has been done on modifying the optical properties of glass surfaces by controlled chemical attack. The production of anti-reflection films by chemical etching is no longer of practical value because of the weak and optically inefficient nature of the films but past work in this field is of wider interest.

Hubbard and Rynders (1948) have studied the attack of glass surfaces by solutions covering a wide range of pH values. They measured by optical interference the depth of the surface dissolved after six hours with the solution at 80°c. Measurements were also made of the change in the transmittance ($\Delta T\%$) of the specimens and the degree to which the attacked surface retained its specular gloss at an incidence angle of 45°.

Shown in Fig. 3.14 are the results of the foregoing tests for a series of glasses with the compositions given in Table 3.8. The curves show that at low pH values (< 6) the transmittance of the various glasses are enhanced with the exception of chemical 'Pyrex' which remains unchanged. The increase in the transmittance is not necessarily the maximum obtainable as the treatment time was not controlled to obtain $\lambda/4$-thick films. Generally the surface gloss is impaired at low pH values because the alkali and heavy metal oxides undergo selective solution leaving a roughened surface. As information is not available on the depth of the silica enriched layer remaining after acid attack it is not possible to say whether impairment of glass would be as bad with $\lambda/4$-films, but the results indicate the light scattering nature of chemically produced coatings.

Table 3.8

Composition in weight % of the glasses tested by
Hubbard and Rynders (1948)

Oxide	BSC 517	BaC 572	F 620	Chemical Pyrex
SiO_2	66·4	49·7	45·6	81·0
B_2O_3	12·4	3·6	—	13·0
Na_2O	8·4	0·4	3·6	3·6
K_2O	11·8	7·7	5·2	0·2
BaO	—	30·8	—	—
PbO	—	—	45·1	—
ZnO	0·5	7·2	—	—
As_2O_3	0·5	0·2	0·5	0·002
Sb_2O_3	—	0·4	—	—
R_2O_3	—	—	—	2·2

At high pH values the alkaline nature of the solution results in
the glass constituents tending to be equally dissolved and generally
in this region the gloss is least impaired and interference films cannot be produced. When borosilicate crown, barium crown and flint
glasses were exposed to a 5% $NaOH^-$ solution at 80°c the rate of
surface attack remained constant with time and the corrosion only
lowered the gloss of the worse affected glass, *i.e.* the flint, by 3%
after 4 hours.

FILM GROWTH IN ALMOST NEUTRAL SOLUTIONS

Pore density. Schroeder (1949a) has investigated the chemical attack
of glass to produce interference films using water solutions of
organic and inorganic salts with pH values near the neutral point.†
He claimed that soda-lime glass on which it is normally difficult to
produce a surface film of interference thickness could be treated in
these solutions. The glasses used in Schroeder's experiments were
plate glass ($n_D = 1·5215$, specific density 2·510) and Schottglass BK7
($n_D = 1·5163$). Schroeder claimed that the surface films formed by
neutral solutions had a pore diameter of 70–100 Å and that the
silica framework was attacked during film formation whereas this
did not occur with acid solutions. An estimation of the number of
pores N per unit surface area in the eroded glass was obtained by

† The compositions of all the solutions were not specified.

assuming that each pore was a cylinder of radius r. Thus if the densities of the solid and porous glass are ρ_g and ρ_f respectively, we have

$$N = \frac{1 - \rho_f/\rho_g}{\pi r^2}$$

Observations on many types of alkali glasses gave a value of N of 5–$10.10^{11}/cm^2$, independently of the nature and concentration of the solution. With strong basic glasses (*e.g.* those containing barium oxide) the value of N reached 5.10^{12}.

Schroeder advances the theory that pores are formed at the sites of faults on the glass surface and since the mean pore distance is $1/\sqrt{N} \simeq 100$ Å this is also the distance between surface defects.

Kinetics of film growth. Schroeder observed that the weight lost by a glass during treatment was greater than could be accounted for by the formation of the porous deposit and found that the film had been eroded from the outside during growth. He reasoned that for a porous film to form the rate of pore formation V_p must be higher than the rate of dissolution of the glass V_g, so that the net rate of porous film growth V_f was

$$V_f = V_p - V_g \tag{1}$$

It is necessary to consider more fully the meaning of this expression. The growth of a porous film is normally limited by diffusion processes in the film so that its rate of growth is inversely proportional to its thickness d, *i.e.* $dd/dt = K/d = V_p$ (see p. 144). At the commencement of attack the film will begin to form as oxides and alkalis are selectively removed from the glass and the remaining silica network will then be eroded chiefly at its outer surface. The presence of the film will decrease its rate of formation until it is equal to the erosion rate (equally, if a film was already present it would be eroded until its thickness was sufficiently reduced for its rate of renewal to equal its rate of erosion). Thus at equilibrium the film attains a constant thickness d_L with a renewal and erosion rate of $V_g = V_p$. At this stage the net film growth would become zero and $V_f = 0$, but a film would be present although equation (1) as interpreted by Schroeder would imply that this was not possible.

If equation (1) was applied to the conditions of film growth for films *less* than equilibrium thickness then V_f would represent an average value depending on the film thickness range chosen for measurement. In his determination of V_p and V_g Schroeder studied the effects of solution concentration and temperature on the formation of anti-reflection coatings which were of similar optical interference thickness. He does not mention a limiting thickness, and we may presume that the thickness of the films were less than d_L, *i.e.* if such a limitation existed. Under these conditions V_f would represent an average value which could be used for assessing the film forming efficiency of different solutions because it would be inversely proportional to the time t taken to form an anti-reflection coating of constant thickness d_s, *i.e.* $V_f = d_s/t$. With these cautionary remarks we shall now discuss Schroeder's method for determining V_f and V_g.

If A is the plane area of the specimen surface, d_s the thickness of a film giving an interference minimum for reflected light and $\Delta\rho = \rho_g - \rho_f$ the change in density in the time t, then the measured weight loss per unit area is given by

$$\Delta G/A = \rho_g V_g t + \Delta\rho d_s$$

As $V_f = d_s/t$ it follows

$$V_p = \frac{1}{t}\left[\frac{\Delta G}{A\rho_g} + \left(1 - \frac{\Delta\rho}{\rho_g}\right)d_s\right] \quad V_g = \frac{1}{t}\left(\frac{\Delta G}{A\rho_g} - \frac{\Delta\rho}{\rho_g}d_s\right)$$

The treated specimens were weighed in a dry atmosphere, because of water absorption by the film. The film thickness was determined from the interference minimum in the reflected light and the measured refractive index. As a check on the experimental results the amount of glass completely eroded ($V_g t$) was also determined by measuring the height of the original specimen surface above the outer surface of the film.

Shown in Fig. 3.15 is log V as a function of $1/T$ for a glass attacked with a $Na_2H.AsO_4$-solution. The porous films are $\lambda/4$-thick at $\lambda = 5500$ Å and have a refractive index of about 1·23. For temperatures under 80°c the activation energies are $E_g = 28$ kcal/g mol and $E_p = 22·4$ kcal/g mol. Fig. 3.16 is for the same system as the previous figure but the solution has a concentration (unspecified) giving a poor film formation rate; for temperatures below 70°c $E_g \simeq E_p \simeq 16$ kcal/g mol.

FILM GROWTH ON WORKED AND HEAT TREATED SURFACES

Film formation will occur only when V_g/V_p is less than one, but if the film grows to a limiting thickness d_L as previously discussed

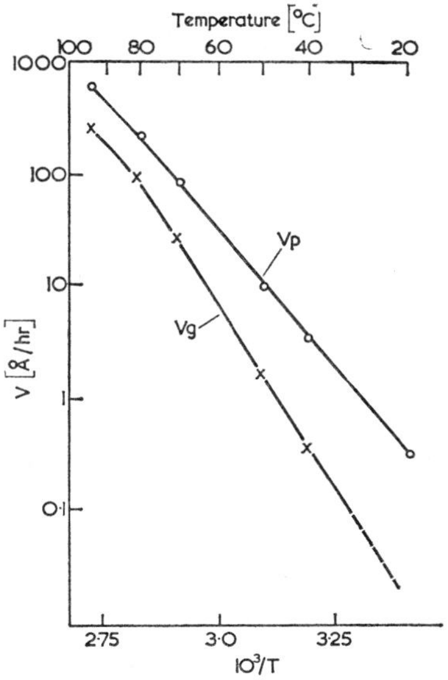

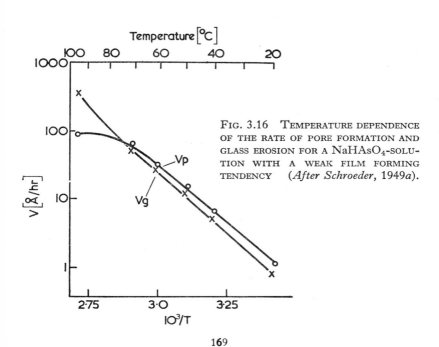

FIG. 3.15 Temperature dependence of the rate of pore formation and glass erosion for a $NaHAsO_4$-solution with a strong film forming tendency (*After Schroeder*, 1949a).

FIG. 3.16 Temperature dependence of the rate of pore formation and glass erosion for a $NaHAsO_4$-solution with a weak film forming tendency (*After Schroeder*, 1949a).

then V_g/V_p will rise to one as d becomes equal to d_L. Fig. 3.17 shows that V_g/V_p *falls* rather than rises as the thickness of the attacked layer is increased beyond the $\lambda/4$ value previously used. This was attributed by Schroeder to the glass having an initial surface layer, *e.g.* a silica enriched film arising from optical working, which had to be removed before film growth could properly commence. For such a film to hinder rather than aid formation of the low index layer it must have a dense structure. The point at which the curve ceases to decrease indicates that the pitch polished BK7 glass has an initial surface layer 3000 Å thick.

The foregoing effect was studied by Schroeder (1949*b*) in another way. It is shown in Chapter 2 that the reflectance of a glass coated with an interference film of low refractive index is approximately proportional to a cosine function of the thickness. Thus, by measuring the change in the reflectivity of a treated glass whilst immersed in the attacking solution, it is possible to follow the film growth. If the film grew according to a parabolic time law then this, combined with the cosine relation, would result in the reflectivity decreasing rapidly. However, as shown in Fig. 3.18, when optically worked glass was chemically filmed the reflectance measured in the solution remained almost constant for a time interval before decreasing to a minimum. The period for which this occurred depended on the glass and the method of finishing. It was longest for BK7 which had been polished on a pitch tool and shortest for plate glass. Some workers believe that polishing glass produces a hard film of glass on the surface. However, the results shown in Fig. 3.18 can be taken to indicate the presence of an alkali leached layer on the surface of the glass which slows down the initial rate of attack, *e.g.* as shown in Fig. 3.5. There is evidence that a thin film of silica gel is formed on a glass surface during polishing by the chemical action of the polishing materials and liquid. It has also been shown that BK7 glass can be polished on a pitch tool with water alone, indicating extensive silica gel formation. Plate glass is more resistant to attack and the growth of a silica gel film during polishing is less marked.

Schroeder reports that surface attack of normal glasses can be reduced by heat treatment, fire polishing and exposure to an intense glow discharge. Fire polishing would tend to denude the surface of alkali and produce a surface free from defects. The action of a glow discharge is more complex because it may heat the glass, remove alkali ions by sputtering or cover the glass surface with organic films if hydrocarbon molecules are present in the residual gas.

Jones (1941) observed that optical glasses which had been chemically attacked to produce a superficial silica coating were less

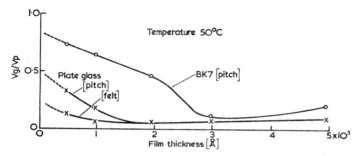

FIG. 3.17   DEPENDENCE OF THE RATIO OF SURFACE ATTACK V_g/V_p ON THE THICKNESS OF THE POROUS LAYER FORMED (*After Schroeder*, 1949*a*).

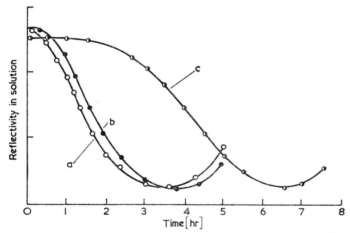

(*a*) plate glass/felt polisher; (*b*) plate glass/pitch polisher; (*c*) BK7/pitch polisher.

FIG. 3.18   CHANGE OF REFLECTIVITY WITH TIME OF IMMERSION IN FILM FORMING SOLUTION (*After Schroeder*, 1949*b*).

easily attacked when the film was sintered by heat treatment. Sodium ions cannot diffuse readily through compact layers of silica.

6. CORROSION OF OPTICAL GLASSES

Glass used for making windows and bottles usually contains oxides of calcium, potassium and sodium combined with silica, whereas chemical ware (*e.g.* 'Pyrex') may contain oxides of boron, sodium and aluminium with silica. To produce optical glasses covering a wide range of refractive indices it is necessary to incorporate many different metal oxides in the glass melts, and optical glass may contain, apart from the oxides already referred to, oxides of lead, barium, zinc, magnesium, antimony, etc., together with silica. The oxides of lead and barium are often present in very high concentrations in optical glasses.

As explained at the beginning of this review various methods have been devised both for accelerating the corrosion of glass and for assessing the extent of the corrosion. Particular attention has been given to optical glasses because of the ease with which certain types can be tarnished, *e.g.* dense flints and barium crowns can be stained by perspiration from finger prints. We shall briefly consider here some of the investigations into the durability of optical glasses.

SURFACE ELECTRICAL CONDUCTIVITY

The British Scientific Instrument Research Association (1922, 1937) have investigated the durability of optical glasses by measuring the electrical conductivity of their surfaces. Optically worked specimens were heated in an oven to about 130°c and then cooled in a nearly saturated atmosphere of water. The process could be repeated several times if required. The electrical conductivity of an adsorbed water layer is mainly determined by its alkali content and the durability test is really one of measuring alkali liberation during weathering. It was found that after pre-treatment the conductivity finally reached a constant value which depended on the history of the particular glass and its composition. Of the glasses tested a light flint had the lowest affinity for water and a fluor crown and dense barium crown had the highest affinities for water.

When a range of optical glasses was exposed in the tropics under corrosive conditions the extent to which their surfaces became filmed could for certain groups of glasses be correlated with the results of the electrical method. Thus there was good agreement between the two sets of placings for hard and soft crowns; barium light flints; medium barium crowns; light flints. There was practically no correlation in the two placings for glasses in the following groups – borosilicate crowns; dense barium crowns; dense flints; extra dense and double extra dense flints.

Durability of glasses and their hygroscopic properties

Hubbard (1946*a*) has stated that the serviceability of optical glasses, *i.e.* their ability to maintain a clear polished surface under normal conditions, is too often confused with the general subject of the *chemical durability* of glasses. He has drawn attention to the fact that some of the common optical glasses are known to possess poor chemical durability over a wide range of conditions, but they still give excellent service. From this Hubbard concludes that many of the methods proposed for assessing chemical durability do not give useful information on optical serviceability.

Hubbard considers that most optical glasses are exposed to air containing water vapour throughout their life and the most useful indication of their serviceability will most likely be obtained from knowledge of their hygroscopic properties. Obviously if one limits testing to the effects of water the performance of an optical glass is likely to appear better than when it is exposed to acid attack. However, one cannot ignore the possible presence of acidic components in the atmospheres of industrial towns and obtaining complete knowledge of glass properties obviously requires testing under various conditions.

The quantity of water sorbed by unit area of glass is very small, and Hubbard used powdered glass to obtain a large area and adequate sensitivity when measuring weight changes. About 1·5 g of powder was dried at 110° c and then exposed in a shallow weighing bottle under humid conditions (95–98% R.H. at 25°c) and the change in weight measured.

Hubbard found that the water sorbed by window and bottle glass was 5 to 10 times greater than that taken up by a group of optical glasses. Precise data on water sorption of glasses will be found in the next chapter and it is sufficient to state here that the water sorbed by a borosilicate crown (517), a flint glass (F620), a lead borate (51·71% PbO) and a barium crown (572) was either comparable to or less than that of chemical-ware such as Pyrex.

In a later paper Hubbard (1946*b*) showed that the pH response of glass electrodes made from different glasses could be related to their hygroscopicity. The optical glasses referred to above all showed a low pH response in agreement with their low water sorption. Thus an alkali electrode glass (Corning 015) had a water sorption of 358 mg/cm^3 and had a response of 59 mV/pH. The optical glasses had a water sorption of 2–5 mg/cm^3 and a response of 33–43 mV/pH. Hubbard suggests that measurement of pH response would indicate the serviceability of glasses.

Hubbard has stated that the ability of glasses to maintain optically clear surfaces is approximately in inverse order to the rate at which water is sorbed by new surfaces. This would appear to be confirmed by the work of Simpson (1953a) who alternately condensed and evaporated water on the surfaces of a number of optical glasses and measured the amount of light scattered by the reaction products.

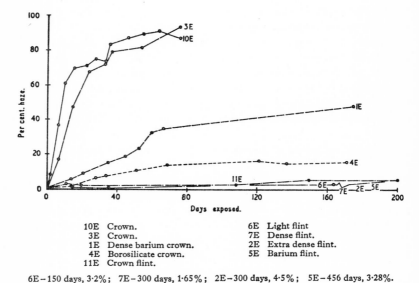

10E	Crown.	6E	Light flint
3E	Crown.	7E	Dense flint.
1E	Dense barium crown.	2E	Extra dense flint.
4E	Borosilicate crown.	5E	Barium flint.
11E	Crown flint.		

6E – 150 days, 3·2%;   7E – 300 days, 1·65%;   2E – 300 days, 4·5%;   5E – 456 days, 3·28%.

FIG. 3.19   HAZE FORMATION ON A RANGE OF OPTICAL GLASSES (*After Simpson,* 1953a).

The glasses were suspended over water and their temperature varied by 5°F in 2 hours. Shown in Fig. 3.19 is the percentage of light scattered by reaction products on the attacked surfaces as a function of the time of exposure. The results show that the flint glasses retain their optical clarity whereas the crown (soda-lime silicate) glasses rapidly deteriorate. These results can be roughly correlated with the water sorption properties of the glasses. It is shown in Chapter 6 that glasses with large polarizable ions of barium and lead adsorbed to their surface have least affinity for water. This has been attributed to the Pb^{2+} and Ba^{2+} ions being adsorbed to the surface in such a way that their electrical forces are directed mainly towards the glass. However, sorption studies of bulk lead oxide glasses indicate that the attractive fields of the surface cations are better satisfied by adsorbed oxygen than water or OH-groups.

Low resistant glasses

Certain optical glasses are in use which are easily tarnished in a humid atmosphere or by perspiration from the fingers when handled. The corrosion of such glasses has been exhaustively studied in Japan by Kinosita and Natsume (1959).† The compositions of most of the glasses investigated will be found in the work by Morey (1954) and with few exceptions we shall only refer to the glasses by type number: these were SK5, SK16, SF2, SF3, BaF10, SSK5, KF2, KF6, LaK13 and F2.

Corroded areas on glass are of two types (*i*) tarnish films of low refractive index showing optical interference effects and (*ii*) coarse corrosion deposits which scatter light and appear white.

Rate of attack and refractive index of films. Natsume (1960) has measured by Abelès method the refractive index n_f of surface films produced on three sensitive optical glasses. The types of glass, the index and treatment were as follows: dense silicate flint SF3(1·760)– $\frac{1}{10}$N HNO₃; dense barium crown SK5 (1·589) – $\frac{1}{1000}$N HNO₃; and LaK13 (40–50% B_2O_3; 20–30% La_2O_3) (1·694) – pure water.

Values of n_f measured at 60°c for SF3 varied between 1·450–1·525, for SK5 between 1·440–1·520, and for LaK13 between 1·450–1·53. Natsume gives the mean indices for films on the previous three glasses in the foregoing order as 1·484, 1·477 and 1·500. However, the indices of the films vary so much there is little importance one can attach to the mean values except that they show that the basic and acidic oxides have been leached from the glass. Also, the indices of the films were affected by moisture sorption. Thus gently warming a film on LaK13 glass with an electric lamp reduced its index from 1·500 to 1·420; the index change was reversible. Heat treating the films at 180°–300°c raised their index.

The growth of the surface films as a function of time was determined from their interference colour, which gives the optical thickness $n_f d$. The index was independently measured so that d could be

---

† The abstracts of the papers are given in English but full translations of the papers were unfortunately not available to the writer.

found. Films grown on SK5 in $\frac{1}{100}$N HNO$_3$ at 60°c grew at a linear rate of 1200 Å/min suggesting that the rate-controlling process was the reaction at the compact glass/film interface and not diffusion through the porous film. Films formed on SK5 with weak acid solutions ($\frac{1}{1000}$N HNO$_3$ at 40°, 50° and 60°c) indicated a diffusion process. Similarly films formed on SF3 in $\frac{1}{10}$ to 1N HNO$_3$ at 40°, 50° and 60°c and on LaK13 in water at 40°, 50° and 60°c indicated growth under diffusion conditions. The time law for the growth under diffusion condition approximated to $d = t^{0.4}$; it has been shown earlier that diffusion controlled growth of a porous layer should be proportional to $t^{0.5}$.

Activation energies for growth of the tarnish layers were determined by measuring the times of formation of 1000 and 1500 Å thick films as a function of temperature. This gave values of 18·9, 14·3 and 9·7 kcal/mol for SF3, SK5 and LaK13 respectively.

Sulphur attack. Kamogawa (1940) studied the surfaces of polished optical glasses using electron diffraction. The glass specimen was bombarded with a beam of low velocity electrons (~ 300 V) during examination with the normal high velocity beam (40–50 kV). This technique prevented the glass accumulating a negative charge because the secondary electron emission of glass reaches a maximum ($\simeq 2$) at a low voltage. Optical glasses containing a high percentage of barium oxide (*e.g.* SK4, BaLF4) and lead oxide (*e.g.* SF2, SF5) were kept at room temperature in a humid atmosphere rich in sulphur dioxide gas. The glasses developed visible interference films which, for barium glass, were identified as BaSO$_4$ and, for lead glass, as a mixture of PbS and PbSO$_4$.

7. IMPROVING CHEMICAL DURABILITY BY SURFACE TREATMENT

We have already shown in a previous section that the durability of alkali glasses can be improved by sulphur treatment, which lowers the alkali content of the surface by forming sodium sulphate. Also, that the durability can be improved by an ion-exchange process in which Na$^+$ ions are first replaced by H$^+$ ions and then the hydrogen is removed combined with oxygen at high temperature. The durability of glass surfaces may also be influenced by treatment with acids and optical working.

Haze formation. Simpson (1953*b*) has studied the effects of varying the temperature of plate glass specimens a few degrees above and below the saturation temperature of water vapour. The saturation temperature was 55°C and the condensed water did not flow off the glass surface, so that the reaction products remained producing a haze, which could be detected optically from the scattered light. Simpson found that fire polished glass taken directly from production was the most resistant to hazing, whereas it deteriorated rapidly if it had been stored. Aged glass which had been washed and cleaned deteriorated more slowly if initially treated with sulphuric acid but finally the haze formation was the same as without treatment. Treatment with hydrochloric acid did not delay hazing and sodium hydroxide hastened it. Adsorbed films of acids or alkali may have remained on the surface and influenced the pH value of the subsequently condensed water vapour. Sulphuric acid is less volatile than hydrochloric acid and may have remained on the surface neutralizing alkalis released from the glass.

Effect of optical working. Attention was drawn to the effect of optical working on the chemical durability of glass by Rosenhain in the discussion of a paper by French (1917). Rosenhain stated that glasses which were easily attacked in the atmosphere showed a relation between their tarnish resistance and the nature of the polishing medium. Badger and Farber (1943) polished *enamel*-type glass with a range of substances – chromic oxide, titania, zinc oxide, zinc sulphide, cuprous oxide, Feldspar, silica, cryolite, zirconium silicate, nickel hydroxide and manganese dioxide. After etching specimens in a 10% solution of citric acid for 15 min they found that the polished regions were practically unaffected, whereas the unworked areas were deeply etched. The enhanced chemical resistance of the polished glass was not dependent on the nature of the polishing medium. The influence of optical working on chemical durability could arise from several causes, but the most likely is that soluble glass components are removed by the polishing slurry leaving a silica rich surface layer which is resistant to acid attack.

Contrary to the above reports for *optical* and *enamel* glasses Simpson (1953*b*) found that grinding and polishing the fire-polished surface of soda-lime glass reduced its resistance to haze formation when water vapour was continually condensed and re-evaporated from its surface. Probably the fire-polishing had previously left a dense glass layer of low alkali content on the surface.

12

The effect of optical working on chemical durability is probably dependent in a complex manner on the nature of the glass and polishing system and the polishing conditions, *e.g.* load on polishing tool, temperature of slurry, etc. However, a study of the chemical properties of optically worked surfaces may give interesting information on the nature of the surface layers and their mode of formation.

Vacuum deposited films. It is understandable that attempts have been made to protect glasses against corrosion with surface coatings. Films of silicon oxides, metal oxides and metal fluorides are regularly deposited on glass for optical purposes (beam splitters, anti-reflection films, etc.) either by evaporation in vacuum or by cathodic sputtering in a glow discharge. Such films are usually stable in corrosive atmospheres and may even impart some protection to the glass substrate. However, it is difficult to produce films which are completely free from pinholes and corrosion of coated glass usually occurs at localized points which may look worse than uniform attack of the uncoated glass. Lohr (1953) claims that films of vanadium and tantalum oxides deposited in vacuum protect boiler sight glasses against attack by alkalis and steam, but to the writer's knowledge these claims have not been realized in practice. In the writer's laboratory films of heat oxidized titanium (TiO_2 rutile) and magnesium fluoride have been deposited on boiler sight glasses, but they did not prevent glass erosion in water at high temperatures. Anti-reflection films of magnesium fluoride deposited on hot glass ($\simeq 300°c$) in vacuum will protect the optical elements against attack when exposed to cutting fluids used in optical centering.

Protection of glass by evaporated or sputtered films might yet prove possible, but apart from the problem of producing pinhole-free deposits there is only a limited range of film materials which have suitable optical properties. Holland (1956) has discussed the preparation of dielectric films by vacuum deposition techniques.

Silicone treatment. Glass surfaces can be covered with chemisorbed films of silicones which make them hydrophobic and the method of treatment is discussed in detail in Chapter 7. Briefly, silicone polymers are constructed of repeating elements such as $[(CH_3)_2 SiO]_n$ in which the structure is based on chains or cycles of —Si—O—Si— atoms. If Na^+ and OH^- ions, which usually satisfy the chemical forces of the incomplete silica network at the surface are absent then the —Si—O—Si— groups of the silicone molecule are able to continue the silica network forming a strongly bonded film with non-polar (CH₃) groups extending outermost from the surface. The chemisorbed silicone film may be prepared by heating the glass in the presence of silicone oil in the form of a spray, water emulsion or solvent solution. At high temperature the adsorbed water and OH⁻ ions are removed exposing the silica network. Alternatively one may use a methylchlorsilane which reacts with water adsorbed to the glass producing hydrochloric acid and thereby leaving the surface unshielded for silicone adsorption.

The resultant adsorbed film may be simply represented as follows:

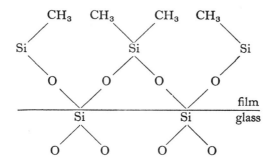

In practice the silicone film may be many times thicker than a monolayer and the chain length of the alkyl group may be increased, thereby producing a more hydrophobic surface.

Wessel (1958) has investigated the effect of silicone films on the chemical durability of a heavy silicate flint glass (SF4) exposed to hydrogen sulphide. The glass was cleaned with soap solution, alcohol and distilled water and heated for 1 hour at 400°c. It was then dipped in a toluene solution of silicone oil for 1 min and again heat treated for ½ hour at 300°c. Shown in Plate 18 is the transmission of the silicone treated glasses after some days' exposure to hydrogen sulphide. The lead component in the glass reacts with sulphur to produce a black lead sulphate which reduces the glass transmission. The photographs show that the glass is better protected after two silicone treatments using silicone oils of high viscosity.

Silicone treated glass has a lower surface electrical conductance than untreated glass because the hydrophobic film prevents the formation of a continuous water layer (see Chapter 9). Edge and

Oldfield (1958) found that silicone films on glasses with a high alkali content (20–30%) became ineffective after exposure to conditions of high humidity as experienced in tropical countries. Removal of alkali ions from the glass surface by controlled leaching in hot water at 50°c for about $1\frac{1}{2}$ hours followed by a 20 min bake at 150°–250°c subsequently gave the most durable silicone film; baking glass after leaching lowers the rate of diffusion of Na^+ ions through the leached layer.

Edge and Oldfield believe that a uniform silicone film does not form on a glass surface in areas where the alkali content is high because alkaline hydrolysis of the silicone compound prevents complete polymerization. Water then attacks the glass and film through these discontinuities.

It is quite possible that due to weathering the glass surface is fissured before treatment and the water molecules enter the glass through cracks which the polymerized silicone film incompletely bridges.

In a later paper Edge and Oldfield (1960) reported the effects of silicone treating four metal electrode sealing glasses, viz. a high alkali glass ($Na_2O + K_2O = 16\cdot3\%$); a lead glass ($Na_2O + K_2O = 13\cdot3\%$); and a borosilicate ($66\cdot0\%$ SiO_2; $2\cdot0\%$ Al_2O_3; $4\cdot0\%$ Na_2O; $3\cdot0\%$ K_2O; 24% B_2O_3). Siliconed specimens of these glasses were subjected to an accelerated climatic test at 55°c and 95% R.H. In all cases the silicone film broke down under these severe conditions. However, leaching and baking the surface before treatment improved the performance of the soda glass, gave a small improvement with the lead-glass, no improvement with the borosilicate glass and even appeared to worsen the attack.

8. SODIUM BOROSILICATE GLASSES

It has been mentioned in an earlier section that a group of sodium borosilicate glasses exist which can be selectively leached in bulk, leaving an almost pure silica framework. This is the method used for preparing articles in a silica glass known as 'Vycor' which is sintered after leaching. The sodium borosilicate glasses have, however, attracted scientific interest outside of their technical value. This is because a special group of compositions can be prepared as transparent glasses which apparently only separate into phases when annealed to produce opalescent glasses. The glasses possessing this property are shown in the hatched zone of the ternary composition diagram in Fig. 3.20 which was prepared by Moltchanova (1957). Also shown in the diagram is the position occupied by 'Pyrex' which is a sodium borosilicate glass which is rendered chemically resistant by the addition of a small quantity of aluminium oxide.

Opalescence in glass is due to the scattering of light by internal boundaries formed between either different glass like phases or the bulk glass and crystalline matter suspended in its interior, *e.g.* opal glass normally contains a crystalline metal fluoride. Recent work suggests that opalescence in sodium borosilicate glasses arises from

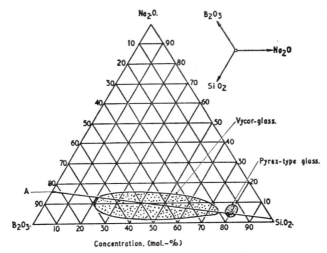

Line A represents the compositions studied by Skatulla *et al.*

FIG. 3.20 PHASE SEGREGATION RANGE IN THE TERNARY GLASS SYSTEM $Na_2/B_2O_3/SiO_2$ (*After Molchanova*, 1957).

the scattering of light by droplets of different glass phases suspended in a glass matrix. However, the important factor to be considered here is that transparent sodium borosilicate glasses can be leached in bulk as well as the opalescent glasses which have visibly undergone phase separation.

The solubility of the clear borosilicate glasses and the dependence of the size of the pores in the leached glass on the annealing period have led many Russian workers to contend that the clear glass also consists of separate phases. Some have gone further and claimed that the behaviour of the sodium borosilicate glasses is evidence for crystalline order on a limited scale in glasses generally. It has now been established by electron microscopy that flint glasses containing a large amount of lead oxide are transparent but contain two glass-like phases.

Much of the Russian work on the chemical leaching properties of the borosilicates indicated the existence of separate phases in the clear glass and this in fact has been confirmed by the electron microscopy work of Skatulla, Vogel and Wessel dealt with further on. However, as always when a new or modified theory is being introduced as a result of fresh experimental evidence, there are those who cling to the work and theory of the past and those who in eagerness tend to apply the new conception unconditionally regardless of confirmation of its validity in each case. Often each of the conflicting theories is valid for the experimental conditions under which it was derived, but the rival groups fail to recognize the limiting effect of the experimental conditions. It would now appear *that optically transparent silicate glasses can exist in which there are one or more separate phases depending upon the nature and concentration of the components.*

PORE SIZE AND COMPOSITION

Zhdanov (1953) has studied the adsorption of water vapour on the surfaces of sodium borosilicate and borosilicate glasses which have been leached by acid treatment. From this he has deduced the volume, area and radii of the pores in the leached glass. Given in Tables 3.9 and 3.10 are the pore volume and internal surface area for different glass compositions.

The tables show that the volume of the pores in a leached glass increases almost regularly with increasing amounts of B_2O_3 and Na_2O in the glass, *i.e.* the components which are dissolved when acids or water act on the glass; the regularity of the pore growth is even more marked in alkali-free borosilicate glasses.

It is of interest to note that the cells in porous glasses are usually much smaller than those in silica gel. Thus in the glasses discussed here the pore size was in the region 10–40 Å in radii, whereas those of silica gel may fall anywhere in the range 20–100 Å. The volume of the pores in silica gel may greatly exceed that of the silica skeleton, whereas in porous glasses the pore size normally does not exceed 50% of the volume of the rigid skeleton.

Table 3.9

Effect of glass composition on the structure of porous glasses
of the system $Na_2O/B_2O_3/SiO_2$
(*After Zhdanov* 1953)

SiO_2 content in original glass (molar %)	75	70		65			60	
Na_2O content (molar %) B_2O_3 ,, ,,	5 25	6 24	4 26	7 28	5 30	4 31	10 30	4 36
Total pore volume of porous glass (c.c/g)	0·143	0·157	0·144	0·161	0·201	0·204	0·280	0·258

Table 3.10

Effect of glass composition on the structure of porous glasses
of the system B_2O_3—SiO_2
(*After Zhdanov* 1953)

B_2O_3 content in original glass (molar %)	40	35	30	25
Total pore volume of porous residue (c.c/g)	0·203	0·190	0·134	0·095
Pore surface (m^2/g)	364	—	286	176

Zak (1953) assumed that all inorganic glasses have a micro-heterogeneous structure and contends that resistant glass, *e.g.* soda-lime silicate, cannot be leached because penetration is prevented by the formation of a protective surface layer. He believed that glass fibres a few microns in diameter of the resistant glasses should be capable of being leached because the solvent could penetrate freely into the whole of the fibre. Thus he found that fibres of an alumino-borosilicate glass dissolved rapidly in acid, leaving behind a silica thread whereas glass rods of the same glass were hardly attacked over a long period.

Zak also studied the solubilities of fibres drawn from simple alkali-silicates. Fibres containing 20 and 26% Na_2O were dissolved by water, leaving behind a porous body composed almost entirely of silica. The material dissolved in the water corresponded approximately to sodium disilicate. From this Zak inferred that alkali-silicates consisted of a silica framework filled with sodium silicate. A porous silica thread was obtained when fibres of complex glasses with large amounts of calcium and aluminium oxides were attacked by acid.

Schmidt (1953) has stated that Zak's results for sodium silicate were fortuitous as the amount of SiO_2 in ratio to Na_2O dissolved by water is dependent on temperature, but Schmidt worked with glass plates where a surface film would be present. The main objection to Zak's results is that they do not conclusively decide between whether the silica framework already *existed* or was *formed* as the glass was attacked.

EFFECT OF HEAT TREATMENT ON PORE GROWTH

Zhdanov found that the pores in a sodium borosilicate glass (7% Na_2O; 23% B_2O_3) grew more rapidly when the glasses had

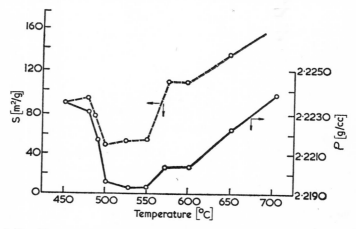

FIG. 3.21   THE FULL CURVE GIVES THE DENSITY OF A 7% Na_2O 23% B_2O_3
GLASS AS A FUNCTION OF THE HEAT TREATMENT TEMPERATURE AND THE DASHED
CURVE THE PORE AREA (*After Zhdanov*, 1953).

been heat treated at 500°–550°c. These glasses also gave the largest pore radii. Shown in Fig. 3.21 is the dependence of the glass density and pore area on the heat treatment temperature. The rate of growth of the leached layer together with the pore volume are plotted in Fig. 3.22 as a function of the heat treatment temperature.

The influence of the heat treatment on the pore formation is particularly pronounced for sodium borosilicate glass with a low alkali content. Thus Zhdanov found that a glass (3% Na_2O; 27%

B_2O_3) quenched from a high temperature and treated with 3N hydrochloric acid gave a typical porous glass with a pore volume of over 0·1 c.c/g indicating that a considerable amount of the boron oxide in the glass had been dissolved. The same glass after being *annealed* at 530°c became incomparably more resistant to chemical attack, did not yield a completely porous product but was merely coated with a thin silica film.

Using a sodium borosilicate glass (7% Na_2O; 23% B_2O_3) Dobychin (1953) found that the amount of material leached remained constant even though the glass had been heat treated to change its appearance from transparent to opalescent. This suggested that phase segregation existed in the clear glass but was insufficient to scatter light. Further work showed that the pore size of the leached glass depended on the annealing temperature and treatment time. Thus the pore size rose from 10 Å to a maximum value of 50 Å when the glass was annealed at 530°c for 100 hours, whereas it remained constant at 15 Å when the glass was treated at a temperature of 650° for 100 hours.

LEACHING OF STRESSED PLATES

It is of interest that stresses are not removed when plates or fibres of sodium borosilicate glasses are leached with acids. Thus Evstropyev (1953) has stated:

'If a plate of sodium borosilicate glass is bent and treated with acid to leach out the sodium borate component, and the bending stress is then removed, the plate resumes the form it had before the deformation and leaching. Therefore, the fundamental structure of the plate remains unchanged during the leaching, and retains the deformed stresses. This experiment provides direct proof of the independent existence of two structures in the glass: silica and sodium borate.'

RATE OF LEACHING

Sodium borosilicate glasses can undergo volume changes when leached (Hood and Nordberg, 1940). Kuehne (1955) observed that acid leached glasses shrunk or swelled depending on the temperature and time of the previous heat treatment. A combination of treatment temperature and time could be found at which dimensional changes did not occur.

Kuehne noted that glasses which swelled during acid treatment could be leached more rapidly than those which shrank. The rate of leaching was controlled by a diffusion process. Thus the data given for the growth in a $2N$ H_2SO_4 solution of a leached layer on a 2 mm thick specimen (which did not change dimensionally during treatment) shows that at $60°$ and $80°c$ the leaching roughly followed the parabolic law $d \propto \sqrt{t}$.

ELECTRON MICROSCOPY EVIDENCE FOR PHASE SEPARATION

Not all Russian workers have inferred that the leached transparent sodium borosilicate glasses are evidence of either a crystallite or microheterogeneous structure in glass. Thus Belov (1953) has argued that:

'It is obvious to every chemist that a system need not be a two-phase system on the macro or micro-scale in order to release boric anhydride or sodium borate under the action of reagents; this applies to silicate systems.'

Belov goes on to argue that boron is present in borates in triangular co-ordination, *i.e.* boron atoms lie at the centre of a triangle of oxygen atoms. However, it has been shown that in borosilicates boron is present in fourfold co-ordination, *i.e.* in tetrahedrons. At high temperature the boron in glass is in threefold co-ordination which changes to fourfold at low temperature. The reordering process is not complete when the glass solidifies and some boron remains in threefold co-ordination which affects the continuity of the molecular framework. Weak spots form in the glass and these are the regions at which water acts and leaches out unsymmetrically the unstably situated boron and sodium atoms. The pores serve merely to drain off the soluble part of the glass.

On this view the porous product obtained by treatment of borosilicate glass with acid is a secondary formation produced as a result of the total breakdown of the structure of the original glass and subsequent coagulation of the silica in the acid solution, as in the formation of silica gel from sodium silicate solutions. The structure of the porous glass or film would then be unrelated to that of the original glass. Alternatively, the structure of the borosilicate glasses is not broken down completely by the etchant and a considerable part of it, consisting of silica, remains unchanged and is preserved as a skeleton in the leached glass. If this is so then there should be a close connection between, on the one hand, the composition and thermal history of the original glass and, on the other, the porous structure of the leached glass. The effect on the porosity of heat-treating borosilicate glasses suggests that for these glasses the second hypothesis is the correct one.

Skatulla, Vogel and Wessel (1958) investigated the structure of the borosilicates using electron microscopy. They used an instrument with a resolution of 20–30 Å and prepared the microscope specimens with the utmost care to avoid the production of granula-

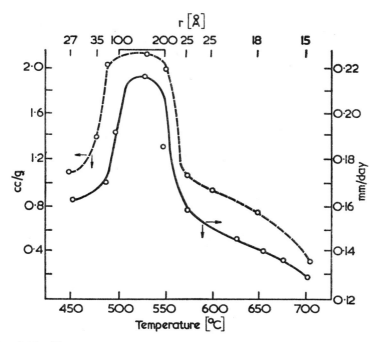

FIG. 3.22 THE FULL CURVE SHOWS THE RATE OF GROWTH OF A POROUS LAYER ON A 7% Na_2O 23% B_2O_3 GLASS AS A FUNCTION OF THE HEAT TREATMENT AND THE DASHED CURVE THE CORRESPONDING PORE VOLUME. THE PORE DIAMETER IS GIVEN ON THE UPPER SCALE (*After Zhdanov*, 1953).

tion in the surface replicas and the atmosphere affecting the glass surface. Replicas of glass surfaces were prepared for the electron microscope by vacuum evaporating on to the glass carbon films which possessed practically no discernible structure. The carbon replicas were floated off the glass in water or dilute hydrofluoric acid and dried on the specimen holders. They were then shadowed to enhance the image contrast by evaporating tungsten oxide in vacuum at an angle to the surface of 30–40°; tungsten oxide films are almost grain free. To avoid attack in the atmosphere or by water vapour in the vacuum vessel the specimen surfaces were prepared by breaking glass *in vacuo* immediately before replication of the fracture surfaces. Some specimens were broken in air and molybdenum oxide smoke crystals condensed on the fresh surfaces. Molybdenum oxide crystals are thin plates with smooth surfaces and it was possible to check that the surface structure of the replica was intrinsically grain free.

Experiments were initially made with sodium borate glasses and it was confirmed that as the Na_2O content was increased the phase separation rose to a maximum at 16 mol % and then declined. The

□ boron oxide   ○ sodium borate   ◉ silica

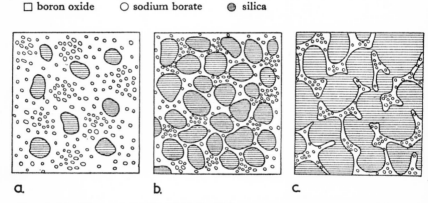

a.   b.   c.

FIG. 3.23   MODEL of a $Na_2O/B_2O_3/SiO_2$ OPALESCENT GLASS WITH (*a*) LOW SiO_2 CONTENT; (*b*) MEDIUM SiO_2 CONTENT; (*c*) HIGH SiO_2 CONTENT (*After Skatulla et al.*, 1958).
Micrographs corresponding to (*b*) and (*c*) are shown in Plate 2.

micrographs of a sodium borate glass (Na_2O 16 mol % B_2O_3 mol 84%) showed that droplets of the sodium rich borate phase had steadily aggregated in a boron oxide rich phase. *All of the glasses showing phase separation on a microscopic scale were transparent and did not scatter transmitted light.*

Skatulla *et al.* explain the behaviour of the Na_2O/B_2O_3 system as follows. Pure B_2O_3-glass is normally composed of a network of [BO_3] groups but when Na_2O is introduced into the glass it results in the production of [BO_4]-tetrahedra with two free electronegative charges partially satisfied by the sodium ions. The surface tension of the sodium borate so formed is higher than that of the pure boron oxide glass and consequently they separate into phases which steadily grow with heat treatment. The heat treatment temperature must be sufficient for the soda to migrate and bunch together without thermal disorder breaking down the accumulated zones.

Skatulla *et al.* investigated sodium borosilicate glasses with the range of compositions given by the line A in Fig. 3.20. The silica content of the glasses was gradually raised with the ratio of the Na_2O to B_2O_3 kept constant at $16:84$ mol %, *i.e.* the concentration showing the greatest phase segregation for the sodium borates. A range of clear glasses was produced which could be changed to opalescent glasses by heat treatment. Shown in Plate 2: (*i*) is a clear glass with a composition similar to that of 'Vycor'. When this glass is heat treated then one obtains opalescent glass with a micro structure as in Plate 2: (*ii*) and (*iii*). Phase segregation could be detected in the micrographs of all the clear glasses ranging up to 70 mol % SiO_2 and above this concentration the borate phase would have been too small to have been detected.

Skatulla *et al.* believed that the borosilicate glasses consisted of three phases as shown in the models in Fig. 3.23, *i.e.* a B_2O_3 rich phase with triangular co-ordination, a sodium borate phase with fourfold co-ordination and a silica rich phase with fourfold co-ordination. Confirmation by microscopy of the models in Fig. 3.23(*b*) and (*c*) was obtained with the heat treated opalescent glasses shown in Plate 3 (*ii*) and (*iii*). Thus the leaching of sodium borosilicate glasses consists in removing the borate phases leaving the silica framework and this explains the chemical behaviour of the porous glasses previously discussed.

CHEMICAL RESISTANCE OF PYREX TYPE GLASSES

Skatulla *et al.* studied Pyrex type glass and found that heat treatment reduced its chemical resistance as shown by the amount of alkali liberated in water. Their results for the alkali liberated from two Pyrex type glasses in water† are given in Table 3.11. Phase segregation could not be detected in the electron micrographs of the normally cooled glasses, *i.e.* within the resolution limitation (20–30 Å) of the instrument. Phase separation could, however, be discerned in the micrographs of the heat treated glasses which had

---

† Measured according to D I N 12111.

Table 3.11

Alkali liberated from Pyrex type glasses
(*After Skatulla et al.*, 1958)

	Pyrex (*Solidex*) (mg Na_2O)	Rasotherm (mg Na_2O)
Normal cooling	30	22
After treatment 2 h at 630°c	138	109

otherwise remained transparent. Large articles of Pyrex glass may have less chemical resistance than small articles because they cool more slowly and phase separation is enhanced.

References

Andrade, E. N. Da C., and Tsien, L. C., 1937, *Proc. roy. Soc.*, **A159**, 346.

Badger, A. E. and Farber, L. G., 1943, *Ceram. Industry*, **40**, 34.

Barrer, R. M., 1951, *Diffusion In and Through Solids*, Cambridge University Press.

Beattie, I. R., 1952, *J. Soc. Glass Technol.*, **36**, 37 (N).

Belov, N. V., 1953, *The Structure of Glass*, p. 275, Acad. Sci. U.S.S.R.; Chapman and Hall, Ltd., London.

Berger, E., 1936, *J. Soc. Glass Technol.*, **20**, 257T.

Brit. Sci. Instrum. Res. Ass., 1922, 'An Investigation into the Stability of Polished Glass Surfaces', Rep. 19.

Brit. Sci. Instrum. Res. Ass., 1937, 'Report on the Stability of Polished Surfaces of Various Optical Glasses and Methods of Estimating the Stability of Polished Glass Surfaces', Rep. 99.

Brueche, E. and Poppa, H., 1957, *Glastechn. Ber.*, **30**, 163.

Charles, R. J., 1958, *J. appl. Phys.*, **11**, 1549.

Cousen, A. and Peddle, C. J., 1936, *J. Soc. Glass Technol.*, **20**, 418; 1937 **21**, 177.

Coward, J. N. and Turner, W. E. S., 1938, *J. Soc. Glass Technol.*, **22**, 309.

Devaux, H., and Aubel, E., 1927, *Compt. Rend. Acad. Sci.*, **184**, 601.

Dobychin, D. P., 1953, *The Structure of Glass*, p. 252, Acad. Sci. U.S.S.R.; Chapman and Hall, Ltd., London.

Douglas, R. W. and Isard, J. O., 1949, *J. Soc. Glass Technol.*, **33**, 289.

Dwight, H. B., 1947, *Tables of Integrals and Other Mathematical Data*, Macmillan, New York.

Edge, J. and Oldfield, L. F., 1958, *J. Soc. Glass Technol.*, **42**, 227T.

Edge, J. and Oldfield, L. F., 1960, *Glass Technol.*, **1**, 69.

Elyard, C. A., and Rawson, H., 1962, *Advances in Glass Technology*, p. 270, Plenum Press Inc., New York.

Ernsberger, F. M., 1960, *Proc. roy. Soc.*, **A, 257**, 213.

Ernsberger, F. M., 1962, *Advances in Glass Technology*, p. 511, Plenum Press Inc., New York.

Evstropyev, K. S., 1953, *The Structure of Glass*, p. 9, Acad. Sci. U.S.S.R.; Chapman and Hall Ltd., London.

Fonda, G. R. and Young, A. H., 1934, *Gen. Elect. Rev.*, **37**, 331.

French, J. W., 1917, *Trans. Opt. Soc.*, **18**, 8.

Geffcken, W. and Berger, E., 1938, *Glastechn. Ber.*, **16**, 296.

Geilmann, W., and Toelg, G., 1955, *Glastechn. Ber.*, **28**, 299.

Gordon, J. E., Marsh, D. M., and Parratt, M. E. M. L., 1959, *Proc. roy. Soc.*, **A, 249**, 65.

Griffith, A. A., 1920, *Phil. Trans.*, **A, 221**, 163.

Holland, L., 1956, *Vacuum Deposition of Thin Films*, Chapman and Hall, Ltd., London.

Holland, L., Putner, T., and Bateman, S., 1957, *J. opt. Soc. Amer.*, **47**, 668.

Hood, H. P., and Nordberg, M. E., 1934, March, Brit. Pat., 442,526.

Hood, H. P., and Nordberg, M. E., 1940, U.S. Pat., 2,221,709.

Hubbard, D., 1946a, *J. Res. Nat. Bur. Stand.*, **36**, 365.

Hubbard, D., 1946b, *J. Res. Nat. Bur. Stand.*, **36**, 511.

Hubbard, D., and Hamilton, E. H., 1941, *J. Res. Nat. Bur. Stand.*, **27**, 143.

Hubbard, D., and Rynders, G. F., 1948, *J. Res. Nat. Bur. Stand.*, **41**, 477.

Jones, F. L., and Homer, H. J., 1941, *J. opt. Soc. Amer.*, **31**, 34.

Kamogawa, H., 1940, *Phys. Rev.*, **58**, 660.

Keppeler, G., 1930, German Pat., 512,904.

Keppeler, G., and Thomas-Welzow, M., 1933, *Glastechn. Ber.*, **11**, 205.

Kinosita, K. and Natsume, K., 1959, 'Experimental Studies on Stains Formed on Polished Surfaces of Optical Glasses', Parts I–IV, Dept. Phys. and Chem., Gakushuin University, Tokyo.

Koenig, H., Loeffler, H. J., and Lappe, F., 1955, *Glastech. Ber.*, **28**, 131.

Kraus, C. A., and Darby, E. H., 1922, *J. Amer. chem. Soc.*, **44**, 2783.

Kubaschewski, O., 1936, *Electrochem.*, **42**, 5.

Kuehne, K., 1955, *Z. phys. Chem.*, **204**, 20.

Lohr, H., 1953, Brit. Pat., 726,312.

Lyle, A. K., 1943, *J. Amer. ceram. Soc.*, **26**, 201.

Marboe, E. C. and Weyl, W. A., 1945, *Glass Ind.*, **26**, 119.

Marboe, E. C. and Weyl, W. A., 1947, *J. Amer. ceram. Soc.*, **30**, 320.

Moltchanova, O. S., 1957, *Steklo i Keram.*, **14**, No. 5, 5.

Morey, G. W., 1954, *The Properties of Glass*, 2nd Ed., p. 101, Reinhold Publishing Corp., New York.

Morey, G. W. and Bowen, N. L., 1927, *J. Soc. Glass Technol.*, **11**, 97.

Mylius, F., 1907, *Z. anorg. Chem.*, **55**, 233.

Natsume, K., 1960, 'Experimental Studies on Stains Formed on Polished Surfaces of Optical Glasses' Part V, Dept. Phys. and Chem., Gakushuin University, Tokyo.

Nordberg, M. E., *Chemical Durability of Glass*, Corning Glass Works.

Philips Gloeilampenfabrieken, 1934, Brit. Pat., 440,551.

Rana, M. A. and Douglas, R. W., 1961, *Phys. Chem. Glasses*, **2**, 179, 196.

Schmidt, Yu. A., 1953, *The Structure of Glass*, p. 253, Acad. Sci. U.S.S.R.; Chapman and Hall, Ltd., London.

Schroeder, H., 1949a, *Z. Naturforschung*, **4a**, 515.

Schroeder, H., 1949b, *Glastechn. Ber.*, **22**, 424.

Sendt, A., 1962, *Advances in Glass Technology*, p. 307, Plenum Press Inc., New York.

Shand, E. B., 1958, *Glass Engineering Handbook*, McGraw Hill Book Co., London.

Simpson, H. E., 1953a, *J. Soc. Glass Technol.*, **37**, 249T.

Simpson, H. E., 1953b, *A. Amer. ceram. Soc.*, **36**, 143.

Skatulla, W., Vogel, W. and Wessel, H., 1958, *Silikattechnik*, **9**, 51; **9**, 323.

Stewart, O. J., and Young, D. W., 1935, *J. Amer. chem. Soc.*, **57**, 695.

Taylor, W. C., and Smith, R. D., 1936, *J. Amer. ceram. Soc.*, **19**, 331.

Wessel, A., 1958, *Silikattechnik*, **9**, 201.

Wheeldon, J. W., 1959, *Brit. J. appl. Phys.*, **10**, 295.

Williams, H. S. and Weyl, W. A., 1945, *Glass Ind.*, **26**, 275, 324.

Zak, A. F., 1953, *The Structure of Glass*, p. 142, Acad. Sci. U.S.S.R.; Chapman and Hall, Ltd., London.

Zhdanov, S. P., 1953, *The Structure of Glass*, p. 125, Acad. Sci. U.S.S.R.; Chapman and Hall, Ltd., London.

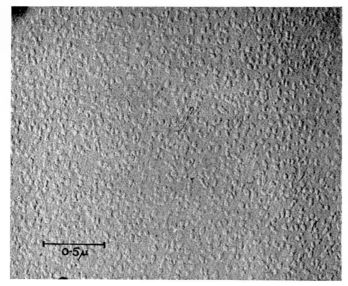

PLATE 1   Polished flint glass with high lead oxide content
(60 mol-% PbO, 40 mol-% SiO$_2$) showing droplets of a
silica rich phase (*After Vogel*, 1959) ×45 000

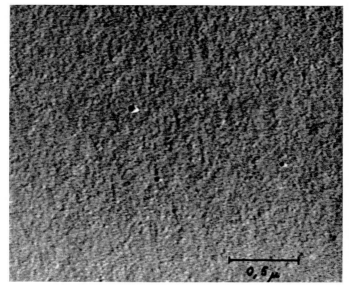

(*i*) Clear glass showing small droplet formation
PLATE 2   Sodium borosilicate glass of the 'Vycor' type
with a composition of 70 mol-% SiO$_2$ and the Na$_2$O and
B$_2$O$_3$ in the ratio 16:84 mol-%

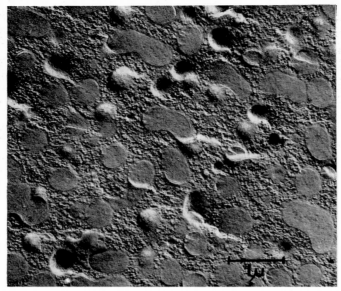

(*ii*) Opalescent heat treated glass showing three glass phases as in Fig. 3.23(*b*), *i.e.* an almost pure B_2O_3 phase containing large droplets of almost a pure silica phase and small droplets of a sodium borate phase

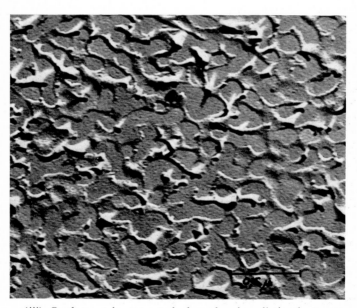

(*iii*) Opalescent heat treated glass showing distinctly two of the three phases present as in Fig. 3.23(*c*) (*After Skatulla, Vogel and Wessel*, 1958)

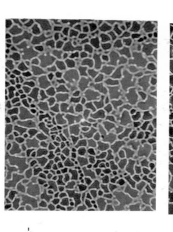

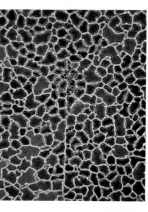

(b) Same area after polishing;

(c) Same area 5 h after polishing

PLATE 4 Condensation patterns taken in transmitted light ($\times 100$) showing effect of polishing a clamped fracture (*After Levengood and Fowler, 1957*)

PLATE 3 Fine ground surface with small cavities some microns deep (*After Brueche, 1956*)

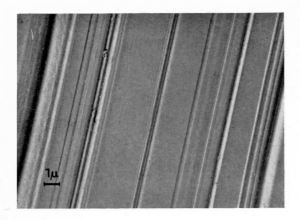

(*a*) Sharp parallel scratches showing surface flow (*After Brueche*, 1956);

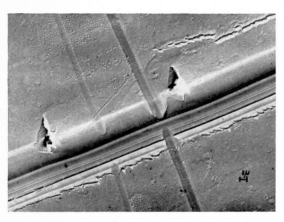

(*b*) Intersecting scratches made with a diamond showing plastic flow (*After Brueche*);

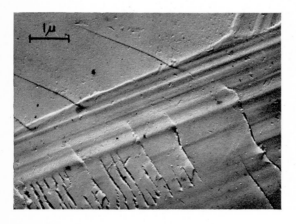

(*c*) Surface scratch showing transverse cracks (chatter flaws) and surface flow (*After Brueche and Poppa*, 1955*a*)

PLATE 5

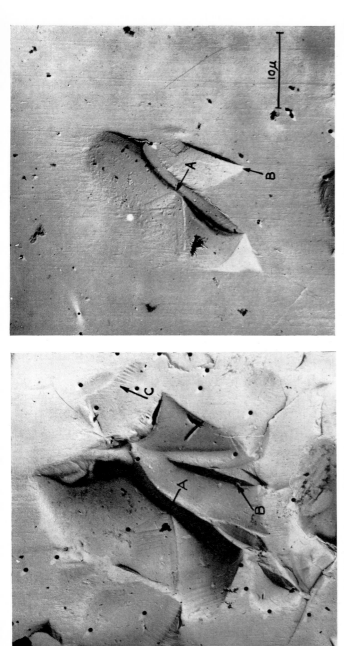

(a) After a short polishing time

(b) After a long polishing time

PLATE 6   Polishing out of a grinding pit on plate glass (*After Brueche and Poppa, 1957a*). A, deep chatter mark in the grinding pit which has not been reached by the polisher; B, a crevice between the surface asperities that has been almost removed by polishing; C, chatter marks which have been polished out. (Faults in the surface replicas have not been removed from the electron micrographs)

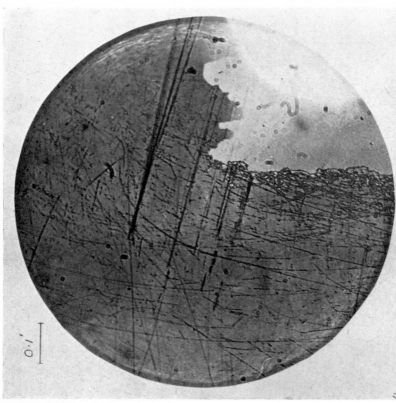

PLATE 8   Polished crown glass etched with hydrofluoric acid showing pattern of scratch marks following the direction of working. Scratches made on the treated glass are more visible on the etched surface (*After*

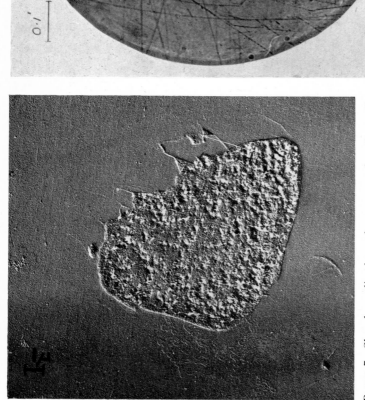

PLATE 7   Sharply outlined rough zone on otherwise well-polished surface (*After Brueche and Poppa, 1957a*)

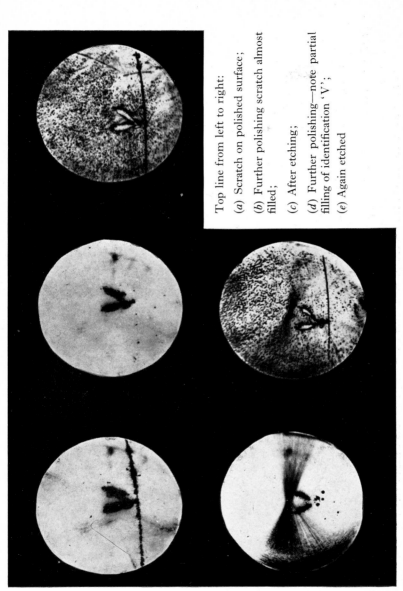

Top line from left to right:

(a) Scratch on polished surface;

(b) Further polishing scratch almost filled;

(c) After etching;

(d) Further polishing—note partial filling of identification 'V';

(e) Again etched

PLATE 9   Reappearance of scratch marks after etching crown glass (*After Rawstron, 1958*)

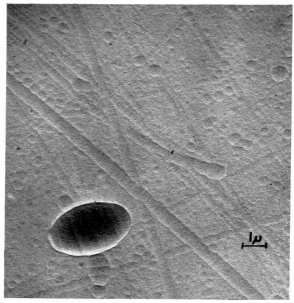

PLATE 10 Electron micrograph of acid etched glass surface showing broadened tracks (*After Brueche, Peter and Poppa*, 1958)

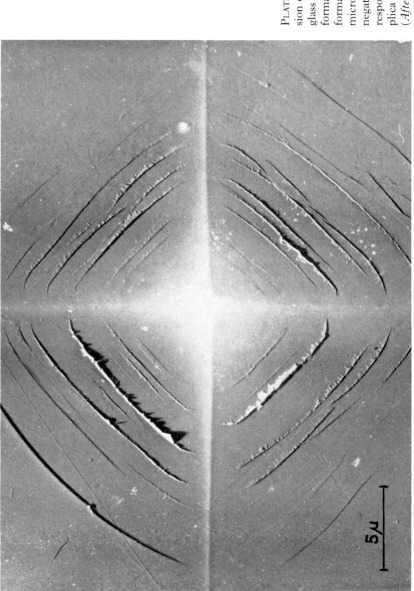

5 µ

PLATE 11 Micro-impression of Vickers diamond in glass showing plastic deformation and fine crack formation. The electron micrograph is taken from a negative replica and corresponds to viewing the replica from the glass side (*After Brueche*)

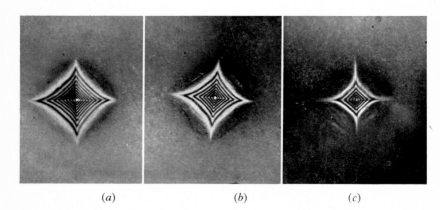

(a) (b) (c)

PLATE 12 Changes in the depth of Vickers hardness indentations in Schott-glass FK6 after heating (*After Diehl and Schulze*, 1957)
   (a) Impression made under 300 g load at room temperature;
   (b) As in (a) but heated at 130°c for 30 min;
   (c) As in (a) but heated at 300°c for 15 min

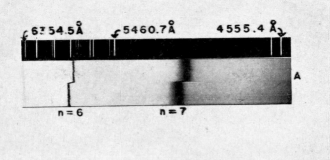

(a)

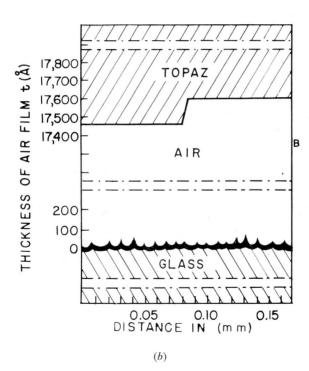

(b)

Plate 13 Examination of polished glass by multiple beam interferometry using fringes of equal chromatic order (*After Koehler*, 1953*b*). The cusps in the fine structure are believed to be contours of cones. Surface polished with 'Barnesite' using bowl feed for 450 min with a polishing pressure of 130 g/cm²

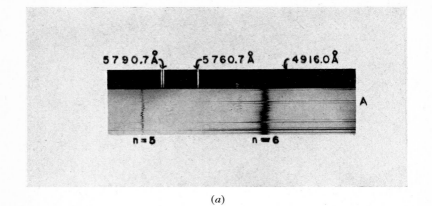

(a)

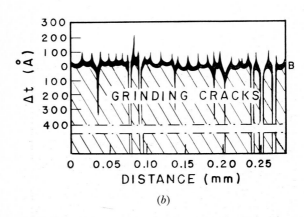

(b)

PLATE 14 Multiple beam interferogram of two glass surfaces (*After Koehler*, 1952*b*). Cones appear on elevated regions between wide grinding cracks. The contour in *b* is the *equivalent* glass surface. Glasses polished for 20 min and as described for Plate 13

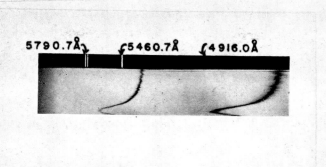

PLATE 15   Multiple beam interferogram of a pit with polishing marks
near the rim (*After Koehler*, 1953*b*). Specimen polished for 330 min
under conditions described in Plate 13

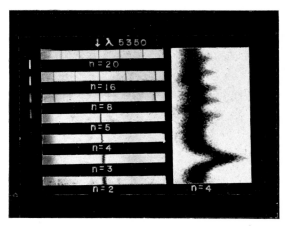

PLATE 16   Multiple beam interference fringes of
different order used for determining surface
roughness of glass plates from measurement of
the fringe half-width (*Koehler and White*, 1955*b*)

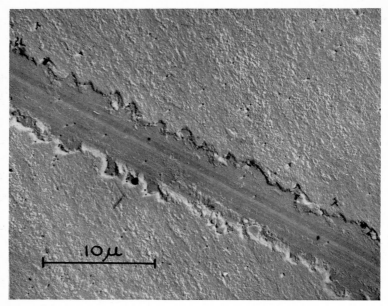

(a) Artificially weathered film on Libbey-Owen-Ford plate penetrated by a broad scratch of about 5 μ width. The weathered film
was visible as a hazy deposit and less than 0·5 μ thick (*After Brueche
and Poppa*, 1957)

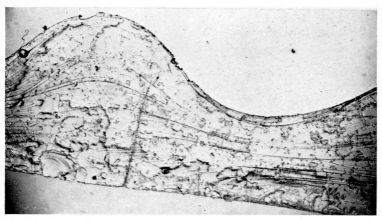

(b) Plastic replica taken from the fractured handle of a third-century
Roman vessel (*After Geilmann and Toelg*, 1955). × 15

PLATE 17

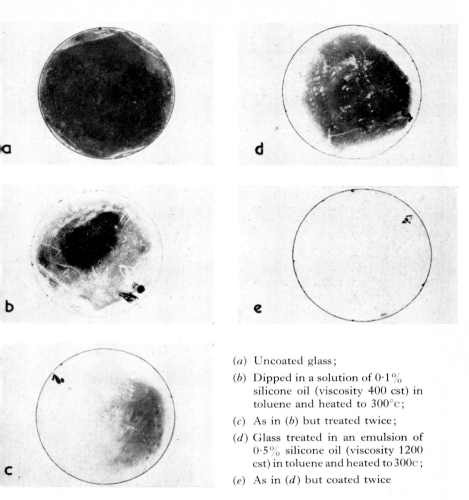

(a) Uncoated glass;

(b) Dipped in a solution of 0·1% silicone oil (viscosity 400 cst) in toluene and heated to 300°c;

(c) As in (b) but treated twice;

(d) Glass treated in an emulsion of 0·5% silicone oil (viscosity 1200 cst) in toluene and heated to 300c;

(e) As in (d) but coated twice

PLATE 18   Transmission photographs of silicone filmed heavy silicate flint glass SF4 (28·4% SiO_2; 2·5% K_2O; 69% PbO) after some days of exposure to hydrogen sulphide (*After Wessel*, 1958)

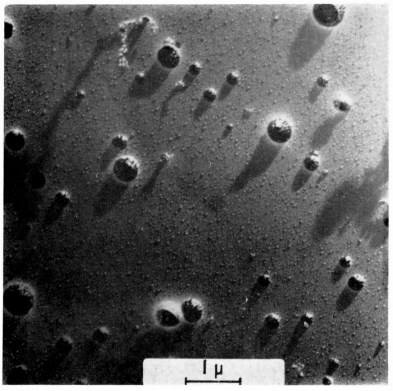

PLATE 19   Microscope slide covered with particles from thermal
decomposition of Pyrex glass (Corning 7740) (*After Donaldson 1962*)

CHAPTER 4

The Sorption of Gases and Vapours by Glass

'Still better instances of the power I refer to, because they are more analogous to the cases to be explained, are furnished by the attraction existing between glass and air, so well known to barometer and thermometer makers, for here the adhesion or attraction is exerted between a solid and gases, bodies having different physical conditions, having no power of combination with each other, and each retaining, during the time of action, its physical state unchanged'. M. FARADAY

'The half-combined and hydrometric state of the alkali appears to be the cause of the deposited film of moisture which is well known to adhere to ordinary glass when exposed to the atmosphere . . .'. M. FARADAY

1. INTRODUCTION

The fact that gas or vapour molecules may be adsorbed † to glass surfaces or absorbed in the bulk material is of both practical importance and academic interest. When glass is used for vacuum envelopes and insulating the electrodes in vacuum devices the sorbed gases must be removed during exhaustion by heating the glass to accelerate desorption. Gas reactions on a glass surface may play an important part in the complex chemical processes which occur in the residual gas of electron tubes. Thus, ionized gas molecules bombarding the envelope of an electron tube may liberate gas and may themselves become embedded in the glass. Undoubtedly the chief stimulant for studying sorption mechanisms of glass has been its extensive use in vacuum apparatus. Langmuir

---

† The term 'adsorption' normally means the binding of gas or vapour molecules to a surface by physical or chemical forces. However, glass is not an inert substance and active gases or vapours may be sorbed in surface layers formed by chemical reactions. Thus, unless the term 'adsorption' is qualified it is used here to imply all mechanisms by which gas or vapour molecules are bound to or within a glass surface.

was probably the first to really appreciate the effects of sorption in high vacuum work and early used his mercury diffusion pump to provide low pressures for sorption studies.

We are concerned primarily in this chapter with the sorption properties of glass rather than with the development of general theories of sorption. However, to aid the understanding of some of the topics discussed limited attention has been given to sorption theories. For a full discussion of the latter the reader should consult the works by Gregg (1934), Roberts (1939) and Trapnell (1955). Useful reviews of the sorption properties of bulk glass and porous silicates will be found in the treatises by Mcbain (1932), Brunauer (1943), Morey (1950), Iler (1955) and Dushman (1962).

Nature of sorption

Gas and vapour molecules may be sorbed by glass by either physical or chemical forces. Thus hydrogen can exist in soda-lime glass as a H^+ ion replacing a Na^+ ion, whereas inert gas atoms in glass are not ionized. Water molecules are held to a glass surface by either chemical or physical forces, whereas inert gas molecules are only physically bound and the glass temperature must be greatly reduced for measurable adsorption to occur.

Binding energies for gas molecules held by physical or van der Waals' forces either in solution or by adsorption are normally comparable to their latent heats. When the sorbed gas is chemically combined either at the sorbent surface ('chemisorption') or in the interior then obviously the energy of binding is higher than that due to physical forces. Thus when water is initially adsorbed by clean glass the heat of adsorption is above 10 kcal/g mol decreasing to about 6 kcal/g mol as the surface becomes covered with strongly bonded OH-groups and chemisorption changes to physical adsorption. The heat of adsorption of gas atoms or molecules usually decreases as a surface becomes covered with gas and the attractive forces of the adsorbent are satisfied.

When gas molecules are chemisorbed by an adsorbent then usually at normal temperature the gas is irreversibly removed from the surrounding atmosphere. If gas molecules are physically adsorbed then gas is taken up until the desorption rate of the adsorbate rises to equal the rate of adsorption. Thus, when a quantity of gas is admitted to an adsorbent at a fixed temperature the pressure decreases until it reaches a value in equilibrium with the amount of gas adsorbed. Physical adsorption often occurs on surfaces which have initially been covered by a chemisorbed layer.

Chemisorption will only extend to a mono-molecular layer if the attractive forces of the valency bonds of both adsorbent and adsorbate are satisfied by their combination. With physical adsorption the adsorbent surface is only covered with a mono-molecular layer when the pressure above the adsorbent is greater than a critical value which increases with temperature. When an adsorbent is completely covered by physically adsorbed molecules then the equilibrium pressure above the adsorbate will be comparable to that of a saturated vapour above a liquid or solid at a similar temperature. If the heat of adsorption of a physically adsorbed monolayer is greater than its heat of condensation on the parent substance then one would expect monolayer formation to be complete at a pressure lower than that of the saturated vapour. A curve relating the amount of gas physically adsorbed as a function of pressure at constant temperature is known as an *adsorption isotherm*.

Raising the temperature of a chemisorbed layer may result in the surface compound being dissociated or evaporated. If dissociation occurs, then an equilibrium amount of surface compound may continue to exist, depending on the composition of the surrounding atmosphere and the temperature. For example when the temperature of borosilicate glass is 200°c or above at a water vapour pressure of 10^{-5} torr or less then chemisorbed hydroxyl groups do not completely cover the active surface. When the glass is allowed to cool water is taken up by the surface with the release of hydrogen.

Adsorption theories. The results of adsorption experiments made with glass have played a big part in the development of adsorption theory. However, unless care is taken in the preparation of the adsorbent surface and in the choice of adsorbate, one cannot know accurately the area and composition of the adsorbent surface or be certain that chemical corrosion does not occur during adsorption. Physical adsorption on virgin glass without initial chemical reaction appears to be limited to inert gases. Nitrogen is physically adsorbed after limited chemisorption.

The amount of gas physically adsorbed at low pressures is for some adsorbent/adsorbate combinations proportional to the equilibrium pressure P_e in a similar manner to the solubility of gases in liquids at low pressures (Henry's law). An early attempt to develop a quantitative relation for the adsorption isotherm outside of the

Henry's law region produced in 1909 the Freundlich isotherm for the amount adsorbed

$$s = kP_e^{1/n}$$

where $1/n$ and k are constants for a given system at a given temperature; n is either equal to 1 (giving Henry's law) or greater than 1.

Langmuir developed a relation known as the 'hyperbolic adsorption isotherm' which was more logically based than the foregoing equation since it sought to explain the processes occurring at the adsorbent surface.

Langmuir assumed that as equilibrium was reached the number of adsorbed molecules had risen until their desorption rate equalled their rate of adsorption from the surrounding gas. From this conception he developed the following equation

$$q = \frac{aq_s P_e}{1 + aP_e}$$

where q is the amount adsorbed at the equilibrium pressure P_e q_s is the maximum adsorbed when the surface is covered and a is a constant. This can be rewritten

$$\frac{P_e}{q} = \frac{1}{aq_s} + \frac{P_e}{q_s}$$

and a plot of P_e/q as a function of P_e at constant temperature should give a straight line. The hyperbolic isotherm not only applies to physical adsorption but also to chemisorption i.e. if the temperature of the system is sufficiently high for surface compound formation to be an equilibrium quantity and the gas above the adsorbent is not changed in composition by the reaction. Often when chemisorption occurs the impinging molecules are dissociated and adsorbed as atoms. Thus from the mass action law the amount of gas adsorbed in the atomic form will be proportional to the square root of the equilibrium pressure and the hyperbolic equation becomes

$$q = \frac{q_s (aP_e)^{1/2}}{1 + (aP_e)^{1/2}}$$

There are many cases where either the amount adsorbed at equilibrium appears to exceed the mono-molecular layer postulated by Langmuir or the hyperbolic relation does not give the best fit to an adsorption isotherm. Brunauer, Emmett and Teller (1938) extended Langmuir's work to explain equilibrium in the presence of multimolecular adsorption.

Obviously if the adsorbent is rough the adsorbed gas may appear to exceed a monomolecular layer when equated to the plane area. It is also possible for the adsorbate to be condensed in surface pores so that the vapour pressure of the condensed liquid is depressed by capillary action as proposed by Zsigmondy. To obtain the vapour pressure P_e in equilibrium with the liquid in the capillaries one may use the Kelvin expression

$$\log_e \frac{P_e}{P_s} = -\frac{2\gamma v \cos \theta}{rRT}$$

where P_s is the saturated vapour pressure of the liquid in free space, r the radius of a capillary, γ the surface tension of the liquid and v its molar volume. When the liquid incompletely wets the adsorbent then allowance must be made for its contact angle θ. If θ has a different value during adsorption to that during desorption, *e.g.* gas contamination prevents immediate wetting of the surface, then the isotherm will show hysteresis. Likewise if the values of r are not randomly distributed but occur within definite limits then the adsorption isotherm will not be smooth but steplike.

Undoubtedly many of the glass substrates used in adsorption studies have had eroded or porous surfaces due to weathering or acid cleaning. It has been fortuitous that baking glass at high temperature to remove sorbed water usually helps to sinter the porous silica on a corroded surface, thereby decreasing the sorbent area.

Pyrex (Corning 7740) is one of the most chemically resistant glasses but absorptive material is emitted from its surface (and from most other silicate glasses) when heated to working temperature. Particles of several thousand ångströms in size are emitted from heated Pyrex together with the vapours of sodium, potassium and boron oxide and these are trapped on the inner surfaces of glass vessels (Donaldson, 1962). Material deposited on the glass surface has an alkaline and boron oxide content many times higher than that of the glass melt.

It is therefore of interest that recent work by Hobson has shown that physical adsorption of nitrogen on Pyrex under ultra-high vacuum conditions follows an isotherm equation developed by Dubinin and Radushkevich for porous adsorbents, whereas the surface density of the adsorbate in equilibrium with saturated vapour was just sufficient to form a monolayer on a smooth substrate (see Section 4). Electron microscopy indicated a surface roughness factor of only about 1·4.

Adsorption theories derived to fit adsorption experiments are usually based on two kinds of model viz. (*i*) a smooth substrate with a uniform distribution of adsorbed molecules on sites of either one or several discrete energy levels and (*ii*) an irregular substrate with the adsorbate condensed in pores. Physical adsorption does not involve valency forces but it is inconceivable that physically adsorbed molecules will have their free energy reduced by the same amount on every site on a glass surface. Physically adsorbed gas molecules will usually be mobile on the substrate and therefore capable of aggregating if their binding energies are higher than those which bind them to the substrate. This would only occur if the pressure of the vapour above the adsorbent exceeded the saturated value and it is not possible to postulate the formation of droplets in the adsorbate under conditions where the surrounding vapour is unsaturated. However, it is possible that plate-like groups of physically adsorbed molecules could form in those regions where certain glass components are most concentrated and there is now ample evidence of phase separation in many glasses.

SORPTION MEASUREMENT

The removal of molecules from the gas phase by sorption processes can be followed in several ways discussed below. Shown schematically in Fig. 4.1 are two basic methods of determining the sorptive capacities of sorbents. The sorbent may be the glass walls of an envelope, a pile of glass plates or a sample of powdered glass. We are considering sorption under reduced pressure where the laws of molecular effusion apply.

(*i*) *Change in pressure* (Fig. 4.1*a*). If a known quantity of gas ($P_1 V_1$) is admitted to an evacuated vessel of volume V containing a sorbent, the mass of gas sorbed is given by $M_s = P_1 V_1 - P_e V$, where P_e is the pressure after sorption. If the gas in the sorbent vessel is in equilibrium with a physically adsorbed layer or with gas dissolved in the solid then M_s will be a function of P_e the equilibrium pressure.

(*ii*) *Constant pressure* (Fig. 4.1*b*). Gas can be admitted to a sorbent vessel from a reservoir via a pipe or aperture of known gas conductance S_c. The pressure P_c can be kept constant above the sorbent during measurement by varying the pressure P_R in the reservoir. The mass sorption rate at any given time is $S_c(P_R - P_c)$. The mass sorbed M after a sorption period t at constant pressure can then be derived by integrating a plot of $S_c(P_R - P_c)$ as a function of t. If M_s is the total mass sorbed when $P_R = P_c$ then the sorption rate can be given as a function of M/M_s. If the volumetric sorption rate of the sorbent is S_g then the mass sorption rate is $S_g P_c$ and $S_g = [S_c(P_R - P_c)]/P_c$. Obviously when M_s is a quantity in equilibrium with P_c then $P_c = P_R = P_e$ as in item (i) above.

Another technique used in sorption measurements is the capillary or time lag method. If two vessels are joined by a capillary and after evacuation the pressure in one is raised to a constant value, then there will be a time lag before the pressure in the second vessel begins to rise. The time lag will depend on the conductance of the capillary and will be lengthened if the capillary sorbs gas (Clausing, 1930; Barrer, 1951). The sorptive capacity may be enhanced by packing the capillary with powdered glass. If a gas molecule is sorbed on first impact on the sorbent surface, then the mass sorbed can be found from the time lag by assuming that each element of the capillary is filled before gas reaches the next element. However, if the mass sorbed is an equilibrium function of pressure then the results of the capillary time lag method would be difficult to interpret as there is a changing pressure gradient along the capillary.

Pressure measurements. Care is required when using the foregoing experimental methods at low gas pressures to ensure that the gas pressure measured corresponds to that above the adsorbent. Thus both the position and the speed of response of the pressure measuring instrument are important. For example, if one followed the sorption process as in Fig. 4.1a under conditions of falling pressure, then the measured rate of pressure change would depend on the conductance of the gauge tubulation if this was small compared with the sorption rate.

Incorrect positioning of the gauge head can also give false results. For example, if the pressure gauge opening faces the end of the calibrated leak in Fig. 4.1(b) then gas will stream directly from the leak into the gauge, thereby raising the measured pressure above the average value.

Another common fault in glass systems is to connect the vacuum gauge in Fig. 4.1(b) into the pipe of the calibrated leak rather than directly into the sorbent vessel. Then if sorption rates are measured under *apparently* constant pressure conditions the true pressure in the sorption vessel is lower than that measured by the gauge and is not, as believed, constant with time. Also, if the conductance of the connecting tube between the gauge and the sorbent vessel is

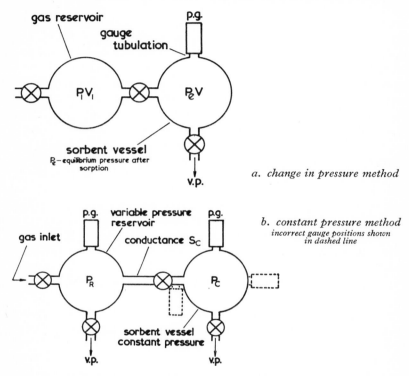

a. change in pressure method

b. constant pressure method
incorrect gauge positions shown in dashed line

FIG. 4.1   METHODS OF DETERMINING THE SORPTION RATE AND CAPACITY FOR DIFFERENT GASES. THE SORBENT MAY HAVE THE LARGE AREA OF A GLASS POWDER OR BE A GLASS VESSEL.

small compared with the true sorption rate one measures an *apparent* sorption rate of the same order as the tube conductance. Thus, even if the sorption rate is decreasing, *e.g.* exponentially as the mass sorbed increases, the *measured* sorption rate will remain constant until the true sorption rate falls to a value near to or less than the conductance. Much confusion has existed in sorption studies because attempts have been made to interpret sorption characteristics that have not been intrinsic.

Mass spectrometry. Great advances have been made in experimental methods for studying sorption because of improvement in vacuum technique. It is now possible to work in the ultra-high vacuum region ($\leqslant 10^{-9}$ torr) and measure pressures with Bayard–Alpert ionization gauges reasonably accurately down to about 10^{-10} torr. Ionization gauges based on the magnetron electrode arrangement have been developed for pressure measurement in the 10^{-13} torr range. Allowance must always be made for ionization gauges having a sorption rate of their own.

Mass spectrometry has recently been used for determining the nature of the gases desorbed by glass and employed in sorption and permeability studies. In the past workers had to determine the nature of desorbed gases, using condensation and trapping techniques which were limited in their sensitivity. Also, should gas reactions have occurred during sorption studies which changed the nature of the gas atmosphere this was at best only indirectly obvious from the pressure gauge readings. Finally, an unknown impurity in a gas atmosphere may have a great influence on the sorption measurements although present in only minute amounts. Consider, for example, a gas containing an impurity flowing into the sorbent vessel in Fig. 4.1(*b*) where the impurity is not sorbed. Then the concentration of the impurity in the sorbent vessel will rise until its pressure is equal to its partial pressure in the reservoir vessel. Thus the pressure measured above the sorbent will not be the true value for the sorbate gas. If the sorbate gas contains a gas which is condensable at the adsorbent temperature then the gas under study may be trapped in a condensed liquid or solid layer. Gas analysis of the atmosphere prevents errors of this kind from being made.

Sorption units. The quantity of gas sorbed by a glass body is usually expressed in terms of a volume of gas at a given pressure and temperature per unit area, volume or mass of glass, *e.g.* $cm^3 N.T.P/cm^2$ or $cm^3 N.T.P/cm^3$. Recently the units *litre micron Hg* (litre μ Hg) or *litre mm Hg* (litre torr) have been used for expressing the quantity of gas sorbed. It follows that (litre μ Hg)/760 = 1000 (litre torr)/760 = cm^3 N.T.P.

Adsorption isotherms. If the mass adsorbed is in equilibrium with the gas above the adsorbent then one may plot values of the mass adsorbed M_s as a function of P_e, the equilibrium pressure at constant temperature; such a curve is termed an *adsorption isotherm*. If adsorption isotherms are determined at a series of temperatures then one may plot *adsorption isosteres* from which the variation of P_e with temperature at constant amount adsorbed can be derived. The isosteres resemble the vapour pressure curves of liquids so that the heat of adsorption E_A can be obtained from the Clausius–Clapeyron equation.

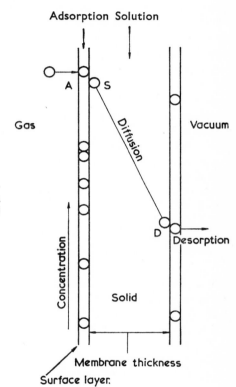

FIG. 4.2   STEPS IN THE PERMEA-TION OF A GAS THROUGH A MEMBRANE (*After Norton*, 1957)

PERMEATION AND DIFFUSION: SYMBOLS AND EQUATIONS

Process. When gas molecules enter and flow through a membrane and return again to the gas phase one can distinguish the following steps in the process as outlined by Norton (1957) and shown schematically in Fig. 4.2:

(*i*) *Adsorption of gas ions, atoms or molecules striking the membrane surface.* For gases not chemically combining with glass, *e.g.* He, N_2, the surface density of the adsorbed layer is an equilibrium quantity depending on the pressure and temperature. Water molecules may be dissociated on striking the surface.

(*ii*) *Solution of the gas in the membrane material.* The amount dissolved at the adsorbing surface depends on the solubility equilibrium.

(*iii*) *Flow of gas within the membrane under a concentration gradient.* Movement of gas ions, atoms or molecules in and across the membrane is termed diffusion; the amount transferred can be derived from Fick's law.

(*iv*) *Transfer of dissolved gas to the desorbing surface.* For physically adsorbed gases the surface density of the desorbing layer will be an equilibrium quantity depending upon the pressure and temperature in the desorption enclosure. If atoms or ions, *e.g.* H^+, OH^-, diffuse through glass then these recombine before being desorbed.

The overall process of transferring molecules in the gas phase from one side of a membrane to the gas phase on the other is termed *permeation*. Transfer of dissolved gas within the membrane is termed *diffusion*.

Permeability. The mass of gas M which permeates in time t through a membrane of uniform thickness l separating two enclosures at different gas pressures is given by

$$M = K \frac{At(P_2 - P_1)}{l} \tag{1}$$

where M/t is the permeation rate, A is the wall area, P_1 and P_2 are the pressures in the respective enclosures and K is the *permeability* of the wall material for the particular gas. If M/t is expressed in g/sec, A in cm^2, l in cm and $(P_2 - P_1)$ in cm Hg then K has the units $g\ cm^{-1}\ sec^{-1}\ (cm\ Hg)^{-1}$.

Generally the mass of gas permeating a wall is expressed in cm^3 N.T.P. with l in mm, A in cm^2 and $(P_2 - P_1)$ in cm Hg and t in sec. The permeability is then the product of a numerical value K and the following units

$$K_1 \frac{(cm^3\ N.T.P.)\ mm}{cm^2\ sec\ (cm\ Hg)}$$

Some workers express the permeability as

$$K_2 \frac{\text{(litre torr) mm}}{\text{cm}^2 \text{ sec (torr)}}$$

so that

$$K_1 = \frac{1000}{76} K_2$$

If a gas is dissociated on adsorption and permeates in the dissociated form then the absorption should be proportional to $\sqrt{P}$ and the mass of gas passing through a membrane given by

$$M = K \frac{At(\sqrt{P_2} - \sqrt{P_1})}{l}$$

It has been tacitly assumed in the derivation of these equations that the concentration of gas in the wall boundaries has the same dependence on pressure as the solubility of the medium under equilibrium conditions.

Suppose that the boundary processes of transferring a molecule from an adsorbed layer to the solid and from the solid to the desorbing surface are slow and comparable in speed with diffusion in the solid. Then much of the material transferred across the entry boundary is removed before the solute concentration can reach equilibrium with the external gas. Likewise, at the exit boundary the slow rate of transfer into the desorbing layer would lead to an accumulation just inside the surface. The concentration gradient in the medium will not then be a simple function of the pressure difference as suggested in the above equations. Normally it is assumed that the low diffusion constants of gases in glass make internal diffusion the rate controlling process. Likewise the permeation rates of permanent gases through glass appears to be directly dependent on the pressure gradient. However, the amount of hydrogen and water absorbed as hydroxyl groups by glass depends on the square-root of the pressure.

Diffusion constant. The quantity q of a given substance which diffuses in time t across an area A of a layer of medium of thickness l is given by

$$q = D \frac{(C_2 - C_1)At}{l} \tag{2}$$

where C_2 and C_1 are the concentrations of the diffusing substance in the medium (mass per unit volume) measured at the boundaries of the layer and D is the diffusion constant. If the concentration is expressed in mass/cm^3, l in cm and t in sec then D has the dimensions cm^2/sec.

Semi-infinite body. A common problem encountered in the degassing of a glass body *in vacuo* is the diffusion of gas from the interior to the surface where it is desorbed. When the diffusion constant has a low value and the gas is readily released from the surface, *i.e.* the rate of desorption is diffusion controlled, then we may consider the desorption as occurring from a semi-infinite body which extends from a bounding layer $x=0$ to $x=\infty$. The mass desorbed can then be found from Fick's law for non-stationary state of flow requiring solution of the equation

$$\frac{\partial C}{\partial t} = D\frac{\partial^2 C}{\partial x^2}$$

Given that the solute concentration C_0 is uniform throughout the body at $t=0$ and $C_0=0$ at $x=0$ for values of $t>0$ then the mass desorbed per unit area at time t is

$$q = 2C_0\left(\frac{Dt}{\pi}\right)^{1/2} \tag{3}$$

(Dushman, 1962; Barrer, 1951).

The diffusion constant calculated from formula (3) is often referred to as 'diffusivity' or 'diffusion coefficient of desorption' (or sorption), because both diffusion in the body and evaporation from the solid occurs in the process. Likewise activation energies calculated from the dependence of D on temperature are also for the combined processes.

Both the diffusion constant and the permeability are generally related to temperature by equations of the kind

$$K = A_k \exp -\frac{E_K}{RT} \tag{4}$$

and

$$D = A_D \exp -\frac{E_D}{RT} \tag{5}$$

where A_K and A_D are constants, E_K E_D are activation energies per g mol, R is the gas constant and T the absolute temperature.

Solubility. The mass of gas dissolved per unit volume by a body exposed to a gas at a given pressure is termed the solubility S. The solubility may be determined by measuring the gas absorbed by a body after permeation into the interior has ceased, *i.e.* the dissolved gas is in equilibrium with that in the gas phase. If the gas molecules dissociate on adsorption before permeating into the interior then S is proportional to the square-root of the gas pressure. The concentration of dissolved gas C at the boundary of a solid through which gas is permeating will be equal to S, providing the permeation rate is diffusion controlled and the solid homogeneous up to the boundary surface. Therefore the permeability, as given by equation (1) above for a membrane, is related to the diffusion constant as follows

$$K = SD$$

where S is a function of the pressure P. If the solubility is a linear function of pressure (as assumed in equation (1)) and expressed as the mass of gas dissolved per unit volume of medium and per unit gas pressure, *i.e.* $g\,cm^{-3}\,(cm\,Hg)^{-1}$ and D has the dimensions cm^2/sec then K has the units $g\,cm^{-1}\,sec^{-1}\,(cm\,Hg)^{-1}$ as given above for permeability. Equation (1) may then be rewritten

$$M = SD\,\frac{At(P_2 - P_1)}{l}$$

2. GASES IN GLASS

ABSORPTION DURING MANUFACTURE

When glass is heated *in vacuo* gas may be released both from the surface and from the solid. The surface gas will usually have been adsorbed from the atmosphere, whilst the gas in the bulk may have been absorbed from the furnace atmosphere during melting and from components in the glass batch. Before one can determine the contribution of surface held gas to a desorbed atmosphere it is necessary to know the nature of the gases absorbed by the solid and the manner of their release. We shall therefore consider here the absorption of gas by a glass melt in a furnace atmosphere and the desorption of gas from molten glass in vacuum. Later in the chapter we shall discuss the desorption of gas *in vacuo* from glass heated from ambient temperature to the softening point; such a process is of importance in many vacuum techniques.

The literature survey in this section is not intended to be exhaustive and the reader will find well documented reviews of the subject in the work by Slavyanski (*Gases in Glass*, translated by Kruszewski, 1959) and in a paper by Harper (1962).

The principal gases found in glass are water vapour, carbon dioxide, sulphur dioxide and oxygen. Many early workers assumed that gases were physically dissolved by glass. For example, Washburn *et al.* (1920) believed that the glass melt dissolved the gaseous reaction products of the batch constituents. Washburn *et al.* suddenly exposed molten glass to a vacuum whereupon the melt frothed over growing six times in volume. Although inert gases, *e.g.* helium, may be dissolved by glass active gases usually enter the glass in combination with the constituents. Thus the subsequent release of such active gases depends on the decomposition temperatures of the compounds formed. If the reaction is reversible then obviously melting in vacuum will alter the equilibrium.

Gas trapped in a glass may be evolved when the solid is fractured *in vacuo*. Thus, Mr. R. W. Lawson† in a private communication reported that '. . . large amounts of gas were evolved when glass was broken under vacuum by means of a stainless steel plunger. The specimens were glass tubes that had been thoroughly washed and baked at 400°c in vacuum before breaking. Glasses tested included W1, Pyrex, Kodial, Lead and Soda and all evolved large quantities of carbon monoxide and methane in roughly equal quantities. For a straightforward fracture of a 30 mm dia. tube the quantity of gas evolved was about 10^{-6}cm^3 N.T.P. It appeared that the quantity of gas released was proportional to the degree of fragmentation of the glass.'

Sulphur dioxide. The sodium carbonate in a batch may react with sulphur dioxide in a furnace atmosphere releasing carbon dioxide and forming sodium sulphate. The amount of sulphate formed by a glass at 1100°c increases with its soda content. As the temperature is further raised the sulphate content reaches a maximum at 1200°c falling almost to zero at 1300°c, because above 1200°c the sulphate begins to thermally decompose. The sulphate content of a glass melt in the range 1200°–1500°c is lowered more rapidly in a reducing atmosphere than in an oxidizing atmosphere because the reducing atmosphere facilitates decomposition of the sulphate.

---

† Post Office Research Station, Dollis Hill, England.

Sulphate can be removed from a glass melt by holding its temperature above that needed for thermal decomposition and bubbling air through the melt. Oxygen in a furnace atmosphere promotes sulphate formation in a melt. Thus a reaction does not occur between sodium borosilicate glass and pure SO_2 at temperatures up to 830°c unless oxygen is present. The solubility limit of glass is about 0·4–0·6% SO_3 and above this value the sulphate separates into droplets.

Fincham and Richardson (1954) measured the amount of sulphur present in aluminate melts at 1350°–1650°c when exposed to atmospheres containing SO_2 in which the oxygen partial pressure was thermodynamically controlled. The balance between sulphide and sulphate in a slag depended on the oxygen partial pressure. The total sulphur content (sulphide and sulphate) reached a minimum at an oxygen partial pressure of 10^{-5} torr. The ability of a binary melt to hold sulphur depended on the activity of the basic oxide.

Carbon dioxide. The amount of carbon dioxide in glass is usually a few thousand times less than that of SO_3. Glasses containing barium oxide may react with CO_2 to form barium carbonate. Dense barium oxide glasses (40% BaO) show a maximum in their CO_2-content at 1300°c. It is believed that above 1200°c barium silicate dissociates to give free BaO which reacts with CO_2 and above 1300°c barium carbonate is thermally unstable.

The absorption of CO_2 by soda-lime, borosilicate crown and lead oxide glass appears to be very small. Eitel and Weyl (1932) investigated the reaction between CO_2 and sodium silicates. The solubility of CO_2 in sodium metasilicate under a pressure of 750 atm decreased from 35 cm³ N.T.P./g at 1050°c to 28·5 cm³ N.T.P./g at 1400°c. The CO_2 content of a melt increased with alkali content and pressure but at a diminishing rate. Mahieux (1956) using a radioactive tracer method with ^{14}C has studied the solubility of CO_2 in soda-lime silicates. The radioactive carbon was present either in the furnace gas in CO_2 ($P_{CO_2} = 7·6$ torr) or in sodium carbonate added to the batch. The equilibrium content of CO_2 in high alkali glass (28·5% Na_2O, 15% CaO) was about 0·05 cm³ N.T.P./g.

Oxygen. Information on the absorption of oxygen is conflicting. Glasses containing the trioxides of arsenic and antimony may absorb oxygen as they are converted to the pentoxides when their temperature is raised and desorb oxygen as the reaction is reversed on cooling. Thus a glass containing 7% of As_2O_3 absorbs as much as 1·7 cm³ N.T.P./g at 500°C; the pentoxide is formed at 400°C and decomposes at above 1000°C (Kühl *et al.* 1938). Möttig and Weyl (1933) reported that at high oxygen pressures up to 1·5 cm³ N.T.P./g of oxygen could be absorbed by glasses containing lead, barium and manganese. The changes in the colour of the manganese glass showed how the oxygen was associated with the oxide. Thus the absorption of oxygen by glass can arise from the presence of lower oxides or metal atoms of variable valency in the melt.

Water vapour. Glasses invariably contain water bound in their structure as hydroxyl groups. Salmang and Becker (1927–28) found that molten glass absorbed water in the presence of water vapour or when steam was bubbled through the melt. Water could not be introduced into small batches of glass melted on a laboratory scale under humid conditions. Also water was not introduced in the glass by adding water-bearing agents to the melt. Salmang and Becker state that it is well known that silica and water become more reactive as their temperature is raised and that water is chemically bound in the structure of many silicates. When a small batch of glass is heated the water may be lost before the melt attains a temperature sufficient for a chemical reaction to occur. With an industrial melt the water in the interior of the batch will not be evaporated before the outside of the melt has attained a temperature promoting chemical reaction (formation of SiOH).

Gas bubbles in glass. During melting of batch materials or reheating of a glass gas bubbles may appear in the molten glass. The bubbles may contain gases introduced into the melt by the batch materials or from the furnace atmosphere, *e.g.* air, water vapour CO_2 and SO_2. When the glass is reheated some of the components may thermally decompose producing bubbles containing gas which reacts with the glass as it is cooled; the effect has been termed 'reboil'. Slavyanski (see Kruszewski, 1959) has reviewed the work in this field.

Detailed discussion of the formation of gas bubbles in glass is obviously outside of the scope of this work. However, certain aspects of the subject are relevant when one is considering the gas sorption properties of glass. For example, Budd *et al.* (1962) heated glass in a platinum boat to 1200°C and rapidly decreased the pressure above the glass to some value P_b. Using a fresh piece of glass for each test, P_b was progressively decreased until a value was found,

14

termed the 'reboil pressure', at which bubbles appeared in the glass. Maintaining a constant temperature during bubble formation ensured that the influence of glass viscosity was similar in all tests. It was found that the reboil pressure of eight soda-lime–silicate glasses (9–11% CaO; 13–16% Na_2O) was dependent on their water content. The water content was determined from the infra red absorption at a wavelength of 2·9 μ, as described in Section 3 of this chapter.

Budd *et al.* observed that a soda-lime glass heated in a gas-fired furnace at either 1200° or 1450°c continuously absorbed water until after ten days the water content was double its initial value. The theory was advanced that both H_2O molecules and OH^- ions coexist in the glass arising from the reaction

$$\overset{|}{\underset{|}{-Si}}-O^- + H_2O \rightleftharpoons \overset{|}{\underset{|}{-Si}}-OH + OH^-.$$

If water is directly dissolved in the glass and released as gas from solution when the external pressure becomes lower than the original equilibrium value then the water content (or partial pressure of H_2O) in equilibrium with Si—OH is given by $P_{H_2O} = K[Si—OH]^2$. As the water content of the glass is measured in terms of the infra red absorption of OH^- groups then a plot of the square root of the reboil pressure as a function of SiOH content should give a straight line. The results presented do not show conclusively whether the reboil pressure is a linear or a square root function of the SiOH content. The absorption and desorption of water from glass melts is discussed in Section 3.

Hydrogen. When glass is melted in hydrogen reduction of some of the oxide components may occur, *e.g.* oxides of lead, antimony and arsenic. Hydrogen readily diffuses into glass, whereas carbon monoxide does not. Thus reduction of glass oxides by CO is limited to the surface. Hydrogen may enter glass to form hydroxyl radicals and undergo ion-exchange with sodium ions. It has been observed with solid silica that if the silica is reduced but OH^- groups are present then at high temperature the hydroxyl radicals oxidize the lower silicon oxide and release hydrogen from the solid.

GASES EVOLVED DURING MELTING IN VACUUM

The nature and quantities of gases evolved from molten glass in vacuum have been studied by Becker and Salmang (1929) and

Dalton (1933, 1935). They found that water, carbon dioxide, sulphur dioxide and oxygen were the principal gases released.

Dalton heated the glass sample to 1400°c in a sillimanite tube joined to a vacuum pump via a Pyrex chemical glass tube. The furnace was heated by a tantalum wire element embedded in alundum on the outside of the ceramic tube. The furnace heater and sillimanite tube were mounted inside a glass container which was evacuated by a separate pump forming a guard vacuum for the sillimanite tube.

Shown in Table 4.1 are the total amounts of gas extracted and their percentage compositions for a range of glasses; two specimens

Table 4.1

Gases evolved by glasses † heated to 1400°c in vacuum
(*After Dalton*, 1935)

Glass type	*Total gas content* (cm³ N.T.P.)	*Percentage composition of gases*				
		H_2O	SO_2	CO_2	O_2	*Inert*
Barium (optical)	0·71	24–22	—	40–37	36–41	0·1–0·1
Soda–lime (milk bottle)	0·93	51–51	33–34	3–3	12–11	0·1–0·1
Soda–lime (bulb)	0·90	44–44	35–36	4·5–7	16–13	—
Borosilicate (heat resistant)	0·36	92–89	0·3–0·3	3–4	5–7	—
Borosilicate (bulb)	0·74	94–94		2·5–3	3–3·5	—
Lead (sign tubing)	0·70	33–39		8–7	59–54	—
Soda–lime (expt.) ‡	1·41	28–28		10–8	62–64	—

† Glass samples weighed one gramme.   ‡ High arsenic oxide content.

were tested of each glass. Dalton states that measurements were complicated because volatile oxides such as those of boron and sodium were evaporated from the furnace on to the walls of the vacuum system where they readsorbed gas. (At 1400°c in vacuum the oxides of lead, iron and arsenic, present in some of the glasses, would evaporate and dissociate releasing oxygen.) Thus the values given in the table must not be taken as precise. Further, they differ considerably for a specific glass depending upon the batch materials used and the initial melting technique.

Generally water vapour was the most abundant constituent evolved. Carbon dioxide was nearly always present although often in small quantities, but carbon monoxide was rarely observed. The barium oxide glass liberated a large volume of carbon dioxide due to the basic character of the oxide; a similar observation was made by Becker and Salmang who vacuum melted a dense barium flint. Hydrogen was rarely found. (At 1400°c oxygen ions from absorbed 'water' would have sufficient mobility to be released in stoichiometric ratio to those of hydrogen.) Only negligible amounts of inert gas were released. Glasses which contained sodium sulphate released sulphur dioxide and those containing higher oxides of lead, arsenic and iron gave off oxygen. The sulphur dioxide was not measured separately from carbon dioxide for the last three glasses in the table and the values given are for the sum of SO_2 and CO_2. The experimental soda-lime glass had an unusually high arsenic content and evolved large quantities of oxygen.

The surfaces of lead and barium glasses which have not been attacked by acids have a lower affinity for water than soda-lime and borosilicate glasses and these also dissolve less water as indicated in Table 4.1.

The gas evolved from three types of glass has been analysed with an Omegtron mass-spectrometer by Garbe and Christians (1962). The glass samples were heated in an ultra-high vacuum system and the compositions of the evolved gas are given in Table 4.2.

Table 4.2

Gases evolved by glasses determined by pressure rise in vacuum and with an Omegatron mass-spectrometer
(*After Garbe and Christians*, 1962)

Glass	Temperature (°c)	Gas content (cm^3 N.T.P. cm^{-3})	Percentage composition of gas						
			H_2O	CO_2	CO	N_2	H_2†	CH_4	$C_mH_n m \geqslant 2$
Soda-lime silicate	1000	1·6	99	1	—	—	0·2	0·1	
Borosilicate	970	1·2	98	0·6	0·7	0·1	0·2	0·2	
Alumino-silicate	970	0·08	98	0·8	1	—	—	0·2	0·1

† Part of the H_2 comes from reaction of H_2O with the hot cathode in the mass-spectrometer.

Naughton (1953) has degassed *in vacuo* a sample of Pyrex (Corning 7740) in a platinum crucible at about 1370°c. Absorption tests were made in another vacuum vessel at 1170°c. No measurable solubility was found for oxygen, argon or helium. For hydrogen at a pressure of 10 torr the solubility was 0·060 cm^3 N.T.P./g the solution process being reversible. Sodium disilicate showed no measurable solubility for any of the foregoing gases when heated up to 800°c.

GASES EVOLVED DURING BAKING IN VACUUM

Nature and quantity of gas. The removal of sorbed gases from glass envelopes is of major importance in high vacuum technology and it was extensively studied by Langmuir (1913, 1916, 1918*a*). Langmuir baked the bulbs of incandescent lamps (200 cm² area) under vacuum and observed that the principal gas evolved was water vapour. Thus, after drying the bulbs at room temperature by pumping them in a vacuum system fitted with a liquid nitrogen trap, they were vacuum degassed by heating to different temperatures. Bulbs baked at 200°c over a 3 hour period evolved the following volumes of gas expressed in mm³ N.T.P.:

$$200 \text{ mm}^3 \text{ H}_2\text{O}, \quad 5 \text{ mm}^3 \text{ CO}_2, \quad 2 \text{ mm}^3 \text{ N}_2$$

Raising the bulb temperature from 200° to 350°c increased the total gas liberated to

$$300 \text{ mm}^3 \text{ H}_2\text{O}, \quad 20 \text{ mm}^3 \text{ CO}_2, \quad 4 \text{ mm}^3 \text{ N}_2$$

Subsequently heating the bulbs to 500°c increased the total gas evolution to

$$450 \text{ mm}^3 \text{ H}_2\text{O}, \quad 30 \text{ mm}^3 \text{ CO}_2, \quad 5 \text{ mm}^3 \text{ N}_2$$

Gas evolution ceased after about half an hour of baking, but began again when the temperature was raised to a higher value.

In a later experiment Langmuir measured the gas evolved by a pile of 200 microscope cover slides (1966 cm² area, 13·6 cm³ volume). To prevent the glasses from becoming closely packed in the test bulb they were slightly bent by heating in a gas flame. The cover slides were cleaned with hot concentrated sulphuric acid and potassium dichromate and washed with distilled water before sealing in the vacuum vessel. The glass bulb containing the slides and an empty glass bulb of the same volume were separately baked at 300°c for 1 hour under vacuum. Langmuir calculated that in terms of the plane adsorbent area the gas evolved was equivalent to 4·5 monomolecular layers of H_2O, 1·05 of CO_2 and 0·9 of N_2. The latter gases appeared to correspond to monolayers. However, the acid cleaning of the glasses would have greatly increased the surface area by forming a layer of porous silica. The heating during degassing would then have partially sintered the porous silica.

Heat-treatment temperature. Langmuir (1918*b*) found that the bulbs (soda–magnesia–borosilicate G-702-P) of incandescent lamps which had been baked at 400°–500°c during exhaust did not blacken in use as quickly as bulbs that had been degassed at 550°–600°c. Langmuir had previously shown that a tungsten filament in an incandescent lamp reacted with water vapour to form a volatile tungsten oxide and hydrogen. The tungsten oxide was deposited on the lamp bulb and reduced by the hydrogen to form a black metallic deposit. Langmuir deduced that the enhanced blackening of lamps with the higher degassing temperature arose as follows. Baking at 400°–500°c liberated water from the surface, whereas at 550°–600°c water was desorbed from the interior of the glass. Thus, at the higher degassing temperature, water diffused to the glass surface providing a higher surface concentration than that obtained at the lower degassing temperature. Langmuir showed that lamps which had been baked at 550°c and then at 400°c subsequently had a very long life, because at the lower degassing temperature surface water was removed after the general degassing.

Langmuir noted that whereas water desorption ceased after about half an hour at temperatures below 500°c at higher temperatures water evolution continued indefinitely. It therefore appeared as if the water evolved at the higher temperature came from a thermal decomposition of the glass. A baking temperature of about 400°c would facilitate the removal of OH⁻groups and condensed water molecules from the surface and desorption of hydrogen from the solid. At high baking temperatures oxygen ions could more easily migrate with the hydrogen ions to the surface. As is shown in Section 3, all of the processes by which 'water' is bound in glass and enters and leaves the solid are not properly understood. However, the formation of hydroxyl groups within glass is well established. It is of interest to note that *if 'water' was uniformly bound and distributed through an homogeneous solid with a plane surface then raising the degassing temperature would more quickly lower the surface concentration, i.e. there would not be an optimum temperature for surface degassing.*

Sherwood (1918*a*, *b*) measured the amounts of water vapour, carbon dioxide and gases (non-condensable at liquid air temperatures) evolved from different types of glass at temperatures up to 600°c. Shown in Fig. 4.3 are the quantities of gas evolved from samples of 350 cm² area made of a high melting point glass (G-702-P) used for incandescent lamp bulbs, a soda glass and a lead oxide glass. The glass samples were progressively raised in temperature in steps and held at each temperature for three hours.

The quantity of gas evolved at each temperature during the heating cycle is given in the figure.

Sherwood's results show that water vapour evolution reaches a maximum in the temperature region 150°–350°c then decreases and

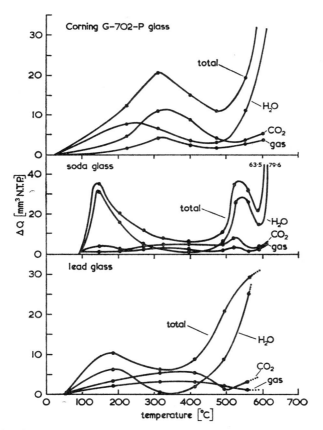

FIG. 4.3   GAS DESORBED FROM SAMPLES OF DIFFERENT GLASSES. THE VACUUM PRESSURE BEFORE BAKING THE SAMPLE WAS $0·1–1\mu$Hg. A SAMPLE OF EACH KIND OF GLASS WAS BAKED AT INCREASING TEMPERATURES; THE PERIOD OF HEATING AT EACH PLOTTED TEMPERATURE VALUE WAS 3 H. THE CURVE MARKED 'GAS' REFERS TO GASES WHICH COULD NOT BE CONDENSED ON A LIQUID NITROGEN COOLED TRAP, VIZ. H_2, N_2, D_2 AND CO_2 (*After Sherwood*, 1918a)

rises rapidly at about 600°c. Such desorption characteristics agree with Langmuir's theory that surface water is removed by baking at 450°c and below and chemically bound 'water' in the interior is dissociated at temperatures above 550°c. Sherwood found that annealing a glass at a high temperature subsequently reduced the amount of gas evolved in vacuum.

Shrader (1919) observed that the vacuum in a sealed-off glass vessel which had been baked deteriorated with time due to desorption. (Most vacuum workers will have noted how the pressure in a sealed-off vacuum system made of glass or metal rises first quickly and then slowly, approaching a constant value. One assumes that the pressure of the water vapour or gas released rises until it reaches an equilibrium value at which the sorption rate equals that of the desorption.) Shrader found that gas and vapour were still released when a sealed-off glass vessel was heated to a temperature under that used to degas the glass during pumping. This is not surprising if one considers that the glass may not have been completely degassed before seal-off since the gas must diffuse to the glass surface. Secondly, the glass will reabsorb gases as it becomes cold after bakeout. It should be appreciated that in Langmuir's study of the blackening of incandescent lamps discussed above the glass bulbs were heated when the lamps were in service. It is probably the temperature rise in service which enhances the liberation of water and indicates more strongly the difference in the water content of the surface layers after different methods of heat-treatment.

Harris and Schumacher (1923) determined the amount of water, carbon dioxide and permanent gas evolved from a series of glasses when heated for 65–80 hours at their softening temperature. The nature of the glasses and their alkali contents are given in Table 4.3 together with the amount of gas desorbed per unit volume and area. The glasses were cleaned with chromic acid and water and dried in vacuum at room temperature before being heat-treated. The results show that the mass of water evolved rose with the alkali content. It was believed that glass no. 5 evolved the least amount of gas because it had the highest softening temperature and had been heated to the highest temperature during manufacture. However, this glass contains boron oxide and has the least alkali content. Glass no. 6 had an exceptionally low gas content, because it had previously been heat treated (not *in vacuo*) by the glass manufacturer at about 1500°c for 1 hour.

The total gas evolved by the glasses listed in Table 4.3 was measured as the temperature was increased in 100 degc steps from 100°c to the softening point. The curves in Fig. 4.4 show a maximum in the amount desorbed at temperatures between 200°–300°c

Table 4.3

Gases evolved from silicate glasses heated to their
softening temperature in vacuum
(*After Harris and Schumacher*, 1923)

Glass	Percentage $(Na_2O + K_2O)$ in glass	Temperature of glass (°c)	Percentage Composition of gas		$\times 10^{-4}$ cm^3 N.T.P. per cm^2 glass	$\times 10^{-4}$ cm^3 N.T.P. per cm^3 glass
1 Soda-lime	21·12	400	H_2O	88·5	46·6	726
			CO_2	10·5	5·5	86
			†P.G.	1·0	0·5	8
				Total	52·6	820
2 Soda-lime	16·87	400	H_2O	92·6	30·0	508
			CO_2	6·3	2·0	34
			P.G.	1·1	0·4	6
				Total	32·4	548
3 Soda-lead	12·30	400	H_2O	96·4	23·7	506
			CO_2	2·2	0·5	11
			P.G.	1·4	0·4	8
				Total	24·6	525
4 Soda-lead	11·90	400	H_2O	97·2	25·4	568
			CO_2	1·4	0·4	8
			P.G.	1·4	0·4	8
				Total	26·2	584
5 Soda-lead-boro	5·35	500	H_2O	33·3	0·6	12
			CO_2	44·5	0·9	16
			P.G.	22·2	0·4	8
				Total	1·9	36
6 Soda-lead	9·99	400	H_2O	49·6	1·0	19
			CO_2	49·6	1·0	19
			P.G.	0·8	0·02	0·3
				Total	2·02	38·3

† P.G. = permanent gas, *i.e.* non-condensable at −190°c.

which was assumed to arise from surface desorption as discussed
above.

Harris and Schumacher found that the carbon dioxide liberated
by the glasses when heated to 200°–300°c was proportional to their
alkali content. They considered that the carbon dioxide was sorbed
by a film of sodium hydroxide on the glass. Krause (1889) observed
that a glass with a high soda content did not adsorb carbon dioxide
if the glass and the gas had been carefully dried. Also, carbon
dioxide was not adsorbed by glass which had been washed with
boiling water to remove the alkali.

The temperature at which the desorption maximum of a glass
occurs does not appear to depend on the nature of the glass but
probably depends on the history of the glass (gas content and

distribution) and the heat treatment cycle used in the test. Thus desorption maxima have been reported by Cartwright (Dushman, 1962) at 150°c for Pyrex (7740), and at 200°c for Corning soda-lime glass (0080). Vycor brand glass (7910) showed a small maximum in the desorption curve at 300°c; the gas desorbed by this glass was

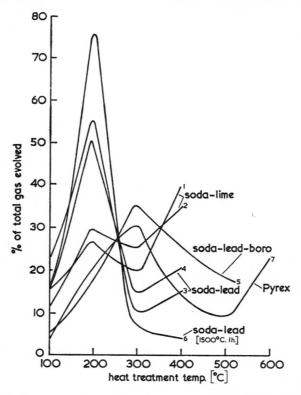

FIG. 4.4 Gas evolved by different types of glass determined at 100°C intervals when increasing from 100°C to their softening points (*After Harris and Schumacher*, 1923)

a tenth or less of that liberated by the soda-lime glass over the temperature range studied (20°–500°c).

Release of fluorine. Fluorine may be present in certain glasses and released if the glass is heated. Francel (1961) has studied the release of fluorine from baria alkali silicates with and without lead oxide and containing about 0·5–1% of fluorine; the commercial glass types were Kimble TM-5, K-52 and TH-8. The glass was crushed and heated in vacuum at 10^{-4} torr. The fluorine released was condensed on a cold trap. The condensate contained soda and potash and it was believed that these were from sodium and potassium fluorides. The remaining condensate appeared to be hydrogen fluoride. Fluorine in the sodium and potassium fluorides accounted for some 20% of the fluorine liberated.

The evaporation rate of the fluorine followed the Arrhenius equation

$$\log F = -\frac{B}{T} + C$$

where F is the evaporation rate in μg dm^{-2} h^{-1}; T is the temperature in °K; B and C are constants. For example, for glass type TM-5 $B = 5020$, $C = 7\cdot65$ and the activation energy $E = 23$ kcal g mol^{-1}. Fluorine evaporation was not detected until the glass sample had been heated to 375°C. The amount of fluorine evaporated in μg dm^{-2} increased with time according to the parabolic law $F = mt^{1/2} + n$, where t is in hours, and m and n are constants. For glass TM-5 over the temperature range 400°–450°C m increased from 4 to 13 and n from $-2\cdot5$ to $-8\cdot5$. The minus value for the constant n arose from an induction period before fluorine evaporation commenced. Francel states that water and alkalis have to be initially removed to make a passage for the fluorine. Equally likely the surface had been denuded of fluorine by atmospheric reaction and the initial washing treatment. Fluorine evaporation was greater for glasses containing lead or boric oxide.

3. SORPTION OF WATER VAPOUR

We have now established in the foregoing section that the principal gas sorbed by glass is water and in this section we shall discuss processes by which water is bound and released from glass.

DESORPTION OF WATER

Diffusion and surface evaporation. Johnson Todd (1955) has studied the manner in which water is released by soda-lime glass tubing (Corning 0080). Mass spectrometry showed that glass samples which had been washed and dried in air and heated for $4\frac{1}{2}$ hours at 100°, 200°, 300° and 480°C liberated respectively 100, 99·7, 98·6 and 98·2% of water of the total gas evolved.

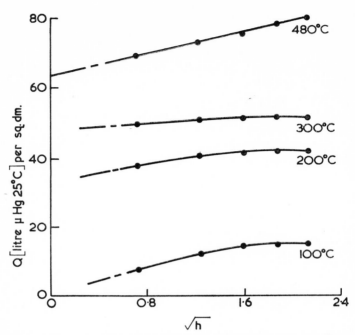

FIG. 4.5 AMOUNT† OF WATER DESORBED BY TWO YEAR OLD TUBING (8 mm O.D.)
SODA-LIME GLASS (NO. 0080) WASHED AND DRIED IN AIR (*After Johnson Todd,*
1955)

For bake-out temperatures above about 300°C the water evolution
could be expressed by the equation

$$Q = mt^{1/2} + n \qquad\qquad (i)$$

where Q is the mass of water evolved per unit surface area after time
t and m and n are constants (Fig. 4.5). Johnson Todd found that the
value of n was higher for glass with an aged surface. Freshly drawn
glass or glass which had been washed with dilute HF gave a low
value of n. Washing aged glass with chromic acid or 2·5M solutions
of HCl, H_2SO_4, NH_4OH and NaOH did not affect the values of
n or m. The value of n could be greatly increased, leaving m unchanged, by storing the glass in saturated water vapour at 90°C.

From these experiments it can be concluded that the constant n
in equation (i) arises from desorption of water by a hydrated layer
on the aged glass surface.

Garbe *et al.* (1960) have also shown the effect of surface water on
the desorption characteristics of aged soda-lime glass. Plotted in

---

† litre μ Hg is one litre of gas at a pressure of 1 μ Hg and is equal to 10^{-3} litre torr.

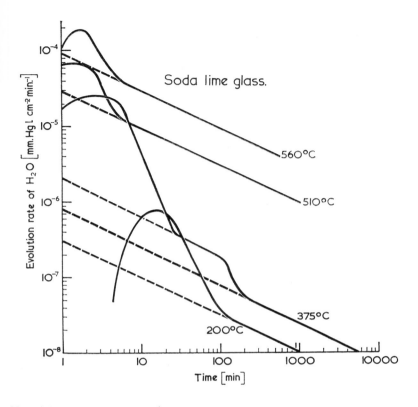

FIG. 4.6 DESORPTION RATE† OF WATER FROM SODA-LIME GLASS AS A FUNCTION
OF TIME (*After Garbe et al.*, 1960)

Fig. 4.6 is the rate of desorption of water dQ/dt as a function of
time and at different temperatures. The amount of water released
from the surface of aged soda-lime glass was 4×10^{-4} cm^3
N.T.P./cm^2, whereas it required 45 hours at 420°c for the same
amount to diffuse to the surface from the interior.

Silica does not adsorb large quantities of gas. Thus Garbe and
Christians (1962) degassed a silica flask at about 1000°c *in vacuo*
and then exposed it to air. The flask was repumped to 10^{-7} torr
and baked liberating $3 \cdot 7 \times 10^{-5}$ cm^3 N.T.P./cm^2 of gas at 380°c
rising to $6 \cdot 1 \times 10^{-5}$ cm^3 N.T.P./cm^2 at 480°c. The foregoing
quantities are consistent with the desorption of a chemisorbed
monolayer. The desorption energy of the layer was 15 kcal/g mol.

† mm Hg l is also written as litre torr.

When the degassing temperature of soda-lime glass is raised the slope m of the curves relating Q to t is increased (Fig. 4.7).

The term $mt^{1/2}$ in equation (i) is related to the equation on p. 205 for diffusion into a vacuum from a semi-infinite body, viz.

$$q = 2C_0\left(\frac{Dt}{\pi}\right)^{1/2} \tag{ii}$$

where q is the mass desorbed. If after the evolution of the surface gas n further desorption of gas $Q - n$ follows equation (ii) then we have

$$mt^{1/2} = 2C_0(Dt/\pi)^{1/2}$$
$$m = 1\cdot13C_0D^{1/2} \tag{iii}$$

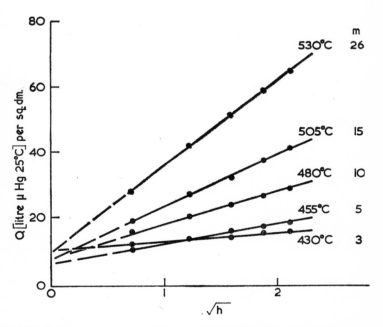

FIG. 4.7 DETERMINATION OF m AT DIFFERENT TEMPERATURES FOR SODA-LIME GLASS (NO. 0080) AFTER WASHING WITH 1% HF AND DRYING (*After Johnson Todd*, 1955)

Removing water in air. In a later paper Johnson Todd (1956) showed that the water content of soda-lime glass (0080) could be lowered by baking in dry air. Thus his experiments established that water diffusion proceeded as well in dry air ($P_{H_2O} < 1\mu$ Hg) as in vacuum with the same water concentration gradient at given times and temperatures. Tests were made to find whether water was absorbed or desorbed when samples were heated in atmospheres containing different partial pressures of water. There was neither permeation in nor out of a sample when the partial pressure of water was 10 torr at 500°c and 12 torr at 550°c. From this one can conclude that the 'water' in the manufactured glass corresponded to an equilibrium amount given by either of the foregoing combinations of pressure and temperature.

Activation energy of desorption. If one measures the water desorbed by glass at different temperatures then the activation energy for 'water' permeation in the glass can be found. Shown in Fig. 4.8 are values of m as a function of the reciprocal temperature as measured by Johnson Todd for a range of glasses heated *in vacuo*.

Tubing made of 96% silica glass ('Vycor' 7910, 7911) develops a low water concentration at the surface during manufacture and this gives a lower value of m than for granular samples of crushed glass. Glass No. 7911 is a vacuum-fired product.

We may find the activation energy of desorption E_m from the relation

$$m = m_0 \exp\left(-E_m/RT\right) \qquad \text{(iv)}$$

where R is the gas constant and T the temperature. Using equation (iii) above Johnson Todd obtained the activation energy for diffusion E_D from

$$m = 1 \cdot 13 C_0 D_0^{1/2} \exp\left(-E_D/2RT\right) \qquad \text{(v)}$$

so that $E_D = 2E_m$. Equation (iv) can be written in the form

$$\log m = -\frac{\mathbf{B}}{T} + \mathbf{C}$$

where $\mathbf{B} = E_m/2 \cdot 303 R$ and $\mathbf{C}$ is a constant. Values of $\mathbf{B}$, $\mathbf{C}$ and E_m for different glasses are given in Table 4.4.

In deriving equation (v) an activation energy has only been allowed for diffusion of 'water' to the desorbing surface, whereas desorption into the gas phase will also be activated. Garbe and

Table 4.4

Constants for the calculation of m (litre μ Hg 25°) per sq dm/$\sqrt{h}$ at an arbitrary temperature from the equation, log $m = (-\mathbf{B}/T) + \mathbf{C}$

(After Johnson Todd, 1955)

Glass code no.	Glass type	**B** (°K)	**C**	E_m ‡ water (kcal/g mol)
7911 †	Vycor brand 96% silica	6230	5·397	28·5
7910 †	Vycor brand 96% silica	8240	9·772	37·5
1720	Lime-aluminium	7000	7·952	32
7740 †	Borosilicate	4510	6·310	20·5
7720	Lead-borosilicate	4150	5·983	19
0080 †	Soda-lime	5420	8·153	25
0120	Potash-soda-lead	3910	6·208	19
9014	Potash-soda-barium	4840	7·799	22

† Samples made of tubing remaining samples granular.
‡ *Note*: Johnson Todd assumed that the activation energy for diffusion equalled $2E_m$; this did not allow for activated desorption of water.

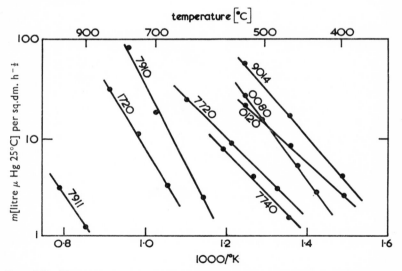

Fig. 4.8 Temperature dependence of m for eight glasses produced by corning glass works. Type of glass given in table 4·4 *(After Johnson Todd,* 1955)

Christians (1962) have allowed for the water concentration (or solubility) C being a function of temperature with an activation energy for desorption from the solid. Assuming the relation

$$C = C_0 \exp\left(-E_c/RT\right) \qquad \text{(vi)}$$

and allowing for this as part of the measured activation energy we have

$$E_m = E_c + \tfrac{1}{2}E_D \qquad \text{(vii)}$$

Given in Table 4.5 are values of E_m obtained by Garbe and Christians for CO_2 and H_2O desorbing from different glasses. The value of E_c for water dissolved by silica has been reported as —6 kcal/g mol (Moulson and Roberts, 1961).

Table 4.5

Activation Energy E_m for desorption of water and carbon dioxide
(*After Garbe and Christians*, 1962)

	E_m (kcal/g mol)	
	H_2O	CO_2
Soda-lime-silicate	29	12
Borosilicate (Pyrex type)	21	10·5
Aluminosilicate	49	16

Diffusion constant. When Johnson Todd (1955) melted a soda-lime glass (0080) *in vacuo* at 1300°c for $\tfrac{1}{2}$ hour it liberated 0·65 cm³ N.T.P. of water per cm³ of glass. Assuming this equalled the water available for diffusion at bake-out temperatures then the diffusion constant can be found from equation (iii) above. The results are given in Table 4.8 in the next section where the chemical form 'water' assumes in permeating glass is discussed at length.

ADSORPTION BY POWDERS

Hygroscopicity. Faraday (1830) regarded glass as a solution of different substances rather than as a strong chemical compound and observed that 'The half-combined and hygrometric state of the alkali appears to be the cause of the deposited film of moisture which is well known to adhere to ordinary glass when exposed to the atmosphere. . . .' If glass is crushed to increase the surface area and reduce the depth required for diffusion to the interior then the amount of water sorbed is greatly increased and may be taken as a measure of the hygroscopicity of the glass. Pike and Hubbard (1957) have measured the water sorbed by a range of powdered glasses when exposed to water vapour at a high humidity. Their results,

15

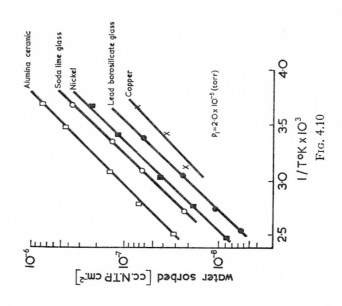

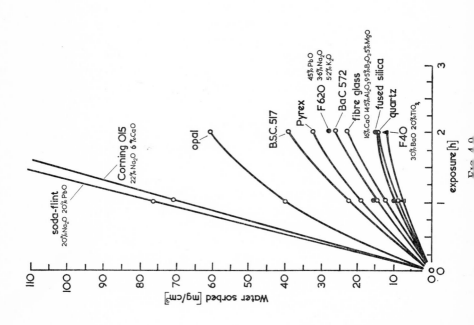

FIG. 4.10

FIG. 4.9

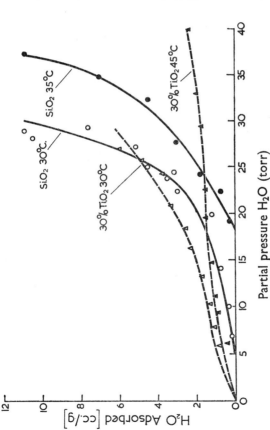

FIG. 4.11

Partial pressure H$_2$O (torr)

FIG. 4.11

FIG. 4.9 HYGROSCOPICITY OF A NUMBER OF GLASS POWDERS GROUND TO PASS A NO. 140 U.S. STANDARD SIEVE. WATER SORBED DETERMINED FROM CHANGES IN WEIGHT OF SAMPLES EXPOSED TO HIGH HUMIDITY MAINTAINED BY SATURATED AQUEOUS SOLUTION OF CaSO$_4$.2H$_2$O (*After Pike and Hubbard*, 1957)

FIG. 4.10 MASS OF WATER SORBED PER UNIT AREA BY DIFFERENT POWDERED MATERIALS AS A FUNCTION OF THE RECIPROCAL OF THE TEMPERATURE (*After Okamoto and Tuzi*, 1958)

FIG. 4.11 ADSORPTION ISOTHERMS FOR WATER ON POWDERED SILICA AND ALKALINE GLASS CONTAINING 30% TiO$_2$ (*After Anderson and Kimpton*, 1960)

plotted in Fig. 4.9, show that quartz, silica and glasses with a low alkali content sorb the least water. The high sorption capacity of the strongly alkaline glasses is attributed to the alkali being leached from the powder and forming an aqueous solution.

Okamoto and Tuzi (1958) have measured the amount of water vapour sorbed by soda-lime and lead borosilicate powders. The glass powder was packed into a tube connecting two glass vessels and the amount of water sorbed was calculated from the time lag for water vapour to pass from one vessel to the other (see p. 199). The amounts of water sorbed per unit area by various substances are given in Fig. 4.10 as a function of temperature. The vapour pressure of water in the reservoir vessel was 2×10^{-5} torr.

Adsorption isotherm. Anderson and Kimpton (1960) have determined the adsorption isotherms for water taken up by powders of silica and sodium silicate glass containing 30% of titanium dioxide. Their results are plotted in Fig. 4.11. It is of interest to note that the silica powder does not show any adsorption until the partial pressure of the water vapour reaches a critical value, which is greater the higher the temperature. The heat of adsorption for water vapour on silica was between 6–7 kcal/g mol and for water vapour on the alkali/titania glass 19 kcal/g mol. The latter value was greater than that expected from hydrogen bonding or van der Waals' forces. (Information was not given on the size of the powder or its degassing treatment.) Presumably the silica surface was initially covered by chemisorbed water and the isotherm is for physically adsorbed water as indicated by the heat of adsorption. If one uses powders for adsorption on large areas it is possible that condensation of vapour may occur in capillaries between the grains.

The view has been advanced that water is only physically adsorbed on sites where hydroxyl groups are chemisorbed. Thus Young (1958) studied water adsorption on silica powder formed by flame hydrolysis of silica tetrachloride. He found that when chemisorbed hydroxyl groups were removed by heating their reformation was reversible, but if the silica was heated to above 400°c it could not be rehydrated by exposure to unsaturated water vapour. Young concluded that above 400°c a change occurred in the nature of a dehydrated site such that it was shielded by oxygen forming tetrahedral and silicon monoxide type bonds. Physical adsorption was also reduced by lowering the number of OH-sites.

Thus even at pressures approaching saturation those portions of the silica surface devoid of bound OH-groups were also bare of adsorbed water molecules and adsorption proceeded by formation of clusters around OH-sites. Since water was not physically adsorbed on a reformed surface the silica could only be rehydrated by exposure to liquid water.

Sidorov (1960) studied water adsorption in porous silica glass formed by leaching a sodium borosilicate. Using infra red absorption spectroscopy he identified two types of OH^- groups, one free, the other with a perturbed hydrogen bond. He contended that pairs of perturbed hydroxyls bound to the surface are the sites for subsequent water adsorption.

APPARENT ADSORBATE THICKNESS

Ideally if one formed a fresh surface on alkaline glass, *e.g.* by melting, then the surface would be smooth on an atomic scale and in an atmosphere of unsaturated water vapour one would expect chemisorption of OH^- ions on active sites and partial surface coverage by physically adsorbed water. However, as exposure continued the adsorbed water would react with the alkali components in the glass. Weyl (1945) has noted that when one breathes on the surface of freshly broken glass the condensed water initially forms an optical interference film. After a time the water reacts with the glass and hydrogen diffuses into the glass so that the inner film boundary vanishes and optical interference ceases.

When an alkaline solution forms on a glass surface the silica in the glass structure is attacked, forming silica gel. If glass with such a corroded surface is degassed by heating *in vacuo*, then its potential adsorptive capacity is much greater than that of a freshly prepared surface. If the weathered glass is washed with acids (other than HF) then the alkali will be leached from the glass surface leaving a porous surface mainly of silica. Such porous layers may have a high adsorptive capacity due to their large area. If now the glass is heated *in vacuo* the adsorbed water will be removed and if the temperature is high enough ($> 300°c$) the porous silica may be sintered into a compact body.

If water is condensed in fissures or holes in the surface of weathered glass then the pressure of water vapour in equilibrium with its liquid at a given temperature will be depressed by capillary action. Thus liquid may continue to exist in the surface fissures when the vapour pressure has fallen below the normal saturated value. A similar effect could occur with silica powders and could explain the critical pressure for adsorption shown in Fig. 4.11; if alkali components existed on the surface then adsorption would occur at the lowest vapour pressure.

It will immediately be inferred from the foregoing that it is almost impossible to obtain consistent values for the adsorption capacity of a given type of glass for water. Moreover, the adsorptive capacities of glass for non-reactive gases or vapours may be enhanced to an unknown extent if corrosion has roughened the adsorbent surface.

If it is assumed that the adsorbed water forms a continuous surface film whose thickness can be derived from the mass of vapour sorbed, then it is invariably found that glass apparently has the ability to hold many molecular layers of water on its surface. This water is so firmly held that it is not released unless the glass temperature is raised several hundreds of degrees in dry air or vacuum. For example, Bunsen (1885) passed dry air through glass wool for periods of up to 12 hours until no more water was transferred from the issuing gas to phosphorus pentoxide. The temperature of the glass was increased on each test. Assuming all of the water was removed at 503°c the amount of water remaining at lower temperatures could be calculated. Bunsen's results are given in Table 4.6. The large amount of water held by the glass could easily arise from alkalinity of the glass or capillary action.

Many early workers believed that the Langmuir theory of monomolecular adsorption should apply to the sorption of water on glass. However, they neglected the effects of chemical reaction and surface roughening on the adsorptive capacity of glass. Garbe and Christians (1962) have deduced from desorption curves the percentage gas evolution from three zones of a glass body, viz. the surface, the boundary film and the interior; their results are given in Table 4.6.

McHaffie and Lenher (1925) devised a method for determining the quantity of gas adsorbed by a surface when a liquid and its vapour were heated in a closed vessel to convert them to the gas phase. A plot of pressure versus temperature of the system should give first a saturated vapour pressure curve until all of the liquid has evaporated followed by a linear curve relating the pressure of a gas in a closed system with its temperature (curve *aoc* Fig. 4.12). The two curves should show a sharp intersection at the point of vapour–gas transition if vapour or gas is not removed from the atmosphere by adsorption.

Table 4.6

Apparent thickness of adsorbed water film on glass wool at
different temperatures
(*After Bunsen*, 1885)

Temperature °C	Apparent H_2O thickness Å†
23	105
107	67
215	55
329	36
415	13
468	4
503	0

† The water film was assumed to have a density corresponding to that at 4°C.

Note: Garbe and Christians (1962) deduced from desorption rate curves such as those in Fig. 4.6 that gas was liberated by glass from three regions, as given below, with their respective percentage contributions after heating for 2 hours at 380°C *in vacuo*.

	cm^3 N.T.P. cm^{-2}	Surface %	Boundary film %	Interior %
Soda-lime-silicate	$3 \cdot 4 . 10^{-4}$	58	31	11
Borosilicate	$10 \cdot 8 . 10^{-4}$	60	32	8
Aluminosilicate	$1 \cdot 6 . 10^{-4}$	100	00	10^{-3}

McHaffie and Lenher allowed the vapour from degassed water to enter a soft Duroglass vessel where it was isolated from the supply. The Duroglass vessel was then cooled and heated to obtain the experimental pressure/temperature curve *abc* shown in Fig. 4.12. The experimental curve below *a* coincides with the saturated vapour pressure curve for water. Also, at temperatures above *c*, the experimental curve follows the theoretical relation for a gas heated at constant volume. The experimental curves were reversible. (The adsorbent surface must have been covered with chemisorbed water so that the water vapour was adsorbed on an existing layer of OH^- ions.)

The number of moles of water n in the gaseous phase at any temperature T above c on the experimental curve is given by $n = PV/(RT)$, where P is the pressure, V the volume of the adsorbent vessel and R the gas constant. If any other temperature T_1 be chosen on the curve *abc* then the number of moles n_1 in the vessel atmosphere can be found. The amount of water remaining on the glass walls is then given by $n - n_1$. In the region of the curve *a* the water held to the glass will be the normal condensate as the vapour pressures are saturated values. However, both the vapour and gas curves have been depressed between *a* to *c* on the curve. Thus it *could* be concluded that the pressure values in this region are in equilibrium with adsorbed water. (It is of course a system in which both *P* and *T* are being changed, *i.e.* it is not isothermal.) Assuming

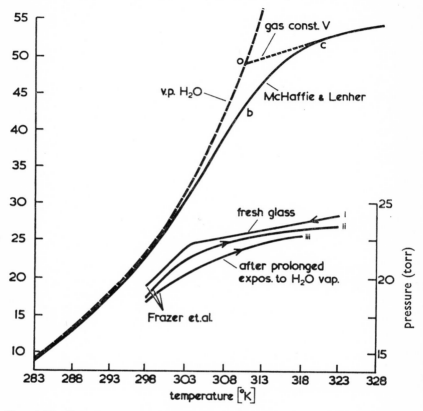

FIG. 4.12 PRESSURE OF WATER VAPOUR IN A CLOSED VESSEL WHEN ITS TEM-PERATURE IS VARIED. CURVE abc FOR AN ACID CLEANED VESSEL (*After McHaffie and Lenher*, 1925). CURVE i FOR A FRESHLY BLOWN VESSEL WITH TEMPERATURE INCREASING, CURVE ii TEMPERATURE DECREASING. CURVE iii AFTER PROLONGED EXPOSURE TO WATER VAPOUR (*After Frazer et al.*, 1927)

the adsorbent surface was plane calculations based on Fig. 4.12 gave *apparent* thicknesses for the water film of 180 molecular diameters at 24 torr (*i.e.* 90% of the saturated vapour pressure) and 27°c falling to 1·4 molecular diameters at 52 torr and 55°c.

McHaffie and Lenher appreciated that the surface of their glass vessel was probably irregular on a fine scale. The glass vessel had been rigorously cleaned with acids which would have removed soda from the surface, leaving a porous silica layer.

In a later paper Lenher (1927) discussed the adsorption of benzene on glass and silica after baking the adsorbents under vacuum (glass at 250°c for 3 hours and silica at 500°c for 2 hours). He found that the *apparent* number of adsorbed molecular layers of benzene was less than a tenth of that measured for water on glass when the pressure was equal to the saturated value.

Frazer *et al.* (1927) repeated the above experiments using a freshly blown glass vessel to obtain a smooth adsorbent surface with toluene as a non-reactive adsorbate. They found a sharp intersection between the vapour and gas curves. The experimental accuracy was insufficient to detect monomolecular adsorption if it occurred. When the glass vessel was cleaned with acid the vapour and gas curves no longer showed a sharp intersection but indicated marked adsorption. Experiments were also made with water vapour in a freshly blown vessel. Care was taken to avoid water condensation when filling the vessel with vapour and the virgin adsorbent gave the sharply intersected curves in Fig. 4.12 when the temperature was lowered. However, the two curves do not intersect on the vapour pressure curve for water. Probably the alkaline in the fresh glass surface entered into a reaction with the absorbed water, thereby depressing the vapour pressure. When the vessel temperature was raised the vapour pressure did not follow the original curve but was depressed at all points. The divergence increased as the glass remained exposed to the vapour. A chemical test indicated that the surface of a virgin glass bulb was strongly alkaline.

Thus water molecules can be held by a glass surface in the presence of unsaturated water vapour or gaseous water in a number of ways. The water may be condensed or physically adsorbed in capillaries and pores in a corroded surface or absorbed by an alkaline solution on a new surface.

Adsorption in ultra-high vacuum

Using ultra-high vacuum techniques Garbe *et al.* (1960) have determined adsorption isotherms for water on borosilicate glass in the pressure range 10^{-9}–10^{-5} torr. The glass was outgassed by baking at 380°c for 15 hours and water vapour admitted through a pipe of known conductance into the sorbent chamber. Partial pressures of water vapour were measured using an Omegatron mass-spectrometer fitted with an oxide cathode working at 700°c to prevent water vapour from being unduly dissociated by the cathode. Plotted in Fig. 4.13 are the amounts of water vapour adsorbed as a function of pressure for different temperatures. From the relation between the pressure and temperature at *constant amount adsorbed* the isosteric heat of adsorption can be calculated and plotted as a function of the amount adsorbed (Fig. 4.14). The amount adsorbed per unit area given in Fig. 4.14 has been calculated using the geometrical plane area of the adsorbent.

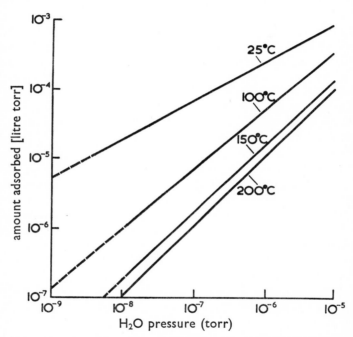

FIG. 4.13 AMOUNT OF WATER ADSORBED ON BOROSILICATE GLASS AFTER DEGASSING FOR 15h AT 380°c. AREA OF SORBENT 700 cm² VOLUME OF SORBENT 0·5 1. (*After Garbe et al.,* 1960)

It appears from Figs. 4.13 and 4.14 that at pressures less than 10^{-7} torr at 25°c and 10^{-5} torr at 200°c water is not held to glass by simple physical adsorption. Thus the heat of adsorption decreases from above 10 kcal/g mol when the amount of water adsorbed is about $3\cdot3 \times 10^{-8}$ cm³ N.T.P./cm² to 7 kcal/g mol at $1\cdot3 \times 10^{-7}$ cm³

N.T.P./cm²; the latter heat of adsorption is comparable to that obtained for physically adsorbed water. At room temperature and a water vapour pressure of 10^{-6} torr the water adsorbed was about 0·1% of that required to form a monolayer on a plane surface. It will be obvious from the discussion in the previous sections that it is almost impossible to obtain repeatable equilibrium conditions for the adsorption of water on glass. Thus part of the water arriving at a

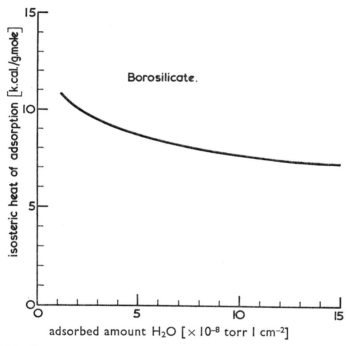

FIG. 4.14   ISOSTERIC HEAT OF ADSORPTION OF WATER ON BOROSILICATE GLASS
(*After Garbe et al.*, 1960)

nascent glass surface will react to form hydroxyl groups and release hydrogen and the degree to which the reaction is reversible with temperatures will depend on the composition of the atmosphere, *i.e.* the ratio of hydrogen to water vapour present. Also after the glass has been in contact with water for a period the chemical composition of its surface undergoes irreversible changes.

Garbe *et al.* (1960) found that lowering the temperature of a glass sealed-off vacuum system from 180° to 35°c reduced the partial pressure of water from about 5×10^{-4} torr to 5×10^{-7} torr. As the water pressure fell so hydrogen was evolved by reaction between the adsorbed water and the glass; some thermal dissociation of water occurred on the mass spectrometer hot cathode.

OXYGEN VERSUS WATER ADSORPTION

Silicate glasses usually have a greater affinity for water vapour than active gases in the atmosphere and are thus easily wetted. However, it is shown in Chapter 6 that lead oxide glasses, *e.g.* an X-ray plate glass, can have a high contact angle ($\simeq 30°$) for water, indicating a lowered affinity. It is also shown in Chapter 6 that adsorption of large, highly polarizable ions such as Pb^{2+} to silicate glass raises the contact angle for water. Anderson and Kimpton (1960) attempted to produce a non-wetting glass by preparing a batch with a high lead oxide content (90% PbO; 10% SiO_2). However, when the glass was cast and cooled it was wetted perfectly by water; freshly broken surfaces were also perfectly wetted. When the wetted glass surface was rubbed with moist cheese-cloth or other pure cellulose material and wiped dry it became non-wetting with a contact angle near 90°. The hydrophobic glass became wettable after a few hours heat treatment in air at 275°c.

When a glass specimen was put in a desiccator immediately after casting and left in dry air for several days the measured contact angles were between 80–90°. This observation suggests that the affinity of aged lead oxide glass for water or air (oxygen) depends upon the gas or vapour initially in contact with the glass and therefore chemisorbed.

Continued investigation showed that certain other glasses with a low silica content could be made non-wetting after being treated as above, *e.g.* glasses containing large amounts of TiO_2, BaO, Bi_2O_3, Sb_2O_3. A study of the wetting properties of different crystalline oxides indicated that those which arranged their metal–oxygen atoms in octahedra, *e.g.* rutile, could become hydrophobic, whereas those with Si—O tetrahedra, *e.g.* quartz, always gave low contact angles. It was believed that non-wetting arose from oxygen adsorbed to the surface octahedra.

Glass samples which had been made hydrophobic by treatment were heated *in vacuo* to find if oxygen was released. All the glasses tested released oxygen when heated to 175°c, but this did not destroy the hydrophobic quality of the lead oxide glass. Thus a

90% PbO glass which had been preheated at 175°c did not release more oxygen until the temperature was raised to 268°c when it also lost its hydrophobic property. This indicated that the oxygen desorbed at the higher temperature had been strongly bound to the surface and a calculation showed that the quantity of oxygen released was sufficient to form a monolayer. Soda-lime glass which had been preheated at 175°c did not give off oxygen nor change its wetting properties when heated to 300°c *in vacuo*.

Optical indication of adsorbed vapours

Various optical techniques for detecting the presence of adsorbed films on glass or the changes in the surface refractive index due to chemical attack are discussed in Chapter 2. Whilst the techniques are valuable for indicating a departure from an ideal homogeneous surface the measured results are often difficult to interpret when attempting to derive the composition and structure of the surface layer.

Ellipticity. When light polarized at 45° to the plane of incidence falls at the polarizing angle on a boundary between two non-absorbing media the reflected beam should be plane-polarized perpendicular to the plane of incidence. Invariably a transition zone is present between the media and the reflected light is elliptically polarized. As shown in Chapter 2 Drude and Vašiček have derived expressions relating the ellipticity γ to the refractive index and thickness of the surface layer. The ellipticity is defined as the ratio of the principal axes of the ellipse, *i.e.* b/a when $\gamma \rightarrow 0$ and a and b are measured parallel and perpendicular to the major axis of the ellipse.

Frazer (1929) has followed the adsorption of water and methyl alcohol vapours on glass by measuring the ellipticity of the reflected light. Initial measurements were made on fracture surfaces of plate glass. Numerous specimens prepared in this way gave a value of $\gamma \simeq 0.01$, which corresponded to a transition layer of about 30 Å thick if its refractive index was assumed intermediate between that of the glass and air. The ellipticity of a fracture surface showed almost no change after 2 days in the atmosphere and also did not change when placed in a vacuum at a pressure of 10^{-6} torr. Adams (1929) did not find the same stability with pressure when working with fracture surfaces of Pyrex glass. Thus a specimen exposed in air for 5 days had an ellipticity of 0·013 which fell to 0·0115 on evacuation.

One must conclude that the fracture surfaces were covered by chemically bound water immediately after their formation. The subsequent resistance to further adsorption indicates the effectiveness of these glasses in protecting their surfaces against atmospheric corrosion.

It would undoubtedly be of value to study the ellipticity of light reflected from glass surfaces formed in ultra-high vacuum ($<10^{-9}$ torr) where adsorption of the first monolayer would proceed slowly. Experiments made at higher vacuum pressures incur possible contamination of the glass surface and are probably limited to physical adsorption or adsorption by hygroscopic substances in the glass, *e.g.* alkalis. Frazer measured the ellipticity of light reflected from a glass specimen exposed in a normal vacuum to water vapour with a saturated vapour pressure of 18 torr. His results are not easy to interpret. Thus the ellipticity was constant until a pressure of about 6 torr was reached, when it rose almost linearly with vapour pressure. At 12·5 torr there was a sharp discontinuity and the curve again increased linearly with pressure but more sharply than before. The ellipticity was reversible with vapour pressure and claimed to be independent of the history of the specimen. Unfortunately the specimen treatment was not given.

Similar results were obtained with methyl alcohol. Thus the ellipticity started to increase linearly with pressure when the pressure had reached 30% of the saturation value. At a pressure of about 90% of the saturated value there was an abrupt break and the ellipticity increased rapidly. The calculated thickness for the break was about 9 Å. Exposure of the glass to vapours of nitromethane, acetone, toluene and formaldehyde showed that these substances did not condense on the glass at saturation pressures.

Adams (1929) measured the ellipticity of fracture surfaces of Pyrex which was broken in air and heated in vacuum at a pressure of 10^{-6} torr. He found that γ decreased from 0·0113 at 20°c to an almost uniform value of 0·011 between 100°–250°c and then fell again to 0·0105 at 300°c.

Surface refractive index. A method due to Pfund is described in Chapter 2 for accurately determining the refractive index of a solid from Brewster's angle. Pfund's method is also useful for detecting small changes in the refractive index of the surfaces of dielectrics.

When the change in index arises from a thin surface film the meaning of the Pfund angle θ_p is difficult to interpret and the index of the film is not simply equal to tan θ_p as for an homogeneous solid. Thus, as explained above, a surface film reflects plane polarized light as elliptically polarized light. In this case the Pfund angle is equal to the angle of incidence at which one of the principal axes of the vibration ellipse of the reflected light lies in the plane of incidence. The reader will find that this follows from the discussion of the polarimetric method of studying surface films in Chapter 2.

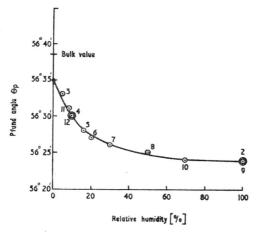

FIG. 4.15 PFUND ANGLE OF A CLEAN GLASS SURFACE AS A FUNCTION OF THE RELATIVE HUMIDITY OF THE AMBIENT ATMOSPHERE. REFRACTIVE INDEX OF THE BULK GLASS WAS 1·5177 GIVING A BREWSTER'S ANGLE OF 56° 37′ (*After Kinosita, 1953*)

Kinosita (1953) has followed the adsorption of water on glass by measuring θ_p as a function of relative humidity at ambient temperature. He used a glass with an index of 1·5177 giving a Brewster angle of 56° 37′ when free from moisture. The plotted values in Fig. 4.15 are numbered in order of measurement and show that the adsorption process is reversible and physical in origin. It is obvious that results obtained by Kinosita differ from those of Frazer described above; neither the kind of glass used by Kinosita nor its cleaning treatment was given.

Optical thickness of corrosion films. When glass is weathered a porous surface film may be formed whose optical thickness varies with the

The Properties of Glass Surfaces

amount of vapour condensed in its pores. Coelingh (1939) has studied the absorption of alcohol in the porous surface of a corroded glass flask (probably soda-lime). The flask was partially filled with alcohol held at a constant temperature (T_1) and the wall tem-

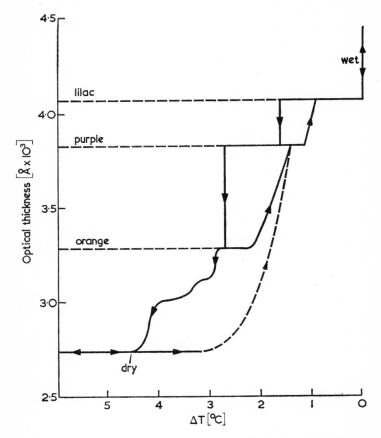

FIG. 4.16 DRYING AND CONDENSATION CURVES FOR WEATHERED GLASS ABSORBING ALCOHOL IN A POROUS SURFACE. GLASS TEMPERATURE INITIALLY 20°C (*After Coelingh*, 1939)

perature (T_g) varied. The interference colour of the surface film and corresponding optical film thickness are plotted in Fig. 4.16 as a function of $\Delta T = T_g - T_1$. The curve indicates that desorption occurs in steps and is subject to hysteresis. Coelingh believed that the sizes of the pores in the weathered surface were not continuously distributed but were grouped. Applying the theory of vapour pressure reduction arising from absorption in capillaries she calculated that the radius of the groups ranged from 20 to 200 Å.

The hysteresis indicated in Fig. 4.16 was attributed to adsorption of air in the pores which delayed wetting and condensation. Coelingh believed that the reason why some workers observed hysteresis effects with silica gel and others had not was due to differences in the pore size of the samples. When the pore radius is about 20 Å or less then the sorption of vapour molecules must occur by adsorption. Certainly the glasses studied in Figs. 4.15 and 4.16 differed in the degree of corrosion of their surfaces and only the weathered glass shows hysteresis. However, adsorption can be subject to hysteresis if a gas layer must be displaced before adsorption can proceed. It is possible that the water adsorbed on the glass studied by Kinosita was absorbed by an *hygroscopic* surface layer.

INFRA RED ABSORPTION BY ABSORBED WATER

Absorption in the 3 *micron region.* Certain of the infra red absorption bands of glasses made from oxides of high or low molecular weight arise from impurities, and the absorption bands due to water are particularly marked. Thus glasses with a high silica or boric oxide content absorb light strongly in the region $2 \cdot 7$–3 μ due to the presence of water. Much work has been done on this subject because of both the use of glass optical components in the near infra red and the information it affords on the glass structure. We are concerned here with the water sorption properties of silicate glasses and infra red studies are discussed primarily from that standpoint. For extensive bibliographies of the infra red properties of silicate glasses the reader should consult Scholze and Dietzel (1955) and Adams (1961*a*).

According to Harrison (1947) it was Gage† in 1933 who first suggested that the absorption band of glass at wavelengths between $2 \cdot 7$–3 μ arose from its water content. Water vapour has a strong absorption band at $2 \cdot 7$ μ and liquid water a much broader band with its centre at 3 μ. In 1935 Dalton† vacuum degassed Pyrex glass and found that the transmission at $2 \cdot 8$ μ was greater than of normal

---

† Corning Glass Works Laboratory.

16

Pyrex as shown in Fig. 4.17. Analysis of the untreated Pyrex showed that it contained 38 cm³ N.T.P. water vapour per 100 g of glass. Water vapour was not detectable in the degassed samples.

Drummond (1934) detected absorption peaks in fused silica at about 2·7 μ and suggested an impurity such as carbon dioxide. Ellis

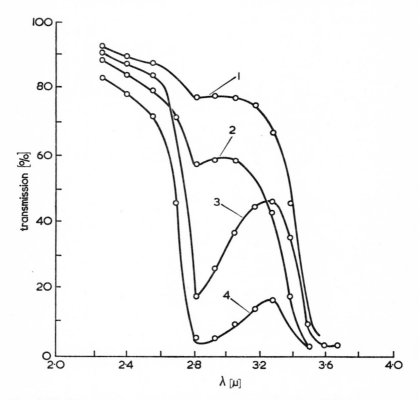

FIG. 4.17 INFRA RED TRANSMITTANCE OF PYREX GLASS (NO. 774) AS REPORTED BY HARRISON (1947). 1, DEGASSED 2 mm THICK; 2, DEGASSED 5 mm THICK; 3, UNTREATED 2 mm THICK; 4, UNTREATED 5 mm THICK

and Lyon (1936, 1937) found little or no optical absorption by fused silica which had had an opportunity to dissolve carbon dioxide and suggested that water was the impurity. More recently Foex (1954) has melted silica in atmospheres of O_2, N_2, A, CO_2 and dry and moist air. Only with a moist atmosphere was an absorption band found at 2·7 μ.

Harrison (1947) studied the infra red transmission of simple glasses. She found that some commercially available fused silica samples showed a strong absorption at $2 \cdot 7 \ \mu$, whereas with others absorption was almost absent (Fig. 4.18). An absorption band at $2 \cdot 85 \ \mu$ obtained with fused boric oxide could be removed by bubbling the melt with boron trichloride and casting between platinum foil.

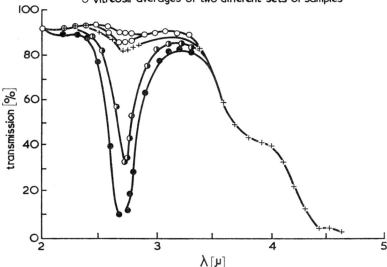

FIG. 4.18   INFRA RED TRANSMITTANCE OF SILICA SPECIMENS ABOUT 5 mm THICK (*After Harrison*, 1947)

An absorption peak at $2 \cdot 95 \ \mu$ shown by fused sodium tetraborate was partially removed by bubbling the melt with dry air.

H_2O *or* OH^- *groups?* Harrison attributed the absorption bands given in Table 4.7 to OH^- vibrational absorption and suggested that the position of the band might be related to the strength of bonding with the principal components of the glass, *i.e.* the absorption band shifts to larger wavelengths with rise in the strength of the hydrogen bonding.

Glaze (1955) and his co-workers were of the opinion that the water was present in silicate glasses as molecular H_2O-groups. Moore and McMillan (1956) believed that the absorption bands of glasses made from oxides of low atomic weights arose in the 3 μ region from OH^- groups, which were associated in the network of the glass former through hydrogen bonding. Heaton and Moore (1957) studied glasses formed from oxides of high molecular weight and were unable to decide whether water was present in the form of molecular H_2O or OH^- groups.

If the infra red absorption of individual H_2O or OH^- groups is independent of their concentration c then Beer's law is applicable and we have $I = I_0 e^{-kcd}$, where I_0 is the intensity of the incident light, k is the absorption due to unit concentration and d the thickness of the glass sample. As the light transmission is given by $T = I/I_0$ then the optical density is $\log_{10}(1/T) = 0.434\, kcd$, *i.e.* the optical density is directly proportional to the concentration of absorbing groups.

Henry's law states that the solubility of a gas in a liquid is proportional to its pressure providing that the solution is dilute and the molecular state of the gas is unchanged on solution. Thus, only if water vapour was absorbed as H_2O would the optical density of a water peak increase linearly with the pressure of water vapour over the liquid glass.

Scholze and Dietzel (1955), working with a soda-lime glass (74% SiO_2; 10% CaO; 16% Na_2O) found that the optical density of the 'water' band rose as the relative humidity of the furnace atmosphere was increased. They also observed that the optical density was higher when sodium carbonate containing water of crystallization was added to the melt in place of dehydrated soda. A plot of optical density as a function of the partial pressure of water vapour appeared to give a linear relation, but inspection of their curves show that insufficient measurements were taken to permit such a conclusion.

If the absorption bands arising from water in glass are due to OH^- groups which are initially produced at the glass surface by a reaction of the kind

$$\frac{O \qquad O}{\diagdown \; \diagup}\!\!\!\!\!Si\!\!\!\!\!\diagup \diagdown \atop O \qquad O \;\; + H_2O \rightarrow \frac{OH \quad OH}{\diagdown \; \diagup}\!\!\!\!\!Si\!\!\!\!\!\diagup \diagdown \atop O \qquad O \;\; + 0.5\, O_2$$

and the OH^- groups diffuse into the glass we have the possible reaction

$$-\overset{|}{\underset{|}{Si}}-O-\overset{|}{\underset{|}{Si}}-O + 2HO \rightarrow -\overset{|}{\underset{|}{Si}}-OH + OH-\overset{|}{\underset{|}{Si}}-$$

The solubility of water in the above reaction should be proportional to the square-root of the water vapour pressure. Tomlinson (1956) and Russell (1957) have found such a relation for silicate glasses containing by weight 30% Na_2O. Scholze (1959), using the soda-lime glass referred to above, has also now confirmed a square-root law.

CO_2 *infra red absorption bands.* During his latter work Scholze reinvestigated the source of the absorption band at about $3 \cdot 6 \mu$, which had been attributed by several workers to the CO_3^{2-} ion. Using the soda-lime glass he found that the intensity of the absorption band was affected by the 'water' content of the glass and remained about the same whether the glass was prepared in dry nitrogen or dry CO_2.

Scholze also showed that an absorption band existed at about $4 \cdot 25 \mu$ but was hidden in the normal spectrum by the steep gradients of the bands due to the glass itself. The band was exposed when the spectrum of a 'wet' glass was subtracted from that of a 'dry' one. Adams (1961a) did not find the absorption peak at $4 \cdot 25 \mu$ affected by bubbling either dry air or D_2O vapour through glass. He therefore concluded, at variance with Scholze, that this peak arose from CO_2 and gave strong evidence that the CO_2 was not in the glass but in the atmosphere.

Deuterium-hydrogen exchange. Hydrogen ions in glass may be replaced by those of deuterium and this has been used to identify absorption bands arising from water. Kats and Haven (1960) found that the wavelength of certain absorption peaks in α-quartz which appeared after heating in water vapour at $1000°c$ were shifted when the quartz was heated in D_2O at 25 atmospheres pressure. 'Water' peaks measured in the 3μ region at $80°K$ are as follows (the shifted values due to D_2O are in brackets); $3 \cdot 01$ ($4 \cdot 06$), $2 \cdot 97$ ($4 \cdot 00$), $2 \cdot 91$ ($3 \cdot 89$) μ. The ratio of the wavelengths of the peaks $\lambda_{OH}/\lambda_{OD}$ has an average value of $0 \cdot 744$.

Adams (1961) has used the deuterium exchange technique with

several glasses and his results are given in Table 4.7. The ratio $\lambda_{OH}/\lambda_{OD}$ determined from Adams' results has an average value of 0·735.

Table 4.7

Infra red absorption peaks arising from presence of water and D_2O in Glasses

Glass	Harrison (μ) OH	Adams (μ)	
		OH	OD
SiO_2	2·7	—	—
Pyrex	2·8	—	—
B_2O_3	2·85	2·79 3·09	3·74 —
$Na_2O.2B_2O_3$	2·95	—	—
HPO_3	> 3·2 – complete absorption	—	—
29·4 mol % Na_2O 70·6 mol % SiO_2	— —	{ 2·88 { 3·62	3·94 N.O. †
55·02 mol % PbO 44·98 mol % SiO_2	— —	{ 2·88 { 3·22 { 3·77	3·95 4·36 N.O.
16·86 mol % Na_2O 15·96 mol % CaO 67·18 mol % SiO_2	— — —	{ 2·94 { 3·50	3·95 N.O.

† N.O. peak not observed because it coincided with region of strong absorption arising from vitreous network.

INFRA RED ABSORPTION BY ADSORBED WATER

Hygroscopic glasses will absorb water in their surfaces on exposure to normal atmospheres. If the water penetrates the glass slowly and tends to be concentrated at the surfaces then the optical absorption will be independent of the specimen thickness. Adams found that the absorption band at 3·09 μ given in Table 4.7 for boric oxide glass, arose from surface absorption.

Water may be adsorbed to the surfaces of glasses and its presence will be more easily detected optically if the glass surface is porous. Benesi and Jones (1959) have made a study of chemisorbed and physically adsorbed water on silica gel. They found that water bound to silica gel consisted entirely of SiOH-groups on the surface. Shown in Fig. 4.19(a) is the spectrum of an evacuated silica gel film (1 mg/cm²) before and after exposure to water vapour. The absorption band between 2·5 to 4 μ is attributed to OH^- groups. Evacuation removes the physically adsorbed water but not the chemisorbed OH^- groups. The chemisorbed hydroxyl can only be removed by heating to 400°C *in vacuo*. The broad OH^- band in the wavelength region 2·8–3·3 μ narrows and becomes asymmetrical upon removal of SiOH-groups.

Water which is physically adsorbed on silica gel has absorption

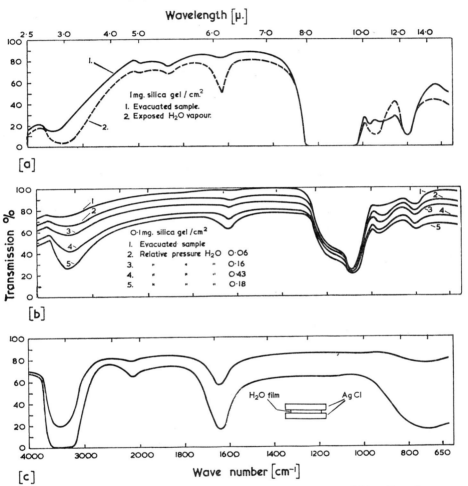

FIG. 4.19   TRANSMITTANCE IN THE INFRA RED OF SILICA GEL (*After Benesi and Jones*, 1959)

bands corresponding to those of water as shown in Figs. 4.19(*b*) and (*c*). Increasing the amount of water adsorbed by raising the water vapour pressure enhances the water peaks as shown in Fig. 4.19(*b*).

Benesi and Jones found that hydrogen in silica gel could be completely replaced by deuterium when evacuated silica gel was exposed to D_2O and the technique could be used for identifying OH-bands.

REMOVAL OF WATER DURING GLASS MELTING

Air-bubbling and vacuum treatment. Water can be removed from a glass if it is melted in dry air or in vacuum. Tomlinson (1956) and Mulfinger and Scholze (1959) measured the water desorbed at high temperatures (1000°–1400°c) and believed that the desorption rate depended on diffusion. A volatile component with a low diffusion coefficient may often be more rapidly removed from a liquid if dry air is bubbled through the liquid, *e.g.* mineral oil is dried by air bubbling. The bubbles have a large area for evaporation and their continuous renewal maintains a high surface concentration of the volatile component. Movement of air past the upper liquid surface carries the vapour away from the liquid. Grove (1955) has used dry air bubbling and vacuum treatment on calcium-aluminosilicate glasses and found that the vacuum treatment was the most effective. However, Florence *et al.* (1948) found that dry air bubbling was superior for removing water from a lead silicate glass.

Adams (1961*b*) has investigated the latter techniques and found that the bubbling treatment was more effective than vacuum treatment which, in turn, was more effective than melting in dry atmospheres. Vacuum melting appeared to be no better than melting in dry air once the initial evolution of bubbles had ceased. Water removal became more efficient the lower the partial pressure of oxygen above the melt. A surface reaction of the type:

$$2OH^- \rightarrow H_2O + \tfrac{1}{2}O_2$$

was tentatively proposed as the rate controlling process in the removal of water rather than diffusion. Presumably for the desorption process to depend on the partial pressure of oxygen the reaction postulated must obey the mass action law.

Fluoride batch addition. Adams (1961*b*) has investigated the removal of water from lead silicate and lead tellurite glasses by the addition of a fluoride. The OH^- ion and the F^- ion have the same charge and are similar in size.† Thus, if the hydroxyl in glass could be

---

† It is shown in Chapter 6 that F^- ions can be chemisorbed to glass surfaces in place of OH^- ions.

replaced by fluorine, as occurs for example in mica, this should improve the infra red transmission of glass in the region of the 'water' peaks.

Adams replaced lead oxide by lead fluoride (PbF_2) in a glass of base composition 55·02 mol % PbO, 44·92 mol % SiO_2. He found that the infra red absorption bands for water were completely removed after replacing 5 mol % PbO by PbF_2 and treating the batch for 4 hours at 1000°c. The fluoride technique was simpler than vacuum degassing for treating glass on a large scale. To obtain 5 mol % PbF_2 in the glass after melting 10 mol % PbF_2 had to be added to the initial batch. Fluorine was lost during melting and heat treatment by evaporation of PbF_2 and SiF_4 and by reaction with water to form HF. The latter did not appear to be present in the treated glass in a free or associated state. As the lead fluoride content in the glass was increased from zero the 'water' peaks in the infra red transmission curve at 2·88, 3·22 and 3·77 μ became much broader. However, when the PbF_2 content in the initial melt was raised to 15 mol % one broad but resolvable peak occurred at about 3·22 μ after 15 min at 1000°c; the peak disappeared after heat treatment for 30 min. The appearance of the absorption peak was attributed to temporary increased bonding of OH^- groups in the glass structure as they preferentially associated with tetrahedra containing fluorine (*e.g.* SiO_3F) before reacting to form HF.

Water can be removed from non-silicate glasses by fluoride treatment. Thus, Adams produced a lead tellurite ($PbO:TeO_2$) glass free from 'water' absorption bands by adding ZnF_2 to the batch.

MELTING AND HEATING SILICA IN DIFFERENT ATMOSPHERES

Dependence of OH^- *content on fusion method.* Garino Canina and Priqualer (1962) state that silica obtained by fusion of quartz in a flame usually has a hydroxyl content between 10^{18}–10^{19} OH^- radicals cm^{-3} depending on fusion conditions and the size of the quartz grains. Vitreous silica prepared from silicon tetrachloride burnt in a flame has a hydroxyl content between 10^{19}–10^{20} OH^- radicals cm^{-3}.

Hetherington and Jack (1962) state that there are three general methods used to make transparent silica, viz.

(1) Electrical fusing of quartz powder producing a silica of negligible 'water content'. Such a product, known as I.R.

Vitreosil,† contains about 3×10^{-4} wt % of OH⁻ radicals.

(2) Flame fusing of quartz to produce O.G. and O.H. Vitreosils † each with about 0·04 wt % of OH⁻ radicals.

(3) The vapour-phase hydrolysis or oxidation of silicon compounds in a flame producing a silica product known as Spectrosil † containing about 0·12 wt % OH⁻ radicals.

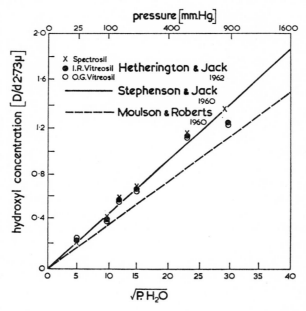

FIG. 4.20 HYDROXYL CONTENT OF SILICA VERSUS THE SQUARE ROOT OF THE WATER VAPOUR PRESSURE FOR SILICA HELD AT 1000°C. HYDROXYL CONTENT DETERMINED AT ORDINARY TEMPERATURE FROM THE OPTICAL DENSITY PER UNIT THICKNESS WHICH IS PROPORTIONAL TO THE OH⁻ CONCENTRATION *c* GIVEN BY $D/d = Ec$, WHERE E IS THE EXTINCTION COEFFICIENT (*After Hetherington and Jack*, 1962)

It is to be noted that the product with the lowest hydroxyl content, I.R. Vitreosil, has the greatest concentration of metallic impurities, whereas Spectrosil, containing less than 2 parts in 10^{-7} of metallic impurities, has the most hydroxyl. I.R. Vitreosil does not show the strong 'water' absorption bands characteristic of the other grades, but it possesses a small absorption throughout the infra red due to the metallic impurities.

†Trade names of Thermal Syndicate Ltd.. Wallsend, England.

'Diffusivity' of 'water', oxygen and hydrogen in silicate glasses at different temperatures

Glass	Expt. method	Temperature (°C)	Diffusivity (cm²/sec)†	$D_0 \exp(-E/RT)$	Gas	Observer
Soda lime (Corning 0080)	Desorption H_2O in vacuo	430	$6 \cdot 1 . 10^{-13}$	—	'Water'	Johnson and Todd(1955)
		505	$2 \cdot 0 . 10^{-11}$	—	'Water'	Johnson and Todd(1955)
Silica	Absorption in vacuo	600–1200	—	$(1 \cdot 0 \pm 0 \cdot 2) . 10^{-6} \exp\left(\dfrac{-18\,300 \pm 500}{RT}\right)$	'Water'	Moulson and Roberts (1960, 1961)
	Infra red absorption (2·7 μ)	1000	$7 \cdot 2 . 10^{-10}$	—	'Water'	Moulson and Roberts (1960, 1961)
Silica	Desorption in vacuo	600–1200	—	$(2 \cdot 7 \pm 1 \cdot 0) . 10^{-7} \exp\left(\dfrac{-17\,300 \pm 2000}{RT}\right)$	'Water'	Moulson and Roberts (1960, 1961)
	Infra red absorption (2·7 μ)	1000	$2 \cdot 9 . 10^{-10}$	—	'Water'	Moulson and Roberts (1960, 1961)
Silica	Thin specimen saturated in H_2O vapour	600	—	Solubility at 760 torr: $6 . 10^{-3}$ OH^- groups/SiO_2 molecule	'Water'	Moulson and Roberts (1960, 1961)
	Infra red absorption (2·7 μ)	1200	—	$3 . 10^{-3}$ OH^- groups/SiO_2 molecule	'Water'	Moulson and Roberts (1960, 1961)
Silica	Desorption in vacuo weight loss	1000	$3 \cdot 4 . 10^{-10}$	—	'Water'	Stephenson and Jack (1960); Hetherington and Jack (1962)
Silica	Absorption in dry H_2	800–1050	—	$9 \cdot 5 . 10^{-4} \exp\left(\dfrac{-15\,800}{RT}\right)$	Hydrogen	Bell et al. (1962)
	Infra red absorption (2·73 μ)	1050	$2 \cdot 4 . 10^{-6}$	—	Hydrogen	Bell et al. (1962)
Soda-lime (16% Na_2O 12% CaO)	Isotope O^{18} exchange	460–525	—	$2 \cdot 1 . 10^{-3} \exp\left(\dfrac{-66\,500}{RT}\right)$	Oxygen	Kingery and Lecron (1960)
		500	$6 . 10^{-16}$	—	Oxygen	Kingery and Lecron (1960)
Alumina-lime (20% Al_2O_3; 40% CaO)	Isotope O^{18} exchange	765–845	—	$4 \exp\left(\dfrac{-69\,000}{RT}\right)$	Oxygen	Kingery and Lecron (1960)
		1000 (extrap.)	10^{-13}–10^{-12}		Oxygen	Kingery and Lecron (1960)

† The term *diffusivity* is used because both solution and diffusion are determined in these studies. Thus the activated energy E contains terms for the activation energy of solution and diffusion, see discussion of this on page 223. The activation energy E_0 for 'water' dissolved in silica as hydroxyl is -6 kcal/g mol (Moulson and Roberts, 1961) and for hydrogen dissolved as hydroxyl -2 kcal/g mol (Bell et al., 1962).

The solubility of 'water' in silica is proportional to the square-root of the partial pressure of water vapour at a given temperature (Moulson and Roberts, 1960; Stephenson and Jack, 1960; Hetherington and Jack, 1961, 1962). Shown in Fig. 4.20 is the hydroxyl solubility of silica at 1000°c as measured by Hetherington and Jack. The hydroxyl content was measured by determining the optical absorption of a specimen at 2·73 μ. Absolute OH⁻ contents were obtained by heating specimens *in vacuo* and assuming the weight loss was water. Relating the weight loss to the optical density gave an extinction coefficient E of 77·5 litres OH⁻ mol⁻¹ cm⁻¹, where the optical density D equals $\log_{10}(1/T) = Edc$, T the transmittance, d the thickness in cm and c the concentration of hydroxyl in moles per litre. The OH⁻ concentration is then proportional to $D/d = Ec$.

Effect of hydrogen. Bell *et al.* (1962) heated 'water' free silica in dry hydrogen and observed that hydroxyl groups appeared in the solid. The hydroxyl concentration gradient was related to the rate of diffusion of hydrogen in silica. The hydroxyl content of the silica was determined from its optical absorption at 2·73 μ. The concentration gradient was found by removing slices from a hydrogen treated specimen and measuring the increase in the optical transmittance. A plot of total optical absorption against the square-root of the treatment time gave a straight line, indicating a diffusion controlled process. The rate at which hydrogen treatment produced OH⁻ groups in the silica was much higher than that obtained by treatment in water vapour. Shown in Table 4.8 are the 'diffusivities' for 'hydrogen' and 'water' in silica.

It must be remembered that the infra red absorption method only gives the concentration of hydroxyl groups produced by a hydrogen reaction, and not the concentration of molecular hydrogen if this is present in the glass. Thus the absorption measurements do not show directly that it is hydrogen or hydroxyl which diffuse through the glass. It has already been stated on p. 244 that water is believed to enter glass as hydroxyl groups formed by a reaction at the surface. It is possible that molecular hydrogen could be dissociated or react at the silica surface so that atomic hydrogen or hydroxyl groups respectively diffuse into the solid. However, the large difference between the *apparent* diffusion constants of water and molecular hydrogen suggests that hydrogen does not enter the silica in the same form as water *e.g.* as hydroxyl groups.

Bell *et al.* (1962) found that the equilibrium concentration of hydroxyl introduced by hydrogen treatment was proportional to the square-root of the partial pressure of molecular hydrogen. The experiments were made using I.R. Vitreosil at temperatures of 800° and 1050°c and over a pressure range of 28–760 torr. The relation between OH^- concentration and hydrogen pressure suggested a reaction equilibrium

$$\tfrac{1}{2}H_2 \; \rightleftharpoons \; \underset{\text{dissolved}}{\tfrac{1}{2}H_2} \; + -O- \; \rightleftharpoons \; \underset{\text{hydroxyl}}{-OH}$$

with the reaction occurring in the solid. The only other reactions giving rise to a square-root law are (i) formation of OH^- groups at the silica surface already rejected above because of the low diffusion rate of OH^- groups and (ii) dissociation of molecular hydrogen at the silica surface (similar to that found for hydrogen entering metals) but it is unlikely that hydrogen could dissociate without forming hydroxyl groups. Thus at present the most probable reaction is that given above.

When silica, *e.g.* O.G. Vitreosil containing hydroxyl radicals, is heated *in vacuo* hydrogen and water are evolved. 'Water'-free silica such as I.R. Vitreosil is usually produced in a partially reduced state and absorbs ultra-violet at 2425 Å. When heated in an oxidizing atmosphere the absorption is slowly reduced at a rate determined by the diffusion of oxygen through the solid. O.G. Vitreosil containing hydroxyl groups also has non-stoichiometric silica giving absorption at 2425 Å. This absorption is removed much more rapidly than with 'water'-free glass when the O.G. Vitreosil is heated in an oxidizing atmosphere or vacuum. It appears that the reduced silica with hydroxyl gives a reaction of the kind

$$Si^{3+}O^{2-}OH^- \rightleftharpoons Si^{4+}2O^{2-} + \tfrac{1}{2}H_2.$$

The diffusivities calculated for removal of the absorbing centres were of the same order as those for hydroxyl appearing in silica when heated in hydrogen. From this it was concluded that the oxidation rate was governed by the outward diffusion and removal of hydrogen.

Vacuum fusion. Moriya (1961) has investigated the properties of silica prepared by melting quartz powder in a molybdenum crucible at a gas pressure of 10^{-5} torr. Shown in Fig. 4.21 are infra red absorption spectra of 1 mm thick specimens of vacuum and flame melted silica specimens compared with that of the original quartz

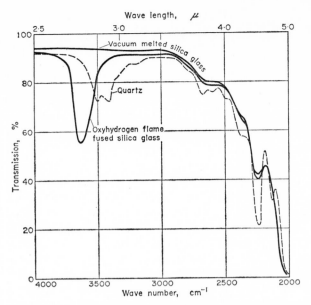

FIG. 4.21 INFRA RED TRANSMITTANCE OF QUARTZ, FLAME-FUSED SILICA AND VACUUM-MELTED SILICA; SPECIMENS 1 mm THICK (*After Moriya*, 1961)

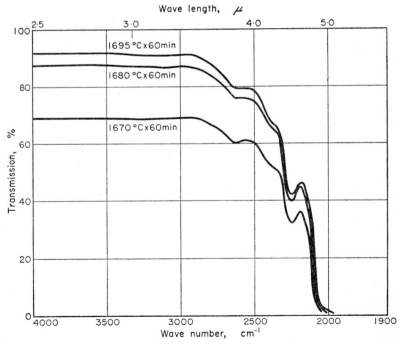

FIG. 4.22 INFRA RED TRANSMITTANCE OF SILICA AFTER MELTING AT DIFFERENT TEMPERATURES IN VACUUM; SPECIMENS 1 mm THICK (*After Moriya*, 1961)

material. The vacuum melted silica has no absorption band at about 3 μ. Shown in Fig. 4.22 is the effect on the transmission of silica of raising the vacuum melting temperature from 1670° to 1695°c. When the melting temperature was raised to 1745°c the silica was black in colour due to molybdenum and molybdenum oxide entering the melt. Water released from the quartz powder reacted with the molybdenum crucible producing volatile molybdenum oxide which became dispersed through the partially sintered quartz grains. The molybdenum oxide was then reduced by free hydrogen according to the reaction

$$Mo + 2H_2O \rightleftharpoons MoO_2 + 2H_2$$

When a small charge of silica is melted in vacuum in a tungsten or molybdenum crucible the silica is reduced by reacting with the crucible and tungsten or molybdenum oxides contaminate the silicon oxide. With a large melt such a reaction will probably be limited to the surface of the melt and the water vapour reaction noted by Moriya will be the principal source of contamination. Pre-heating the silica powder before melting to remove adsorbed water might reduce the risk of subsequent contamination by formation of molybdenum oxide. If silica is melted *in vacuo* in contact with carbon heating elements there is also an interfacial reaction producing a lower oxide of silicon, carbon oxide gas and silicon carbide.

4. PHYSICAL ADSORPTION

When an inert gas is in contact with a glass surface measurable adsorption only occurs when the glass is cooled to low temperature and the amount of inert gas adsorbed is not *permanently* removed from the atmosphere but is in *equilibrium* with the surrounding gas. In this case the heat of adsorption is of the same order as the latent heat of condensation. A gas which has some affinity for a glass may only be physically adsorbed if the valency forces of the glass surface have already been shielded by a chemisorbed layer. If water has been adsorbed by an alkaline glass before being exposed to a particular gas (*e.g.* CO_2) then the gas may be dissolved by an aqueous layer on the glass.

Most of the early adsorption studies of glass were done under conditions where the adsorbent surface if clean rapidly became covered with gas from the vacuum atmosphere before the adsorbate gas was admitted. (If every molecule arriving at a surface at a pressure of 10^{-6} torr sticks then a monolayer of, say, oxygen molecules would form in 1–2 sec.)

When physical adsorption occurs on a surface, then it follows from the discussion in Section 1 that surface coverage will tend to be complete as P_e/P_0 approaches unity, where P_e is the equilibrium pressure above the adsorbent and P_0 is the saturated vapour pressure of the adsorbate gas at the temperature of the system. Thus the amount of surface covered may be negligible if $P_e \ll P_0$. If the adsorbent temperature is sufficiently reduced the equilibrium (or saturated) pressure above a completed monolayer may be quite low. Thus the saturated vapour pressure of hydrogen has been given as $3 \cdot 5 \times 10^{-7}$ torr at $4 \cdot 2°K$.

Normal temperature. Langmuir (1918a) measured the amount of gas adsorbed by two hundred microscope cover-slides spaced apart to give an adsorbent area of 1966 cm². The glasses were cleaned with acids and baked to 300°c *in vacuo*. Adsorption was negligible at room temperature in the pressure range 0·03–0·1 torr for H_2, N_2, CO, A and CH_4; CO_2 was sorbed in a measurable quantity.

Under certain conditions a long period may be required for equilibrium to be reached when gas is introduced to an adsorbent. Bangham and Burt (1924) studied the sorption of gases by fine glass wool which had been acid cleaned, washed with distilled water and dried. The glass wool was degassed *in vacuo* at 200°c for several days using charcoal cooled with liquid air to remove the evolved vapours. It was found that the sorption of carbon dioxide observed at 0°c over periods of 50 hours obeyed the equation $S^x = kt$, where S^x was the mass sorbed at a time t and the index x was a function of the pressure in the range studied 4–650 torr; x had larger values at higher pressures. Similar results were obtained with several other gases. It would appear from the equation that there was no upper limit to the sorption indicating the protracted nature of the process.

After sorption had occurred Bangham and Burt reduced the pressure in the system in steps allowing 24 hours for equilibrium to be attained. They found that the quantity of gas sorbed was related to the corresponding pressure by the Freundlich equation $S^n = k'P_e$. Arranging the gases studied in order of increasing amount sorbed over the pressure range 10–400 torr the sequence was C_2H_2, N_2O, CO_2, SO_2 and NH_3. The index n also increased with the sorptive capacity. Apart from their practical value the results of early experiments of this kind are impossible to explain. The results indicate, as Bangham and Burt noted, that the amount of gas sorbed exceeded a monolayer in thickness. Further, there was a rough correlation between the amount of gas sorbed and the solubility of a gas in water. Certainly the glass wool would have been corroded by the cleaning and surface water inadequately removed by heating to 200°c. This was appreciated by Burt (1932) in a later paper.

Durau (1926) studied the adsorption of gases by powdered glass, which had been evacuated at 570°c for several days. Glass powder thoroughly degassed at 600°c gave off further gas at 740°c and still more at 1060°c. At each temperature the degassing rate fell to a negligible quantity. Powders which had been rigorously degassed did not measurably sorb N_2, H_2 or dry air at 18°c. Carbon dioxide was reversibly sorbed but only to the extent of 16% of a monomolecular layer at atmospheric pressure.

Low temperature. When the microscope slides used by Langmuir (1918a), described above, were cooled to 90°κ after cleaning and baking the amount of oxygen and argon adsorbed agreed with the 'hyperbolic' equation (given on p. 196)

$$q = \frac{aq_sP_\theta}{1 + aP_\theta}$$

The results for carbon monoxide did not yield a straight line when P_e/q was plotted against P_θ as expected from the 'hyperbolic' equation but they did satisfy the modified equation

$$q = q_1 + \frac{a_2q_sP_\theta}{a_2P_\theta}$$

where a_2 was a constant and q_s was the mass of gas adsorbed when the surface was covered.

The addition of the constant q_1 indicates that a quantity of gas is adsorbed which is not pressure dependent. Langmuir found that the adsorption of carbon monoxide occurred in two stages. At a carbon monoxide pressure of 10^{-3} torr a part of the glass surface became saturated with 6·6 mm³ N.T.P. of gas, but after raising the pressure to about 0·1 torr a further 16·2 mm³ N.T.P. of gas was adsorbed. When the pressure was reduced above the adsorbent 17·6 mm³ N.T.P. of the adsorbed carbon monoxide was released.

17

Thus 5·2 mm³ N.T.P. of gas was irreversibly adsorbed. A similar effect but to a lesser degree was noted with methane.

Langmuir showed that at 90°K the amount of gas adsorbed increased in the order O_2, A, N_2, CO, CH_4, whereas the boiling points of these gases increased in the order N_2, CO, A, O_2, CH_4.

Zeise (1928) extended Langmuir's experiments using a pile of one thousand microscope cover-slides separated by fibres of similar soft glass. The glasses were baked at 420°c for $2\frac{1}{2}$ hours and at a higher temperature for 1 hour whilst under vacuum. The isotherms

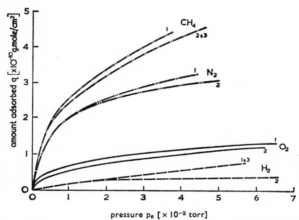

FIG. 4.23   ISOTHERMS FOR THE ADSORPTION OF DIFFERENT GASES ON GLASS MICROSCOPE COVER-SLIDES AT 90°K. THE NUMBERS ON THE CURVES REFER TO SEPARATE EXPERIMENTAL RUNS (*After Zeise*, 1928)

obtained for H_2, O_2, N_2 and CH_4 at 90°K are shown in Fig. 4.23; several experimental curves are given for each gas studied. At the highest value of P_e given the amount of methane adsorbed was 52% of that required to form a monolayer, 29 or 77% with nitrogen (depending on the calculation), 10 or 36% with oxygen and much less with hydrogen.

Zeise noted that for pressures between $2 \times 10^{-4} - 7 \times 10^{-2}$ torr for the gases studied the adsorption isotherm at 90°K followed the relation

$$q = \sqrt{\frac{k_1 k_2 P_e}{1 + k_2 P_e}}$$

The equation is near to that given in Section 1 for the case of gas molecules which are dissociated on adsorption. If the surface forces had been satisfied by chemisorption then it is difficult to believe that dissociation could occur when gases were physically adsorbed on the cooled glass. It is shown further on that recent work on the physical adsorption of nitrogen on glass does not indicate dissociation.

NITROGEN

Nitrogen appears to have negligible chemical affinity for silicate glasses and can only be adsorbed appreciably by van der Waals' forces.

Hobson (1959a, 1961a) has determined the nitrogen adsorption isotherm for Pyrex glass (Corning 7740) at temperatures from 63·3° to 90·2°K using the interior of a ½-litre flask as the adsorbing surface. At liquid nitrogen temperature (77·4°K) the surface coverage ranged from 0·001 to 0·3 of a monolayer for the pressure range 10^{-9}–10^{-3} torr. Measurements were made in an ultra-high vacuum plant exhausted by a mercury diffusion pump with liquid nitrogen traps. The vacuum system and Pyrex adsorption vessel were degassed by baking at 500°C for 12 hours; the vessel was not treated with solvents of any kind. Before taking measurements a pressure of 10^{-10} torr was obtained in the adsorption vessel with an ionization gauge operating as a sorption pump and with the mercury diffusion pump isolated. The background pressure was the result of the gauge pumping against the helium diffusing through the Pyrex envelope. Nitrogen was admitted to the cooled adsorbent vessel and the equilibrium pressure measured after adsorption had ceased. The flask was then warmed and the amount of nitrogen released measured from the pressure rise. The adsorption measured was therefore for *physically* bound gas as any chemisorbed gas would remain on the surface.

When adsorption measurements were made the Pyrex envelope was cooled in liquid nitrogen and the ionization gauge was used solely for pressure measurement and not for sorption pumping. The rate at which the helium pressure in the system increased under these conditions was separately determined so that the partial pressure of the nitrogen over the adsorbent could be found. The nitrogen pressure P above the cooled adsorbent differs from that P_1 measured by the gauge at room temperature and can be found from the relation

$$\frac{P}{P_1} = \sqrt{\frac{T}{T_1}} = \sqrt{\frac{77·4}{295}} = 0·512$$

which is applicable when the mean free path of the gas molecules exceeds the diameter of the gauge tubulation (Dushman, 1962).

The adsorption isotherm measured under the above conditions is shown in Fig. 4.24. The curve for 77·4°κ was taken with adsorbing areas of 32 and 60 cm² with the pressure increasing and decreasing. The ionization gauge was operated at different electron currents to prove that ion-pumping had a negligible effect on the results. The curve in Fig. 4.24 has practical as well as theoretical value, because it shows the behaviour of a glass cold trap in a ultra-high vacuum system.† If one takes 16·2 Å² as the area of a nitrogen molecule then

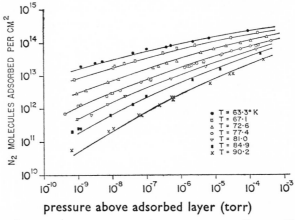

FIG. 4.24 ADSORPTION ISOTHERMS OF NITROGEN ON PYREX. POINTS ARE EXPERIMENTAL. LINES ARE CALCULATED FROM THE DUBININ–RADUSHKEVICH EQUATION (*After Hobson*, 1961a)

to cover one square centimetre of surface with a monolayer would require $6·2 \times 10^{-14}$ molecules. In Fig. 4.24 the fraction of the surface covered varies from 10^{-4} to 0·3. These calculations are based on the assumption that the sorbent surface is plane.

Given in Fig. 4.25 are experimental results of other workers for nitrogen physically adsorbed on different materials at temperatures near the boiling point of nitrogen; it should be noted that P is the pressure above the adsorbed layer and P_0 the saturated vapour pressure above liquid nitrogen at the same temperature, *i.e.* 760 torr at 77·4°κ.

Hobson found that for values of P/P_0 from 10^{-6} to 10^{-11} the

† The saturated vapour pressure of nitrogen has been reported as $2·2 \times 10^{-11}$ torr at 20°κ.

adsorption isotherms could be represented by an equation due to Dubinin and Radushkevich (1947), viz.

$$\log \sigma = \log \sigma_m - D \, [\log (P/P_0)]^2$$

where σ is the amount adsorbed (mol/cm^2), P/P_0 is the relative pressure, σ_m is a constant Kaganer (1957) has identified with the number of molecules in a monolayer, and $D = AT^2$ where A is a constant. Values of $\sigma_m = 6.4 \times 10^{14}$ and $A = 3.28 \times 10^{-6}$ gave a good

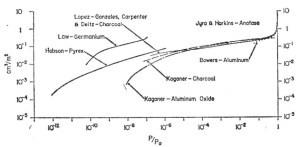

FIG. 4.25 COMPARISON OF EXPERIMENTAL RESULTS ON THE PHYSICAL ADSORPTION OF NITROGEN NEAR $T = 77.4°$K. THE VOLUME OF GAS ADSORBED cm^3/m IS AT N.T.P. (*After Hobson,* 1959a)

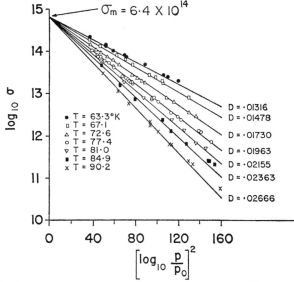

FIG. 4.26 ADSORPTION ISOTHERMS FOR NITROGEN ON PYREX IN THE CO-ORDINATES OF THE DUBININ–RADUSHKEVICH EQUATION (*After Hobson,* 1961a)

fit to the experimental data and were found by trial and error. Plotted in Fig. 4.26 are curves of $\log_{10} \sigma$ as a function of $(\log_{10} P/P_0)^2$ which fit the experimental values. The same equation constants were used to derive the curves in Fig. 4.24. Hobson (1961a) states that by assigning a small temperature variation to σ_m an even better fit to the measured values could be obtained.

Hobson concludes—

'(1) The adsorbing surface is nonporous and nearly flat. This conclusion rests on the absolute magnitude found for $\sigma_m = 6\cdot4 \times 10^{14}$, which is close to $6\cdot2 \times 10^{14}$ mol/cm^2 for nitrogen molecules in a monolayer.† The uncertainty in the absolute accuracy of the Bayard–Alpert (ionization) gauge was about $\pm 10\%$. Examination of the adsorption surface with an electron microscope using platinum-carbon replica techniques showed a rolling surface with an approximate periodicity less than 300 Å and a roughness factor less than about 1·4.

'(2) The appearance of the Dubinin–Radushkevich equation in the present context is surprising for two reasons. First, it is a particular equation within the Polanyi potential theory, which is a theory of condensation and might not be expected to apply to physical adsorption at very low coverage. Second, most of the adsorbents to which the Dubinin–Radushkevich equation have been applied (Kaganer 1957) have been porous, whereas our conclusion (1) above suggests that Pyrex is nonporous for nitrogen. Thus, unless and until a basic derivation for this equation is provided, it can only be considered as a useful empirical relation.'

There are certain inconclusive aspects of the above. For example, if nitrogen does not have appreciable chemical affinity for glass then the physically adsorbed gas will be mainly in contact with the glass components. However, there is evidence that separate domains (phases) may exist in Pyrex as shown in the introduction to this work and in chapter 3. If the adsorbent is chemically heterogeneous then the idea of a monolayer even on a plane surface may only extend to the calculation of the number of molecules per unit area, because in reality the nitrogen molecules during their lifetime on the surface form clusters in preferred regions.

Hobson and Armstrong (1961) have given the heat of adsorption of nitrogen on 'Pyrex' as 6·7 kcal/g mol at a fractional surface coverage of 10^{-3} falling to 4·3 kcal/g mol at 0·3.

---

† There has been some uncertainty in the cross-sectional area of a nitrogen molecule. A value of 16·2 Å^2 has been calculated from the density of liquid nitrogen and 13·8 Å^2 from the density of solid nitrogen. Livingstone (1949) has discussed these determinations and prefers a value of 15·4 Å^2.

HELIUM

The adsorption isotherm for helium on Pyrex (Corning 7740) has been measured by Hobson (1959b) at 4·2°K. Absorption measurements were made on surfaces with geometrical areas of 10–70 cm², using an ultra-high vacuum apparatus (as described above for nitrogen) over a pressure range of 10^{-4}–10^{-12} torr. The Pyrex absorber was cooled in liquid helium. Pressure measurements were made with Bayard–Alpert and Magnetron type ionization gauges. Only the Magnetron gauge was used for measuring pressures below 5×10^{-10} torr. The ionization gauge readings were corrected to give true helium pressure. The pressure P_1 measured by the gauge at room temperature T_1 was corrected to that of P at the absorbent temperature T using the relation

$$\frac{P}{P_1} = \sqrt{\frac{T}{T_1}} = \sqrt{\frac{4·2}{295}} = 0·119.$$

Shown in Fig. 4.27 are the number of atoms adsorbed per square centimetre of geometrical area as a function of the pressure above the adsorbent. Three distinct adsorption regions appear in the figure. These were explained as follows.

The limiting pressure of $1·5 \times 10^{-12}$, where the points lie almost vertically, is the lowest pressure recorded by the gauge due to helium diffusing into the vacuum system from the atmosphere. The helium is pumped by the adsorbent but due to its continuous flow there is a pressure drop in the system between the regions of entry and the adsorbent. It was assumed that at the limiting pressure the true pressure above the cooled adsorbent was negligible compared with that in the gauge arising from helium diffusion. The measured pressure values in Fig. 4.27 have therefore been corrected by subtracting the limiting pressure. The corrected values are represented by arrows and the points are shifted progressively less for higher pressures.

From $1·5 \times 10^{-12}$ to 5×10^{-10} torr the amount adsorbed is roughly proportional to the measured pressure. If the heat of adsorption is independent of coverage then this result is to be expected for a partial monolayer, but Hobson suspected that this part of the curve arose from the design and operation of the adsorption apparatus. Thus as the measurements were made the level of the liquid helium cooling the trap continuously decreased, releasing adsorbed gas. The desorbed helium was pumped by the remaining cooled surface of the adsorber and by the vacuum gauge.

Calculation of the rate of evolution of helium and the pumping speed indicated that the pressure measured in the system was the equilibrium value at which the desorbed gas was repumped. The calculation was made assuming that the true pressure above the adsorbed helium was negligible.

Pressures measured above 10^{-9} torr were considered to represent the true condition above the adsorbed layer.

Shown in Fig. 4.28 is a comparison made by Hobson of his results with those of other workers. Hobson concluded that no changes in slope are shown in the curves which can be interpreted as decisive evidence for the completion of the first adsorbed monolayer. Further, he believed that no authors to date had made true pressure measurements above a partial monolayer of helium on a solid adsorbent for $T = 4.2°$K. His experiments suggested the first adsorbed layer was complete at $P/P_0 \leqslant 10^{-12}$ and that the heat of adsorption in the first layer had a lower limit of 250 cal/g mol.

The curve for Keeson and Schweers (1941) was taken with pre-adsorbed gases on Thüringian glass. Hobson observed that Ne and H_2 preadsorbed on Thüringian glass reduced the heat of adsorption for the first He-layer so that the layer was complete at $P/P_0 > 10^{-5}$. With preadsorbed O_2 the first He-layer was complete at $P/P_0 < 10^{-7}$ and with preadsorbed N_2 at $P/P_0 < 10^{-9}$. Preadsorbed H_2, Ne, O_2 and N_2 lowered the heat of adsorption of helium on Thüringian glass in the same order as their permeabilities decrease (see Table 4.12; Norton, 1957). Hobson advanced the theory that if diffusion occurred through holes with surface sites then physical adsorption may occur on similar sites. Preadsorption would saturate the sites and lower the heat of adsorption.

In a later paper Hobson (1961*b*) stated that the adsorption isotherms for helium at $4.2°$K and argon at $77.4°$K were consistent with the Dubinin–Radushkevich equation previously given for nitrogen above. He therefore considered it permissible to extrapolate the measured results in Fig. 4.27, *i.e.* the region for $p > 10^{-9}$ torr, considered to be the true pressure above the adsorber; alternatively one could extrapolate the full curve in Fig. 4.28 to obtain values of P/P_0 lower than 10^{-12}.

Gomer, Wortman and Lundy (1957) have immersed the Pyrex bulbs of field emission microscopes in liquid helium to maintain low pressures. Cooling Pyrex reduces the helium diffusion rate (Rogers, Buritz and Alpert, 1954) and also makes the bulb serve as a sorption trap. Hobson (1961) calculated that if a Pyrex bulb with a volume of half a litre was exhausted to a pressure of 5×10^{-10} torr of helium gas then on immersion in liquid helium the number of atoms adsorbed would be about 3×10^7 per cm^2 and the pressure should fall to about 10^{-33} torr! Steele and Halsey (1955) have given the heat of adsorption of helium on porous glass as 680 cal/g mol. Hobson estimated that this would give a value of $P = 10^{-35}$ torr at $4 \cdot 2°$K. These pressures would be lower than that of interstellar gas.

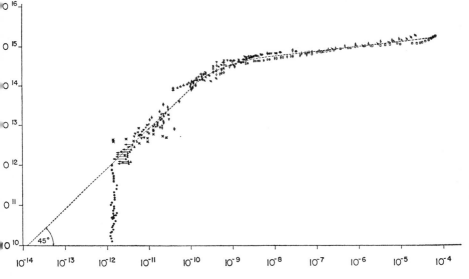

FIG. 4.27 ADSORPTION ISOTHERM FOR HELIUM ON PYREX AT $4 \cdot 2°$K. EACH SYMBOL REPRESENTS A DIFFERENT RUN. SOLID SYMBOLS ARE FOR PRESSURES MEASURED WITH A MAGNETRON GAUGE AND OPEN SYMBOLS FOR A BAYARD-ALPERT GAUGE (*After Hobson*, 1959b)

5. DIFFUSION AND PERMEATION OF GASES†

HELIUM

Silica and silicate glasses are measurably permeable to helium at all temperatures, and to hydrogen and other gases at high temperatures. Helium at a pressure of 760 torr permeates into a vacuum through a silica plate of 1 mm thickness at a rate of 10^{11} atoms per square centimetre per second at room temperature. Helium is present in the atmosphere in the proportion of one

† Symbols and equations referred to in this section are defined and discussed on p. 202.

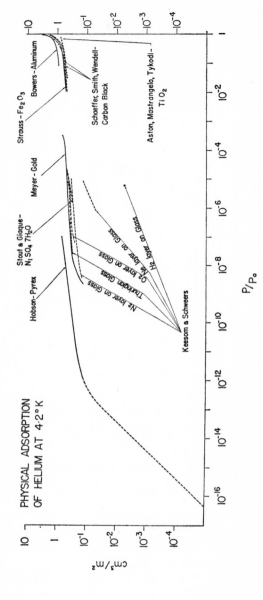

Fig. 4.28 Comparison of experimental results for the physical adsorption of helium at 4·2°k. The dotted part of Hobson's curve represents an upper bound on the pressures above the adsorbed layer. Extrapolation of the full curve for P/P_0 lower than 10^{-12} can be used for estimating surface coverage at low relative pressures (*After Hobson*, 1959b)

volume of helium to two hundred thousand volumes of air. Therefore, atmospheric helium will permeate a silica plate 1 mm thick at a rate of about 5×10^5 atoms $cm^{-2} sec^{-1}$. This permeation rate is several times higher than that of hydrogen and a hundred times greater than that of neon, the next gas in the scale. Helium has been purified by selective diffusion through silica (Watson, 1910) and 'Vycor' glass (Leiby and Chen, 1960).

The permeation of helium tends to set a lower limit to the ultimate pressure attainable in a glass vacuum system which has been thoroughly degassed by baking (Alpert, 1953). Cooling the glass envelope or surrounding the envelope with a continuously pumped guard vacuum are methods used to reduce helium permeation. Norton (1957) states that vacuum Dewar flasks lose their vacuum in a day or two after being used to store liquid helium.

Effect of glass composition. Helium permeates through glass less easily as its acid content decreases in favour of the basic content (Voorhis, 1924; Urry, 1932). Thus, the glass formers boron oxide and phosphorus pentoxide tend to raise the helium permeability of glass in a similar manner to silica. A smooth curve is obtained when values of the helium permeability are plotted as a function of the sum of the glass formers, viz. $SiO_2 + B_2O_3 + P_2O_5$, as shown in Fig. 4.29. The curve is drawn through values of K measured at 100°c by Norton (1953, 1957) using a mass-spectrometer. Also plotted on the same graph are values of K at 25°c determined by Garbe and Christians (1962) with an Omegatron type mass-spectrometer.†

---

† Since this chapter was written information has been published on two new types of glasses. These are the aluminosilicates (Corning 1720) and glass-ceramics (Corning 'Pyroceram'). The latter are crystalline ceramics prepared by heat-treating glasses containing nucleating agents. The Pyrocerams are not definite chemical compounds but can have a variety of compositions like glasses. Miller and Shepard (1961) have given the following values for the permeability in terms of $\dfrac{cm^3 \text{ N.T.P. mm}}{cm^2 \text{ sec (cm. Hg)}}$

	Air		Helium	
Temp °c	450	800	400	500
Pyroceram 9606	6.10^{-15}	6.10^{-14}	$1.5.10^{-9}$	3.10^{-9}
alumino-silicate 1720	4.10^{-16}	—	3.10^{-11}	$1.5.10^{-10}$

Lord Rayleigh (1937) found that the permeability of quartz for helium was immeasurably small and lower than that of silica by a factor of at least 10^{-6}.

Effect of Temperature. The permeation of helium through glasses is an activated process as shown by its dependence on temperature for a range of glasses in Fig. 4.30 after Norton.

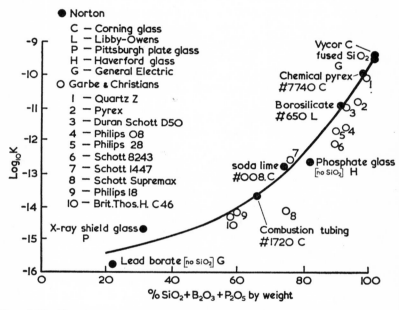

FIG. 4.29   RATE OF PERMEATION OF HELIUM THROUGH VARIOUS GLASSES AS A FUNCTION OF THE TOTAL PERCENTAGE AMOUNTS OF $SiO_2 + B_2O_3 + P_2O_5$. THE CURVE WAS DETERMINED BY NORTON (1957) AT $100°C$. ALSO PLOTTED ARE PERMEABILITIES MEASURED AT $25°C$ BY GARBE AND CHRISTIANS (1962).

$$K \text{ IS IN UNITS OF } \frac{(cm^3 \text{N.T.P.) mm}}{cm^2 \text{ sec (cm Hg)}}$$

Smith and Taylor (1940) found that the permeation rate of helium through four different types of glass at temperatures between $300°–500°C$ depended in each case on the previous heat treatment of the glass. Also a plot of log K versus $1/T$ was only linear over part of the temperature range. Heat treatment raised the permeability of two kinds of borosilicate glasses and lowered it for a lead oxide glass. The activation energies measured for the different glasses were: stabilized Pyrex (7740) 7·1 kcal/g atom; boro-silicate (29% B_2O_3) 8·1–9·2 kcal/g atom; lead oxide (23% PbO) < 410°c 9·9 kcal/g atom, > 410°c 18·1 kcal/g atom; soda-lime (17% Na_2O) the activation energy was not constant from 421° to 478°c but at 421°c equalled 5·1 kcal/g atom. The foregoing activation energies have been plotted in Fig. 4.31 together with values derived by Norton, from Fig. 4.30, as a function of the percentage content

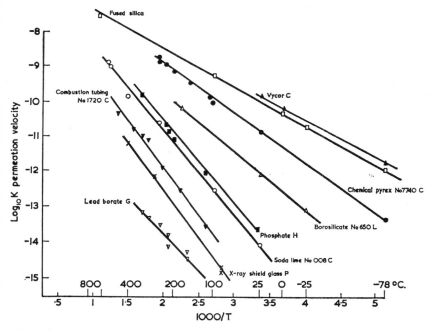

FIG. 4.30   RATE OF PERMEATION OF HELIUM THROUGH VARIOUS GLASSES AS A FUNCTION OF THE RECIPROCAL OF THE TEMPERATURE. (*After Norton,* 1957)

$$\text{K IS IN UNITS OF } \frac{(cm^3 \text{N.T.P.}) \text{ mm}}{cm^2 \text{ sec (cm Hg)}}$$

of glass-forming oxides. Although there is poor agreement between the plotted values the graph shows that the activation energy decreases as the acid content of a glass rises.

PERMEATION CONSTANTS OF SILICA

The permeability of helium in fused silica has been measured by several workers with good agreement. A thorough analysis of the results of past investigators has been made by Swets *et al.* (1961), who also determined the diffusion constants and permeation rates in the temperature range 24°–1034°c. A hollow cylinder made of silica was surrounded with helium and permeation of gas into the inner vessel determined with a mass spectrometer. Permeation rates were measured under a stationary state of flow. The diffusion coefficients were determined from the time lag for helium to appear

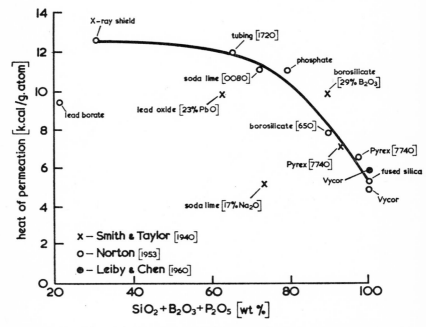

FIG. 4.31 ACTIVATION ENERGIES FOR HELIUM PERMEATING DIFFERENT GLASSES

in the inner vessel after diffusion had commenced and also from the decay curve obtained when helium was removed from the outer vessel. The solubility was calculated from the relation $K = DS$ (see p. 206).

Permeability. The permeability of helium in silica measured by Swets *et al.* and others as a function of temperature is plotted in Fig. 4.33; permeability values reported by Barrer (1934) are not included because they are much lower than those given in the graph. The solid curves in the figures are the *least mean square lines* calculated by Swets *et al.* from their experimental points. The dotted lines are the 95% confidence limits on the solid curves.

Some tests were made to establish the relationship between the permeation rate and pressure at temperatures above 300°c. It was found that the permeation rate could be expressed as $q = KP^n$ where P was the pressure and n varied from 0·93 to 0·97.

The diffusion constant had one of two values depending on the temperature range. In the temperature range 24°–300°c it followed the relation

$$D = 3\cdot04 \times 10^{-4} \exp\left(\frac{-5580 \pm 56 \text{ cal/g atom}}{RT}\right) \text{ cm}^2/\text{sec}$$

and in the temperature range 300°–1034°c

$$D = 7\cdot40 \times 10^{-4} \exp\left(\frac{-6613 \pm 40 \text{ cal/g atom}}{RT}\right) \text{ cm}^2/\text{sec}$$

Values of the diffusion constant were obtained with two specimens of silica of different thickness. The results were in excellent agreement, indicating that D was independent of thickness.

The solubility of helium in silica at a pressure of 760 torr determined by Swets *et al.* and others as a function of temperature is plotted in Fig. 4.32; the plotted values are in good agreement. In the lower temperature range the equation for the line is

$$S = 1\cdot99 \times 10^{17} \exp\left(-\frac{680 \pm 60 \text{ cal/g atom}}{RT}\right)$$

$$\text{atoms cm}^{-3} (760 \text{ torr})^{-1}$$

and in the high temperature range

$$S = 1\cdot28 \times 10^{17} \exp\left(-\frac{1174 \pm 120 \text{ cal/g atom}}{RT}\right)$$

$$\text{atoms cm}^{-3} (760 \text{ torr})^{-1}$$

Leiby and Chen (1960) have determined the permeation constants for helium in Vycor glass and their results are given in Table 4.9. It should be noted that the values for the diffusion constant and permeability at 26°C are higher than what would be expected for activated diffusion, whereas the solubility at 26°c is one half of that at 100°c. The solubility of helium in fused silica rises as the temperature approaches ambient (Fig. 4.32). One concludes that Vycor must contain flaws in its structure permitting

Table 4.9

Permeation constants for helium in Vycor glass
(After Leiby and Chen, 1960)

$T(^\circ c)$	$K\left(\dfrac{cm^3\ N.T.P.\ mm}{cm^2\ sec\ (cmHg)}\right)$	$T(^\circ c)$	$D(cm^2/sec)$	$S\left(\dfrac{cm^3\ N.T.P.}{(cm^3\ SiO_2)\ cmHg}\right)$
26	$4\cdot74 \times 10^{-12}$	26	$6\cdot3\ \times 10^{-8}$	$5\cdot7 \times 10^{-5}$
100	$2\cdot03 \times 10^{-11}$	26	$5\cdot9\ \times 10^{-8}$	$6\cdot1 \times 10^{-5}$
200	$1\cdot15 \times 10^{-10}$	100	$1\cdot26 \times 10^{-7}$	$1\cdot2 \times 10^{-4}$
300	$2\cdot98 \times 10^{-10}$			
400	$6\cdot26 \times 10^{-10}$			
450	$9\cdot05 \times 10^{-10}$			
455	$1\cdot06 \times 10^{-9}$			

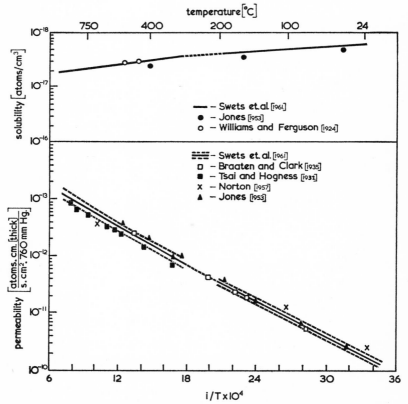

FIG. 4.32 PERMEABILITY AND SOLUBILITY OF HELIUM IN SILICA GLASS
(Swets et al., 1961).

non-activated flow of helium. Thus the permeation rate probably comprises two terms, one activated and one non-activated. Vycor is made by acid leaching a sodium borosilicate and sintering the porous silica body obtained. Thus one would not expect the silica to have the compactness of structure of the *fused* material.

PERMEATION CONSTANTS OF H_2, Ne, N_2 AND A

It has already been explained in Section 3 that hydroxyl groups are formed in silica that is heated in hydrogen. It is believed that hydrogen enters glass in molecular form and reacts with oxygen in the silica network to form hydroxyl (Bell *et al.*, 1962). Thus it is improbable that flow of hydrogen through glass will be a physical process. Further, values for the solubility of hydrogen in silica may really refer to hydroxyl. Shown in Table 4.10 are reported values of the permeability of hydrogen in silica compiled by Bell *et al.*, together with their own measured values.

Table 4.10

Permeability of 'hydrogen' in vitreous silica, cm³ N.T.P. mm sec⁻¹ cm⁻² cm Hg⁻¹†

	600°	700°	800°	900°	1000°c
Barrer (1941)	14	25	43	64	100×10^{-10}
Norton (1953)	13	21	—	—	100×10^{-10}
Altemose (1961)	23	[39]	[71]	—	100×10^{-10}
Bell *et al.* (1962)	31	73	138	271	442×10^{-10}

† Compiled by Bell *et al.*

Wüstner (1915) and Williams and Ferguson (1922) reported that the rate of permeation of hydrogen through silica was proportional to pressure. However, the solubility of hydrogen in terms of hydroxyl concentration is proportional to the square root of pressure. Possibly the rate at which adsorbed hydrogen enters the dissolved phase is of a similar order to its rate of flow through the silica so that the concentration of hydrogen within the silica surface does not reach equilibrium during steady state of flow. Also, a linear dependence of flow rate on pressure suggests that the hydrogen does not dissociate at the surface. It is impossible to believe that hydrogen could dissociate at a glass surface without forming OH⁻groups and it is shown in Table 4.8 that hydroxyl has a much lower diffusion constant than hydrogen.

18

Values of the permeabilities for neon, nitrogen and argon in silica together with some results for Vycor glass are given in Table 4.11; all of the gases have been reported as giving a rate of permeation proportional to pressure. It can be seen that the permeability of argon is very low and decreases to a negligible quantity if the silica is heat-treated (Barrer, 1934). Table 4.12, prepared by Norton (1957), shows the relation between the rate of permeation of different gases and their atomic or molecular diameter.

Table 4.11

Permeability of neon, nitrogen and argon in fused silica

Temperature (°c)	Permeability $\left[\times 10^{-9} \dfrac{cm^3 \text{ N.T.P. mm}}{cm^2 \text{ sec [cmHg]}} \right]$		
	Neon†	Nitrogen‡	Argon‡
400	0·0065 (Vycor)§	$8·3 \times 10^{-5}$ (Vycor)	—
450	0·012 (Vycor)	—	—
500	0·139‡	—	—
550	—	—	—
600	0·282	—	—
650	—	0·066	—
700	0·50	0·146	—
750	—	0·271 [0·161]	—
800	0·81	0·39	—
850	—	0·64	0·0161
900	1·18	0·95	
950	—	1·44 [0·65]	$\begin{cases} 0·062{-}0·031 \\ [0·00022] \end{cases}$
1000	1·63	—	[0·00050]

† T'sai and Hogness (1932).
‡ Barrer (1934) values in brackets obtained after prolonged heating of silica specimen.
§ Leiby and Chen (1960) note Vycor has a lower density than fused silica being a sintered body.

Table 4.12

Relation between rate of permeation of gases through silica glass
at 700°c and their molecular dimensions
(*After Norton, 1957*)

Gas	Permeation rate, K,† at 700°c	Atomic or molecular diameter (Å)
Helium	$2·1 \times 10^{-8}$	1·95
Hydrogen	$2·1 \times 10^{-9}$	2·5
Deuterium	$1·7 \times 10^{-9}$	2·55
Neon	$4·2 \times 10^{-10}$	2·4
Argon	Under 10^{-15}	3·15
Oxygen	Under 10^{-15}	3·2
Nitrogen	Under 10^{-15}	3·4

† cm³ N.T.P. mm thickness, sec⁻¹, cm⁻² area, cm⁻¹ Hg ΔP.

NATURE OF DIFFUSION

Several theories have been advanced to explain the high rate of permeation of helium through silica and glasses with a large silica content. Vitreous silica has a less closely packed structure ($\rho =$ 2·20 g/cm^3) than quartz ($\rho = 2 \cdot 65$ g/cm^3) and as the latter is almost impermeable to helium this suggests that helium flows through the more extended silica structure. The presence of large cations such as those of sodium in silicate glasses helps to fill discontinuities in the silica network and thereby obstruct the flow of helium atoms.

If helium in the gas phase effused through pores in the silica structure then such a mechanism would require the permeation rate to be proportional to the square root of the absolute temperature. This would be in contradiction to the experimental results given above where log K is proportional to $1/T$. However, it is clear that Vycor glass with a higher helium permeability than silica does show non-activated diffusion at low temperatures. Also, curves of log K versus $1/T$ for permeation of helium and hydrogen in silica and silicate glasses have shown that for small values of T the permeation rate is higher than would be expected.

Alty (1933) suggested that gas molecules entered glass directly from the gas phase and diffused along cracks into the body obeying the Lennard–Jones equation for surface diffusion. Such a process would not explain the activated diffusion of helium in silica at temperatures above about 100°c, as discussed in the previous section. Barrer (1934) found that the permeation rate of air decreased after prolonged heating of silica, but it did not affect the permeation rates of hydrogen and helium. He concluded that diffusion of nitrogen, argon and air predominately occurred down faults and cracks of molecular dimensions in the silica, but hydrogen and helium diffused through the silica lattice.

McAfee (1958) has studied the effect of stress on the diffusion constant for helium in Pyrex (7740) glass. He found that when the Pyrex glass was submitted to a tensile stress the diffusion constant was unchanged until the stress became about one-half of the breaking stress of the glass. Beyond this point the diffusion constant increased until under a large stress it was ten times its normal value. No apparent change was produced in the glass and reducing the stress gave the same diffusion constant as previously showing that the effect was reversible. Even larger compressional stresses on the same glass specimen had almost no effect on the diffusion constant.

A further investigation was made to find the effect of a shear stress on the diffusion constant of helium in glass. A disc of glass (7052) 0·005 in. thick had a torque applied to one of its faces by a metal rod sealed to the centre of the glass. Shear strains up to $\gamma = 4 \times 10^{-3}$ did not alter the diffusion constant appreciably. Shear stresses in the glass ranging from 0 to $5·7 \times 10^5$ g/cm^2 only raised the diffusion constant at 30°c from $10·9 \times 10^{-9}$ to $12·5 \times 10^{-9}$ cm^2/sec, which was not much above the experimental error. It was concluded that only tension produces large changes in the helium flow by reversible opening of submicroscopic fissures in the random glass network.

Swets *et al.* observed a change in the activation energy for diffusion of helium in silica as the temperature was raised above 300°c and wondered whether this arose from short range ordering in the glass as discussed on p. 8. They reasoned that the activation energy[†] for the diffusion of impurities in a crystalline lattice is considered to be the energy required for an impurity atom to jump from one interstitial site to another. If the structure of silica corresponds to a random array of the basic tetrahedra then the measured activation energy for diffusion would be an average of all possible 'jumping' energies. Although vitreous silica does not exhibit the presence of inversion points in the volume versus temperature curve the crystalline forms of silica do. Cristobalite and tridymite show pronounced inversions in the temperature range of 160°c to 280°c. There are also inversions in the birefringency in this temperature range. Swets *et al.* conclude that fused quartz may in some subtle way retain some of the properties of cristobalite and this is responsible for the change in the activation energy for helium diffusion in the region of 300°c.

There is conflicting evidence about the relationship between the permeation rate of helium and pressure. Taylor and Rast (1938) found that the rate of flow of helium through Pyrex into a vacuum was proportional to the pressure on the high pressure side. Urry (1932) observed that the permeation rate of helium through a range of glasses obeyed the relation $q \propto P^n$ where $n = 0·88$ for Pyrex glass; $n = 0·56$ for lead oxide glass; $n = 0·64$ for soda-lime glass and $n = 0·66$ for Jena 16 glass. Swets *et al.* found that n was between 0·93–0·97 for helium flowing through silica.

---

† When E_k is derived from sorption phenomena it must include a term for the solution.

The relation $q \propto P^{1/2}$ is normally characteristic of gases which dissociate on entering a sorbent, but this is not possible with helium. Barrer (1951) states that the only other explanations are

(1) helium enters glass from an adsorbed phase which does not obey a distribution law $x = kP$, where x denotes the amount adsorbed. He considered that helium should, at room temperature, be adsorbed according to Henry's law $(x = kP)$ and
(2) irreversible changes occur in the structure of the glass.

Another possibility is that the surface sites for diffusion became filled.

6. SORPTION PROCESSES IN IONIZED AND ACTIVE GASES

CLEAN-UP IN LOW PRESSURE DISCHARGES

Sputtering. When a glow discharge is passed at low gas pressures in a glass envelope the pressure usually rises at first as gas is liberated from the metal electrodes and glass vessel. As the glow discharge continues the pressure gradually decreases and falls below its initial value. Positive gas ions are sorbed by the metal cathode and the glass envelope. Gas molecules are also trapped in metal films sputtered on to the envelope from the cathode. Plücker (1858) observed that the pressure in a Geissler tube was reduced during the passage of the glow discharge. Willows (1901) and Hill (1912) found that gas was sorbed during the passage of an electrodeless high frequency discharge in a glass vessel. Swinton (1907, 1908) observed that the inner surface of a vacuum tube exposed to electron bombardment became roughened and upon heating the glass with a blow-pipe minute bubbles of hydrogen were formed in the glass; the effect also occurred with electrodeless discharges.

Several investigators have observed that electrodeless discharges in glass vessels produce optically absorbing deposits on the chamber walls and it is possible that part of the gas sorbed in an electrodeless discharge is trapped within a film sputtered from the glass. A glass wall exposed to a glow discharge usually becomes negatively charged because the electrons in the discharge have a higher mobility than the positive ions. Positive ions may then be accelerated to the wall where they can sputter components of the glass and enter the glass structure. The writer (1958) has observed that sodium is readily sputtered from soda-lime glass bombarded by positive ions with low energies; this and other effects of sputtering glass with positive ions are discussed in Chapter 5. Most workers have found that soda-lime glass is more effective than potash-lime or lead oxide glass in cleaning-up gas.

Ions trapped in glass. When argon is mixed with neon in glow discharge lamps or sodium lamps then the argon can be selectively sorbed by the glass envelope. Argon removal during normal operation of the discharge can be prevented by running a discharge in argon to saturate the glass before finally filling the lamp (Verweis and Weijer, 1959).

Jěch (1956) observed that radioactive radon or Xenon-131 is taken up by a glass surface when the gas is ionized in a low pressure discharge by a high frequency supply. Covering the glass with a single monolayer of calcium stearate about 25 Å thick is sufficient markedly to reduce the sorption. The radioactive gas penetrates the glass to a depth of about 200 Å and can be released by etching with hydrofluoric acid. Grinding the surface with carborundum or etching with HF reduces the amount of gas subsequently sorbed.

Jěch (1958) showed in a later paper that five monolayers (125 Å) of calcium stearate on glass were sufficient to prevent radon being taken up from an electrodeless discharge.

Helium has a high permeation rate in silica and borosilicate glass so its positive ions are not likely to be trapped in these glasses. However, there is evidence that helium ions can be trapped on glass surfaces covered with metallic coatings.

Gaseous impurities. When electrical discharges are passed in gases in the presence of a chemical sorbent, *e.g.* evaporated metal film, gas may be taken up at an increased rate. Some have attributed the effect to the production of active or atomic species in the gas and this undoubtedly could occur with hydrogen. The writer has drawn attention to the possibility of atomic hydrogen or nitrogen entering porous sorbents more readily than diatomic molecules when the pore size approaches molecular dimensions. However, the effect may arise from a different cause if impurities such as hydrocarbon vapours, which are poorly sorbed, are present in the residual gas. The ionization can then dissociate the impurity molecules permitting their constituents to be sorbed. This gives the impression that ionization is enhancing the sorption rate of the gas being studied. A hot filament in an electronic device can also promote dissociation.

Hydrogen. Langmuir (1912, 1915) observed that hydrogen was dissociated when it struck a heated tungsten filament at a temperature above 1000°c. He found that the atomic hydrogen was sorbed by the glass bulb of an incandescent lamp which had been degassed at a temperature above 360°c. (Clean-up for nitrogen occurred at a filament temperature of 1900°c. Methane was dissociated by a hot tungsten filament with the carbon being taken up by the tungsten and the hydrogen released.) When a lamp bulb had sorbed 35 mm^3 N.T.P. of hydrogen only 4 mm^3 N.T.P. of gas was recovered after heating the bulb to 115°c. Cooling the bulb to 80°K gave surface coverages of $1 \cdot 5 \times 10^{15}$ atoms-H/cm^2. On warming to room temperature about half of the adsorbed hydrogen atoms recombined whilst the rest were evolved on further heating. This topic is discussed further on p. 282.

Johnson (1929) found that hydrogen was readily taken up when exposed to an electrodeless discharge in a glass vessel which had been baked at 200°c *in vacuo*. The quantity of hydrogen sorbed was sufficient to form $0 \cdot 3$–$0 \cdot 6$ of a monolayer having a heat of adsorption of about 11 kcal/g mol. It is possible that the hydrogen was dissociated by the discharge and occupied sites similar to Na-ions. Dry hydrogen is not dissociated to a measurable degree in a low pressure discharge operated at moderate power input (Finch, 1949), but can be detected at a high power input of several hundred watts in a small tube (Coffin, 1959).

CLEAN-UP IN IONIZATION GAUGES

Sorption processes. The glass walls of an ionization vacuum gauge with a hot cathode emitter are exposed to electron bombardment and normally assume a negative potential because the secondary electron emission is less than unity at the anode potential commonly used ($\simeq 200$ V). Positive ions are attracted to the negatively charged wall and neutralization of the surface charge is quickly destroyed by the intense electron stream. Schwarz (1940, 1943) has reported that glass is more efficient than metals for absorbing positive gas ions. Alpert (1953) has used these sorption techniques for attaining pressures of 10^{-9} to 10^{-11} torr termed 'ultra-high vacuum'. The pumping action of the glass walls of an ionization gauge has been confirmed by Young (1956). Comsa and Musa (1957) have described an ionization pump with a hot cathode and anode grid in which only the glass envelope serves as the positive ion collector.

Some difficulty has been experienced in attributing the clean-up of helium in ionization gauges to absorption by the glass envelope because of the readiness with which helium permeates glass. Varnerin and Carmichael (1955) found that helium ions were trapped in a metal deposit which had evaporated from the metal electrodes on to the gauge wall during the degassing cycle. Helium is not dissolved by metals so presumably the gas is sorbed by helium ions bombarding the metal coated glass.

Glass surface potential. According to Carter and Leck (1959) the surface potential of a glass envelope used with a hot cathode ionization gauge of the Bayard–Alpert type may be zero or positive with respect to the cathode. Secondary electron emission from heat-treated and contaminated glass surfaces is discussed in Chapter 9, where the bistable operation of the Bayard–Alpert gauge is also considered. The surface potential of a glass ionization gauge can influence the accuracy of the pressure readings and the pumping action of the gauge. Thus clean-up of positive ions cannot occur if the surface potential approaches that of the electron collector. Likewise, if the secondary emission ratio is high (positive surface potential) then secondary electrons will flow to the anode grid and be falsely counted as part of the electrons producing ionization. Cobic *et al.* (1961) found that the inner wall of a Bayard–Alpert gauge which had been thoroughly degassed by baking always stabilized at cathode potential for pressures in the range 10^{-9}–10^{-4} torr and electron acceleration potentials below 250 V. (An electron accelerating voltage of 250 V was also the optimum value for the highest ionization efficiency.) When the anode potential was increased above 250 V with a low emission current ($\frac{1}{4}$ mA) then the wall potential became unstable and possibly increased to the anode value. The effect was pressure dependent, with instability occurring at electron collector potentials of about 385 V at 3×10^{-7} torr and 320 V at 10^{-5} torr.

Ionization gauges have been used by several workers for studying ion-pumping by the glass envelopes. The measured sorption rates thereby obtained are of practical value to vacuum physicists but it is often difficult to be certain of either the source of the sorption or of its mechanism. Gas can be sorbed in an ionization gauge by gas ions striking and becoming embedded in the collector electrode, glass envelope and in a metal film deposited on the glass walls during degassing. Chemically active gas can also be sorbed by forming surface compounds on the metal electrodes, glass wall or evaporated metal deposit. Finally, gas may be dissolved in the gauge components. If the mechanism of ion pumping by glass is to be studied then it can hardly be done satisfactorily in the presence of so many other sorption processes and without reasonable knowledge of the energy of the impinging gas ions.

Argon. Blodgett and Vanderslice (1961) studied the sorption of argon ions in Bayard–Alpert ionization gauges with different types of glass envelope. The filament potential was +30v, the grid +180v and the axial ion collector grounded. The inner surface of the glass was shielded to keep it clean during degassing. It was found that the rate of pressure fall (or 'clean-up') during ion pumping increased in the following order: Pyrex, Nonex, FN, Corning 7040 BA, Corning 7056. This is in reverse order to the diffusion rate of helium in these glasses.

When an equilibrium pressure is reached the number of ions entering the glass is balanced by the number diffusing out. The number diffusing out is a function of the number of atoms in the glass and the distribution of their concentration. Blodgett and Vanderslice found that at equilibrium the rate of recovery of atoms after a time t was proportional to $n_0 t^{1/2}$ where n_0 was the total number of atoms sorbed. The diffusion energy for argon recovery was about 3 kcal/g mol, which was low compared with a value of 42 kcal/g mol reported by Reynolds (1957) for argon diffusion in potash-lime silica. From the foregoing it was concluded that ion bombardment had altered the structure of a layer on the glass surface within which argon had a low diffusion energy and a uniform concentration at saturation.

Nitrogen. Hobson (1961*c*) has measured the pumping speed for nitrogen of a typical Bayard–Alpert ionization gauge in the pressure region 10^{-9}–10^{-7} torr using an ultra-high vacuum system. Nitrogen was admitted to the gauge after bake-out and attainment of an ultimate pressure of 10^{-10} torr or lower. The highest pumping speed determined after bake-out was about 1 litre/sec for a new gauge and about 0·1 litre/sec for a degassed gauge that had previously pumped some 10^{17} molecules. These sorption rates were mainly due to chemical pumping. After some 10^{15} molecules of nitrogen had been pumped the chemical sorption rate decayed leaving an ion-pumping speed of about 0·25 litre/sec, *i.e.* with an electron current of 8 mA; ion collector zero potential; electron collector grid $+300$ V; filament $+45$V. The ion-pumping speed was roughly constant until nearly 10^{17} molecules had been sorbed, and then the pumping speed fell sharply. The re-emission probability of nitrogen molecules after chemical pumping was $< 10^{-6}$ molecule^{-1} sec^{-1} and 1 hour after ion-pumping between 10^{-5} to 10^{-6} molecule^{-1} sec^{-1}. Hobson concludes that most of the chemically sorbed gas was taken up by the clean metal electrodes.

Carter *et al.* (1962) recently studied the sorption of spectroscopically pure nitrogen in a diode pump of the Comsa–Musa type which had been baked at 400°c under vacuum. The ultimate pressure of the pump was 10^{-8} torr. The pump was operated in a constantly flowing stream of gas at a pressure of 10^{-4} torr. Gas which had been sorbed after bake-out and operation of the ionization system could be released by heating the pump to about 350°c. When the temperature of the pump was raised to remove the sorbed gases a peak was obtained in the desorption rate curve at about 180°c. (A desorption peak was also found at 180°c for a number of other sorbed gases, viz. H_2, He, Ne, A, Kr and Xe.)

Nitrogen is only chemisorbed by glass to a negligible degree and Carter *et al.*, attribute its high sorption rate in ionization gauges to the formation of active nitrogen which is chemisorbed by the glass. They consider that in the ionized atmosphere dissociation may occur in the gas phase or by dissociation of N_2^+ ions and N_2^* metastable molecules on the glass surface. It is of interest that nitrogen begins to be sorbed in an ionization gauge when the electron accelerating potential reaches only 8 eV (Jaeckel and Teloy, 1960) which is less than that required to form atomic nitrogen in the gas phase (9·76 eV).

Interaction of atomic hydrogen with glass

The formation of atomic hydrogen (by an incandescent tungsten filament or in a glow discharge) and its clean-up by glass has already been discussed above. Hickmott (1960) has investigated the clean-up of atomic hydrogen by Pyrex glass, using an ultra-high vacuum apparatus. Atomic hydrogen was produced with a tungsten filament inside a Pyrex vessel which had a geometrical area of 255 cm². A gas pressure of 2×10^{-10} torr could be obtained before admitting hydrogen. Pressures were measured with a Bayard–Alpert ionization gauge fitted with a tantalum cathode coated with lanthanum boride, which had a lower emission temperature ($\simeq 800°$c) than tungsten and therefore produced less atomic hydrogen.

The gas atmosphere was analysed with an 'Omegatron' mass-spectrometer and analysed reagent grade hydrogen used for leaking into the adsorbent vessel. During bake-out of the system the chief gas liberated was water followed by carbon oxides. After bake-out these were the only two gases present and they were barely detectable. When hydrogen was admitted at a pressure of 4×10^{-7} torr the atomic hydrogen formed by the hot tungsten filament ($730°$–$1700°$c) reacted in the system forming CO, H_2O and CH_4. Carbon monoxide was the chief gas present and its concentration in the residual atmosphere rose with increase in the tungsten temperature. The production of the contaminant gases was greatest where the atomic hydrogen could impinge on the glass walls of the system. It was concluded that atomic hydrogen reacted with the metal oxides in the glass releasing water which dissociated on the hot tungsten filament. The tungsten contained carbon as an impurity which reacted with the oxygen from the water to produce carbon monoxide.

A study was made of the number of hydrogen atoms bound to Pyrex glass at normal temperature and at $77°$k. The Pyrex was degassed at $250°$c before each test. There appeared to be two distinct binding sites on Pyrex that were occupied simultaneously at low temperatures and had roughly equal populations, even at low surface coverages. At a sorbent temperature of $77°$k and a tungsten filament temperature of $1460°$k the number of hydrogen molecules adsorbed as atoms after 50 min was $2 \cdot 5 \times 10^{13}$ cm^{-2} (assuming a plane adsorbing surface). About half of the adsorbed hydrogen atoms were desorbed as molecules at room temperature and the remainder at $525°$k. When hydrogen was adsorbed at $300°$k with the filament at $1460°$k the number of molecules sorbed as atoms was $1 \cdot 4 \times 10^{13}$ cm^{-2} and about two-thirds of the sorbed atoms were released as molecules at $525°$k.

EMISSION OF GLASS COMPONENTS

Bills and Evett (1959) have noted that sodium and potassium are liberated from Pyrex (Corning 7740) and Nonex (7720) glasses either by heating the glass to above $350°$c *in vacuo* or by bombarding the glass with low energy gas ions. They found that particles of glass containing sodium and potassium were deposited on a tungsten filament if glassware was baked at $350°$c near the filament.

When the tungsten filament was slowly raised in temperature K$^+$ions were liberated at 765°c and Na$^+$ions at 815°c (Fig. 4.33(A)). Ions were not emitted at these temperatures if the glass was not heated. If the glass was maintained at a high temperature whilst the filament was hot ions were emitted in transient bursts from the filament at random intervals. Presumably large aggregates of glass containing up to a thousand alkali ions struck the filament during bake-out. The existence of particles emitted by Pyrex during thermal degassing

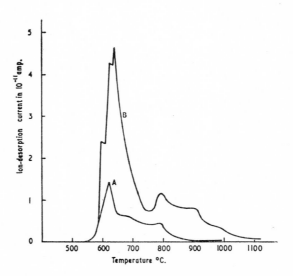

FIG. 4.33 POSITIVE ION DESORPTION CURRENT VERSUS FILAMENT TEMPERA-TURE OBTAINED AFTER EXPOSING A TUNGSTEN FILAMENT TO: A—HOT PYREX GLASS AND B—SPUTTERED COMPONENTS OF PYREX (*Bills and Evett*, 1959)

has recently been shown in electron micrographs prepared by Donaldson (1962) as in Plate 19.

When the glass was exposed to bombardment by positive gas ions formed by 18 eV-electrons the amount of sodium and potassium deposited on an adjacent filament was enhanced (Fig. 4.33(B)).

ELECTRON BOMBARDMENT OUTGASSING

Todd *et al.* (1960) have measured after bake-out in vacuum the amount of gas released from glass when bombarded with an electron beam which scanned the target as in a cathode ray tube. The beam current was 200 μA and the electron accelerating potential 20 kV. To prevent the glass surface acquiring a negative charge which diminished the electron current the glass was coated with an evaporated aluminium film 100 Å thick. Calculation showed that 96% of the incident electrons passed through the metal film with an average energy of 19·7 keV after transmission. When the aluminium film was deposited directly on the glass the gas evolved by electron bombardment was trapped under the metal coating and escaped from blisters in the aluminium film. To prevent gas being trapped the aluminium was deposited on a nitrocellulose film applied to the glass. The nitrocellulose film was removed by baking, leaving behind a loosely adherent and porous metal deposit. Using the same bombardment conditions about three times as much gas was evolved with the loosely attached film as with directly evaporated aluminium.

The glass samples were 1 mm thick and bombarded using a raster of $3 \times \frac{1}{4}$ in. At least 95% of the gas evolved was oxygen the remainder being carbon monoxide and hydrogen; part of the CO and H_2 came from the components of the electron gun. The samples reached a temperature of about 250°c and the gas evolution increased with temperature. When a number of Corning glasses were bombarded for 20 hours the amounts of oxygen evolved in cm³ N.T.P. were as follows: (7940) fused silica $< 0·001$; (7740) Pyrex 0·015; (0120) potash-soda-lead 0·016; (0081) soda-lime 0·06; (8603) lithia-alumina-silicate 0·08. The electron beam penetrated the glass to a depth of 2 μ and if all the oxygen contained in this depth had been released from the lithia-alumina-silicate glass then 0·88 cm³ N.T.P. of gas would have been evolved. In fact some 10% of this amount had been released after 20 hour bombardment. These results show how electron bombardment of glass can cause dissociation of the oxide components.

More recently Lineweaver (1963) reported that soda and potash in glass are the most easily dissociated by bombardment to a depth as given for the electron penetration by the Thomson–Whiddington relation discussed in Chapter 9.

References

Adams, R. V., 1961a, *Phys. Chem. Glasses*, **2**, 39.
Adams, R. V., 1961b, *Phys. Chem. Glasses*, **2**, 50.
Adams, A. S., 1929, *Phys. Rev.*, **34**, 1438.
Alpert, D., 1953, *J. appl. Phys.*, **24**, 860.

Altemose, V. O., 1961, *J. appl. Phys.*, **32**, 1309.

Alty, T., 1933, *Phil. Mag.*, **15**, 1035.

Anderson, S., and Kimpton, D. D., 1960, *J. Amer. ceram. Soc.*, **43**, 484.

Bangham, D. H., and Burt, F. P., 1924, *Proc. roy. Soc.*, A, **105**, 481.

Barrer, R. M., 1934, *J. chem. Soc. Lond.*, 378.

Barrer, R. M., 1951, *Diffusion In and Through Solids*, Cambridge University Press.

Becker, A., and Salmang, H., 1929, *Glastechn. Ber.*, **7**, 241.

Bell, T., Hetherington, G., and Jack, K. H., 1962, *Phys. chem., Glasses*, **3**, 141.

Benesi, H. A., and Jones, A. C., 1959, *J. phys. Chem.*, **63**, 179.

Bills, D. G., and Evett, A. A., 1959, *J. appl. Phys.*, **30**, 564.

Blodgett, K. B., and Vanderslice, T. A., 1961, 2nd Inter. Congr. Vac. Sci. Technol., p. 400, Pergamon Press, London.

Braaten, E. O., and Clark, G. F., 1935, *J. Amer. chem. Soc.*, **57**, 2714.

Brunauer, S., 1943, *The Sorption of Gases and Vapours*, vol. 1, *Physical Adsorption*, Princeton University Press, Princeton, N.J.

Brunauer, S., Emmett, P. H., and Teller, E., 1938, *J. Amer. chem. Soc.*, **60**, 309.

Budd, S. M., Exelby, V. H., and Kirwan, J. J., 1962, *Glass Technol.*, **3**, 124.

Bunsen, R. W., 1885, *Ann. Phys. Chem.*, **24**, 321.

Carter, G., and Leck, J. H., 1959, *Brit. J. appl. Phys.*, **10**, 364.

Carter, G., James, L. H., and Leck, J. H., 1962, *Vacuum*, **12**, 213.

Clausing, P., 1930, *Ann. Phys., Lpz.*, **7**, 489, 569.

Cobic, B., Carter, G., and Leck, J. H., 1961, *Vacuum*, **11**, 247.

Coelingh, M. B., 1939, *Kolloid Zeit.*, **87**, 251.

Coffin, F. D., 1959, *J. chem. Phys.*, **30**, 593.

Comsa, G., and Musa, G., 1957, *J. sci. Instrum.*, **34**, 291.

Dalton, R. H., 1933, *J. Amer. ceram. Soc.*, **16**, 425.

Dalton, R. H., 1935, *J. Amer. chem. Soc.*, **57**, 2150.

Donaldson, E. E., 1962, *Vacuum*, **12**, 11.

Drummond, D. G., 1934, *Nature*, **134**, 739.

Dubinin, M. M., and Radushkevich, L. V., 1947, *Proc. Acad. Sci. U.S.S.R.*, **55**, 331.

Durau, F., 1926, *Z. Physik*, **37**, 419.

Dushman, S., 1962, *Scientific Foundations of Vacuum Technique*, 2nd Ed., edited by J. M. Lafferty, John Wiley & Sons Inc., London.

Eitel, W., and Weyl, W. A., 1932, *J. Amer. ceram. Soc.*, **15**, 159.

Ellis, J. W., and Lyon, W. K., 1936, *Nature*, **137**, 1031.

Ellis, J. W., and Lyon, W. K., 1937, *Nature*, **139**, 70.

Faraday, M., 1839–55, *Experimental Researches in Electricity*, Everymans Library, p. 99. J. H. Dent and Sons, Ltd., London.

Faraday, M., 1830, *Phil. Trans. roy. Soc.*, London, Part 1, p. 1.

Finch, G. I., 1949, *Proc. phys. Soc.*, Lond., **62A**, 465.

Fincham, C. J. B., and Richardson, F. D., 1954, *Proc. roy. Soc.*, **A223**, 40.

Florence, J. M., Glaze, F. W., Hahner, C. H., and Stair, R., 1948, *J. Amer. ceram. Soc.*, **31**, 328.

Foex, M., 1954, *Bull. Soc., chim.* France, Mém., **21**, 767.

Frazer, J. H., 1929, *Phys. Rev.*, **33**, 97.

Frazer, J. C. W., Patrick, W. A., and Smith, H. E., 1927, *J. phys. Chem.*, **31**, 897.

Francel, J., 1961, Amer. Soc. Test Mater. Spec. Tech. Pub. No. 300. 'Symposium on Materials and Electron Device Processing', 1961.

Garbe, S., Klopfer, A., and Schmidt, W., 1960, *Vacuum*, **10**, 81.

Garbe, S., and Christians, K., 1962, *Vakuum-Technik*, **11**, 9.

Garino Canina, V., and Priqualer, M., 1962, *Phys. Chem. Glasses*, **3**, 43.

Glaze, F. W., 1955, *Bull. Amer. ceram. Soc.*, **34**, 291.

Gomer, R. Wortman, R. and Lundy, R., 1957, *J. chem. Phys.*, **26**, 1147.

Gregg, S. J., 1934, *The Adsorption of Gases by Solids*, Methuen and Co. Ltd., London.

Grove, F. J., 1955, *Symposium sur l'Affinage du Verre*, Paris.

Harper, T. J., 1962, *Glass Technol.*, **3**, 171.

Harris, J. E., and Schumacher, E. E., 1923, *J. ind. engng. Chem.*, **15**, 174.

Harrison, A. J., 1947, *J. Amer. ceram. Soc.*, **30**, 362.

Haven, Y., and Kats, A., 1960, Colloque 'Silice' de l'Association belge pour favoriser l'étude des Verres.

Heaton, H. M., and Moore, H., 1957, *J. soc. Glass Technol.*, **41**, 3T.

Hetherington, G., and Jack, K. H., 1961, *Bull. Soc. Franç. Céram. Internat. Colloquium*, Paris.

Hetherington, G., and Jack, K. H., 1962, *Phys. Chem. Glasses*, **3**, 129.

Hickmott, T. W., 1960, *J. appl. Phys.*, **31**, 128.

Hill, S. E., 1912, *Proc. phys. Soc., Lond.*, **15**, 35.

Hobson, J. P., 1959a, *Canad. J. Phys.*, **37**, 1105.

Hobson, J. P., 1959b, *Canad. J. Phys.*, **37**, 300.

Hobson, J. P., 1961a, *J. Chem. Phys.*, **34**, 1850.

Hobson, J. P., 1961b, 2nd Internat. Vacuum Congress, Washington, D.C., Pergamon Press.

Hobson, J. P., 1961c, *Vacuum*, **11**, 16.

Hobson, J. P., and Armstrong, R. A., 1961, 18th Internat. Congress Pure Appl. Chem.

Iler, R. K., 1955, *The Colloid Chemistry of Silica and Silicates*, Cornell University Press, Ithaca, New York

Jaeckel, R., and Teloy, E., 1960, *Z. Naturforsch.*, **15A**, 1009.

Jěch, C., 1956, *Nature*, Lond., **178**, 1343.

Jěch, C., 1958, *Radioisotopes in Scientific Research*, vol. 2, p. 491, Pergamon Press (London).

Johnson, M. C., 1929, *Proc. roy. Soc.*, A, **123**, 603.

Johnson Todd, B., 1955, *J. appl. Phys.*, **26**, 1238.

Johnson Todd, B., *J. appl. Phys.*, **27**, 1209.

Johnson Todd, B., Lineweaver, J. L., and Kerr, J. T., 1960, *J. appl. Phys.*, **31**, 51.

Jones, W. M., 1953, *J. Amer. chem. Soc.*, **75**, 3093.

Kaganer, M. G., 1957, *Proc. Acad. Sci. U.S.S.R.*, **116**, 603 (English transl.).

Keesom, W. H., and Schweers, J., 1941, *Physica*, **8**, 1032.

Kingery, W. D., and Lecron, J. A., 1960, *Phys. Chem. Glasses*, **1**, 87.

Kinosita, K., 1953, *J. opt. Soc. Amer.*, **43**, 924.

Krause, 1889, *Ann. Physik*, **36**, 923.

Kruszewski, S., 1959, *Trans. Soc. Glass Technol.*, **43**, 359, transl. of Slavyaski, V. T., 1957, *Gases in Glass* (Oborongiz).

Kühl, C., Rudow, H., and Weyl, W., 1938, *Glastechn. Ber.*, **16**, 37.

Langmuir, I., 1912, *J. Amer. chem. Soc.*, **34**, 1310.

Langmuir, I., 1913, *Trans. Amer. inst. elec. Engrs.*, **32**, 1921.

Langmuir, I., 1915, *J. Amer. chem. Soc.*, **37**, 417.

Langmuir, I., 1916, *J. Amer. chem. Soc.*, **38**, 2221.

Langmuir, I., 1918a, *J. Amer. chem. Soc.*, **40**, 1361.

Langmuir, I., 1918b, U.S. Pat. 1, 273, 629.

Leiby, C. C., and Chen, C. L., 1960, *J. appl. Phys.*, **31**, 268.

Lenher, S., 1927, *J. chem. Soc.*, **129**, 272.

Lineweaver, J. L., 1963, 2nd. Inter. Conf. Residual Gases in Electron Tubes, Milan.

Mahieux, F., 1956, *Verres et Réfr.*, **10**, 277, 342; 1957, **11**, 9.

McAfee, Jr., K. B., 1958, *J. chem. Phys.*, **28**, 218, 226.

Mcbain, J. W., 1932, *The Sorption of Gases and Vapours by Solids*, G. Routledge and Sons Ltd., London.

McHaffie, I. R., and Lenher, S., 1925, *J. chem. Soc.*, **127**, 1559.

Miller, C. F., and Shepard, R. W., 1961, *Advances in Electron Tube*.

Moore, H., and McMillan, P. W., 1956, *J. soc. Glass Technol.*, **40**, 66T.

Morey, G. W., 1950, *The Properties of Glass*, Reinhold Publishing Corp. New York.

Moriya, Y., 1961, *Vacuum*, **11**, 158.

Mottig, M., and Weyl, W. A., 1933, *Glastechn. Ber.*, **11**, 67.

Moulson, A. J. and Roberts, J. P., 1960, *Trans. Brit. ceram. Soc.*, **59**, 388.

Moulson, A. J., and Roberts, J. P., 1961, *Trans. Faraday Soc.*, **57**, 1208.

Norton, F. J., 1953, *J. Amer. ceram. Soc.*, **36**, 90.

Norton, F. J., 1957, *J. appl. Phys.*, **28**, 34.

Naughton, J. J., 1953, *J. appl. Phys.*, **24**, 499.

Okamoto, H., and Tuzi, Y., 1958, *J. phys. Soc. Japan*, **13**, 649.

Plücker, J., 1858, *Pogg. Annal.*, **103**, 91.

Pike, R. G., and Hubbard, D., 1957, *J. Res. Nat. Bur. Stand.*, **59**, 127.

Rayleigh, Lord, 1937, *Proc. roy. Soc.*, A, **163**, 376.

Reynolds, M. B., 1957, *J. Amer. ceram. Soc.*, **40**, 395.

Roberts, J. K., 1939, *Some Problems in Adsorption*, Cambridge University Press, London.

Russell, L. E., 1957, *J. soc. Glass Technol.*, **41**, 304T.

Salmang, H., and Becker, A., 1927/8, *Glastechn. Ber.*, **5**, 520.

Schwarz, H., 1940, *Z. Phys.*, **117**, 23.

Schwarz, H., 1943, *Z. Phys.*, **112**, 437.

Scholze, H., 1959, *Glastechn. Ber.*, **32**, 81, 142.

Scholze, H., and Dietzel, A., 1955, *Glastechn. Ber.*, **28**, 375.

Shrader, J. E., 1919, *Phys. Rev.*, **13**, 434.

Sherwood, R. G., 1918a, *J. Amer. chem. Soc.*, **40**, 1645.

Sherwood, R. G., 1918b, *Phys. Rev.* **12**, 448.

Sidorov, A. N., 1960, *Optics and Spectroscopy*, 8 (Optical Soc. Amer. Transl. p. 424).

Smith, P. L., and Taylor, N. W., 1940, *J. Amer. ceram. Soc.*, **23**, 139.

Steele, W. A., and Halsey, G. D., Jr., 1955, *J. phys. Chem.*, **59**, 57.

Stephenson, G. W., and Jack, K. H., 1960, *Trans. Brit. ceram. Soc.*, **59**, 397.
Swets, D. E., Lee, R. W., and Frank, R. C., 1961, *J. chem. Phys.*, **34**, 17.
Swinton, A. A. C., 1907, *Proc. roy. Soc.*, A, **79**, 134.
Swinton, A. A. C., 1908, *Proc. roy. Soc.*, A, **81**, 453.
Taylor, N. W., and Rast, W. L., 1938, *J. chem. Phys.*, **6**, 612.
Tomlinson, J. W., 1956, *J. Soc. Glass Technol.*, **40**, 25T.
Tsai, L. S., and Hogness, T., 1932, *J. phys. Chem.*, **36**, 2595.
Trapnell, B. M. W., 1955, *Chemisorption*, Butterworths Scientific Publications, London.
Urry, W. D., 1932, *J. Amer. chem. Soc.*, **54**, 3887.
Varnerin, L. J., and Carmichael, J. H., 1955, *J. appl. Phys.*, **26**, 782.
Verweij, W., and Weijer, M. H. A. V. d., 1959, Internat. Commission on Illumination. XIV session, Brussels, communic., P-59.22.
Voorhis, C. C., Van., 1924, *Phys. Rev.*, **23**, 557.
Washburn, E. W., Footitt, F. F., and Bunting, E. N., 1920, *Univ. Ill. Eng Expt. Sta. Bull.*, No. 118, **18**.
Watson, W., 1910, *J. chem. Soc.*, **97**, 810.
Weyl, W. A., 1945, *Glass Ind.*, **26**, 557.
Williams, G. A., and Ferguson, J. B., 1922, *J. Amer. chem. Soc.*, **44**, 2160.
Williams, G. A., and Ferguson, J. B., 1924, *J. Amer. chem. Soc.*, **46**, 635.
Willows, R. S., 1901, *Phil. Mag.*, **1**, 503.
Wustner, H., 1915, *Ann. Phys.*, **46**, 1095.
Young, G. J., 1958, *J. colloid Sci.*, **13**, 67.
Young, J. R., 1956, *J. appl. Phys.*, **27**, 926.
Zeise, H., 1928, *Z. phys. Chem.*, **136**, 385.

CHAPTER 5

The Cleaning of Glass

1. INTRODUCTION

Clean glass surfaces must be prepared for a variety of purposes in both industry and research, and methods of treating glass with organic solvents, acids, detergents and ionized atmospheres, such as flames and electrical discharges to remove grease layers, have received much attention. The effects of such techniques on the chemical and physical properties of glass surfaces have also been well investigated, as is shown in Chapters 3 and 7. Countless processes have been advocated for cleaning glass and it is apparent that many workers treat the subject more as an *art* than a *science*. It is hoped that the discussion here will clarify many aspects of the cleaning techniques, which are often surrounded by mystery. First we shall review the historical background of the subject and then consider the principal cleaning techniques in greater detail. The cleanliness of a glass surface may be assessed by measuring:

(*i*) the contact angle of liquids, which affects the form assumed by breath figures,

(*ii*) the frictional resistance to rubbing solids and,

(*iii*) the adhesion of other solids and superimposed films.

Apart from their value in determining surface cleanliness such measurements are of interest in studies of the force fields of glass surfaces and of practical importance when dealing with bonding of glass to other substances or the coating of glass with metal or dielectric films for optical purposes. The related topics of wetting and friction are dealt with in the next two chapters which should be read in conjunction with this chapter.

HISTORICAL BACKGROUND

Breath figures. Quincke (1877) found that glass could be more easily wetted with water after treatment with *hot* sulphuric acid. Aitken

(1893) observed that a chemically cleaned surface, which formed a condensed water film that diffusely reflected light, would condense a smooth specular film of low reflectance if the surface was flamed with the tip of a blow lamp; the two kinds of water condensation are now generally known as *grey* and *black* breath figures respectively. The smooth water film which is of lower refractive index than the glass can be seen to form an anti-reflection coating of interference thickness as its depth is reduced by drying. The water droplets in a grey breath figure have appreciable contact angles to glass, whereas the contact angles of the droplets in a black figure approach zero (see, for example Plate 20).

Aitken was of the opinion that the uniform water condensation he obtained was promoted by invisible nuclei deposited on the glass by the blow lamp flame. Lord Rayleigh (1911–12) further investigated both the acid and flaming treatment of glass. He found that, with the exception of hydrofluoric acid, reagents such as sulphuric acid, chromic acid, aqua regia and strong potash had to be heated to be effective in producing a black figure. Lord Rayleigh concluded that the uniform water layer was due to the high affinity of clean glass for water. He observed that when a glass plate was heated in a bunsen flame a black figure was only obtained on the unflamed side if the glass temperature almost reached the softening point.

Clean glass showing a black breath figure has an abnormally high coefficient of friction† ($\mu_s \simeq 1$) when rubbed with glass or metal, but as shown in the next section an adsorbed mono-molecular layer of a fatty acid, such as stearic acid, is sufficient to have a marked lubricating effect ($\mu \simeq 0\cdot3$).

Croft (1892) has stated that Professor Karsten (Berlin, 1852) electrified a coin resting on a glass and found it made a latent impression which was revealed when breathed on. Croft studied the effect, using a Wimshurst machine, and observed a black breath figure where the glass surface was exposed to electrical sparks. He examined the form of the water condensation with a microscope and noted that the water droplets were larger in the black zone. Croft also observed that the breath figure reproduced an image of the coin with a black figure opposite the more projecting parts of the metal surface.

---

† Throughout this chapter we shall use μ_s to denote the coefficient of static friction and unless otherwise stated the friction is measured using a plane glass rider of 2·5 cm by 5 cm under a load of 120 g and maintained clean by vapour degreasing in *iso*-propyl alcohol.

Baker (1922) investigated the cleaning of both glass and metal and found that a black breath figure could be obtained by sparking and flaming, but that a low temperature flame did not produce a black figure. Ritschl (1931) and later Strong (1934) used a glow discharge for cleaning glass substrates before evaporating thin films in vacuum and this is now general practice.

Strong (1935) subsequently reported that a black breath figure was obtained if chemically cleaned glass was dried in a desiccator or exposed to a glow discharge at low gas pressure. Also, he confirmed an observation by Baker that the electrical conductivity of a black figure was some thousand times greater than that of a grey figure. Strong observed a faint breath figure on a glass placed at the focus of a quartz lens which collected ultra-violet light from a mercury arc. Kinosita *et al.* (1949) have studied the spectrum from a glass during sparking of the surface and detected C_2 and CN when grease was present and sodium and calcium when the glass was clean or covered with soap.

Jěch (1954) has shown that polystyrene can be more easily wetted by water after irradiation with α rays. The change in the wetting properties did not occur when the irradiation was in vacuum. This suggested that ionization of the surrounding gas by the α rays was responsible for the change in the wetting properties of the plastic, and Jěch compared the effect to that observed with bombarded glass. However, the writer (1959) has pointed out that the effect cannot arise from the same cause. Thus, bombardment of glass by ionized gases removes grease films which prevent wetting, whereas bombardment of a plastic desaturates the surface molecules which become hydrophilic. Flaming a polyethylene surface tends to make it wettable not because grease is removed but because hydrogen bonds are broken, leaving unsaturated surface molecules.

EFFECT OF CLEANING ON SURFACE COMPOSITION

It is unlikely that glass cleaned in the various ways outlined above has a resultant composition at the surface similar to that of the bulk material, or that the boundary composition produced by the various techniques is the same. Thus the foregoing processes can produce surface changes which show an effect on the breath figure long after the surface has again become contaminated. Lord Rayleigh (1911–12) observed that the breath figures produced on glass by acids and flames continued to show the treated regions for a long time. The writer has confirmed that the treated part of a glass surface may show a small difference in the breath figure long after treatment, but the clean surface, as manifested by a black figure and high coefficient of friction, is destroyed quickly after exposure to normal atmospheres. Lord Rayleigh considered that the contaminant film actually penetrated the glass surface and after removal took a long time to be replaced. The writer believes that harsh cleaning can change the form of the surface structure of the treated glass and this may still influence the contact angle of the droplets in the breath condensate when the surface has again become contaminated. It is also shown in the next chapter that a well cleaned surface may adsorb substances which are more hydrophobic than those on the uncleaned surface. Glass surfaces cleaned by vapour degreasing in *iso*-propyl alcohol or by bombardment of low energy positive ions in the positive column of a glow discharge do not show permanent changes as indicated by the breath figures on more harshly treated surfaces.

FRACTURED GLASS SURFACES

One would expect that the easiest way of producing a clean glass surface would be to fracture a piece of glass. Oddly enough such surfaces can show breath figures which vary from black to almost grey. Rayleigh studied glass fracture surfaces and found that there were always regions where the condensed droplets were more aggregated. The black and less black parts of two fractured surfaces were those which had been contiguous before fracture. The writer has found that water droplets on the fractured surfaces of soda-lime glass had a high contact angle if the glass was fractured *in vacuo* in the presence of silicone vapours. Normally when the glass is fractured in air it is immediately covered by adsorbed gas molecules or OH^- groups by reacting with water in the atmosphere. Hydroxyl groups are not repellent to water but there may be a finite time for a water droplet to dissolve an adsorbed gas layer. The surface of aged glass has usually undergone complex chemical reactions with the water in the atmosphere and after cleaning with water or acid the surface is roughened and porous. The porous surface layer could act like a sponge and readily adsorb condensed water, thereby giving externally a low contact angle. Studies of water absorption by silica gel have shown that the interior wetting of the pore surfaces is subject to an hysteresis effect because of existing adsorbed molecules.

Frazer (1929) has studied the adsorption of water on glass surfaces fractured in air and held at room temperature in vacuum. He found that there was no measurable adsorption until a vapour pressure of 6 torr was reached. Above this point the surface gradually became covered with clusters of water molecules until at a pressure of 12·5 torr a continuous layer was formed. If the glass surface had been clean, smooth and chemically uniform then one would have expected a monolayer of OH⁻ groups to cover the glass at the lowest vapour pressure and condensation to occur on this monolayer. The formation of clusters is typical of the growth of liquid films from vapour atoms incident on weakly binding surfaces, *e.g.* mercury films on glass. When the intensity of the vapour molecules striking the surface is sufficient for the temporarily adsorbed and migrating molecules to collide with one another on the surface then nuclei are formed on which condensation occurs. Droplets may also occur in the vapour and be deposited on the surface where they act as centres for condensation.

Frazer's results are understandable if either (i) his glass surfaces were contaminated or (ii) the fracture glass surface was chemically heterogeneous. The contamination of fresh glass surfaces by organic vapours in vacuum is discussed at the end of this chapter.

2. CHEMICAL CLEANING OF GLASS

ACID TREATMENT

When glass is treated with acids to remove grease layers it is inconceivable that the contaminants are removed without the reagent attacking the glass surface. If the products formed by reaction between the contaminants and reagent are not soluble in the reagent then the porous surface of aged glass may continue to retain foreign matter. Agitation of the reagent may also be insufficient to dislodge the reaction products. It has been noted in a previous section that acids, with the exception of hydrofluoric acid, must be used hot to produce clean glass showing a black breath figure. Silica is not readily dissolved by acids, apart from hydrofluoric, and the surface layer on aged glass is invariably finely divided silica. Raising the reagent temperature may aid the dissolution of silica so that a new surface is created on the glass. Some glasses, such as those with a high lead or barium oxide content, are leached in mild acids which leave a loose silica film on their surfaces. Thus acids must not be used on many types of optical glasses and such reagents are usually only suitable for cleaning glassware, as described below.

A universal reagent. Hydrofluoric acid has a strong etching action on glass but in dilute solutions its effect is reduced. Crawley (1953) claims that a cold solution containing 5% hydrofluoric acid, 33% nitric acid, 2% Teepol and 60% water is an excellent reagent for cleaning glass and silica. The hydrofluoric acid removes a thin layer of the glass by solvent action so that the contaminating deposit is stripped from the surface. Thus the cleaning action of the reagent is independent of the nature of the surface film. Obviously if the surface layer is not dissolved then the reagent can only attack the glass through pinholes or discontinuities in the surface coating.

Examples of materials that were removed from glass with the cleaning mixture were: silica deposits on glassware; carbonaceous deposits (more rapidly removed than with hot chromic acid); sputtered platinum film; Perspex polymer film. When the cleaning solution is used with graduated glassware the volume of the vessel is increased by the removal of surface material. Thus a flask of 100 ml. capacity increased in volume by 0·04 ml. after 5 min immersion in the reagent.

Chromic-sulphuric acid. A common method of cleaning glass in chemical laboratories is to immerse the glass in a concentrated sulphuric acid solution of potassium dichromate. The solution normally used is:

$$K_2Cr_2O_7 + 4H_2SO_4 = K_2SO_4 + Cr_2(SO_4)_3 + 4H_2O + 3O$$

Thus one molecule of potassium dichromate supplies three atoms of active oxygen which oxidize carbonaceous matter on the glass surface.

GLASS CLEANING FORMULATIONS

Lesser (1945) has reviewed the formulations used in preparing cleaning solutions for glass. Such cleaning agents can be divided into some five groups which are based on solutions of the following substances: glycol, alcohols, organic solvents, alkalis, synthetic detergents. Some of the commercial cleaning solutions contain chalk, which is useful in removing adherent particles from glass. Wax is sometimes added to the commercial products to give lustre and water repellent properties to the glass and this would negate the object of providing a clean surface. *Iso*-propyl alcohol is extensively used for cleaning glass and in commercial cleaners. This alcohol has the advantage over ethyl alcohol that it can be used in the pure state without excise restrictions.

A simple method of removing superficial dirt from glass is to rub the surface with cotton wool dipped in a mixture of precipitated chalk and alcohol or ammonia. There is evidence that traces of chalk can be left behind as a thin film on a glass surface after cleaning. Thus films of gold condensed from the vapour stage on glass have been found to have a higher energy of binding to glass surfaces cleaned with chalk. Very likely the calcium ions in the chalk replace the sodium ions in the glass, as discussed on p. 135.

The calcium and magnesium salts present in hard water react with many detergents to form insoluble compounds. Some of the precipitates so formed can attach themselves to glass surfaces. Wilson and Mendenhall (1944) have studied the mode of growth of hard water films using a 'hard' water made by adding calcium chloride and magnesium sulphate to soft water. Controlled weights of cleaning materials were added to the hard water. The amount of precipitate formed by successively washing a glass slide in the agitated water was determined by measuring the optical transmittance of the specimen. These results showed that the three alkaline materials commonly used in commercial washing compounds gave an increasing order of contamination as follows: trisodium phosphate ($Na_3PO_4 . 12H_2O$); sodium metasilicate ($Na_2SiO_3 . 5H_2O$) and soda ash (Na_2CO_3). Hard water films were least produced by the polyphosphates and a cleaning agent containing 32% sodium tetraphosphate ($3Na_2O . 2P_2O_5$), 40% sodium metasilicate pentahydrate and 20% sodium carbonate produced a very small amount of surface coating.

Fletcher *et al.* (1962) studied the resistance of soda-lime glass to industrial detergent additives. They found that the alkaline phosphate preparations were more corrosive than silicate preparations of similar alkalinity. Organic detergents, discussed below, had a much less corrosive effect.

SOAPS AND DETERGENTS †

The advent of the so-called 'synthetic' detergents has greatly simplified the cleaning of glass in water. The two principal groups of compounds from which detergents have been developed are alkylsulphate and alkylbenzolsulphonate. The structural forms of these compounds resemble normal soap as shown below.

Soap is the alkali salt of a fatty acid:

$$CH_3.CH_2.CH_2. \quad . \quad . \quad . \quad .CH_2{-}C \underset{ONa}{\overset{O}{\big<}}$$

alkylsulphate‡ or sulphated fatty alcohol has the composition

$$CH_3.CH_2.CH_2. \quad . \quad . \quad . \quad .CH_2{-}O{-}S \underset{ONa}{\overset{O}{\lessgtr}} O$$

and alkylbenzolsulphonate contains a phenyl group

$$CH_3.CH_2.CH_2. \quad . \quad . \quad . \quad .CH_2 \big< \bigcirc \big> SO_3Na$$

Substances may also be used which contain bromide or chloride groups§ thus:

$$CH_3.CH_2.CH_2. \quad . \quad . \quad . \quad .CH_2N \big< \bigcirc \big> Cl$$

All of these substances are long chain molecules terminated by non-polar and polar groups. Thus the CH_3-group is hydrophobic, whereas the sodium and chloride groups are hydrophilic. When these substances are dissolved in water they dissociate and form electrolytes, the molecule becoming an anion when the positive sodium ion is detached and a cation when the negative chloride ion is detached. There are several hundred commercial preparations available but these can be divided into three main classes of compound. These are: (1) anionics, (2) cationics and (3) non-ionics. In

---

† The word 'detergent' refers to any cleansing or purifying agent, *e.g.* common soap. However, in recent years the word has become commonly identified with *synthetic* detergents possessing a particular molecular form and it will be used in this sense here.

‡ Synthetic detergent used in the preparation of the commercially available product 'Dreft'. 'Teepol 514', a product of the Shell Chemical Co. Ltd., is a detergent and wetting agent containing 27% active matter being a mixture of secondary alkyl sulphates and alkyl aryl sulphonates.

§ 'Suma', Joseph Crosfield Ltd., contains an anionic synthetic detergent, an organic chlorine compound and Na_2SO_4.

the latter case the molecule contains a hydrophobic and hydrophilic group as before.†

A very interesting review of the physics and chemistry of washing using detergents has been made by Kling (1950). He has shown that when a contaminant such as oil on a glass surface is exposed to water containing a detergent the oil is gradually displaced at the glass surface and forms a spherical droplet on the surface. The oil is not immediately dispersed in the liquid but requires agitation to release it from the surface. Thus a detergent does not render oil soluble in water but with agitation aids its emulsification. The removal of oil films from surfaces by detergent or soap solutions has been attributed to the adsorption of the detergent molecules on the non-polar oil surface with their hydrocarbon groups inwards and their ionized groups outwards to give wetting by water. If the substrate was non-polar then the detergent molecule would be adsorbed in the same way and the oil would suffer a repulsion due to the like charges of the terminal groups. However, this could not explain the detergent action with a polar glass surface. Adsorption of detergent molecules to the glass surface with its unshielded silicon cations could only occur with the anion terminals of the detergent molecule inwards. Glass surfaces which have been exposed to water are covered by OH⁻ ions and it is usually supposed that the negative charge due to these repels the negative groups of the oriented detergent film on the oil. A similar explanation to the foregoing has been advanced to explain the removal of solid dirt particles.

If detergent molecules were adsorbed to glass by their polar or ionic terminals then this would render the glass surface hydrophobic. However, when freshly fractured surfaces of soda-lime glass are covered with the detergent Teepol they remain hydrophilic although OH⁻ groups would not be initially present to prevent adsorption. We can therefore conclude that OH⁻ ions adsorbed to the glass surface are the active centres for repelling detergent covered oil.

The theory of electrical charging of substrate and dirt is used to explain the cleaning effect of the alkali compounds. Thus, when a glass is immersed in water, a potential is set up between the glass surface and the water as the glass adsorbs negative hydroxyl groups

---

† 'Lissapol N', Imperial Chemical Industries Ltd., is an aqueous solution of a non-ionic surface active agent with a polyethylene glycol chain.

from the water. Adding alkali to the water raises the concentration of the OH⁻ ions and these attach themselves to the dirt and glass, thereby repelling the dirt from the surface. In fact it has been found that both the surface charge and cleaning efficiency of a solution can be related to its pH value. Thus the negative charge developed by oil droplets and solid particles dispersed in water is increased by the addition of, for example, soap. With water/soap solutions the negative charge on dissolved particles passes through a maximum potential as the soap concentration rises. Urbain and Jensen (1936) have measured a potential as high as 90 mV on carbon particles at a concentration of about 1·5 g of sodium oleate per litre of water at 28°c, and this agrees with practical experience that an optimum washing efficiency is achieved with low concentrations of soap.

The foregoing explanation of detergent action is based on the assumption that the organic matter comprising the dirt is non-polar. However, Lawrence (1959) has drawn attention to the fact that dirt may be formed from polar compounds such as fatty acids. Thus explanation of detergent action based on the assumption of wetting and reduction of surface-free energy is in this case unsatisfactory. He has studied the phase diagrams of systems based on water, soap and polar compounds such as the higher homologues of the aliphatic acids. He found that at nearly equal ratios of soap to aliphatic acids there was a very large depression of the freezing point of the polar *dirt*. Further observation of soap and fatty acids in contact showed that when water was present there was a minimum temperature above which the detergent penetrated fairly rapidly into the fatty acid. The minimum temperature for penetration was always less than the melting point of the fatty acid tested. These observations led Lawrence to contend that detergence is due to cryoscopic forces. It could be argued that the high soap concentration required for suppression of the melting point of the polar compound is not in agreement with the small concentration at which detergents are found to be effective. However, as Lawrence has stated, there will be a close packed adsorbed monolayer of soap at the solution-dirt interface and the conditions for suppression of the melting point occur in this region.

WASHING IN DEMINERALIZED WATER

Several workers clean glass by washing in a continuous flow of demineralized water measuring the electrical conductivity of the water to assess the presence of contaminants released by the glass. Organic filters working on the ion exchange principle can now be obtained for providing low conductivity water. Reames (1959) has described a closed system in which water is filtered and demineralized by inorganic and organic filters. A submicron filter is used to remove all particles above 0·45 μ in size. The system was made of stainless steel and Teflon. Glass slides were first cleaned in a detergent and then placed in a container in the filtered water system. Water was pumped by a centrifugal pump through the container and the conductivity of the water measured on the inlet and outlet sides. The conductivity of the outlet stream rose for a few minutes and then fell to that of the inlet. At this stage the glass was assumed clean. The water will obviously not dissolve oil or grease films. Also it is difficult to evaporate the water from the cleaned surface without picking up atmospheric contaminants. However, the technique can be used in combination with, say, vapour degreasing or glow discharge cleaning as discussed below.

Vapour degreasing

A simple method of preparing highly clean glass surfaces is to use vapour degreasing in alcohol vapour. A practical arrangement for the degreasing vessel is shown in Fig. 5.1. The alcohol is boiled at the base of the vessel by hot water piping and condensed on a glass sheet or optical components at the top of the chamber. Condenser pipes at the top of the vessel create convection currents in the air so that the vapour does not unduly escape when the lid is removed.

Assessment of organic solvents. It has been usual for some time to use *iso*-propyl alcohol for cleaning glass by vapour degreasing, and T. Putner (1959) working in the writer's laboratory has compared its cleaning efficiency with that of several organic solvents. The solvents were vaporized in a glass beaker heated by an electric hot plate with plate glass specimens hanging from the top of the beaker. The solvents tested were carbon tetrachloride, trichlorethylene and *iso*-propyl alcohol. The glass specimens were first washed in a detergent (Teepol) to remove heavy contamination and then suspended in the solvent vapour for periods ranging from 15 sec to 15 min. Maximum cleaning was achieved after an immersion period of some 2 min, which generally corresponded to the time taken for

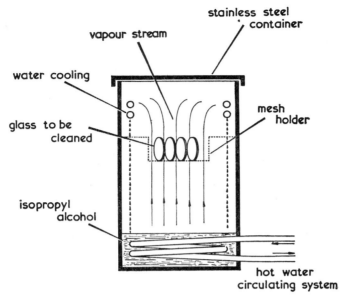

FIG. 5.1 VAPOUR DEGREASING APPARATUS USED FOR CLEANING GLASS

the condensing vapour to heat the glass to the temperature of the saturated vapour so that condensation ceased. Obviously the greater the thermal capacity of the glass the longer would be the time for which condensing vapour washes the exposed surface. If the specimen had a small thermal capacity and a large area then condensation could cease before the surface was clean and it would be necessary to immerse the specimen in the vapour a number of times.

The highest value for the coefficient of friction obtained by vapour degreasing was 0·6 using *iso*-propyl alcohol as the cleaning agent (see Table 5.1). This solvent gave a value of μ_s near to that obtained by glow discharge cleaning, which is discussed further on. The cleanliness of the surfaces was also demonstrated by the adhesion of evaporated aluminium films which resisted stripping with scotch tape as shown in Plate 21. The results obtained with *iso*-propyl alcohol are maintained when the cleaning is carried out in a large stainless steel container suitable for cleaning 2 ft square glass plates. It is necessary when cleaning glass components of high thermal capacity to withdraw them slowly from the vapour allowing

Table 5.1

Coefficients of static and kinetic friction of glass on glass after
solvent and detergent cleaning
(*After Putner, 1959*)

Method of cleaning	Coefficient of friction	
	Static	Kinetic
Vapour degreased in *iso*-propyl alcohol	0·5–0·64	0·4–0·62
Vapour degreased in trichlorethylene	0·39	0·31
Vapour degreased in carbon tetrachloride	0·35	0·28
Teepol washed and cloth dried	0·07	0·04
Teepol wash and glow discharge cleaned	0·8	0·6
Teepol washed, cleaned with alcohol and chalk, wiped with cotton wool	0·33	0·27
Teepol washed, cleaned with alcohol wiped with cotton wool and glow discharge cleaned	0·8	—
Vapour degreased in *iso*-propyl alcohol and glow discharge cleaned	0·8	0·6
Teepol washed, cleaned with alcohol and chalk, wiped with cotton wool and flamed with gas flame	0·41	—

The value given for each cleaning method is a mean result for several tests.

time for any condensate tears on the surface to evaporate off. If liquid tears are left to dry in air then their outline persists even when the glass is vacuum coated and in these regions the adhesion of superimposed films, etc., is always poor.

When used in a vapour degreaser both carbon tetrachloride and trichlorethylene produce low values of μ_s and evaporated films are poorly adherent to the cleaned glass. Also, with vapours of these solvents, a white chalky deposit is often formed on the glass surface. If the deposit arose from volatile impurities in the solvents then it should re-evaporate from the glass when it becomes hot. The writer believes that the chlorine in the solvent reacts with adsorbed water on the glass to form hydrochloric acid; it is known that carbon tetrachloride will react with water and form corrosive compounds when hot. The acid would leach alkali from the glass and evaporate leaving the alkali compounds as a loosely bonded deposit. The residues of liquid tears remaining after vapour degreasing in *iso*-propyl alcohol could be silica gel. It is known that sodium will react readily with the OH^- groups of the alcohol molecule thereby releasing hydrogen. Such a reaction could remove the sodium from the glass and replace it by hydrogen which forms silicic acid as already discussed on p. 135; see also the discussion on the effect of rubbing glass in alcohol on p. 377.

Kinosita (1953) has determined the coefficient of static friction of soda-lime glass cleaned by chemical, sparking and flaming techniques using a watch glass as the rider. His values of μ_s for certain of the cleaning techniques are high. Thus he obtained values of $\mu_s = 0.903$ and 0.935 for washing with soap and chromic-sulphuric acid respectively. However, in both cases, he dried the treated glass by washing it in hot distilled alcohol. Later in his paper he recognized the cleaning effect of the alcohol. The coefficient of friction of untreated glass after washing in hot distilled alcohol three times rose from about 0.3 to 0.6, which roughly agrees with that reported here for alcohol vapour degreasing after detergent cleaning.

ULTRASONIC CLEANING METHODS

Ultrasonic cleaning is a valuable method of removing heavy contaminants from surfaces and it has been used for removing pitch and rouge from optically worked glass. It is of interest to compare the standard of cleanliness obtained with this technique with that of the foregoing methods.

Atherton (1957) has discussed the use of both low and high frequency ultrasonic agitation of cleaning fluids for industrial cleaning purposes. He shows that cavitation in the agitated fluid occurs at low frequencies (20–100 kc/sec) which greatly assists the removal of gross particles from contaminated surfaces. High cavitation energies can damage the surface of an article undergoing cleaning and therefore the energy output of a low frequency system must be carefully controlled. Greater energies can be used with high frequency systems having frequencies of the order of 1 Mc/sec because the cleaning action is more gentle and free from cavitational bombardment of the irradiated surface. Noltingale and Neppiras (1950) have investigated the problems of cavitation and its dependence on vibration frequency, internal pressure and the presence of nuclei of suitable size for its production.

If the gas pressure above the agitated liquid is lowered two effects are promoted which may or not be advantageous to the cleaning action, these are:

(1) Dissolved gases which provide suitable nuclei for cavitation centres are removed and therefore cavitation effects may be reduced.

(2) Air trapped in deep holes in the surface of intricately shaped components may be removed, thereby permitting the solvent to completely cover the surface to be cleaned.

The influence of these two effects on the cleaning of glass in ultrasonically agitated solvents was studied by Putner (1959) using the apparatus shown in Fig. 5.2. With this equipment cleaning could be conducted either at atmospheric or at reduced pressures.

Ultrasonic cleaning apparatus. The cleaning chamber was exhausted by a gas ballasted rotary pump. The solvent was evaporated at the base of the chamber and was condensed on water-cooled pipes from

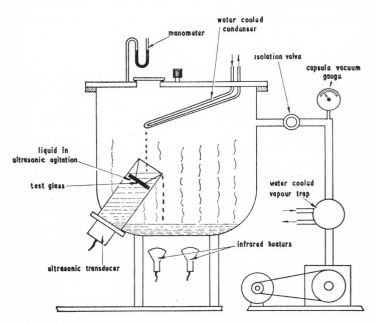

FIG. 5.2 APPARATUS USED FOR ASSESSING THE EFFECT OF ULTRASONIC AGITA-
TION OF CLEANING FLUIDS AT HIGH AND LOW GAS PRESSURES (*After Putner*, 1959)

which it ran continuously into a vessel containing the ultrasonic transducer. By this means the agitated fluid was kept clean and the liquid surface through which the specimen had to pass was constantly changed. The ultrasonic power was provided by either a high or low frequency ultrasonic generator. The high frequency unit operated at 1 Mc/sec and had a 300 watt output. A thin slice of barium titanate crystal was used as the transducer with an effective area of 4 cm × 8 cm. The low frequency unit operated at 25 kc/sec at an output of 250 watts using a magnetostrictor for the trans-ducer, the vibrating plate was approximately 10 cm in diameter. *Iso*-propyl alcohol was used as the solvent because it had proved to be an effective glass cleaner when used in a vapour degreaser.

The chamber was exhausted and the cleaning liquid degassed until the pressure was between 30–50 torr, *i.e.* in the region of the saturated vapour pressure of the solvent at room temperature. Further degassing occurred when the liquid was ultrasonically agitated. In fact, when using the low frequency agitation the boiling of the liquid was violent unless the generator was operated at reduced power. At high frequency the liquid was more stable and maximum power input could be used. The slides were cleaned for periods of 15 sec up to several minutes. After each operation the solvent was allowed to dry by evaporation to ensure that the final state of the surface was that due to the ultrasonic cleaning. Tables 5.2 and 5.3 and Plate 21 indicate the standard of cleanliness obtained using ultrasonics under these conditions.

Table 5.2

Coefficients of static and kinetic friction of glass on glass obtained with ultrasonic cleaning
(*After Putner, 1959*)

Time (sec)	H.F. (1Mc/sec) (300 watts) *cleaning*		L.F. (25 kc/sec) (125 watts) *cleaning*	
	Static	Kinetic	Static	Kinetic
15–20	0·39	0·28	—	—
30–45	0·39	0·27	—	—
60	—	—	0·3	0·2
120	0·4	0·27	0·28	0·2
5 min	0·37	0·25	0·3	0·2

The values given are mean values resulting from many tests.

The highest value achieved for the coefficient of static friction was 0·4. It is not easy to explain why there should be a difference in the cleaning results between the vapour degreasing and ultrasonic cleaning methods. In the first technique the test surfaces were im-mersed in pure alcohol vapour, and in the second the surfaces were immersed in the distilled liquid. If volatile contaminants were present in the agitated liquid then these would have had to evaporate

20

Table 5.3
Wetting† observations after different cleaning methods
(*After Putner, 1959*)

Method of cleaning	Observation
Ultrasonically cleaned in *iso*-propyl alcohol using H.F. at reduced pressure	Only slight indication of wetting
Ultrasonically cleaned in *iso*-propyl alcohol using L.F. at reduced pressure	Only very slight indication of wetting
Vapour degreasing in *iso*-propyl alcohol	Surface wets
Glow discharge cleaned in shielded cathode system	Surface wets
Teepol washed and polished with Selvyt Cloth	No wetting
Vapour degreased in either carbon tetrachloride or trichlorethylene	Partial wetting

† Water on plate glass.

from the main solvent charge and similar contaminants would have been present during vapour degreasing. Radiant heating the glass surface to accelerate drying after removal from the fluid did not alter the results. However, glow discharge cleaning *in vacuo* removed the residual contamination responsible for the low friction values as shown by adhesion tests (see Plate 21). The writer believes that the greater cleaning efficiency of vapour degreasing may be connected with the higher temperature reached by the solvent and glass; the ultrasonic experiments were made with the liquid at 15°c.

Some tests were made by Putner on unwashed slides which showed that heavy contaminants, such as greasy finger prints, could be removed from the glass surface by ultrasonic agitation providing the fluid was agitated at a low frequency (see Table 5.4). These results confirm that cavitation is essential for removing gross contamination.

The ultrasonic cleaning of enclosures was studied, using glass capillary tubes of 1·5 mm bore and 2 cm length with closed ends. The inside surfaces were contaminated with colloidal carbon ('Dag') or grease. The tests showed that it was necessary to reduce the gas pressure above the cleaning medium to remove the air trapped in holes, which prevented irradiation of the whole of the surface. However, for the most effective removal of dirt layers the liquid should be in the undegassed state as shown in Table 5.5, and thus, after initial reduction of the pressure, the cleaning should be carried out in the atmosphere.

Table 5.4

Effect of various cleaning techniques on the
removal of grease and oil deposits
(*After Putner, 1959*)

Method of cleaning	Comments
Immersed in *iso*-propyl alcohol for 2 min	Oil film incompletely removed
Immersed in trichlorethylene for 2 min	Oil film incompletely removed
Ultrasonically cleaned in atmosphere for 2 min in *iso*-propyl alcohol using H.F. transducer	Removed visible grease and dirt, but not a finger print impression
Ultrasonically cleaned at reduced pressure for 2 min in *iso*-propyl alcohol using H.F. transducer	As above
Ultrasonically cleaned in atmosphere for 2 min in *iso*-propyl alcohol using L.F. transducer	Removed both grease and dirt and completely removed finger print impression. Removed visible oil film in 30 sec
Ultrasonically cleaned at reduced pressure for 2 min in *iso*-propyl alcohol using L.F. transducer	As above
Vapour degreased in *iso*-propyl alcohol	Removed grease and dirt but not finger print impression

The glass slides were heavily finger printed with grease and dust. Two greases were used, Apiezon vacuum grease and ordinary lubricating oil.

Table 5.5

Ultrasonic cleaning of glass capillary tubes
(*After Putner, 1959*)

Method of cleaning	Comments
Ultrasonic cleaning in atmosphere using L.F. transducer in *iso*-propyl *alcohol*. Trapped gases not removed	No cleaning
Ultrasonic cleaning at reduced pressure using L.F. transducer in *iso*-propyl alcohol	Partial cleaning after 4 min
L.F. transducer in *iso*-propyl alcohol. System pumped out to remove trapped air from capillary. Air admitted to system. Ultrasonic cleaning done in atmosphere in un-gassed medium	Complete removal after some 4 min

The tubes were 1 mm bore and 2 cm long. Their interior was covered with colloidal carbon (Dag).

ADVANTAGES AND USES OF THE CLEANING PROCESSES

The foregoing discussion shows that vapour degreasing in *iso*-propyl alcohol produces a higher standard of surface cleanliness than can be achieved with either detergents or ultrasonic cleaning. Unlike acid reagents *iso*-propyl alcohol does not unduly corrode glass. Vapour degreasing in *iso*-propyl alcohol produces glass surfaces of a cleanliness almost comparable to those obtained by glow discharge cleaning. However, vapour degreasing is not effective for removing gross contamination and must therefore be used in combination with either a manual washing process or with ultrasonic cleaning. If contamination of the surface by dust particles is to be kept low then cleaning techniques involving polishing of the glass should be avoided, because polishing electrostatically charges the glass, which then attracts dust particles binding them to its surface.

3. CLEANING GLASS IN FLAMES

It has already been noted above that only high temperature flames produce black figures on glass. Thus, Aitken (1893) found that an alcohol flame did not produce a black figure, whereas Rayleigh (1911–12), using a similar flame with a mouth blow-pipe, found it did. With a coal gas/compressed air flame a black figure can be obtained without difficulty but gross contaminants must first be removed from the glass. The coefficient of friction of flamed glass surfaces is given in Tables 5.1 and 5.7 and it can be seen that the values are lower than those obtained with several other techniques.

Composition of typical flames. It will be useful here to consider briefly the composition of different types of flames and their possible effects on the treated glass. A flame contains ions of various kinds and impurity atoms as well as molecules of high thermal energy. Knewstubb and Sugden (1958) have extracted ions from different flames and analysed them in a mass spectrometer. In hydrogen-air flames the chief ion in the gases above the reaction zone appeared to be H_3O^+ together with a fair amount of H_2O^+. There were traces of Na^+ and K^+ which appeared to be inevitable when using a compressed air supply. Similar results have been published by Deckers and Tiggelen (1958).

Knewstubb and Sugden found that in the reaction zone of pre-mixed hydrocarbon flames the fuel rapidly polymerized forming hydrocarbon radicals and molecules with mass numbers up to 150. The extent of polymerization was greater for the unsaturated hydro-carbon fuels (ethylene, acetylene) than the saturated (ethane, methane). The presence of the polymerized molecules could be detected over an appreciable proportion of the height of the flame when it was rich in fuel, *i.e.* low in oxygen. Luminous flames of high fuel content are known to form solid carbon particles and these probably arise from the degradation of the polymerized material.

Deposition of hydrocarbons. It is a matter of common observation that if a flame containing hydrocarbons is not operated at high temperature the combustion is not complete and carbonaceous material is deposited on the flamed surface. Hydrocarbons deposited from a flame would most likely be unsaturated and therefore have some affinity for water. When the surface of solid polyethylene is flamed the contact angle of water is reduced from 90° to about 40° by the presence of unsaturated molecules at the surface. However, it is unlikely that the contact angle of an unsaturated hydrocarbon film would be sufficiently low to produce a black breath figure similar to that on clean glass.

Cleaning process. The cleaning effect of a flame is probably very similar to that of a glow discharge which is also an ionized atmo-sphere. The fact that only high temperature flames effectively remove grease films may not arise from the gas particles striking the glass having higher thermal energies, but may be due to the absence of deposits from incomplete combustion, which would be the reason for using the tip of the flame. It is shown further on that glass can be freed from contaminants remaining after chemical cleaning by exposure to the plasma of a glow discharge where the gas temperature rarely exceeds about 100°c and the equivalent temperature of the positive ions is not much higher. The possibility that grease films are removed from glass by chemical reactions with the hot gases cannot be excluded. However, Rayleigh did not find that glass exposed to ozone for long periods was effectively cleaned. Also, as shown further on, glass can be cleaned in a glow discharge using both inert and chemically active gases. Thus the removal of material from a glass surface in a flame is probably due to the high energy particles in the flame imparting their energy to the adsorbed molecules. Recombination of ionized particles on the glass surface will liberate heat and may help in removing adsorbed molecules.

4. EFFECTS OF A GLOW DISCHARGE ON GLASS

When a glass is immersed in a glow discharge its surface is bombarded by electrons, positive ions, chemically active atoms and molecules, neutral molecules of high thermal energy and radiations covering a range of wavelengths. Thus both chemical and energy exchange processes may be occurring at the glass surface and it cannot be expected that a simple explanation can be given of the cleaning action in such a 'complex' atmosphere. However, it is shown below that chemical action of the ionized gas on the contaminated surface, *e.g.* oxidation of organic layers, is not an essential part of the cleaning process and that glass can be cleaned by bombardment of neutral or ionized molecules which energetically sputter the surface layer (Plate 22).

We shall start by discussing the effects on a glass surface of the different active components in the ionized atmosphere. For information on methods of controlling glow discharge cleaning arrangements the reader should consult the writer's work (1956). Since the latter was published the writer has made new discoveries about the mode of cleaning in glow discharges. We shall be mainly concerned here with the cleaning mechanism and the principles underlying the design of electrode systems. The cleaning process is generally carried out in vacuum systems of the *kinetic type*, *i.e.* continuously exhausted systems using oil diffusion pumps and rubber to metal seals. Usually the main components of the residual atmosphere in such systems are water and organic vapours, *i.e.* apart from the gas bled into the chamber for sustaining the discharge. The glow discharge electrodes are normally constructed of aluminium because this has a low sputtering rate.

ELECTRON BOMBARDMENT AND HYDROCARBON DECOMPOSITION

Optically absorbing layers. When molecules of hydrocarbon vapours are present in a glow discharge they are bombarded by ionized particles which break main or side chains liberating hydrogen. The unsaturated molecules produced by the bombardment polymerize and condense to form yellowish liquids and films on the container walls. When a glow discharge is operated in a kinetic vacuum system a glass specimen can sometimes be contaminated with a a yellowish tinted deposit rather than be cleaned. The vapour pressure of organic substances in a glow discharge may be quite low and it has not been clear whether the contaminant is polymerized material or comes from other sources. The writer (1958a) has observed that glass plates which are mounted facing a plane cathode made of pure aluminium (99·99%) become yellow tinted when bombarded in a vessel sealed with rubber gaskets† and exhausted by an oil diffusion pump. For example, when the glow discharge was operated at 5 kV and 1 mA/cm²‡ for about 10 min the glass developed a brown tint which was deeper in colour the nearer the glass was to the edge of the cathode dark space. Glass exposed to electron bombardment at high accelerating voltages (> 20 kV) may become optically absorbing due to the oxides in the glass interior being dissociated. However, examination of the treated surface by multiple beam interferometry showed that the optical absorption arose from a deposit on the glass surface. The absorbing coating was extremely hard and could not be removed with organic solvents or common acids, which is characteristic of many polymerized compounds.

There was still some uncertainty whether the surface deposit was a partially oxidized film of aluminium or impurity metals sputtered from the metal cathode. The oxide on aluminium does not readily sputter and Hiesinger and Koenig (1951) were only able to prepare sputtered films of aluminium oxide in a moderate time by using a very high current density of 20 mA/cm². The tinted deposits produced on glass in kinetic vacuum systems did not become more metallic when the residual atmosphere was changed from air to argon, as would a sputtered metal oxide film. Also, the optical absorption remained constant when the cathode surface was coated with a highly pure film of evaporated aluminium. Both of these tests indicated that the deposit came from the residual atmosphere.

Bent electron beam. Using the apparatus shown in Fig. 5.3 the writer was able to study the effect of electron bombardment, without the risk of cathode sputtering on to the glass. A cylindrical

---

† Buna N 'O' ring seals and a Neoprene 'L' gasket on the chamber base.

‡ The glow discharge current is expressed throughout this section as *current density*, *i.e.* the current per unit area of cathode, unless otherwise stated.

anode and cathode were used with an anode shield surrounding the cathode and within the cathode dark space thus confining the glow discharge to the cathode interior. In operation a pencil beam of electrons was obtained which could be bent by a magnet to strike a second anode on which a glass was rested.

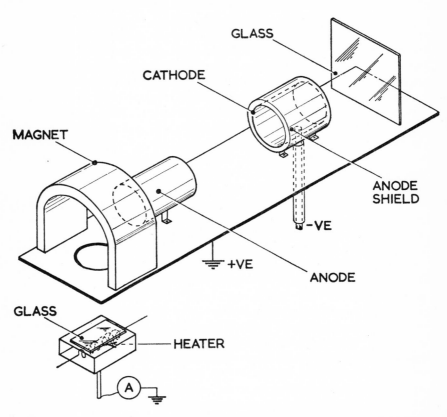

FIG. 5.3 ELECTRODE SYSTEM USED FOR DETECTING DEPOSITION OF ORGANIC CONTAMINANTS IN A GLOW DISCHARGE WITHOUT THE EFFECTS OF CATHODE SPUTTERING

The apparatus was operated at 5 kV with a current of 0.2 mA/cm^2 flowing to the second anode for 1 hour in air at low pressure. On removal the test plate was coated with a roughly circular deposit where the electrons had impinged. Such deposits grew at a rate of about 10 Å/min. The growth rate was of the same order as that obtained with a glass facing a cathode electrode and it was concluded that the deposit was a layer of decomposed hydrocarbon, as observed by Ennos (1953–54) and Koenig (1953) for thermally emitted electrons striking a target in high vacuum.

Ennos found that the rate of decomposition could be decreased by raising the target temperature, presumably because the period of adsorption of a hydrocarbon molecule was reduced, and with it the probability of decomposition. The target electrode was therefore heated by an element mounted under the second anode and inside a closed copper box so that material could not vaporize on to the target surface. It was found that the deposit formed after 1 hour of bombardment at a support temperature of 150°c was too thin to be accurately measured (< 100 Å) and at 200°c only a slight optical absorption could be discerned together with a breath pattern showing the area of bombardment.

Experiments were also made with sources of organic vapour near the target electrode, *e.g.* neoprene rubber, and the rate of surface contamination was always greatly increased.

Decomposition of adsorbed molecules. Goche *et al.* (1950) have admitted hydrocarbon vapours to a glow discharge and observed the deposition of their reaction products on the target of an electron beam focused by a magnetic field. They contend that the electrons collide with the vapour molecules in transit and that the decomposed material is only deposited where the electron bombardment has cleaned the surface. If this was so it is difficult to see why the hydrocarbon products are not also deposited on surfaces exposed to the positive column of a glow discharge, because, as shown further on, random bombardment in a plasma cleans surfaces but does not remove decomposed hydrocarbon films. It is unlikely that the electron induced deposits in normal vacuum systems are caused by electrons colliding with hydrocarbon molecules in transit and carrying them to the target. The hydrocarbon vapours present in typical kinetic vacuum systems would have a partial pressure less than 10^{-6} torr and the mean free path of electrons in the vapour would be large. If one assumes the presence of hydrocarbon molecules with a molecular weight of 400 and diameter of 10 Å, then the mean free path of electrons given by kinetic theory is 400 cm even at a pressure of 10^{-5} torr. From this it may be concluded that collisions in space between electrons and hydrocarbon molecules will normally be negligible for transit lengths of a few centimetres.

The number of molecules striking the unit area of the target with the foregoing mass and pressure at room temperature is 10^{15} cm^{-2} sec^{-1} and the number of electrons impinging on the target at a current density of 0·2 mA/cm^2 is $1·2 \times 10^{15}$ cm^{-2} sec^{-1}. These values are sufficiently similar to indicate that hydrocarbon decomposition on the target surface is the most probable process. Raising the current density to 0·4 mA/cm^2 under the vacuum conditions discussed here did not increase the rate of film formation which suggested that the rate of decomposition was limited by the rate at which hydrocarbon molecules were adsorbed.

Hydrocarbon decomposition zones

Contamination of glass by polymerized organic films is limited to regions exposed to bombardment of high velocity electrons traversing the cathode dark space (Holland, 1958b). This can be shown by using a large diameter aluminium cathode as drawn inset in Fig. 5.4 with a glass specimen inclined to its surface so that each part of the glass sees the cathode without obstruction. With a tray containing butyl phthalate (vapour pressure at 20°c 10^{-5}–10^{-4} torr) in the vacuum vessel the optical transmittance of the glass is reduced as shown in Fig. 5.4. The glass specimens have been bombarded at different voltages and gas pressures for a constant time of 5 min and at a current density of 0·2 mA/cm^2. The reduction in transmittance is greater the thicker the organic deposit.

Cathode dark space. Fig. 5.4 shows that at high gas pressures the glass inside or on the fringe of the cathode dark space was coated with a deposit, whereas the zone within the positive column was uncoated. Glass surfaces in the positive column near to the anode often developed the high coefficient of friction characteristic of clean surfaces. When the gas pressure was reduced the glass outside the cathode dark space was contaminated because the electrons falling through the cathode dark space travelled considerable distances in the rarefied gas. When the glow discharge was passed in silicone vapour the glass was coated with an optically absorbing deposit in a similar manner to that obtained with organic vapours, but the deposit had a high coefficient of friction and could be wetted as shown in Plate 23. Silicone vapour decomposed by electron bombardment in high vacuum is known to form deposits containing a high percentage of silica.

If the current density of the bombardment is increased (> 1 mA/cm^2) then the glass target may attain an appreciable temperature near to the cathode and the rate of growth of organic contaminants is decreased, because vapour molecules have a shorter period of adsorption and thus less probability of decomposition by

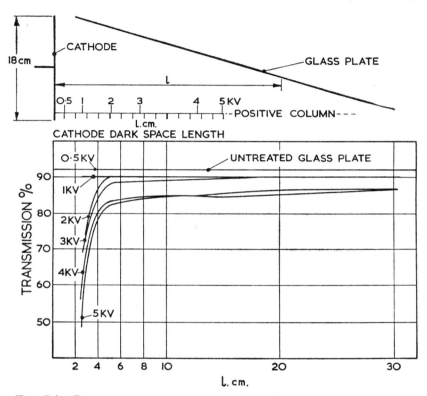

FIG. 5.4 CHANGE IN THE TRANSMITTANCE OF GLASS SPECIMENS (MEASURED AT $\lambda = 4600$ Å) WHEN ARRANGED AT DIFFERENT DISTANCES FROM AN ALUMINIUM CATHODE OPERATED AT CONSTANT CURRENT DENSITY 0·2 mA/cm^2 AND DIFFERENT VOLTAGES IN THE PRESENCE OF ORGANIC VAPOUR

electron impact. This does not necessarily apply to silicone oil contamination because chemisorption of silicone molecules is aided by removal of water from the glass surface at high temperature (see, for example, the discussion on this on pp. 338 and 341).

Karasev and Izmailova (1954) produced clean glass in a glow discharge, although they mounted their cathode above the glass to be treated and used a glass apparatus with grease seals. The glasses were cleaned in argon and a preliminary discharge was run in oxygen before exposing the glass to oxidize organic vapours. However, an appreciable vapour pressure of organic vapour must have always been present. Their failure to observe the deleterious effects of high velocity electron bombardment must be attributed to the use of a small cathode dark space in relation to the cathode to glass spacing. Thus the cathode was 9 cm from the glass and operated at 700 V and a pressure of 0·06 torr so that the cathode dark space was about 1 cm in length; the electrons passing through the cathode dark space would have been scattered before reaching the glass as demonstrated above.

Positive column. Glasses exposed within the positive column of a high pressure glow discharge may remain free from contamination because either (*i*) the electrons accelerated within the plasma only possess sufficient energy to excite hydrocarbon molecules but not to degrade them, or (*ii*) polymerized organic films are formed but are removed by the bombardment of positive ions and neutral molecules striking the wall.

It is shown in a later section that bombarding glass with positive ions of high energy in the cathode dark space removes polymerized organic material previously deposited by electron bombardment. However, if similar deposits are exposed in the positive column they are not removed. Thus the absence of hydrocarbon decomposition products in the positive column is not due to the cleaning action of positive ions or neutral molecules of high velocity, but arises from the electrons having insufficient energy to desaturate the hydrocarbon molecules. The weakly adsorbed substances remaining on glass surfaces after chemical cleaning can be removed by exposure to the plasma in the positive column, providing the glass is not exposed to high-speed electrons passing into the positive column from the cathode dark space. Thus one side of a glass exposed to the cathode dark space may become contaminated whilst the remote side in the plasma may be cleaned. It is probable that adsorbed organic molecules are removed in the plasma by directly impinging positive ions and neutral gas molecules. Evaporation of contaminant molecules may occur due to the glass becoming heated by the glow discharge. However, if the temperature rises unduly (> 200°c) organic molecules in the residual gas may be cracked on the hot substrate as shown in Section 6.

Radioactive Xenon 131 or radon is taken up by a glass surface when ionized at low gas pressure by a high frequency supply. A monolayer of calcium stearate ($\simeq 25$ Å thick) adsorbed to the glass surface is sufficient to produce a distinct decrease in the gas sorption (Jěch 1956). The conditions in a high frequency discharge resemble those in the positive column of a glow discharge.

Bombardment of glass by positive ions

The experiments discussed in the previous sections show that when using kinetic vacuum systems electron bombardment of glass

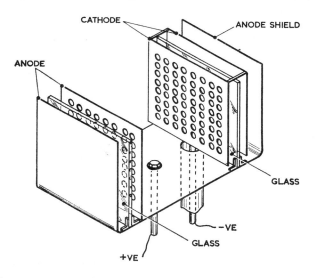

Fig. 5.5 Perforated electrodes used for studying the effects of electrons and positive ions bombarding glass in a glow discharge

cannot be an effective method of cleaning. Thus claims for cleaning glass by electron bombardment in high vacuum must be treated as suspect. Apart from chemical processes it would appear that the larger particles present in the glow discharge are really the agents for effective cleaning. The separate effects of electron and positive ions were investigated by the writer (1958a, b) using the electrode system shown in Fig. 5.5. Both the anode and the cathode electrode were made from perforated aluminium plates behind which test plates of soda-lime glass were situated. The glow discharge was suppressed from the back of the cathode by an anode mounted within the cathode dark space. The charged particles were accelerated through the electrode apertures and struck the test glasses.

The distribution of the current between positive ions and electrons at the cathode was not known, but from data on the secondary electron emission of oxidized metals it was believed that the positive ion current was about one-third of the total current flowing in the circuit. The electron current at the anode was equal to the current flowing in the external circuit. The cathode dark space filled the gap between the electrodes and the electrons leaving the cathode must have struck the anode with energies almost equal to that attained by falling through the applied voltage.

Reduction of refractive index. With a discharge at 3 kV and 0.2 mA/cm^2 in air or argon, a yellow glow was emitted by the glass bombarded by positive ions. After a time the yellow glow spread to the cathode electrode as the sodium or its compounds vaporized from the glass. When the glasses were removed from the vessel, the electron bombarded plate was coated, as expected, with a polymerized film of hydrocarbons where the glass had been exposed behind the holes in the anode electrode. The glass bombarded by positive ions was free from any deposit, and had a higher optical transmission in the bombarded zones, because of the formation of a low reflectance interference film attributed to the growth of a porous silica layer on the glass surface. The glass used contained some 13% of sodium oxide and if this had been removed by bombardment then the porous layer formed would have had a refractive index of about 1.3, which was consistent with the decrease in the glass reflectance. It is shown in Chapter 2 that the refractive index of a glass surface may be lowered by acid treatment if this selectively leaches the surface constituents. The selective removal of sodium from soda-lime glass by positive ion bombardment can be demonstrated by evaporating aluminium on to the glass, which reacts with the sodium compounds remaining in the untreated regions, as shown in Plate 22.

Glasses which are intensely bombarded by positive ions form a whitish deposit around the exposed zones when exposed to air because the sodium condensed on the untreated areas becomes converted to the hydroxide. Continuous bombardment of the glass not only removes the sodium content but the surface of the silica skeleton is slowly sputtered. Thus bombarding for 1 hour under the conditions given above produces the usual low index layer but the bombarded zones as shown by multiple beam inter-ferometry form pits of some 1000 Å depth.

Other workers have detected changes in the refractive index of glass exposed to positive ion bombardment but attributed it to changes in surface structure rather than selective removal of surface material. Thus Koch (1948–49) claims that crown glass, flint glass and quartz develop an anti-reflection film on their surfaces when bombarded with inert gas ions at an accelerating potential of 60 kV for 5 hours at 10 μA/cm^2. Hines (1957) has bombarded soda-lime glass with 40 keV A$^+$ ions and found that the surface had a de-creased refractive index (1·34). He believed that the glass structure had been changed in a manner similar to that found with neutron irradiated quartz. The surface damage, observed by the writer with a glow discharge, occurred at only 3 kV in both argon and air and obviously arose from selective removal of the glass components. Recently workers using vacuum ionization gauges have observed that sodium and potassium ions are liberated when Pyrex and Vycor are bombarded with positive ions in high vacuum.

When metals and semi-conductors are sputtered by positive-ion bombardment gas ions enter their bodies and similar sorption effects can be expected with glass.

Hines and Arndt (1960) report that low energy (7·5 keV) bom-bardment of silica by H$_2$$^+$, D$_2$$^+$ and He$^+$ ions produces contaminant films in the presence of organic vapours, whereas bombardment by Kr$^+$ and Xe$^+$ has a negligible effect. Ions of small mass should be the most effective for desaturating organic molecules and the least effective for sputtering the resultant polymerized layer.

Hines and Arndt noted that bombardment of silica with gas ions with energies between 7·5 and 45 keV produced a layer of changed refractive index on the silica. The depth of the layer depended on the ion energy and mass. They attributed the effect to alteration of the silica structure by the impacting ions, in a similar way to the structural changes produced in silica by fast neutrons. However, apart from collision and sputtering effects, gas ions would be trapped in a surface layer and their presence might also effect the index.

Sputtering of glass. The sodium removed from glass by positive ion bombardment may be sputtered or evaporated if the glass tem-perature rises. However, components of low volatility can un-doubtedly be sputtered from glass by positive ion bombardment.

Thus, the writer coated soda-lime glass with evaporated $\lambda/4$-films of titanium dioxide and silicon monoxide which, due to their effect on the surface reflectance, permitted changes in the surface condition to be easily observed. Both oxide films were completely removed after 1 hour of bombardment in air or argon at 3 kV and $0\cdot2$ mA/cm². It is known that these oxides can be sputtered from the surface of the parent metal in a glow discharge. A $\lambda/4$-film of magnesium fluoride was removed by positive ions of air or argon, but in this case the compound must have been partially reduced because a metallic grey coating was formed on the glass during its removal.

Tests were also made using silica blanks placed alongside soda-lime glass plates at each electrode to determine whether the positive ion bombardment could remove silica by sputtering. After treatment for 1 hour at 3 kV and $0\cdot2$ mA/cm² it was found that the silica blank exposed to positive ions had been etched but to a less extent than the soda glass.† The electron bombarded silica blank had a slightly less absorbing coating than that of the glass plate. Selective sputtering of sodium oxide from glass would produce a porous surface. However, the porous surface which forms on silica is more difficult to explain. It is known that a large amount of the material removed from a surface by sputtering may be recondensed on the surface by collision with surface asperities or gas molecules. Further, that the energy of the surface molecules may be raised without them leaving the surface. This would result in a migrating surface layer which forms a new structure on the surface. Microcrystalline structures are formed on the surfaces of cathodically sputtered metals due to selective sputtering and migration of the surface atoms.

---

† Since completing this section the writer has found that Belser (1952–55) has observed the etching of quartz crystal and glass under ion bombardment. He used a 5 cm dia. aluminium cathode with holes through which the positive ions bombarded the specimens. Bombarding at 3 kV and 100 mA for 5 min was sufficient to etch the surface of polished quartz for electron microscopy examination. A surface etched for 20 min showed a series of parallel markings which were the ledges of crystallites terminating at the surface. The polish did not appear to be marred to the naked eye and the etching penetrated only some 100 Å deep. The etch pattern resembled that obtained by chemical methods. The direct ion-bombardment produced a very clean surface. Thus metal deposited on glass surfaces etched by ion-bombardment had high interfacial bond strengths (300 lb/in² for gold and 1000 lb/in² for platinum, iridium and rhodium).

The efficiency of positive ion bombardment in removing hydrocarbon films from glass is illustrated by the following example. If a glass plate is placed behind a perforated anode electrode as shown in Fig. 5.5 for 1 hour to produce a polymerized hydrocarbon layer of about 600 Å on its surface and the glass is then transferred to the cathode electrode for a similar time the positive ion bombardment will completely remove the surface coating. This effect occurs in glow discharges in both air and argon which indicates that removal of the surface material is due to an energy exchange process rather than a chemical effect.

DIFFUSION OF SODIUM

The writer has observed that soda-lime glass resting on a cathode electrode in a glow discharge forms on the cathode side a white deposit of sodium hydroxide when exposed to air. It appears that the surface of the glass bombarded by positive ions becomes positively charged with respect to the cathode electrode, due either to the emission of secondary electrons or to the adsorption of positive ions. The positive surface charge results in sodium ions diffusing to the cathode. Neither the excitation of sodium atoms or the effects of their diffusion can be detected on the anode glass so that it is improbable that its surface becomes charged.

BOMBARDMENT WITH ALTERNATING POTENTIALS

It follows from the above that a glass exposed to the alternate bombardment of electrons and ions in the cathode dark space of a glow discharge containing hydrocarbon vapours should not become covered with a polymerized layer. Thus the electrodes shown in Fig. 5.5 were operated from an alternating current supply at 3 kV and 0·2 kV/cm² for 1 hour in both air and argon without visible signs of contamination. Likewise glasses of 2 in. square were not contaminated when clamped to two opposing aluminium electrodes 4 in. square as in Fig. 5.6(c). The glasses remain free of contamination when the electrodes are connected to an a.c. supply and Neoprene rubber is introduced into the glow discharge, but a deposit forms rapidly on the anode when the high tension is rectified. The individual effects of ions and electrons are thus disguised by the use of an a.c. power supply as in Fig. 5.6(c). Rozhdestvesnki (1948) studied the cleaning of a glass slide supported on an

21

aluminium table forming one electrode of an opposing pair connected to an a.c. supply. His specimen was undoubtedly exposed to electron and positive ion bombardment. His success in obtaining

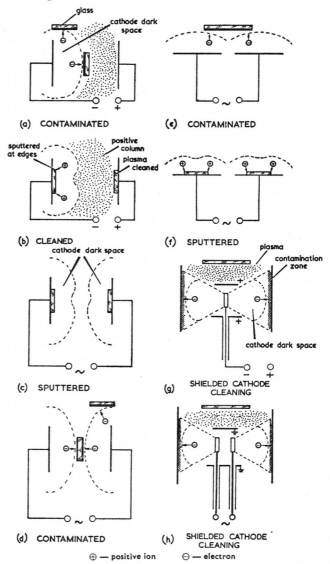

FIG. 5.6 THE CLEANING AND CONTAMINATING EFFECTS OF GLOW DISCHARGE ELECTRODE SYSTEMS USED WITH D.C. AND A.C. HIGH-TENSION SUPPLIES

clean glass surfaces with this arrangement was probably the reason why he did not investigate the process further.

If the glass is placed on the fringe of the cathode dark space as in Figs. 5.6(*a*), (*d*) and (*e*), then it is exposed predominantly to electron bombardment and the risk of contamination irrespective of whether the current is uni-directional or not. When the glass is rested on adjacent a.c. electrodes as in Fig. 5.6(*f*), it is exposed mainly to positive ion bombardment as in Fig. 5.6(*b*) for a d.c. system.

Summary. Summarizing the foregoing discussion on the effects of submitting glass to a glow discharge in a kinetic vacuum system we can state:

(*i*) High velocity electrons traversing the cathode dark space desaturate and polymerize hydrocarbon molecules adsorbed to glass surfaces in their path, whereas electrons accelerated within the positive column have insufficient energy to decompose organic compounds.

(*ii*) Positive ions accelerated in the cathode dark space sputter components from glass, and also superimposed metal oxide and organic films, whereas ion bombardment in the positive column removes at most weakly adsorbed molecules from glass surfaces.

(*iii*) Positive ions accelerated in the cathode dark space sputter polymerized organic films from glass, whereas random bombarding ions of low velocity in the positive column do not.

(*iv*) In the cathode dark space the rate of sputtering of polymerized deposits by the positive ion stream is normally greater than their rate of formation by the electron stream so that contaminants are not deposited on surfaces exposed to alternate bombardment of these particle streams.

(*v*) Glass surfaces may be freed from weakly bound organic contaminants by exposure to the positive column. The adsorbed molecules are most likely removed by random bombardment of positive ions and molecules of high thermal energy. Local heating due to the recombination of ions and electrons on the surface or by conduction from the gas is likely to promote thermal decomposition and deposition of organic matter if the glass is heated to 200°c or above.

BOMBARDING ORGANIC POLYMERS

It has been shown that electron bombardment of organic vapours produces desaturated molecules which polymerize to form thin films with a high carbon content. Treatment of plastic materials, such as the glass-like resins, with high energy particles, may lead to fracture of side chains forming radicals which link adjacent molecules together, or fracture of main chains, reducing the average molecular weight. Both processes may occur together with either cross-linking or degradation predominating. The writer (1958c, 1958d) has studied the effects of bombarding glass-like polymers in a glow discharge where the liberation of energy by the impacting particles is limited to the outer surface because of their moderate energy. Although we are not primarily concerned with solid organic polymers, the processes which occur during their bombardment illustrate and confirm the theories advanced above for the role of the most energetic electrons and ions in a glow discharge containing organic vapours.

The plastic specimens to be bombarded were mounted behind apertures (0·5 × 0·5 in.) in the centres of two opposing electrodes made from aluminium sheet of 4 × 3 in. spaced 4 in. apart. As in the previous experiments, the current densities of the particles bombarding the specimens were not known, but it was assumed that they were of similar order to those flowing to the metal electrodes, because surface tracking and internal breakdown did not occur with either specimen. Also a stable discharge was obtained with a continuous cathode dark space in the region of the electrode aperture. The glow discharge was operated at 5 kV at 0·13 mA/cm² with the cathode dark space almost filling the electrode spacing.

Perspex. 'Perspex' specimens of ⅛ in. thick sheet were bombarded for different times. During the first 5 min of bombardment the reflectivity of both anode and cathode specimens rose from 4% to about 9% and their optical absorption increased to about 10%. During further bombardment the adsorption of the cathode specimen remained constant, whereas the electron bombarded specimen became dark brown and almost opaque, as shown in Fig. 5.7. When the bombardment period was increased to 1–2 hours, being carried out in stages so that the specimens did not exceed 100°c in temperature, the cathode specimen became deeply etched as material was removed from its surface, whereas the anode specimen was completely destroyed, as shown in Plate 24. Similar changes in the optical absorption were obtained with polystyrene but the cathode specimen was not etched.

Epoxy resins. Coatings of epichlorhydrin resin cross-linked with melamine were applied to glass slides by dipping and stoved for 40 min at 170°c. The films ranged in thickness from 0·001–3 in. and were almost colourless before bombardment. The change in the transmittance of the specimens as the bombardment proceeded was similar to that observed for Perspex, *i.e.* a continuous decrease in the transmittance of the electron bombarded specimen, whereas the cathode specimen reached a constant value, as shown in Fig. 5.7. When the bombardment time was increased to $4\frac{1}{2}$ hours, the resin films were completely removed by the positive ion bombardment.

The foregoing experiments were carried out in argon to avoid oxidation of either target. However, exactly similar results have been obtained in air. From the optical characteristics of the specimens it appears that the damaged layer produced by electron bombardment has a carbon concentration which rises with the bombardment time. On the other hand, the constant optical absorption attained under positive ion bombardment is probably due to the initial formation of a damaged layer which is partially removed by the impacting ions as the carbon content of the surface rises. The resultant optical absorption would then be an equilibrium value depending on the interaction of the two processes. To prove this hypothesis Perspex specimens which had been electron bombarded to promote degradation were exposed to positive ion bombardment, and it was found that their optical absorption was reduced to that of a cathode specimen as the damaged material was removed from the surface (1958c). The experiments discussed here show that synthetic glasses cannot be treated in a glow discharge for cleaning purposes without degradation of the surface material.

5. GLOW DISCHARGE CLEANING OF GLASS IN EVAPORATION PLANT

ELECTRODE DESIGN

It is shown in the preceding sections that glass can be cleaned, *i.e.* manifests a high coefficient of friction and black breath figure, if exposed to a glow discharge in a kinetic vacuum system providing high energy electrons do not reach the surface. Thus a glass specimen may be cleaned when rested on a cathode electrode. However, there are many obstacles to the use of this method, particularly in vacuum evaporation plant. At high current densities (0.2 mA/cm^2) the glass surface is sputtered by positive ions in the cathode dark space. Also, the bombarded surface becomes electrically charged so that ions in the glass, such as sodium, migrate under the induced field. The system can only be used with a glass of limited area,

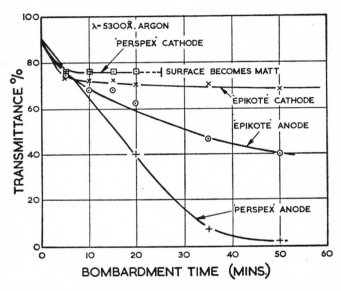

Fig. 5.7   Changes in the transmittance at $\lambda = 5300$ Å of 'perspex' sheet and 'epikote' lacquers films under bombardment by positive ions and electrons at 5 kV and 0.13 mA/cm^2 in argon

otherwise the configuration of the cathode dark space is affected, and only the edges of the glass are bombarded by positive ions. Finally, when used in an evaporation plant films may be deposited from the vapour source on to the open cathode electrode and these can sputter on to the glass during a subsequent bombardment. Fortunately, contaminants remaining after chemical cleaning are removed from glass by random bombardment in the positive column.

Benson *et al.* (1950) describe an electrode system for use in the bell jars of normal evaporation plants or in large evaporators

(72 in. dia). They used a flat annular cathode facing the work-surface and arranged it at a large distance from the work to obtain uniformity of heating. As their system must have contained organic vapour one must attribute cleaning to the positive column. How-

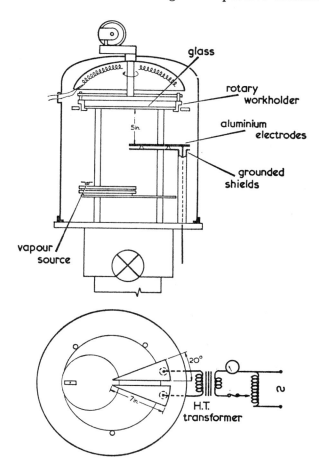

FIG. 5.8   SECTOR CATHODES USED WITH A ROTARY WORK-HOLDER IN A VACUUM
EVAPORATION PLANT

ever, with exposed cathode electrodes there is a risk of contamination even when using low applied voltages because, if the pressure should fall, the cathode dark space lengthens so that the glass becomes exposed to the bombardment of high energy electrons which quickly induce surface contamination if organic vapours are present. This may be avoided by using the shielded cathode system (Holland, 1957, 1958*a*) described below.

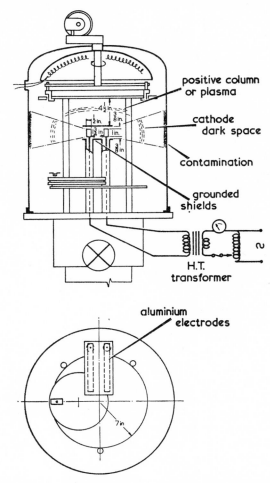

FIG. 5.9   SHIELDED ELECTRODES USED WITH A ROTARY WORK-HOLDER IN A
VACUUM EVAPORATION PLANT

Shielded cathode system. The electrons liberated from or near the cathode in a glow discharge tend to travel in straight paths through the cathode dark space, whereas the positive ions with their smaller mean free path are scattered by colliding with gas molecules. The rectilinearly propagated electrons can be prevented from striking the work by shielding the cathode, and an alternative path made available to sustain ionization. Thus, the high velocity electrons can be made to travel in directions which will avoid collision with the work surface, whereas the positive ions and neutral molecules of high velocity may be considerably scattered and strike the work. The work surface is also exposed to the positive column or plasma region of the discharge. Electrode systems based on the foregoing principle of design are illustrated in Fig. 5.6(*g*) and (*h*).

Electrode system for rotary work-holder. Shielded cathode systems have been used effectively in several types of evaporation plants, and we shall consider first that used in a plant fitted with a rotary plane work-holder. For purposes of comparison a conventional system has been used consisting of a pair of sector-shaped electrodes mounted under the work-holder and connected to an a.c. power supply as shown in Fig. 5.8. Hiesinger (1951) has described a similar system using a single sector cathode.

Shown in Fig. 5.9 is the modified electrode system. It consists of two h.t. electrodes made from aluminium bar arranged radially under the work-holder. The gap between the electrodes is too small for sustained ionization at the gas pressure and current density used, and the glow discharge follows the longer path shown. The electrodes are covered with two horizontal shields so that the electrons traversing the cathode dark spaces are accelerated almost parallel to the plane of the glass. When operated at high pressures (0·5 torr) and low voltage (500 V) the glass is exposed only to the positive column and at low pressures (0·01 torr) and high voltages (5 kV) the glass is also exposed to the random bombardment of high energy ions and neutral molecules from the greatly extended cathode dark space. Under neither of these conditions can high energy electrons reach the glass. Prolonged operation of the electrode system at high voltages and low pressures results in intense heating of the glass. Whilst the latter is useful when the properties of an evaporated deposit are improved by deposition on to a hot substrate organic molecules in the vacuum atmosphere may be thermally decomposed on the substrate.

OPTICAL MEASUREMENTS

Table 5.6 compares the optical absorption produced by contaminating films on glass using the unshielded cathodes with that

Table 5.6

The effect of the glow discharge on the optical absorption of glass at
$\lambda = 5300$ Å when exposed to different electrode arrangements

H.T. electrode design	Residual gas	Treatment time (min)	T (%)	R (%)	A (%)
Unshielded	air	60	80	8·5	3·5
Unshielded	air	180	86·5	7·5	6
Shielded	air	60	91	9	0
Unshielded	argon	60	88	8	4
Shielded	argon	60	91	9	0
Unshielded	air–Neoprene	10	10	10	80
Shielded	air–Neoprene	10	91	9	0

All glasses were mounted on a 14 in. dia. rotary holder and exposed to a glow discharge of 5 kV at 160 mA with flowing gas at 10^{-2} torr pressure. Chamber exhausted by a silicone oil diffusion pump giving an ultimate pressure before gas admission of 10^{-5} torr. Demountable vacuum system with Buna N and Neoprene vacuum seals.

due to the new design. Both systems were operated at 5 kV and 160 mA at 0·01 torr pressure with a cathode dark space of about 4 in. in depth. Under these conditions the edge of the cathode dark space almost reached the work surface when using the open sector electrodes. The exposed glass remained free from absorption even when a piece of Neoprene rubber was placed in the cathode dark space near to one of the shielded electrodes, whereas a dense brown deposit was formed on the glass using unshielded electrodes, as shown in Plate 25a. Fairly clean glass could, in fact, be prepared in the presence of the Neoprene so that when a stick of titanium was lightly rubbed over the glass surface, a heavy trace of metal was left on the treated portion of the glass as shown in Plate 25b. Undecomposed hydrocarbon molecules would not be readily adsorbed to the glass because its temperature rose to about 150°c during the treatment. The electrons accelerated in the cathode dark space of the shielded electrodes struck the wall of the vessel where an organic deposit slowly appeared as indicated in Fig. 5.9.

Certain types of optical glass which were rendered optically absorbing by electron bombardment in a glow discharge could be cleaned with the shielded cathode system without damage.

It has been claimed (1945) that a chemically cleaned glass surface may be protected against contamination whilst in the atmosphere by a film of an organic substance, e.g. lanolin, which is thermally evaporated or oxidized in a glow discharge. Tests have shown that at low pressures the electrode system in Fig. 5.8 decomposes grease films (*e.g.* Apiezon 'L') spread on a glass surface because the glass is exposed to bombardment by high energy electrons, whereas grease layers are removed from glass using the shielded electrodes.

A second type of cleaning system based on the shielded cathode method designed for use with a stationary work holder is shown in Fig. 5.10. The discharge takes the longer path from the circular electrodes and the glass is not exposed to high speed electrons. In a kinetic vacuum system the decomposed hydrocarbon deposits appear directly above and below the electrodes as shown.

SOME PROPERTIES OF BOMBARDED GLASS

The coefficient of friction. The coefficient of static friction was measured for glasses cleaned with the shielded and unshielded electrode systems. With shielded electrodes the value of μ_s measured in air immediately after treatment was substantially the same whether the rider was glow-discharge cleaned or vapour degreased in *iso*-propyl alcohol, the latter was generally used. Table 5.7 shows the values of μ_s measured using different cleaning techniques and is largely self-explanatory.

Table 5.7

The coefficient of static friction of glass on glass using glow discharge and other cleaning techniques

Cleaning techniques	μ_s
Baked *in vacuo* (300°c, 1 hour)	0·2
Flamed (coal gas and air)	0·4
Unshielded h.t. electrodes in air (silicone contamination)	0·7
Unshielded h.t. electrodes with silicone oil bath	0·6
Unshielded h.t. electrodes in air/Neoprene rubber	0·3
Shielded h.t. electrodes in air	0·8
Shielded h.t. electrodes in air/Neoprene rubber	0·6
Shielded h.t. electrodes in A, N_2, H_2 and O_2	0·7–0·9
Evaporated silica on silica	0·7
Evaporated cryolite on cryolite	0·55

All glasses treated in a glow discharge were mounted on a rotary support of 14 in. dia. and exposed for 10 min at 5 kV and 160 mA in flowing gas at 10^{-2} torr pressure. The chamber was exhausted by a silicone oil diffusion pump giving an ultimate pressure before gas admission of 10^{-5} torr. Demountable vacuum system with Buna N and Neoprene vacuum seals.

The glasses treated in a glow discharge were mounted on a rotary support and exposed for 10 min at 5 kV and 160 mA in flowing gas at 0·01 torr pressure, using the apparatus shown in Figs. 5.8 and 5.9. The surprising observation was made that glasses bombarded with the open sector cathodes as shown in Fig. 5.8 were coated with optically absorbing deposits which were readily wetted by water and possessed a high value of μ_s (see Plate 20). The effect was attributed to the decomposition of silicone vapours emitted by the diffusion pump which formed silica-like films on the glass. To confirm this a tray of silicone oil was placed near to the sector electrodes and the treated glass still had a high value of μ_s and could be wetted. If the electron bombardment was very intense the deposit showed interference colours and had negligible absorption. Using a method based on Brewster angle measurement, Mr T. Putner, of the writer's laboratory, found that the deposits had a refractive index of 1·58. Durable coatings of aluminium have been produced on soda-lime glass coated with decomposed silicone films and undoubtedly many workers using these fluids must have un-wittingly produced such base coatings. The values of μ_s for glasses treated in the presence of hydrocarbon vapours from Neoprene rubber were low and the decomposed deposits could not be wetted.

Absorption-free glasses with a high coefficient of friction and showing a black breath figure were always obtained with the shielded electrodes irrespective of the nature of the residual gas. As the friction was not measured *in vacuo* it would be dangerous to attribute different cleaning efficiencies to the different gases because the test glasses must have been partially contaminated in the atmosphere.

When the shielded electrodes were operated at high pressure and low voltage (500 V) so that the glass was in the positive column between the electrodes clean glass was obtained with $\mu_s \simeq 0 \cdot 8$. Karasev and Izmailova (1954) have reported a value of 0·8 for clean silica and 1·07 for clean glass, compared with the average value measured here for clean glass of 0·8; from their experimental data it would appear that their surfaces were cleaned in the positive column of the discharge. The shielded electrode system has been used in vacuum evaporation plant for cleaning astronomical mirrors and plate glass of up to nine feet in diameter. Values of μ_s between 0·85–1 have been obtained over the work surface.

ELECTRODE SYSTEM FOR SPHERICAL WORK-HOLDER

It is common practice to evaporate films, *e.g.* anti-reflection layers, on to small glass components using a spherical work-holder to obtain uniform coating from a single vapour source. The writer (1956) has already described elsewhere a bombardment system for a stationary holder similar to that shown in Fig. 5.10. The system consists of aluminium rod electrodes connected to the output terminals of a h.t. transformer. The discharge rods are shielded on the inside with a grounded metal cylinder to prevent evaporated material from the vapour source condensing on their surface. A second outer cylinder is fitted to prevent the discharge from unduly heating the vessel. In its original form no conscious attempt was made to prevent electrons from the cathode dark space reaching the work-holder and the provision of the inner shield ring for-

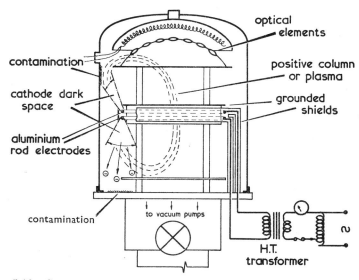

FIG. 5.10 SHIELDED ELECTRODES FOR GLOW DISCHARGE CLEANING IN AN EVAPORATION PLANT USED WITH A FIXED SPHERICAL WORK-HOLDER CARRYING OPTICAL COMPONENTS

tuitously limited the electron bombardment zone. When the cleanliness of glasses treated in the work-holder was determined by measuring their coefficient of friction and optical absorption it was found that a narrow annular region at the edge of the work-holder was adversely affected. An additional annular mask was fitted in the horizontal plane to the inner cylinder and this completely prevented electrons from the cathode dark space from bombarding the work-holder. When operated from an alternating supply (3 kV at 500 mA) cleaning is effected in a few minutes with the glass exposed to scattered high energy positive ions and to the positive column in the centre of the vessel.

ELECTRODE SYSTEM FOR ASTRONOMICAL MIRROR

Shown in Fig. 5.11 is a shielded electrode system used for cleaning an astronomical mirror before evaporating aluminium on to its surface. The system consists of two aluminium ring electrodes

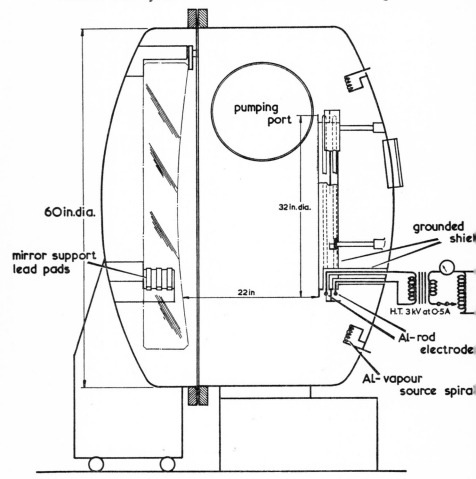

FIG. 5.11   SHIELDED ELECTRODE SYSTEM USED FOR GLOW DISCHARGE CLEANING
AN ASTRONOMICAL MIRROR BEFORE ALUMINIZING *in vacuo*

connected to the output of a h.t. transformer. The large circular shield is grounded and prevents high energy electrons from reaching the mirror surface. Using the apparatus dimensions shown in the figure and operating the system for 20 min at 3 kV and 500 mA raised the temperature of a metal test plate (20 s.w.g.) by some 3 °c as measured with nine thermocouples distributed over the plate. The weak heating effect was due to the mirror zone only being exposed to the positive column. However, this was sufficient to obtain values of μ_s between 0·8–1 after 10 min bombardment.

6. CONTAMINATION OF CLEAN GLASS IN KINETIC VACUUM SYSTEMS

CHEMISORPTION ON FRESH GLASS AND SILICA SURFACES

Bateson (1952) has shown that a glass surface cleaned in a glow discharge becomes contaminated by hydrocarbon molecules if left for a few minutes in the vacuum of a kinetic pumping system. When making the tests discussed in the previous section (Holland, 1958b) the glasses were removed from the vessel immediately the cleaning was completed. Tests were therefore made to find the speed of surface contamination in a normal kinetic vacuum plant using rubber seals and an oil diffusion pump. The diffusion pump was of the fractionating type and fitted with a water-cooled oil baffle.

Fresh evaporated films of silica-on-glass were prepared and exposed for different periods *in vacuo* after deposition. It was observed that the silica deposits could be readily wetted with water after a certain period of vacuum exposure, and then their surfaces rapidly became hydrophobic supporting spherical water droplets. It was deduced that the adsorbed layer was silicone oil from the diffusion pump; chemisorbed silicone films on glass are strongly water repellent.

A series of clean silica and glass surfaces were prepared and exposed in air and vacuum and the following observations made:

(a) *Silica coated glass.* Films which had been rendered hydrophobic by exposure *in vacuo* could not be made wettable by vapour degreasing in *iso*-propyl alcohol vapour, but could be by flaming or glow-discharge cleaning. However, the cleaned films did not become hydrophobic when re-exposed *in vacuo* as found with new coatings. Evaporated silica films initially exposed to the atmosphere immediately after formation also did not become hydrophobic after long periods *in vacuo*.

(b) *Fractured glass surfaces.* The fresh surface of a fractured piece of glass was readily wetted by water when the glass was broken in air. The surfaces of glass broken *in vacuo* could not be wetted after exposure for 4 min at the reduced pressure. However, glass fractured in air and transferred to the vacuum plant continued to be wettable after hours of exposure *in vacuo.*

(c) *Clean glass.* Glasses cleaned by a glow discharge or chemical methods remained wettable and did not develop a hydrophobic surface after hours of exposure *in vacuo.*

From these observations it is obvious that a new surface of glass or silica rapidly becomes contaminated by strongly adsorbed substances when exposed in air and these screen the cations in the glass surface and prevent the subsequent adsorption of silicone molecules. (It should be noted that the vapour pressure of the silicone in the vacuum chamber was below the saturated value so that oil could not condense on the glass.) Water vapour would have been present in the glow discharge gas and also formed in the flame so that cleaned surface would constantly be covered with OH^- ions. It is shown in Chapters 6 and 7 that silicone molecules can be chemisorbed to glass by using dimethyl silicon chloride which chemically reacts with the OH^- ions and removes them from the surface. Silicone molecules do not possess reactive groups and they are only chemisorbed when water or hydroxyl groups are not present on the glass.

Silicones have been chemisorbed by nascent glass surfaces and silica films at vacuum pressures between 10^{-6} to 10^{-4} torr. Analysis of the residual gas showed it contained N_2, O_2, CH_2, CO_2. H_2O as well as the silicone molecules. The vapour pressure of the silicone in the vessel ranged from 10^{-10} to 10^{-8} torr depending on the fluid and the temperature of the cold baffle above the diffusion pump. The partial pressure of water vapour was about half the residual pressure, i.e. between 5×10^{-7} and 5×10^{-5} torr. Thus many hundreds of water molecules competed with each silicone molecule for the adsorption sites. In spite of this silicone surface layers were chemisorbed at room temperature having a contact angle for water of 90°. The partial pressure of the silicone vapour in the vessel ranged from a tenth to its full saturated value whereas that of the water vapour was about a millionth or less of its saturated value. Therefore silicone molecules could move into the chemisorbed state

PLATE 20   'Black' breath figure. The upper half of glass (*a*) has been glow discharge cleaned and the upper half of glass (*b*) flamed. When the glasses are cooled a smooth invisible water film is condensed on the cleaned zones whilst the uncleaned lower halves of the glasses are covered with water droplets

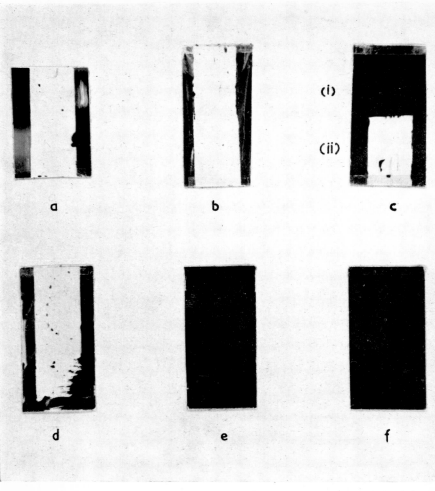

PLATE 21 'Sellotape' stripping test of adhesion of evaporated aluminium films to plate glass pre-cleaned by different methods (*After Putner*, 1959)

(a) Washed in a detergent (Teepol) and water and polished with a cloth;
(b) Vapour degreased in *iso*propyl alcohol, immersed in Teepol/water solution and allowed to dry;
(c) (i) vapour degreased
    (ii) immersed in liquid *iso*propyl alcohol and allowed to dry;
(d) Ultrasonically cleaned using continuously distilled *iso*propyl alcohol;
(e) Vapour degreased in *iso*propyl alcohol;
(f) Vapour degreased and discharge cleaned

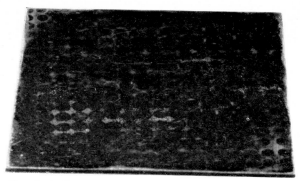

PLATE 22   Soda-lime glass bombarded by positive ions through a grid and aluminized to enhance outline of sputtered pattern (*After Holland*, 1958*b*)

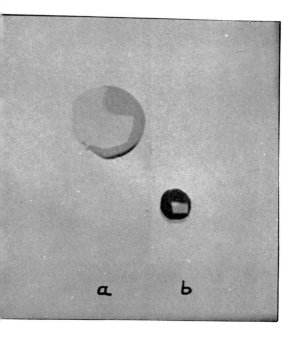

PLATE 23 Glass surface which has been discharge cleaned in the presence of silicone oil vapour from a diffusion pump. Electron bombardment of the surface has formed a desaturated silicone layer

(*a*) Part of surface exposed to electron stream from the cathode dark space of a 'V' cathode (h.t. power 3 kV at 500 mA for 2 h). The bombarded surface shows a low contact angle but reduced optical transmission because of the decomposed silicone film;

(*b*) Part of surface masked during exposure to discharge shows high contact angle due to poor chemical cleaning

untreated   ion bombarded   electron bombarded

PLATE 24   Surface damage produced on Perspex after bombardment for 2 h at 5 kV and 0·13 mA/cm² in argon. The positive ion bombarded specimen has been aluminized to enhance the contrast of the surface etching (*After Holland*, 1960)

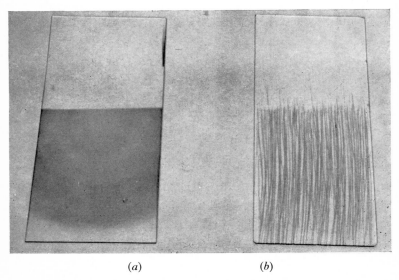

(*a*)   (*b*)

PLATE 25   The glasses have been partially masked and exposed to a glow discharge using a rotary holder with Neoprene rubber in the cathode dark space.

Glass (*a*) shows on the exposed lower half the pattern of the hydrocarbon decomposition which varies with the intensity of the impinging electrons;

Glass (*b*) cleaned with shielded cathodes has a high coefficient of friction on the lower treated surface which has been permanently exposed by rubbing with titanium (*After Holland*, 1958)

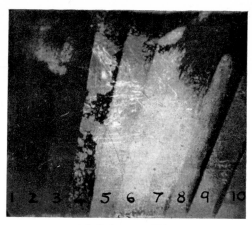

(a) Substrate 50°C

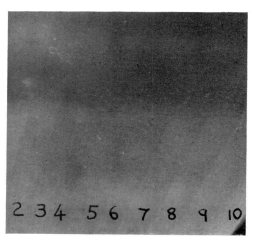

(b) Substrate 230°C

PLATE 26   Reduction of the adhesion of zinc sulphide films to a new silica surface as the substrate becomes covered with a chemisorbed layer from silicone (704) vapour. Silica surface exposed to vapour in 1min steps (*After Holland and Bateman*, 1960)

(a) Chemically cleaned glass

(b) Glass coated with an organic resin (Durez 12687)

PLATE 27   Use of captive bubble for measurement of contact angle of water on glass (*After Moser*)

PLATE 28   Reaction between titanium and soda-lime glass when the metal film is heat oxidized at 400°c. The right-hand side of the glass has been covered with a barrier layer of aluminium oxide, which prevents the reaction (*After Holland et al.*, 1957)

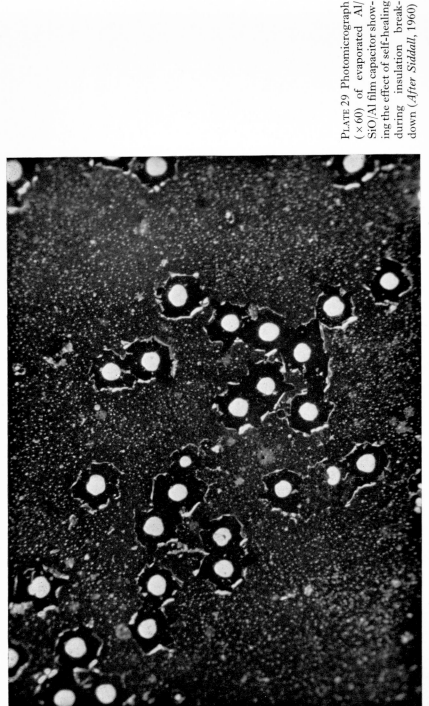

PLATE 29 Photomicrograph (×60) of evaporated Al/SiO/Al film capacitor showing the effect of self-healing during insulation breakdown (*After Siddall*, 1960)

from a physically adsorbed monolayer, whereas water molecules did not linger on the surface sufficiently long to find reaction sites. Due to this effect a silicone layer could still slowly form on a fresh SiO_2-film over a period of $1\frac{1}{2}$ h when the vapour pressure of the silicone was about 10^{-10} torr and that of water 10^{-5} torr.

An experiment was made to ensure that the hydrophobic surface was not produced by hydrocarbons emitted from the rubber gaskets. A quantity of rubber shielded from heat radiation was placed inside the vacuum vessel and a silica film deposited. When removed from the vessel the coating smelt strongly of sulphur and was obviously contaminated, but a black breath figure could still be condensed and the surface was readily wetted. This proved that the principal material deposited from the rubber at normal temperature was not hydrophobic and also that a black breath figure was not a criterion of cleanliness under all conditions. (Most elastomers emit water, nitrogen, oxygen, hydrocarbons, *e.g.* methane, and carbon dioxide. Sulphur will be released if used for vulcanizing. With Buna N Neoprene, and Silastic water vapour desorption predominates.)

From measurement of the time required to render a silica film hydrophobic, the writer concluded that the vapour pressure of the silicone in the vessel was less than the equilibrium value due to the fresh silica coating on the chamber interior having a gettering action. To avoid this, a tray of silicone oil was placed in the coating vessel. With the diffusion pump fluid silicone 704 in the vessel the contamination time was constant at 3 min and with silicone 703 the time was 1 min.

Holland and Bateman (1960) have observed that when a silicone film is chemisorbed by an evaporated silica film it subsequently prevents an evaporated zinc sulphide film from adhering to the silica as shown in Plate 26. When such a film combination is exposed to atmosphere the ZnS-film spontaneously breaks up as it absorbs moisture. This effect did not occur when ZnS-films were evaporated on aged glass held at normal temperature because silicone contamination had been prevented by the shielding effect of the absorbed OH^- ions.

The period of time was measured for a silica film to become covered completely by a chemisorbed silicone layer as manifested by the instability of a superimposed ZnS-film. The freshly evaporated silica film was covered by a shutter and progressively exposed in vacuum to the vapour from a silicone fluid held in a water-

22

cooled container. When the silica film was held at a constant temperature of 50°c the exposure time required for subsequently destroying the adhesion of a ZnS-film was between 3–5 min for silicone 704 and 1 min for silicone 703 (these values agree with those determined by measuring the hydrophobicity of the silica described above). Silica films held at 50°c did not strongly adsorb the vapour molecules emitted from the mineral oil Apiezon 'C' which is a diffusion pump fluid. This was probably because the oil molecules lacked polar groups with an affinity for the film surface and thus at normal temperature only a partial surface coverage by physical adsorption was possible.

When the temperature of a fresh silica film was raised to 230°c in the presence of silicone 703 or 704 the adhesive force of the silica for zinc sulphide was not destroyed completely until the silica had been exposed for 75 min. Zinc sulphide adhesion tests were not made on silica base layers heated in Apiezon 'C' vapour. However, it is shown below that glass becomes permanently contaminated by an organic film when heated to 230°c in Apiezon 'C' vapour, because the oil is easily decomposed on hot surfaces.

The manner in which silicone molecules are chemisorbed by silica or glass surfaces in vacuum is worthy of consideration. Silicone 704 consists of molecules with a constant molecular weight of 484 and a diameter of about 10 Å, thus some 10^{14} molecules cm^2 are required to cover a surface. The vapour pressure of silicone 704 has been reported as 5×10^{-9} torr at 15°c by Huntress *et al.* (1957) who extrapolated a curve determined at high vapour pressures. Using these values and assuming the vapour molecules are adsorbed on first impact one obtains a time for a monolayer to form of about 3–4 min. This agrees with the measured time of 3–5 min for a fresh silica surface to attain maximum hydrophobicity or completely lose any affinity for zinc sulphide.

When the temperature of a fresh silica coating is raised to 230°c it takes 75 min for chemisorption to lower the adhesive forces of the surface, from which it can be deduced that only five out of every hundred molecules are chemisorbed on first impact.

The silicone molecules will strike the substrate by either their polar or non-polar terminals and the chemisorbed layer must be formed as follows. At normal temperature, silicone molecules which strike the substrate by non-polar terminals will be physically adsorbed and linger on the surface for a sufficient time to orientate themselves in the chemisorbed state, because the sorption coefficient is known to approach one. When the substrate temperature is raised, the period for which physically adsorbed molecules linger on the surface decreases so that the formation of a chemisorbed layer increasingly depends on the oil molecules striking the surface by their polar terminals.

It is fortuitous that chemisorbed oil films do not readily form on 'aged' glass surfaces, but they can form on 'aged' glass during baking in vacuum. It has been current practice in vacuum evapora-

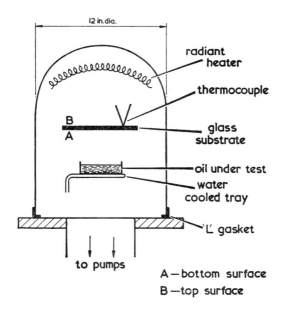

FIG. 5.12 APPARATUS FOR DETERMINING THE CONTAMINATION OF BAKED GLASS BY ORGANIC VAPOURS FROM DIFFUSION PUMP OILS

tion plant to glow-discharge clean glass before baking, but it was shown by Holland and Bateman that the hardest and most water-resistant zinc sulphide films were produced on surfaces which were first baked and then glow-discharge cleaned.

BAKING GLASS IN VACUUM

Effects of oils and greases. Baking glass *in vacuo* may remove sorbed gases but dirt films of non-volatile greases may be thermally decomposed and remain as carbonaceous deposits on the surface. Similarly cracked carbonaceous films may form on the heated glass if it is exposed to the organic vapours emitted by rubbers, vacuum greases and rotary mechanical or diffusion pump fluids. Vacuum oils and

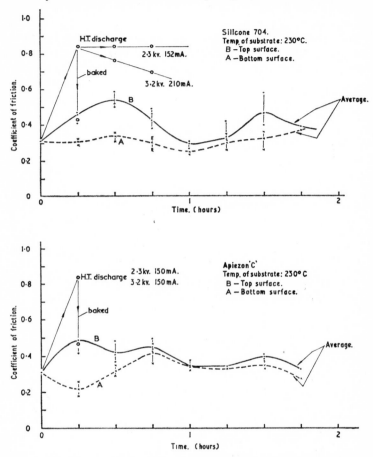

Fig. 5.13   Friction of glass on glass baked *in vacuo* in the presence of different diffusion pump fluids. Glow discharge cleaning gives a high and constant value of μ_s providing the specimen is not overheated as bombardment proceeds

greases derived from mineral oils, such as the Apiezon types, are easily decomposed whereas silicone oils and greases are more resistant to cracking. However, when glass is baked in the presence of a silicone oil the glass surface becomes strongly hydrophobic as the surface water evaporates and is replaced by a chemisorbed silicone layer.

The writer (1960) has determined the value of μ_s of soda-lime glass slides baked for different times in the presence of vapours from diffusion pump fluids. As shown in Fig. 5.12 the glass specimen was placed above a water-cooled tray containing the test fluid to ensure constant concentration of the vapour in the vessel during baking. The glass surface facing the oil was designated A and that remote from the oil B. The glasses were cleaned with cloth dipped in a detergent and then *iso*-propyl alcohol giving a value of μ_s of 0·3. Values of μ_s as a function of baking time are shown in Fig. 5.13. When the glasses were baked at 230°c in either Silicone 704 or Apiezon 'C' vapour the coefficient of friction of the surface facing the liquid oil remained at a low value as oil molecules replaced contaminants evaporated from the glass. The glass surface remote from the liquid oil showed after baking for different periods an initial rise in μ_s and then a decrease. Presumably the thermally evaporated contaminants were more slowly replaced by the oil molecules on the remote glass side because the oil molecules struck this surface at a lower rate.

Heating by a glow discharge. If glass surfaces can be covered with either thermally decomposed or chemisorbed organic films when baked in oil vapour then a similar effect can occur when glass is cleaned in a glow discharge if its temperature is unduly raised by the bombardment. Normally there is ample water vapour in the atmosphere of a low pressure glow discharge to ensure that the surface is covered with hydroxyl groups as organic contaminants are removed; OH^- ions shield the surface against chemisorption of silicone vapour molecules. However, if the glass is unduly heated during bombardment then the hydroxyl groups can be evaporated leaving the surface exposed. Also, thermal cracking of oil molecules on the glass surface will be promoted.

Using an ionic bombardment apparatus with shielded electrodes, as in Fig. 5.9, produced high values of μ_s in a glow discharge providing the h.t. power did not exceed 2·3 kV at 152 mA. Raising the power to 3·2 kV at 210 mA reduced the cleaning efficiency as the specimen temperature rose. Likewise baking a bombarded surface immediately reduced the friction.

Improved vacuum materials and apparatus. The rate of contamination of clean glass by organic vapours in kinetic vacuum systems can now be greatly decreased. Rubber vacuum seals made of Neoprene and Buna N can be replaced by a fluorinated hydrocarbon with elastomer properties called Viton (Du Pont de Nemours) which has a degassing rate about one tenth of the former materials. A silicone oil known as 705 is available for use in diffusion pumps. This fluid has a vapour pressure at 15°c of about 2×10^{-9} torr. Thus it should take three times longer for a glass surface to be covered with a chemisorbed layer of silicone 705 as that for silicone 704 discussed above.

Hickman (1960) has used a class of fluids known as the polyphenyl ethers and polyphenyl benzenes in diffusion pumps, because of their exceptionally high decomposition temperature ($> 400°c$) and low vapour pressure ($\leqslant 10^{-9}$ torr) at normal temperature. Nothing is known about the adsorption of vapours of these fluids on clean or heated glass.

When the partial pressure of organic vapour in a vacuum system is low a polymerized film may not form on an electron bombarded target in a glow discharge in air, because the unsaturated organic molecules are removed from the target by oxidation. However, electron bombardment of a target using a hot cathode emitter in high vacuum will produce a polymerized layer under the same conditions of organic vapour pressure. Using a stainless steel vacuum system with 'Viton' and metal seals and exhausted by a diffusion pump (silicone 705), the writer (1963) could not detect a polymerized film on a target intensely electron bombarded in an air glow discharge (10^{-2} torr) although mass spectrometry had shown organic vapour with a partial pressure of about 10^{-8} torr to be present. However, after several hours of bombardment in air a nonabsorbing coating of aluminium oxide was sputtered on to the glass target from the aluminium cathode. Reducing the vacuum pressure to 10^{-6} torr and bombarding the target with electrons from a thermal emitter gave an organic growth rate of 50 Å/h. Condensing the vapours on a liquid nitrogen trap placed in the vacuum vessel reduced the contamination rate to 22 Å/h.

To prevent clean surfaces from becoming contaminated by organic vapour or gas molecules over long periods one must use ultra-high vacuum apparatus with which pressures of 10^{-9} torr or less are attainable. Such systems must be baked to reduce their desorption rate and are constructed from either glass or stainless steel. When the latter is used the vacuum gaskets are made from compressed metal rings. Ultra-high vacuum systems are exhausted by either getter-ion pumps or diffusion pumps (mercury or oil types). When diffusion pumps are used they must be fitted with refrigerated vapour traps. The writer (1960a) has observed that during bake-out of an u.h. vacuum system oil vapour from a diffusion pump contaminated a glass specimen in the vessel. The diffusion pump was charged with silicone 704 and fitted with a liquid nitrogen trap I near the vessel and a water-cooled trap II directly over the pump. Trap I was only charged with liquid nitrogen after bake-out and the vapour pressure of the oil in equilibrium with the water-cooled trap II was sufficient to cause contamination of the hot glass. Refrigerating trap II with liquid nitrogen prevented contamination during the baking cycle. However trap II had to be refrigerated even when trap I was charged otherwise appreciable oil vapour was condensed on trap I and this was transferred to the vessel during the subsequent baking cycle (Holland, Laurenson and Priestland 1963).

Some interesting observations were made with the vacuum system when trap II was water-cooled. Thus soda-lime glass slides present in the vessel during bake-out had a higher value of μ_s when a diaphragm was inserted into the pumping port *to limit the pumping speed*. Although this would have raised the chamber pressure during baking it also restricted the rate at which oil vapour entered the vessel. (A vessel principally desorbs water vapour during the bake-out unless it has been contaminated by solvents when cleaned.) The coefficient of friction was also lower for glass specimens facing the pumping aperture. Values of $\mu_s \simeq 0.84$, approaching that of clean glass, were only obtained when the oil vapour in the vessel was reduced to a negligible quantity.

The various kinds of surface contamination which can occur on glass treated in kinetic vacuum systems containing organic vapours are collected together in Table 5.8. It will be obvious from the foregoing that whilst oil diffusion pumps can produce ultra-high vacuum conditions there is great danger of surface contamination during initial exhaustion unless the system is carefully designed and operated. There is less risk of surface contamination by organic vapour if a vacuum system is exhausted by a mercury diffusion pump or Penning type getter pump using a Zeolite sorption pump in place of a rotary mechanical oil pump for initial exhaustion. With modern ultra-high vacuum systems it is possible to reduce organic contaminant growth rates on electron bombarded targets to below 5 Å/h.

Table 5.8

Types of contamination of chemically cleaned and fresh† glass surfaces in kinetic vacuum systems containing oil vapours

Process	Surface	Nature of contaminant layer	Comments
GLOW DISCHARGE CLEANING			
(i) Cathode sputtering of h.t. electrodes.	Chemically cleaned or fresh.	Metal or oxidized metal film when glow discharge in oxygen bearing gas, *e.g.* air.	Negligible when using super-pure aluminium cathodes and shielded electrode system.
(ii) Bombardment of glass by c.d.s.‡ electrons.	Chemically cleaned or fresh.	Polymerized organic film.	Produced by organic vapours from elastomers, mineral oils.
		Polym. silica–organic film.	Produced by silicone vapours. Deposit can be wetted with water.
			Avoided by either preventing c.d.s.‡ extending to glass surface or using shielded electrode system.
(iii) Heating of glass by glow discharge either in positive column or by c.d.s. electrons.	Chemically cleaned or fresh.	Decomposed organic film.	Organic vapours cracked on hot glass.
		Chemisorbed silicone.	Silicone molecules replace OH^- ions on glass.
			Avoided by keeping glass temp. $< 200°c$ using moderate h.t. power.
			Shielded electrode system prevents electron bombardment heating.
ELECTRON BOMBARDMENT (HOT CATHODE)	Chemically cleaned or fresh.	Polymerized organic film.	Produced by organic vapour.
		Polym. silica–organic film.	Produced by silicones vapour.
ADSORPTION	Chemically cleaned.	Physically adsorbed gas or organic layer.	Non-polar contaminant molecules can only be physically adsorbed on an existing chemisorbed water layer.
		Polar compounds.	Molecules with $-(COOH)$, $-(OH)$, groups can form oriented layers.
	Fresh.	Chemisorption of water or silicone vapours.	Nature of surface contaminant dependent on composition of vacuum atmosphere.
BAKING	Chemically cleaned or fresh.	Decomposed organic film.	Organic vapours cracked by hot glass.
		Chemisorbed silicone.	Silicone molecules replace OH^- ions on glass.
			Baking fresh SiO_2-film delays silicone chemisorption. Vacuum melted glass may be contaminated on cooling.

7. MELTING GLASS IN AIR AND VACUUM

Fray and Nielsen (1961) have attempted to produce a clean glass surface by melting and quenching glass in vacuum and in air. They compared the effectiveness of various cleaning techniques with vacuum melting glass by determining several factors such as the load required on a titanium point to leave a visible scratch mark; coating the glass with an evaporated zinc film which exposes microscopic surface defects and polishing marks; determining the magnetic properties of Permalloy films deposited on the glass surface.

Shown in Table 5.9 is a selection of their results after treating

Table 5.9

Effectiveness of cleaning techniques compared with
vacuum melting glass †

(After Fray and Nielsen (1961)

Cleaning procedure	Weight on Ti (g)	Domain wall coercivity ($H_c(Oe)$)	Rotational coercivity ($H_k(Oe)$)	Appearance of zinc layer‡
(1) None	400	> 8	> 8	Much structure
(2) Teepol swab, $h+c$ H_2O, HNO_3, ethanol, flame dried	50	5–6	7–8	Structure where alcohol evaporates
(3) Teepol swab, $h+c$ H_2O, chromic acid	100	—	—	Much structure
(4) Teepol swab, $h+c$ H_2O, ethanol, ethanol vapour	30–40	3–4	4–6	Less structure
(5) As (4) + ion bombardment with shielded ring electrodes 1 h at 200°c	30–40	3–4	4–6	Less structure
(6) As (4) + flamed to red heat	30	3–4	4–6	Less structure
(7) As (4) + flame-melted, held vertically	10	1·5–2·5	3–4	No structure
(8) As (4) + flame-melted, horizontal C support	10	—	—	No structure
(9) As (4) + vacuum-melted in Pt tray	10	1·5–2·0	2–3	No structure
(10) Vacuum-melted lead germanate glass	—§	1·3–2·0	2–3	No structure
(11) Cleaved mica surface	1–2	—	—	—

† With exception of (10) all tests were made on soda-lime microscope slides.
‡ Zn-films examined in a low power microscope × 50.
§ Did not show a Ti- mark.

soda-lime slides. The results indicate that ion bombardment produces a surface of about the same cleanliness as ethanol vapour degreasing. It is shown earlier that in terms of μ_s ionic bombardment usually produces a cleaner surface than degreasing in *iso*-propyl alcohol vapour. Also, allowing a glass to reach 200°c in a kinetic system (as stated in Table 5.9) could promote the deposition of cracked hydrocarbon films. However the results given in Table

5.9 show that the highest surface affinity is obtained when the glass surface has been *melted*. Obviously when soda-lime glass is melted *in vacuo* the sodium can evaporate, changing the composition of the glass and this may influence the surface properties. However, from the practical viewpoint of evaporating pure metal films on glass the reduction in the sodium content may be as valuable as removal of other surface contaminants. Fray and Nielsen also vacuum melted a lead germanate glass but titanium did not leave a mark on its surface.

Soda-lime glass has been melted in a molybdenum foil crucible in a kinetic system in the writer's laboratory. A silicone oil diffusion pump was used for exhausting the vessel. The glass melt was readily wetted by water providing it was immediately removed to atmosphere on cooling. Vacuum melted glass exposed for a few minutes to the silicone vapour in the vessel became hydrophobic.

Note Silicone 704 referred to in this chapter is a tetra-methyl tetra-phenyl tri-siloxane, mol. wt. 484 and silicone 705 a tri-methyl penta-phenyl tri-siloxane, mol. wt. 546.

References

Aitken, J., 1893, *Proc. roy. Soc. Edin.*, **20**, 94.
Atherton, L., 1957, March, *Brit. Commun. and Electronics*.
Baker, T. J., 1922, *Phil. Mag.*, **44**, 752.
Bateson, S., 1952, *Vacuum*, **2**, 365.
Belser, R. B., 1952–1955, *Aging Study of Metal Plating on Quartz Crystals*, Interim Reports, Eng. Exp. Stn., Georgia Inst. Technol.
Benson, N. C., Hass, G., and Scott, N. W., 1950, *J. opt. Soc. Amer.*, **40**, 687.
Crawley, R. H. A., 1953, *Chem. and Ind.*, **45**, 1205.
Colbert, W. H., and Weinrich, A. R., 1945, U.S. Pat., 2,383,469.
Croft, W. B., 1892, *Phil. Mag.*, **34**, 180.
Deckers, J., and Tiggelen, A. Van., 1958, *Nature, Lond.*, **181**, 1460; **182**, 863.
Ennos, A. E., 1953, *Brit. J. appl. Phys.*, **4**, 101.
Ennos, A. E., 1954, *Brit. J. appl. Phys.*, **5**, 27.
Fletcher, W. W., Keir, E. S., Johnson, P. G., and Slingsby, B., 1962, *Glass Technol.*, **3**, 195.
Fray, A. F., and Nielsen, S., 1961, *Brit. J. appl. Phys.*, **12**, 603.
Frazer, J. H., 1929, *Phys. Rev.*, **33**, 97.
Goche, O., Bouillon, F., and Frère, A., 1950, *Acad. roy. Belg., Bull. Classe Sci.*, **36**, 330.
Hickman, K. C. D., 1960, Brit. Pat. No. 924,784.
Hiesinger, L., 1951, *Festschrift 100 Jahre*, Heraeus Platinschmelze, Hanau.
Hiesinger, L., and Koenig, H., 1951, *Festschrift 100 Jahre*, p. 376, Heraeus Platinschmelze, Hanau.

Hines, R. L., 1957, *J. appl. Phys.*, **28**, 587.

Hines, R. L., and Arndt, R., 1960, *Phys. Rev.*, **119**, 623.

Holland, L., 1956, *Vacuum Deposition of Thin Films*, Chapman and Hall Ltd., London.

Holland, L., 1957, Brit. Pat. No. 903,473; U.S. Pat. No. 2,985,756.

Holland, L., 1958a, *Nature, Lond.*, **181**, 1451.

Holland, L., 1958b, *Brit. J. appl. Phys.*, **9**, 410.

Holland, L., 1958c, *Nature, Lond.*, **181**, 1727.

Holland, L., 1958d, 'The Effects of a Glow Discharge on Glass and Organic Materials', 1st Intern. Conf. on Vacuum Tech. Namur Pergamon Press, London.

Holland, L., 1959, March, *Plastics*, 112.

Holland, L., 1960, *7th Nat. Symp. on Vacuum Technology Trans.*, p. 168, Pergamon Press, London.

Holland, L., 1963, *Vacuum*, **13**, 173.

Holland, L., and Bateman, S. K., 1960, *Brit. J. appl. Phys.*, **11**, 382.

Holland, L., Laurenson, L., and Priestland, C. R. D., 1963, *Rev. Sci. Instrum.*, **34**, 377.

Huntress, A. R., Smith, A. L., Power, B. D., and Dennis, N. T. M., 1957, *Vacuum Sympos. Trans.*, p. 104, Pergamon Press, London.

Jěch, C., 1954, *Z. phys. Chem.*, **203**, 309.

Jěch, C., 1956, *Nature, Lond.*, **178**, 1343.

Karasev, V. V., and Izmailova, G. I., 1954, *Zh. techn. Fiz.*, **24**, 871.

Kinosita, K., 1953, *J. phys. Soc. Japan.*, **8**, 782.

Kinosita, K., Sumi, M., and Owaki, T., 1949, *J. phys. Soc. Japan*, **4**, 30.

Kling, W., 1950, *Angew. Chem.*, **62**, 305.

Knewstubb, P. F., and Sugden, T. M., 1958, *Nature, Lond.*, **181**, 474; 1261.

Koch, J., 1948, Brit. Pat. 677,784.

Koch, J., 1949, *Nature, Lond.*, **164**, 19.

Koenig, H., 1953, *Vacuum*, **3**, 3.

Lawrence, A. S. C., 1959, *Nature, Lond.*, **183**, 1491.

Lesser, M. A., 1945, Jan., *Soap and Sanitary Chemicals*, **21**, 28.

Noltingale, B. E., and Neppiras, E. A., 1950, *Proc. phys. Soc., Lond.*, B, **63**, 674.

Putner, T., 1959, *Brit. J. appl. Phys.*, **10**, 332.

Quincke, G. H., 1877, *Wied. Ann.*, **2**, 145.

Rayleigh, Lord, 1911, *Nature, Lond.*, **86**, 416.

Rayleigh, Lord, 1912, *Nature, Lond.*, **90**, 436.

Reames, J. P., 1959, *Rev. sci. Instrum.*, **30**, 834.

Ritschl, R., 1931, *Z. Phys.*, **69**, 578.

Rozhdestvesnki, V. N., 1948, *J. tech. Phys., U.S.S.R.*, **18**, 579.

Strong, J., 1934, *Pacific Publ. astro. Soc.*, **46**, 18.

Strong, J., 1935, *Rev. sci. Instrum.*, **6**, 97.

Urbain, W. M., and Jensen, L. B., 1936, *J. phys. Chem.*, **40**, 821.

Wilson, J. L., and Mendenhall, E. E., 1944, *Ind. Engng. Chem. Anal. Ed.*, **16**, 253.

Chapter 6

Wetting Glass Surfaces

1. SURFACE ATTRACTIVE FORCES

The surfaces of most solids exhibit attractive forces for other substances and in this and the following two chapters we shall be concerned with phenomena arising from surface forces of glass. Such attractive forces are due to the unbalanced electrical forces of the atoms in the surface and many materials attempt to neutralize their surfaces by adsorbing foreign atoms and molecules. Materials in which the electrical forces between the atoms in the molecules are more or less balanced do not manifest strong surface forces. Simple polymerized hydrocarbons such as polyethylene, and polymerized fluorocarbons such as polytetrafluorethylene, do not adhere to other substances without chemical modification of their surfaces. On the other hand, fresh glass surfaces exhibit attractive forces due to the unbalanced ions in their surfaces. Thus the surfaces of freshly blown glass stick when touched together. A number of phenomena depend upon the existence of attractive forces at a glass surface, *e.g.* adsorption of gas, wetting by liquids, frictional resistance to sliding and adhesion to solids. It is obvious that the foregoing surface properties will be affected by the structure and composition of the glass surface and as shown in earlier sections the surface condition depends on the history of the glass as well as its bulk composition.

Types of adhesive bond

We shall briefly consider the nature of the adhesive forces between a clean glass surface and superimposed substances. Some substances may chemically combine with the glass so that the adhesive forces arise from electro- or covalent bonds. The high adhesion of a metal oxide coating to glass can be explained by the tendency of the glass to continue its network structure with the atoms in the metal oxide. Likewise the high adhesion of most base metals to glass arises from the existence of a metal oxide layer between the glass and metal interface. Organic compounds may be adherent to glass if they are unsaturated or possess polar groups. The attraction of the glass surface for a particular atomic group of a compound may orient the initial layer of superimposed molecules with respect to the surface. The attractive forces of a glass surface may be modified by foreign atoms or molecules. If the molecules in the superimposed material contain active radicals these may react with the surface coating producing an unsaturated compound which in turn reacts with the glass surface. Such a process occurs when methylchlorosilane reacts with water adsorbed to glass and renders the surface hydrophobic as discussed further on.

Adhesion between a substance and glass may arise from van der Waals' forces, which are responsible for cohesion in liquids. Van der Waals' forces have been attributed to atoms or molecules possessing incompletely balanced electrical charges. Thus, an electrically unbalanced molecule will form a dipole which can be held to the glass surface by the unneutralized ions in the glass surface. Likewise the ions in the surface may induce a dipole in an electrically balanced molecule when it is in contact with the surface. A type of van der Waals' force known as London's dispersion force is manifested even by inert atoms. Rotation of the electrons within an inert atom leaves the nucleus unshielded for a time interval which produces temporary polarity although the average polarity may be zero. Adhesive bonds due to chemical combination are referred to as *primary* bonds whilst those arising from van der Waals' forces are termed *secondary*. Adhesion caused by secondary bonds which arise from polar groups in the molecules of the superimposed layer may reach the strength of chemical bonds.

2. WETTING BY LIQUIDS

THEORETICAL CONSIDERATIONS

The theory of the wetting of solids by liquids will be dealt with briefly as a prelude to a full discussion of the wetting properties of glass.

Contact angle. When a drop of liquid is placed on a solid the factors deciding whether the drop will spread uniformly over the surface or form a lens shape depend upon the relative affinities of the particles in the liquid for the solid and for themselves. Thus, when the attractive force between the unlike particles of the liquid and solid is equal to or greater than that between the particles in the liquid, then uniform spreading of the liquid results, but when the forces between the unlike particles is the lesser then the liquid forms a droplet on the surface. The angle which the liquid makes to the solid surface is usually referred to as the contact angle θ and depends on the relationship of the surface tensions of the three boundaries at their common junction.

The solid surface may be covered by an adsorbed film which has been condensed directly from the vapour phase of the liquid or migrated from the droplet over the surface. The adsorbed film can be expected to lower the surface attractive forces of the solid and

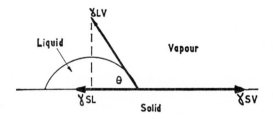

FIG. 6.1   RELATION OF SURFACE TENSION FORCES FOR EQUILIBRIUM OF LIQUID DROPLET ON A SOLID SURFACE

therefore its surface tension. Thus, if we designate the surface tensions of the solid–vapour, liquid–vapour and solid–liquid interfaces as γ_{SV}, γ_{LV} and γ_{SL} respectively, then for equilibrium as shown in Fig. 6.1.

$$\gamma_{SL} + \cos\theta\, \gamma_{LV} = \gamma_{SV} \tag{1}$$

$$\therefore\ \cos\theta = \frac{\gamma_{SV} - \gamma_{SL}}{\gamma_{LV}} \tag{2}$$

If we designate the surface tension of the uncontaminated solid γ_{SO} then $\gamma_{SV} = \gamma_{SO} - \pi$, where π is the surface pressure of the adsorbed film.

Significance of surface tension. The foregoing explanation of the relation between the stability of a liquid droplet and surface tension forces is that usually given in standard physics texts. It is apparent, however, from the diagram in Fig. 6.1, that the forces promoting or opposing wetting will be those acting across the boundary surfaces and not in them as shown. Undoubtedly there is an unbalanced inward pull of the atoms in the surface of a liquid or solid which results in an inner pressure, which can be simulated by imagining that the body is surrounded by a tautened membrane. This has given rise to the idea that surface tension is a fiction which is useful in the solution of problems. However, 'surfaces' that are studied apart from the bulk material, *e.g.* soap films, do exhibit restoring forces. There is, however, a complete identity between the surface tension force of a film and the attractive force at the surface of the same material in bulk form. Thus the inner forces which need to be overcome for an atom or molecule to move into a surface of a stretched film will be equal to the unbalanced forces of a surface atom of the bulk material. From this it follows that if the cohesion of the atoms in a solid or liquid is very high and unbalanced at the surface then this will be represented by a high surface tension. Likewise if the attractive forces across a boundary are partially balanced by the presence of another substance then the surface tension will be lowered. Thus the surface tension is a measure of the degree to which the attractive forces of the surface particles are unsatisfied.

Surface roughness and contact angle. Wenzel (1936) has shown that the measured value of θ is influenced by the roughness of the solid surface. Thus if the true surface area is x times the apparent plane area then the average contact angle $\bar{\theta}$ of the roughened surface is given by

$$\cos \bar{\theta} = x \cos \theta. \tag{3}$$

The equation can be derived by considering surface energy. Thus the energy gained in forming *unit projected area* of solid/liquid is $x(\gamma_{SV} - \gamma_{SL})$, whereas the surface energy of the smooth liquid is γ_{LV} per unit area. Equation (2) then becomes

$$\cos \bar{\theta} = \frac{x(\gamma_{SV} - \gamma_{SL})}{\gamma_{LV}}.$$

When θ is below $90°$ $\bar{\theta} < \theta$ but for values of θ above $90°$ $\bar{\theta} > \theta$.

Hysteresis of contact angle. If a droplet of liquid is allowed to run down an inclined plane the contact angle of the advancing edge is greater than that of the receding edge. Various reasons have been advanced to account for the *hysteresis* of the contact angle. One is that the surface roughness permits the droplet during movement to occupy states where the surface energy has subsidiary minima different from the absolute minimum related to equation (3) (Shuttleworth and Bailey 1948). Another explanation is that there is a finite time for the advancing liquid to replace contaminants on the surface of the solid. Weyl (1953) has observed how very dry sand sprinkled on water remains suspended on the surface for a period before it becomes wet and sinks. Jebsen-Marwedel and Reumuth (1956) have made a study of the edges of water droplets on glass using phase contrast microscopy. They found minute droplets had condensed near to the main water droplet. The boundary of the droplet had a different appearance depending on whether the glass had been dealkalized or weathered before examination.

Sonders *et al.* (1950) have studied the effect on the wetting of glass of bringing ions of different polarizability into the glass surface. They consider that the hysteresis of the contact angle can arise from the presence of polarized ions at the surface which are replaced by the molecules in the superimposed liquid droplet. The effect of a number of different adsorbed ions on the capillary rise of water in glass tubes is discussed on p. 362.

Sonders *et al.* (1950) give an interesting example of the effect on the wetting properties of ion exchange at the surface of soda-lime glass which has been cleaned in sulphuric acid containing potassium dichromate. Sulphuric acid molecules can attach themselves to the cleaned surface by hydrogen bonds owing to the presence of adsorbed OH^- groups on the glass surface. Adding a trace of sodium fluoride to the sulphuric acid causes the OH^- groups to be replaced by F^- ions according to the equation:

$$\overset{|}{\underset{|}{-Si}}-OH + HF = \overset{|}{\underset{|}{-Si}}-F + H_2O$$

The dehydrating effect of the concentrated sulphuric acid causes this reaction to proceed to completion. After a few seconds fluorine ions have replaced the OH^- groups and the lack of affinity of the new surface for H_2SO_4 molecules causes the acid to form little droplets on the glass surface similar to water in a greasy container. Sonders *et al.* state that:

'The substitution of F^- for OH^- has completely changed the interfacial forces between glass and sulphuric acid, because the fluorine ion under the strongly polarizing influence of the silicon ion cannot exert a Coulomb force upon H_2SO_4 molecules which is sufficiently strong to overcome the cohesion forces of the liquid and to produce wetting. In the absence of water the silicon fluoride layer is stable and, if the glass tube with the sulphuric acid is sealed, the inner surface retains its repellency indefinitely. However, in the presence of water, hydrolysis takes place and the OH⁻ groups are restored. The glass surface again is completely wet by water; that means it has a zero contact angle.'

Contact angle and adsorption area. Doss and Rao (1938) have derived an equation relating θ to the fraction S_A of the area of a solid surface covered by molecules adsorbed from the saturated vapour. Consider a solid surface which, in the presence of a saturated vapour is immersed in the liquid emitting the vapour, then the change in free energy per unit area is

$$\Delta F = \gamma_{SL} - \gamma_{SV}$$

When the solid is immersed in the liquid that part of the surface covered with adsorbed molecules is replaced by a liquid interface with a decrease in free energy equal to the surface tension of the liquid, so that for unit area of the partially covered solid

$$\Delta F = -\gamma_{LV} S_A$$

Where the solid is not covered by adsorbed molecules a new liquid surface must be created so that the increase in free energy is

$$\Delta F = \gamma_{LV}(1 - S_A)$$

and the resultant change in free energy per unit area due to these two terms is

$$\Delta F = \gamma_{LV}(1 - S_A) - \gamma_{LV} S_A$$

equating this to the change in free energy of the solid on immersion we have

$$\gamma_{SL} - \gamma_{SV} = \gamma_{LV}(1 - 2S_A)$$

but from equation (2)

$$\gamma_{LV} \cos \theta = \gamma_{SV} - \gamma_{SL}$$
$$\therefore \ \gamma_{LV} \cos \theta = \gamma_{LV}(2S_A - 1)$$
$$\cos \theta = 2S_A - 1 \qquad (4)$$

This expression is applicable where the adsorbed molecules do not have a preferred orientation on the surface, *i.e.* it is based on the assumption that the free energy at the surface of the adsorbed molecules is the same as that at the surface of the liquid from which

23

they are emitted. Thus it could not apply to say organic molecules containing hydrocarbon and hydroxyl groups if the adsorbent surface showed preferred attachment to a particular group.

Livingston (1944) has examined the validity of equation (4) and stated that it has only been experimentally established for the case where $\theta = 0$ and $S_A = 1$. Thus, experimental confirmation does not appear to exist for $\theta > 0$ and $S_A < 1$ for a particular combination. The contact angle of mercury on glass has been reported as between 128–148° so that if equation (4) is applicable the fraction of the surface area covered by adsorbed mercury atoms in the presence of the saturated vapour should be about 0·07–0·2, *i.e.* the number of molecules adsorbed to the surface are about a tenth or so of the number occupying unit area of liquid mercury and which would be required to cover the glass surface. This qualitatively agrees with the known fact that to condense a visible film of mercury on a glass surface the glass must normally be held at a temperature well below that corresponding to the saturated vapour pressure. The low affinity of mercury for glass must, however, be attributed to the presence of adsorbed layers on the glass which weaken the surface forces as discussed on p. 361.

Work of adhesion. The work done in increasing the surface area of a solid or liquid is the product of the surface tension and the change in area. Likewise the work of adhesion W_{SL} is the work required per unit area to create a new surface by separating a liquid from a solid and is related to the surface tensions

$$W_{SL} = (\gamma_{LV} + \gamma_{SV}) - \gamma_{SL} \tag{5}$$

If the attractive forces on both sides of an interface are completely balanced so that $\gamma_{SL} = 0$ then this implies that the surface tensions with respect to vacuum γ_{LO} and γ_{SO} are equal. The work of adhesion, however, would be equal to the sum of the surface tensions of the liquid and solid each with respect to the vapour phase. A similar result can be obtained by combining equations (1) and (5) which gives

$$W_{SL} = \gamma_{LV}(1 + \cos \theta) \tag{6}$$

so that when $\theta = 0$ then $W_{SL} = 2\gamma_{LV}$ and this quantity is equal to the work of cohesion of the liquid W_{LL}, *i.e.* the work done in pulling apart a column of the liquid of unit cross-sectional area.

Obviously θ can only be equal to or exceed zero but not be negative and equation (6) shows that at $\theta = 0$ the adhesion force between the liquid and the solid covered with the adsorbed film is at least equal to the cohesion force in the liquid. In point of fact the adhesion at the interface of the solid could exceed the cohesion in the liquid but the contact angle would only refer to the adhesion of the liquid for the solid covered with an adsorbed layer. Gregg (1951) has pointed out that the contact angle cannot give information on the adhesion of a liquid to a clean solid. However, when the contact angle is high ($\theta > 90°$) adsorption will likewise be low and may not significantly influence the contact angle. Thus Zisman (1957) found that a range of liquids with a high contact angle on poly-tetrafluorethylene gave the same value of θ in saturated and unsaturated vapour.

3. CONTACT ANGLE OF WATER AND OTHER LIQUIDS

DEPENDENCE OF SURFACE CLEANING METHOD

A very extensive study of the contact angle of water on glass and its dependence on the method of cleaning the glass surfaces has been made by Pohlack and Wendler (1958). Glass specimens made of Schottglas BK7 and pitch polished were cleaned as follows:

(1) with an organic solvent (unspecified) and dried with linen,
(2) immersed for 18 hours in chromic acid, rinsed in distilled water and dried,
(3) treated as in (2) and then exposed to a glow discharge for $3\frac{1}{2}$ min at 3·8 kV and 0·2 A using two aluminium electrodes each of 450 cm² area. The glass specimen was rested on the anode electrode facing the cathode electrode with an electrode spacing of 32 cm.

The distribution of the contact angles for a large number of specimens cleaned by the different techniques is shown in Fig. 6.2. The results are plotted to show the distribution of the measured values $\delta = (\varDelta N/N)/\varDelta\theta$, where $\varDelta N/N$ is the fraction of the total number of measurements ($N = 700$) that fall in a contact angle interval of $\varDelta\theta = 5°$. Thus δ is the fraction of the total number of tests falling in a constant angle interval of $1°$ when averaged over $5°$. The results in Fig. 6.2 confirm the high cleaning efficiency of the glow discharge as already shown in Chapter 5. It is of interest to note that the glass must have been immersed in the positive column of the glow discharge with a cathode dark space of about 8 cm. If the specimen had been moved nearer to the cathode to expose it to bombardment of high energy electrons from the cathode dark space then the glass might have been contaminated by dissociated hydrocarbon molecules as described on p. 314.

It is shown in Chapter 5 that only when chromic acid is hot does it produce a black breath figure on glass similar to that obtained

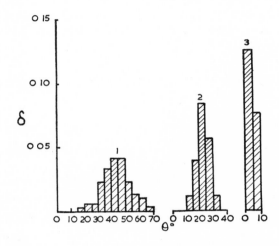

FIG. 6.2 FRACTIONS OF THE TOTAL NUMBER OF TESTS THAT FALL IN CONTACT ANGLE INTERVALS OF 5° WHEN CLEANING GLASS (SCHOTT BK7) WITH —1, ORGANIC SOLVENT; 2, CHROMIC ACID AT NORMAL TEMPERATURE; 3, GLOW DISCHARGE (*After Pohlack and Wendler*, 1958)

with an electrical discharge. Thus, had Pohlack and Wendler used hot chromic acid rather than a long immersion time, they would have probably obtained lower values of θ.

Shown in Fig. 6.3 is the increase in θ measured at different times after glow discharge cleaning at two different high tension power inputs. Pohlack and Wendler suggest that the more effectively the glass is cleaned the quicker it becomes contaminated when exposed to the atmosphere. One would have expected the asymptotic values of θ for the two curves to be the same if the glass had been exposed to the same type of contaminant after cleaning. However, if the initial contaminants on glass 1 incompletely covered the surface after partial cleaning and were less hydrophobic than those of the atmosphere this would account for the difference between the curves.

Pohlack and Wendler have demonstrated how the initial condition of the glass influences the value of the contact angle measured

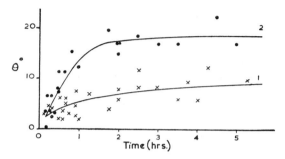

Fig. 6.3 Change in the contact angle of water on glass (schott BK7) with time after ionic bombardment at 1, 2kV, 0·2A, 3·5 min and 2, 3·8 kV, 0·2A, 3·5 min (*After Pohlack and Wendler*, 1958)

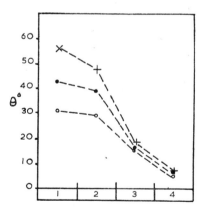

Fig. 6.4 Change of contact angle of water on glass after cleaning as follows 1, polished and dried; 2, organic solvent; 3, chromic acid; 4 glow discharge (*After Pohlack and Wendler*, 1958)

after each cleaning operation. Thus glasses freshly polished with a pitch polisher and dried on a linen lap gave values of θ ranging from 20° to 70°. The two sides of the same glass blank did not give

similar contact angles. When an organic solvent was used for cleaning the contact angle fell but continued to show a relation with the
initial value. Glow discharge cleaning always gave a low contact
angle as shown in Fig. 6.4. Small differences in the contact angle
when θ is near to zero are difficult to detect and it is not possible
to be certain whether glow discharge cleaning destroys the memory
of the initial condition of the surface.

If the glass surfaces used in Fig. 6.4 had different roughness
values then the measured contact angle would be related to the

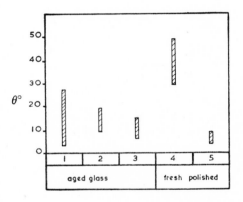

FIG. 6.5   CONTACT ANGLE OF WATER ON AGED AND POLISHED CROWN GLASS
AFTER THE FOLLOWING TREATMENT: 1, ORGANIC SOLVENT; 2, CHROMIC ACID;
3, GLOW DISCHARGE; 4, ORGANIC SOLVENT; 5, GLOW DISCHARGE (*After Pohlack
and Wendler,* 1953)

true contact angle as shown in equation (3) on p. 351. From this it
can be deduced that the relative areas x_1/x_2 of two surfaces with the
same contact angle θ are related to the measured contact angles as
follows $\cos\theta_1/\cos\theta_2 = x_1/x_2$. Thus, on this explanation, the surface area of the specimen with the lowest initial contact angle in
Fig. 6.4 would be about 1·5 times that of the specimen with the
highest value of θ; however, such a relationship is not sustained at
lower contact angles.

Pohlack and Wendler investigated the dependence of θ on the
ageing of the glass. A number of specimens of crown glass were
polished on a pitch polisher and kept in a wooden box for nine

months. At the end of that period the glass was cleaned by various techniques and the measured values of θ are given in Fig. 6.5. The contact angle for the aged specimens was quite low, but vacuum evaporated films which were normally adherent to clean glass surfaces were poorly adherent to the aged glass. The aged glass probably had a porous surface which absorbed moisture and lowered the mechanical strength of the superimposed films.

CONTACT ANGLE FOR VARIOUS GLASSES AND FLUIDS

Moser (1956) has measured the contact angle of water on glasses of different composition and his values are given in Table 6.1. The

Table 6.1

Contact angle of water on glasses of different composition
(*After Moser, 1956*)

Basic ingredients	Type of glass	Contact angle (deg)
SiO_2 72%; Na_2O 13·7%; CaO 11·5%; MgO 2·5%; Al_2O_3 0·3%	Soda-lime	0
SiO_2 29%; BaO 8·4%; PbO 62%; Sb_2O_5 0·6%	Lead	35–37
P_2O_5 67·51%; Al_2O_3 13·49%; CaO 6·90%; B_2O_3 5·05%; SiO_2 5·02%; Fe_2O_3 2·03%	Phosphate	18–20
SiO_2 61·3%; Na_2O 8·8%; B_2O_3 13·3%; ZnO 12·5%; Al_2O_3 2·2%; Na_2SO_4 0·7%; NaCl 0·7%; As_2O_3 0·5%	Zn Boro-silicate	18–20
SiO_2 80·6%; B_2O_3 11·9%; Al_2O_3 2·0%; Na_2O 4·4%; (Ca as Mg) 1·1%	Boro-silicate (Pyrex)	10–12
SiO_2 96%; B_2O_3 3·6%; Al_2O_3 0·4%	Vycor	10–12
SiO_2 71·42%; Na_2O 13·78%; CaO 12·9%; Na_2SO_4 0·85%; NaCl 0·85%	Solex	22–24
SiO_2 71·66%; Na_2O 13·14%; CaO 11·8%; MgO 2·52%; Al_2O_3 0·15%; Na_2SO_4 0·62%; NaCl 10·09%	Iron free plate	20–22
SiO_2	Silica	7–10
SiO_2 59·13%; Na_2O 15·45%; SrO 25·42%	Strontium	17–20
SiO_2 39·0%; K_2O 15·5%; BaO 45·5%	High barium	20–22

measurements were made with a captive air bubble pressed against the substrate which was covered with liquid as shown in Plate 27. The results show that for most glasses θ is generally in the range 0–20°, whilst lead glass appears to be least polar with θ equal to about 35°. However these results do not agree with those of Bartell and Merrill (1932) for organic fluids on glasses of different composition as shown in Table 6.2. It can be seen from the table that a

Table 6.2

Contact angles of various liquids on glass
(*After Bartell and Merrill, 1932*)

Liquid	Silica θ	Pyrex θ	Lead glass θ	Soda-lime glass θ
Acetylene tetrabromide	28° 00′	30° 20′	22° 30′	21° 15′
Alphabromnaphthalene	21° 00′	20° 30′	6° 45′	5° 00′
Methylene iodide	33° 00′	29° 30′	30° 00′	29° 00′
Tribromhydrin	20° 15′	—	15° 30′	17° 00′
Alphachlornaphthalene	15° 00′	—	13° 30′	10° 30′
Ionobenzene	12° 10′	—	12° 15′	0° 15′
Bromoform	24° 30′	—	13° 00′	16°
Turpentine	0°	0°	0°	0°
Acetic acid	0°	0°	0°	0°
Glycerine	0°	0°	0°	0°
Carbon tetrachloride	0°	0°	0°	0°
Xylene	0°	0°	0°	0°
Olive oil	20° 00′	21° 45′	—	—
Oleic acid	27° 00′	27° 30′	—	—

large number of fluids give a zero contact angle irrespective of the nature of the glass. Bartell and Merrill measured the contact angle of the meniscus on fresh drawn tubes having found that acid cleaning affected the glass. It is shown in Chapter 2 that the surface of freshly drawn glass may have a different silica content from that of the bulk material and it is possible that the glass tubes were affected in a similar way.

Moser's results for the contact angle of water on lead glass could be of the right order because, as shown in the next section, the lead ion has a strong shielding effect on the surface forces.

The contact angle of a number of organic liquids on glass has also been determined by Moser (1950) using the captive bubble technique, see Table 6.3. His value of θ for glycerol is 8–10° whereas it is reported as zero in Table 6.2. One would consider that glycerol with its known affinity for water and possession of OH⁻ groups would have given a zero contact angle to glass.

It appears that the reported values for the contact angles of liquids on glass have been influenced by atmospheric modification or contamination of the glass surface and the effects of bulk composition on θ are still uncertain. This is well illustrated by the examples given below for mercury and gallium.

Table 6.3

Contact angles of various organic fluids on glass †
(*After Moser, 1950*)

Liquid	Contact angle (deg)	Liquid	Contact angle (deg)
Distilled water	0	Toluene	0
Methyl ethyl ketone	0–4	Xylene	0
Acetone	0	N-butyl alcohol	0
Ethyl alcohol	0	Glycerol	8–10
Ethyl acetate	10–12	Sulfonamide (MS 80)	3–5
Benzaldehyde	5	'Arochlor 1248'	14–17
Petroleum ether	0–3	Tricresyl phosphate	4–6
Carbon tetrachloride	0	Butyl diglycol carbonate	4–7
Monochlorobenzene	0	Styrene (monomer)	0
Lactic acid	10–12	Methyl methacrylate (monomer)	0
Diethylene glycol	7–10	Vinyl acetate (monomer)	0

† Plate glass.

Mercury and gallium. The contact angle for mercury on glass is usually taken as about 128° and it is generally accepted that mercury does not wet glass. However in complete contradiction to this Briggs (1953) has found that *pure mercury does adhere to degassed glass kept under vacuum.* Vacuum physicists have observed that a portion of the mercury column sometimes sticks to the top of a clean capillary in an evacuated McLeod gauge when the mercury is lowered. This condition which is at the limit of measurement has been popularly termed a 'sticking' vacuum. Briggs used mercury which had been purified by a technique due to Wichers (1942). Air was bubbled through the mercury and the purified metal drawn off from below to separate it from the oxidized base metals floating on the surface. Metal impurities can be reduced to one part in ten million by this method. Wichers observed that purified mercury in evacuated glass ampoules had a flat meniscus and Briggs states that this condition has been retained in sealed ampoules after ten years. When air is admitted to the tubes the mercury meniscus immediately assumes the normal spherical shape.

Briggs experimented with a Pyrex U-tube manometer of 5 mm bore which was degassed at 500°c and exhausted with a mercury diffusion pump. A mercury column distilled into the U-tube remained attached to the sealed end of the manometer when the manometer was mounted vertical and the open leg evacuated. This occurred although the height of the mercury in the closed tube was 52 cm above the meniscus in the open side. Thus the wetting of clean glass by mercury was sufficient to sustain a negative pressure exceeding two-thirds of an atmosphere. This experiment was repeated several times but when the mercury column was released by tapping it would not normally stick again. Capillary tubes were also filled with mercury and sealed off with a small vacant volume at the sealing end. The tubes were then mounted on a rotor with the rotation axis passing through the mid-point of the mercury column so that the centrifugal force on either side of the centre tended to break the mercury column. Such a test would give the force of cohesion within the liquid. Tubes which had been degassed almost at the softening temperature gave a pressure for breaking the column of 425 atmospheres at 27°c.

When gallium is melted (m.p. 29·8°c) in a beaker it adheres to the glass and when poured from the beaker it leaves behind a mirror-like coating. Briggs (1957) found that when gallium was in an evacuated tube it no longer adhered to glass. Gallium behaves in a similar way to indium (see p. 374), in that it wets glass when an oxide film is present.

EFFECT OF ADSORBED IONS ON CAPILLARY RISE

Sonders *et al.* (1950) have shown that some of the H^+ ions of the OH^- groups on a glass surface can be replaced by other cations in an aqueous solution of a salt. They treated glass capillaries of a nominal 0·3 mm bore with diluted HCl and after rinsing exposed them to a salt solution for several days. The treated glass was then rinsed in distilled water to remove the excess salt and dried at 110°c. Complete replacement of H^+ ions by a given cation is not possible because the process is reversible and some of the newly adsorbed cations are re-exchanged for H^+ ions when the salt is washed from the treated surface. The number of ions adsorbed on the glass from a salt depend on the time of exposure, nature of the compound, its concentration and temperature.

Shown in Table 6.4 is the capillary rise in glass tubes after treatment in salt solutions for different periods up to 120 hours. Salts containing cations of the noble gas-type did not exert a measurable effect on the capillary rise, viz. those obtained from nitrates of Li^+, Na^+, K^+, Be^{2+}, Mg^{2+}, Ca^{2+}, Sr^{2+} and Al^{3+}. Thus, with the exception of the large and therefore, polarizable

Table 6.4

Influence of adsorbed cations on the capillary
rise of water in glass tubes
(*After Sonders, et al., 1950*)

Adsorbed cation	Example of the capillary rise in mm *for different treatment times*				Average decrease in rise (%) *for different treatment times*		
	Blank	24 h	48 h	120 h	24 h	48 h	120 h
Ba^{2+}	62	62	59	56	0	5·4	9·2
Tl^{+}	63	63	63	57	0	0	10·2
Fe^{3+}	60	56	55	53	8·5	10·8	12·5
Co^{2+}	64	60	57	55	5·8	10·5	13·1
Zn^{2+}	61	57	55	53	6·9	11·7	13·8
Cu^{2+}	64	58	55	55	9·0	13·3	14·4
Cd^{2+}	60	57	52	50	5·4	13·5	15·7
Cr^{3+}	63	58	53	53	7·5	13·9	10·1
Mn^{2+}	62	55	52	50	10·1	16·5	18·0
Ni^{2+}	62	55	49	48	12·2	20·2	21·8
Hg^{2+}	60	46	40	40	24·1	32·8	32·8
Pb^{2+}	61	44	39	37	29·0	38·1	40·8

The value for blank (H^{+} glass) varied between 60 and 64 mm, depending on the exact diameter of the tube ($\simeq$ dia. 0·3 mm).

Ba^{2+} ion, all cations with eight outer electrons (noble gas-type ions) did not noticeably affect the wettability of the surface. As the capillaries stood in the water a gradual rise occurred. Sonders *et al.* (1950) state that as the water vapour from the meniscus condenses on the glass surface the polarized surface ions gradually become more symmetrical so that the strength of the attraction forces from the surface ions increases. The liquid is able to rise and replaces both adsorbed ions and gas molecules by OH^{-} groups. The time to reach equilibrium height in the glass tube varied from one ion to another. It was greatest for Hg^{2+} (144 h) and Pb^{2+} (120 h), least for Ni^{2+} (72 h) and Cd^{2+} (48 h). The effect of the lead ion on the wetting qualitatively agrees with the high value of the contact angle of water on lead oxide glass shown in Table 6.1.

EFFECTS OF GAS ADSORPTION ON CONTACT ANGLE

Silicate glasses which contain high proportions of lead oxide or are covered with adsorbed Pb^{2+} ions appear to have the least affinity for water. Anderson and Kimpton (1960) attempted to produce a hydrophobic glass by preparing a batch with 90% PbO and 10% SiO_2. To their surprise both freshly cast glass and freshly broken surfaces were readily wetted by water. When the wetted glass surface was rubbed with moist cheesecloth (or other pure cellulose material) and dried it gave a value of $\theta = 90°$. Heating the glass to 275°c in air restored its affinity for water. When a specimen was stored for several days in dry air after casting the measured contact angle was about 80–90°. The high contact angle obtained by polishing with wet cheesecloth was maintained even when 5% Na_2O was added to the glass. The contact angle decreased rapidly when the $PbO:SiO_2$ ratio was below 7:3.

Anderson and Kimpton suspected that the high contact angles obtained did not arise from polarizability of lead ions as suggested for adsorbed Pb^{2+} ions by Sonders *et al.* above. When a series of glasses were prepared with and without large polarizable ions the contact angles obtained after rubbing with wet cheesecloth did not relate to the ionic content of the glass. Thus a glass with 70% BaO, 15% SiO_2, 15% B_2O_3 gave after rubbing $\theta = 30°$, whereas a glass containing 22·6% TiO_2, 46·5% SiO_2, 7% CaO, 2·8% B_2O_3, 21·1% Na_2O gave after rubbing $\theta = 45\%$. The titanium ion has a small radius and cannot be as highly polarized as lead. Anderson and Kimpton state that Gaiser (1949) has observed that TiO_2-coated glass becomes hydrophobic ($\theta = 90$) when cleaned with wet cloth and they obtained the same high contact angle after similarly treating a rutile crystal. They believed that adsorption of oxygen in preference to hydroxyl was responsible for the non-wetting phenomenon. Experiments to remove the adsorbed oxygen by thermal degassing *in vacuo* appeared to support this hypothesis. Likewise it was believed that non-wetting was a property of substances possessing Me-O octahedra in contrast with Si-O tetrahedra.

MENISCUS RESISTANCE TO FLOW

It is well known that a droplet in a tube will sustain a pressure if the contact angle of the meniscus is high (Jamin effect).

Calderwood and Mardles (1954) have observed that the liquid which clings to the walls of a glass tube behind a moving liquid column is part of the meniscus and acts as a variable and elastic resistance. The advancing menisus also possesses friction, but to a smaller extent than that of the receding meniscus. The resistance of the upper meniscus to flow is higher the greater the contact angle.

Experiments were made to ascertain the actual resistance in dynes per centimetre of meniscus periphery. A glass tube of 0·18 cm diameter was cleaned with chromic acid for about 1 hour and

rinsed and dried. The glass tube was tilted so that an index of distilled water began to move along the bore. The force acting on the

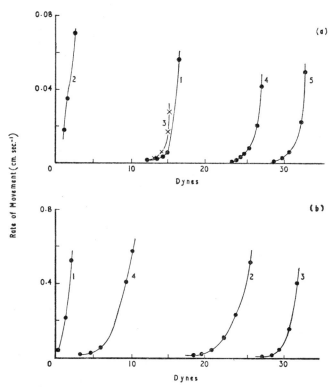

(a) 1. Freshly distilled water in clean dry tube
2. Freshly distilled water in clean dry tube rear meniscus touched with wetting agent
3. Freshly distilled water in clean dry tube front meniscus touched with wetting agent
4. Freshly distilled water in tube contaminated with trace of mineral oil
5. Freshly distilled water in tube coated with thin film of paraffin wax
(b) 1. Silicone fluid (20 cs viscosity) in clean glass tube
2. Index of 2·5 cm silicone fluid and 2·5 cm water (water in front) in clean glass tube
3. Index of 2·5 cm silicone fluid and 2·5 cm water (water in rear)
4. Index of 2·5 cm silicone fluid and 2·5 cm water (water in rear) rear meniscus touched
with wetting agent

FIG. 6.6   THE EFFECT ON RATE OF MOVEMENT OF TOUCHING THE REAR MENIS-
CUS OF AN INDEX OF WATER IN A TUBE WITH A WETTING AGENT; INTERNAL
DIAMETER OF TUBE 0·18 cm, LENGTH OF INDEX 5 cm (*After Calderwood and
Mardles*, 1954)

water index was obtained from the angle of tilt and the corresponding rate of movement of the index measured. The results are given
in Fig. 6.6. For perceptible movement of the water index in the

clean glass tube a force of about 10 dynes was required, which taking into account the irregular liquid periphery, gave a resistance to flow of about 5 dyn cm^{-1}. When the upper meniscus was touched with a wetting agent the force required for movement was lowered, whereas when the glass was made hydrophobic the force required was increased. Also shown in Fig. 6.6 are the effects of placing silicone fluid at the front and rear of the water index.

The liquid film in the wake of the moving index showed elastic properties. Thus if the tube was placed in a horizontal position after movement the index returned more or less completely to its original position depending on the extent and rate of the initial movement. The effect must arise from contact angle hysteresis, *i.e.* a finite time is required even at the rear of a moving droplet for adsorbed gas to be dissolved in the liquid.

References

Anderson, S., and Kimpton, D. D., 1960, *J. Amer. ceram. Soc.*, **43**, 484.
Bartell, F. E., and Merrill, E. J., 1932, *J. Phys. Chem.*, **36**, 1178.
Briggs, L. J., 1953, *J. appl. Phys.*, **24**, 488.
Briggs, L. J., 1957, *J. chem. Phys.*, **26**, 784.
Calderwood, G. F. N., and Mardles, E. W. J., 1954, *Proc. phys. Soc.*, **B67**, 395.
Doss, K. S. G., and Rao, B. S., 1938, *Proc. Indian Acad. Sci.*, **7A**, 113.
Gaiser, R. A., 1949, U.S. Pat. No. 2,478,817.
Gregg, S. J., 1951, *The Surface Chemistry of Solids*, 1st Ed., Chapman and Hall Ltd., London.
Jebsen-Marwedel, H., and Reumuth, H., 1956, *Glastechn. Ber.*, **29**, 128.
Livingston, H. K., 1944, *J. phys. Chem.*, **48**, 120.
Moser, F., 1950 Oct., *Amer. Soc. test. Mat. Bull.*, No. 169, 62.
Moser, F., 1956 April, *The Glass Industry*.
Pohlack, H., and Wendler, S., 1958, *Jenaer Jahrbuch*, p. 41, VEB Carl Zeiss, Jena.
Shuttleworth, R., and Bailey, G. L. J., 1948, *Discussions of The Faraday Society*, No. 3, 11.
Sonders, L. R., Enright, D. P., and Weyl, W. A., 1950, *J. appl. Phys.*, **21**, 338.
Wenzel, R. N., 1936, *Ind. and eng. Chem.*, **28**, 988.
Weyl, W. A., 1953, *Structure and Properties of Solid Surfaces*, p. 147. Edited by R. Gomer and C. S. Smith, University of Chicago Press.
Wichers, E., 1942, *Chem. eng. News*, 20, Sept. 1111.
Zisman, W. A., 1957, 'Relation of Chemical Constitution to the Wetting and Spreading of Liquids on Solids', U.S. Nav. Res. Rep. 4932.

CHAPTER 7

Frictional Properties of Glass
and Effects of Boundary Lubricants

1. MODERN THEORY OF FRICTION

The resistance to sliding exhibited by contacting solids has been intensively studied and many attempts have been made to derive a complete theory to account for the phenomenon. However, it is now generally accepted that the most likely explanation of friction is as follows. When solid surfaces are brought together they make contact on their surface asperities and on either side of the contacting zones the surfaces may be separated by several tens or hundreds of ångströms even when the solid surfaces have been polished. The short range forces of the surface atoms limit their interaction to the contacting asperities. Bowden and Tabor (1956) have shown how at the contacting regions the deformation will first be elastic, but with materials capable of undergoing plastic flow the smallest loads will produce stresses exceeding the elastic limit and plastic deformation will occur. If the load is increased the asperities are plastically crushed until they are large enough to support the load by elastic strains in the underlying material. Under these conditions the area of real contact is proportional to the load, inversely proportional to the hardness of the solid and more or less independent of the macroscopic shape or size of the surfaces.

Normally two types of measurement are made in friction studies. These are to determine the coefficients of static and kinetic friction which are designated here μ_s and μ_k respectively. μ_s is the ratio of the force required to initiate movement of the rider to the load and μ_k is the ratio of the force required to maintain sliding to the load. Both coefficients are usually found to be independent of the load over wide limits and this follows directly from the discussion of the frictional mechanism in the previous paragraph.

When sliding occurs the contacting zones may stick and cold weld together and the junctions so formed may pull out surface material.

The attractive forces at the boundaries of the asperities may be weakened, by adsorbed films or by separating the solid surfaces with thick lubricant layers.

It is shown in Chapter 1 that the tracks formed on glass by scratching the surface may be smooth sided or splintered. The smooth tracks are produced when the glass undergoes plastic flow and are only produced when the load on the stylus is under a critical value. Such surface tracks can be expected to have different effects on the frictional properties but they have not been considered by students of the frictional properties of glass.

2. FRICTION BETWEEN UNLUBRICATED SURFACES

GLASS RUBBING ON GLASS

The coefficient of friction of clean glass on glass is exceptionally high. An early study was made by Hardy and Hardy (1919), using a weighted watch glass resting on a plane glass. They found that the static coefficient of friction was independent of load but depended on the kind of glass. Shown in Table 7.1 are the results of using different weighted watch glasses on two types of plate glass after cleaning with soap in running water. The glass compositions were not specified, but it is stated that glass (ii) was green plate.

Table 7.1
Static coefficient of friction of glass on glass
(*After Hardy and Hardy, 1919*)

(i)		(ii)	
load (g)	μ_s	*load (g)*	μ_s
54·25	0·85	14·58	0·93
58·5	0·85	14·58	1·1
57·79	0·85	58·25	0·93
170·2	0·84	46·95	0·96

Hardy and Hardy noted that the glass rider did not slide on the glass but that the surfaces seized during its movement. This produced a scratch on both surfaces that was not continuous, but which was composed of an irregular collection of shallow pits and thin plates which had been torn from the opposite surface. The track became wider as the sliding proceeded, due to the watch glass vibrating sideways because the internal glass rupture following seizure was not always in line with the pull. The microscope showed that the contacting faces seized before movement started. Clean glasses show a distinct tendency to stick together, but the elastic stresses in the loaded solid break most of the junctions when the load is removed, otherwise the adhesion would persist as it can between freshly melted glasses.

Shaw (1927) has measured μ_s of glass on glass using a machine in which two rods slid on one another at right angles. The glass rods were boiled in chromic acid. Values of μ_s are given in Fig. 7.1.

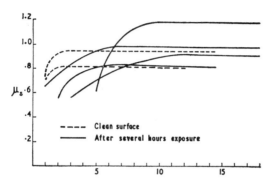

FIG. 7.1   THE EFFECT ON THE COEFFICIENT OF STATIC FRICTION OF REPEATED RUBBING OF GLASS RODS (*After Shaw*, 1927)

The dotted lines are for glass rods tested immediately after cleaning whereas the full lines are for rods exposed to the air for several hours. It is obvious that rubbing the surfaces removes the lubricating contaminants. Also the seizure and tearing of the contacting asperities probably increases the area of fresh surface which is exposed, so that when the rods again pass over the same track the seizure of the surfaces is enhanced.

Southwick (1957) has studied the effect of load on the friction between a microscope slide moving at a constant speed beneath a glass rod with an hemispherical end. The rod was 3 mm diameter and fire polished. The results in Table 7.2 show that the kinetic coefficient rises slightly with decreasing load. The friction was measured with the glass surfaces flooded with water to keep them free from contaminants.

24

Table 7.2

The effect of sliding velocity and load on glass to glass friction †

(*After Southwick, 1957*)

Velocity (mm/sec)	μ_k ‡	load (g)	μ_k §
0·00004	0·70	1000	0·69
0·0007	0·75	500	0·73
0·0003	0·74	200	0·80
0·006	0·75	100	0·78
0·01	0·73	50	0·78
0·02	0·69	30	0·79
0·1	0·67	10	0·87
1·0	0·70		

† All specimens flooded with distilled water.
‡ 1000 g load.
§ 0·02 mm/sec sliding velocity.

Surface roughness. Friction has been attributed to the interlocking of surface asperities, but Hardy and Hardy found that ground glass had a lower coefficient of friction than polished glass. This could have been due to the difficulty of cleaning the ground surface but it also discounts the roughness theory of friction.

Bikermann and Rideal (1939) studied the effect on the friction of raising the load and then decreasing it again. Soft materials gave a higher value of μ_s after the load had been raised, whereas hard materials gave a constant value. From this they contended that the friction between hard surfaces (*e.g.* glass on glass) was not due to adhesion but probably arose from the need to lift the rider over surface irregularities. Obviously, if friction is due to adhesion and the surface asperities undergo plastic flow when the load is increased, the coefficient of friction will remain high when the load is again lowered (*e.g.* indium or tin on glass). Local welding of the asperities can still occur with hard bodies but when the load is raised the asperities may only be elastically deformed so that the surfaces spring apart and break the junctions when the load is removed; under these conditions μ_s would tend to remain constant.

Sliding velocity. Southwick (1957) has studied the effect of the sliding velocity on the kinetic coefficient of friction. His results for microscope slides moving under a glass rod with a hemispherical end are given in Table 7.2, where it is shown that μ_k remains almost constant over a wide velocity range. These results were taken with the glasses flooded with water.

Effect of humidity. Kinosita (1953) has found that μ_s for clean glass is independent of the atmospheric humidity when it is between 50–80% R.H. For lower values of relative humidity μ_s decreases and for higher R.H. values it rises and at 100% R.H. approaches the value for glass flooded with water. Typical values of μ_s were 0·7 in very dry air, 0·90 in normal atmosphere and 0·99 in a damp atmosphere. The change in μ_s was reversible and attributed by Kinosita to physical adsorption of water. It is difficult to see how physical adsorption of a monolayer or less on a plane surface could account for such changes but adsorption within a porous surface would greatly increase the water present.

It has been shown in Chapter 1 that a chemical reaction occurs between glass and the slurry during polishing. Similarly the water

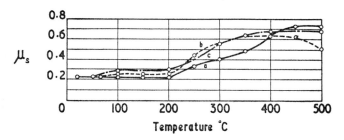

Fig. 7.2 Dependence of the static coefficient of friction of glass on the pre-treatment temperature. Each type of glass was baked for 30 min at plotted temperature (*a*) schottglas BK7 felt polished (*b*) fire polished window glass (*c*) fire polished 'rasotherm' (*After Wessel, 1958*)

adsorbed to glass during friction tests may promote chemical reactions. Even if the water does not function as a boundary lubricant it can take sodium ions into solution. The alkali solution so formed could attack the silica network producing a silica gel interlayer. When the rider presses on the surface water could be squeezed from the gel which now solidifies and forms a cement between glass and rider. It is an interesting fact that if glass articles rub together when washed in strongly alkaline solution a kind of surface marring occurs termed 'scuffing'. It had also been found that glass scratched *in vacuo* (dry surface) under a light load shows an irregular surface that is characteristic of a brittle surface layer, whereas glass scratched in a humid atmosphere shows a smooth sided furrow.

Effect of heat treatment. When glass is heat treated the coefficient of friction gradually rises as surface contaminants are evaporated. Wessel (1958) found that the friction remained almost constant for baking temperatures up to 200°c as shown in Fig. 7.2. It is of interest to note that the friction for plate glass rose to a maximum value at 400°c and then decreased. Shaw and Leavey (1930) observed that the friction of a soda-lime glass was low after baking *in vacuo* ($\mu_s = 0.3$) and rose to $\mu_s = 1$ when treated with chromic acid. The fall in the friction sometimes observed when glass is heated in vacuum or air might arise from diffusion of sodium to the glass surface. Weyl (1949) states that when glass is heated and then rubbed with aged glass the previously heated glass acquires a negative charge, because sodium ions that have migrated to the surface of the heated glass are removed during the rubbing.

Holland (1960) reports that glass heated in continuously pumped vacuum systems to a moderate temperature of 200°c becomes covered with thermally decomposed materials if organic vapours are emitted by rubber joints, etc., in the vacuum apparatus.

Southwick (1957) gives a value of μ_s equal to 0·6–0·9 for microscope slides which have been vacuum baked (250°–400°c). Holland has found a similar range of values for soda-lime glass heat treated in a ultra-high vacuum plant. It is of interest to note that more consistent values of μ are obtained when glass is cleaned in a glow discharge ($\mu_s \simeq 0.8$–1) or by vapour degreasing in *iso*-propyl alcohol ($\mu_s \simeq 0.7$, *e.g.* see Putner, 1959).

Wessel found a persistent difference between the friction values for different types of glass when alternately polished and baked as shown in Table 7.3.

Table 7.3

Coefficient of static friction of glass measured after alternate
heat treatment† and mechanical polishing
(After Wessel, 1958)

Glass type	Nature of surface and number of specimens		Cleaned specimen	Coefficient of friction‡							
				T_1	P_1	T_2	P_2	T_3	P_3	T_4	P_4
Microscope slide	5	fire polished	0·21	0·42	0·19	0·47	0·19	0·62	0·19	0·78	0·19
Window glass	5		0·19	0·49	0·19	0·58	0·21	0·58	0·19	0·51	0·19
'Tempax'	5		0·21	0·62	0·21	0·75	0·19	0·73	0·19	0·70	0·19
BK 7 (Schott)	5	mechanically polished	0·19	0·65	0·19	0·65	0·19	0·65	0·19	0·70	0·19
'Duran'	5		0·21	0·67	0·19	0·73	0·19	0·73	0·21	0·75	0·21

† ½ hour treatment at 500°c.
‡ Average values of ten measurements on each test measured with glass rider with three spherical feet under a load of 1·4 g.

3. RUBBING METALS ON GLASS

COEFFICIENT OF FRICTION

Tomlinson (1929) has measured the coefficient of static friction of metals on glass, using a machine in which a rod with a hemispherical end moved over a flat plate. His results for a range of metals on glass are given in Table 7.4, and these show that the soft metals tin and lead have a high friction when in contact with glass. Tomlinson attempted to develop a theory of friction in which he showed that the value of μ_s for any two surfaces was a function of the elastic moduli of the materials. However, he apparently ignored the effect of the adhesive force between the glass and a particular metal or metal oxide layer. Thus, although platinum is normally covered by a strongly adsorbed layer of oxygen molecules, it is not

Table 7.4

Coefficients of friction of metals on glass
(*After Tomlinson, 1929, and Southwick, 1958*)

Metal	Plati-num	Hard steel	Copper	Mild steel	Nickel	Alumin-ium	Brass	Glass	Tin	Lead
μ_s† μ_k‡	0·569 —	0·605 —	0·675 —	0·721 0·600	0·775 —	0·845 0·400	0·873 0·300	0·940 0·750	0·941 —	2·420 —

† Tomlinson.
‡ Southwick, 1000 g load, 6 mm tip radius, velocity $6·6 \times 10^{-4}$ mm/sec.

covered with a thick oxide film as, for example, mild steel. Soft metals will deform easily under pressure, thereby producing a large area of true contact between the metal and glass. If these metals are also highly adherent by virtue of an oxide layer, *e.g.* that of tin or lead, then such a combination of softness and adhesion would produce a high resistance to sliding.

METAL TRACES ON GLASS

Some metals adhere readily to glass even when the surface is imperfectly clean. Thus, Wooster and Mcdonald (1946) noted that titanium strongly adhered to glass when rubbed over its surface; zirconium also frictionally adheres readily to glass when rubbed on its surface. If the glass surface is sufficiently clean to give a black breath figure, as described in Chapter 5, then it is not possible to pull a titanium wire under its own weight over the surface without leaving a metallic trace (see Plate 25). Aluminium can be made to leave a metallic trace by rubbing a glass surface but it requires a thoroughly clean glass and a high load. When the foregoing metals are rubbed on glass in air they undoubtedly adhere to the surface via an oxide layer. Aluminium is softer than titanium and should make contact to the glass over a larger area when under the same load. However, the ease with which unclean glass can be marked with a pointed titanium wire or rod compared with aluminium is probably due to the harder metal penetrating the surface contaminants.

Writing with indium. Indium adheres to clean glass with similar intensity to that of titanium, but because of its greater softness heavy traces of indium are formed on the rubbed glass. Belser (1953) has made a study of the adhesion of indium to glass and found that indium wetted glass when spread on its surface with a soldering iron. If a flux was used the metal would not wet the glass, from which it could be deduced that oxide formation was essential for adhesion.

Belser soldered with indium a small brass tag of $\frac{1}{8}$ in. $\times \frac{1}{8}$ in. area to glass and measured the strength of the indium–glass bond. The highest strengths were obtained on clean glass and that treated with fired metal films as shown in Table 7.5.

Table 7.5
Bond strengths of indium-soldered joints
(*After Belser, 1953*)

Material soldered	Shear strength (lb/in²)
Solid indium	910
Glass cleaned with detergent, $KMnO_4$ and NaOH	735
Glass intensely heated	600
Glass positive ion bombarded	610
Evaporated aluminium film on glass	560
Aluminium film (heated to oxidation)	760
Fired silver coating on glass with solder 95% In, 5% Ag	>1090

Belser also studied the frictional adhesion of a number of other metals to glass. He pressed a rotating disc of metal against the surface of a glass and found that at low rotary speeds metal was invariably transferred to the glass but at high speeds the glass surface was usually eroded because it melted as it became heated by friction. Noble metals such as gold and silver did not always adhere to the glass. Belser attributed this to their high thermal conductivity removing heat from the rubbing zone so that the metals did not melt and smear out over the surface; the absence of an oxide cementing layer was probably the true reason for poor adhesion. It has been shown that evaporated gold and silver films which are weakly adherent to silicate glasses can only be effectively bonded by pre-coating the glass with certain metal oxides.

MARKING GLASS WITH METALS

Glass can be marked by metals of much less hardness number, because the friction between a metal abrader and glass results in locally welded regions which exert a pull against the glass. With soft metals the glass is not removed from the surface but it is marked by a series of crescent-shaped cracks in the wake of the abrader. The cracks arise as the metal rod yields under the frictional force and jumps on the surface. Similar cracks are produced in glass by hard abrading materials, as discussed in an earlier section.

Table 7.6

Load required on hemispherical metal point to produce
scratch mark on glass
(After Ghering and Turnbull, 1940) †

Metal	Initial load for scratching (kg)	Remarks
Cr	0·20	Scratching without metal mark
Fe	0·23	
Cu	0·51	
Al	1–2	Scratching with metal mark
Ni	1–2	
Brass	1·2–2	
Zn	2–3	
'Monel'	2–3	
Mg	—	
Sn	—	No scratching but metal mark
Pb	—	

† Loaded metal rod ¼ in. dia. and inclined at 45° to surface. Glass pulled in direction to which rod inclined.

Ghering and Turnbull (1940) have measured the minimum load required to produce a metal mark on a glass surface when using a metal rod with a hemispherical end and their results are given in Table 7.6. Cracks in the glass became visible when the metal mark was removed from the surface with acid. It is not clear whether the crescent cracks were due to the impact of the abrader as it jumped on the surface or to the glass yielding under a tensile stress. Thus, as the abrader moved over the glass, the friction produced a compression stress in front and a tensile stress behind. When a rod with a rounded tip is pressed against a glass plate the maximum tensile stress in the plate occurs near the rim of the contact area and there is a critical load for a given tip radius which will produce a ring crack. When the rod is moved over the glass the frictional tension in the surface is added to that due to the static load and the glass may yield under a load less than the static yield value.

As evidence of this hypothesis Southwick (1958) found that the higher the load and the smaller the radius of the metal tip the more easily were surface cracks produced during rubbing. Also, the coefficient of friction of steel, aluminium and brass generally tended to rise with increase of the radius of the abrading tip; values for μ_k under a given load are included in Table 7.4. Brass did not produce crescent cracks but left a smooth track suggesting that the glass had plastically flowed, as described on p. 70.

4. FRICTIONAL BEHAVIOUR OF GLASS IN LIQUIDS

As would be expected, the frictional behaviour of glass when covered with a liquid film is usually strongly dependent on the nature of both the liquid and the rider. Several types of effect may occur and these can be summarized as follows:

(i) The liquid film may dissolve or react with the glass or rider so that friction occurs at a plastic interface; a reaction may also occur between the liquid and the glass or the rider which produces compounds that influence the friction.

(ii) The molecules in the liquid may be adsorbed to the glass or rider so that the friction depends on the nature of the outer terminals of the adsorbed molecules or the degree to which the rubbing surfaces have been separated, *i.e.* the size of the adsorbed molecules.

(iii) The liquid film may be neutral and easily squeezed from between contacting asperities at the rubbing interface; the frictional properties may still be influenced by a neutral liquid if it is a solvent for adsorbed molecules contaminating the rubbing surfaces.

We shall now consider the frictional behaviour of glass for systems in which the foregoing processes are known to occur.

Nature of rider

Hardy (1925) observed that thick water layers on glass had normal hydrodynamical lubricating properties but thin films had properties depending on the nature of the rider. Thus, water films a few molecules in thickness acted as follows:

> anti-lubricant for glass on wood,
> lubricant for glass on ebonite,
> neutral for glass on sulphur,
> neutral for glass on glass.

Thus, with certain combinations of rider and fluid, one is not studying friction between chemically inert components but rather the result of an interaction within the system. It is shown in Chapter 1 that the chemical theory of polishing contends that glass is optically polished by the production of silica gel on the glass surface which is then smoothed by the polishing tool. It has also been shown that some glasses can be polished with water alone providing certain materials are used as the polisher.

Nature of lubricating fluid

Bourdillon (1957) has studied the effects of scratching with a glass rod the wall of a glass vessel containing a number of different liquids. Three types of effect are observed:

(*i*) *The rod slips* with aromatic compounds (except benzene and some simpler derivatives); some other cyclic compounds; open chain compounds of more than about ten carbon atoms.

(*ii*) *The rod bites* and produces glass dust varying in amount and texture. This arises with non-polar compounds of low molecular weight, most ketones and with sulphuric acid.

(*iii*) *The rod bites* and produces dust which sticks to the wall on which it can be smeared. The glass dust also contains particles of 1–2 μ dia. in intense Brownian motion in the liquid. This arises in decreasing order with (a) water and monohydroxyalcohols, (b) dihydroxyalcohols, primary amines, (c) aliphatic acids, some esters, aldehydes, ketones, secondary amines. Group (c) is intermediate between groups (ii) and (iii).

Bourdillon notes that mixtures of the above groups of compounds rarely produce effects which are intermediate between those of the separate components. In fact the results show that there is an interaction between the molecular compounds. Thus water/sulphuric acid mixtures produce slippery zones on the glass surface.

The compounds in group (i) possess molecules of a size and shape which, when linked to the glass surface, prevent frictional adhesion of the glass, as will be discussed below. The results given in group (ii) are those to be expected when the compound does not influence the frictional adhesion between the glass surface because the molecules do not adhere to the surface or are small in size. The compounds in group (iii) are also ineffective in reducing the friction, but they must play some role at the rubbing interface due to their influence on the form assumed by the glass dust. It would appear that hydroxyl groups or hydrogen in the liquids tested react with the glass surface forming silicic acid (silica gel) which is removed under abrasion. The effects of immersing glass in liquids with different pH values are discussed in Chapter 3.

BOUNDARY LUBRICATION

Langmuir (1920) first demonstrated that a monomolecular layer of a fatty acid could greatly reduce the coefficient of friction of glass and many years later (1934) showed that a multimolecular layer of the acid salt did not reduce the friction significantly more than did a monolayer. Hardy and his colleagues made extensive pioneering studies of the effects of adsorbed organic layers on the frictional properties of glass and these will now be discussed.

Active and inactive liquids. Hardy and Hardy (1919) identified two types of liquid in their studies of the influence of fluids on the friction of glass. One type of fluid was *active* in reducing the friction even when the watch glass used as a rider pressed the separating liquid out to a thin film. Examples of *active* fluids were castor oil and oleic acid. The second type of fluid only reduced the friction when present as thick layers between plane glass surfaces and was *inactive* in reducing the friction when present as a film. With *inactive* liquids only a slight pressure sufficed to displace a thick layer so that the solid faces seized. Examples of such liquids were: ethyl alcohol, ethyl ether, benzene, water and ammonia. Also a glycerine film failed to reduce the friction as shown in Table 7.7.

Table 7.7

Static coefficient of friction of glass on glass in the presence of glycerine

(*After Hardy and Hardy, 1919*)

	Clean	Films†	Smear	Plate flooded and drained	Heavily flooded
μ_s —	0·87	0·87	0·73	0·51	0·1

† Films deposited from a 0·002% solution in alcohol, the plate was covered with solution and dried off four successive times without change in μ.

The shape of the rider influences the speed with which it penetrates the liquid layer when loaded. Thus, Hardy (1925) found that a spherical rider more quickly gave a constant value for the coefficient of friction than a flat rider.

An interesting effect noted by Hardy and Hardy was that whereas ammonia was *inactive* the compounds of increasing molecular weight, trimethylamine, triethylamine and triproprylamine, all showed increasing activity in reducing the friction.

If an *inactive* liquid was present with an *active* one then although the surfaces might be flooded the coefficient of friction was higher than that of the active film. Thus the value of μ_s for a film of medicinal paraffin was raised four times by flooding the surface with water; a similar effect occurred with castor oil. When a paraffin wax film was used flooding with water had no effect. It was concluded that the *inactive* water displaced the *active* liquid on the surfaces thereby raising the friction.

Oriented films. Hardy and Doubleday (1922) studied the effect of various organic substances on the coefficient of friction of a weighted watch glass on a glass plate. The glass plates were cleaned in a mixture of sulphuric and chromic acid and rinsed with water, the rider was cleaned with soap and water. The value of μ_s of glass on glass was 0·94 and did not vary over a load of 21–61 g.

The friction of the glass when coated with a specific group of compounds was independent of whether the glass surface was flooded with liquid, held in the presence of saturated vapour or a drop of liquid allowed to migrate over the surface. Thus the liquids used were of the *active* kind described in the previous paragraph

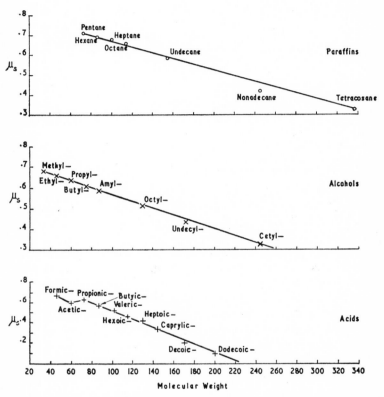

FIG. 7.3 COEFFICIENT OF STATIC FRICTION OF GLASS ON GLASS TREATED WITH ORGANIC MATERIALS OF INCREASING MOLECULAR WEIGHT (*After Hardy and Doubleday,* 1922)

and the modification of the glass friction must have arisen from the existence of a boundary layer of molecular thickness.

When the glass plate was exposed to alcohol vapour the friction steadily decreased as the alcohol vapour pressure was raised to the saturated value. This indicated that the glass surface was gradually being covered with strongly adsorbed alcohol molecules.

Shown in Fig. 7.3 are the values of μ_s measured when three different series of organic compounds of increasing molecular weight were used as lubricants. Each curve can be represented by a relation of the type

$$\mu = b - aM$$

where M is the molecular weight of the lubricant and a and b are parameters. Parameter a is independent of the nature of the solid but is dependent on the nature of the chemical series of the lubricant. The parameter b is dependent on the nature of the solid and is different when metal is used in place of glass for the rider. It is to be noted that the value of b does not coincide with the friction of the unlubricated glass. When the rider and plate are of dissimilar material the coefficient of friction is between that for each pair of similar materials.

When fluid lubricants were polished with a clean cloth the fluid film could be removed, whereas solid lubricants could not be removed. Thus undecyl alcohol melts at 11°c and only in the fluid state could it be removed from the glass. Polishing a liquid lubricant without removing it from a surface greatly decreased the friction for a short period, whereas polishing a solid lubricant permanently lowered the friction. The data given in Fig. 7.3 are for unburnished films.

Hardy and Doubleday account for the dependence of the friction on the molecular mass of the lubricant by assuming that

'... the molecules of the lubricant are oriented by the attraction fields of the solids so that their long axes are at right angles to the solid faces. Let us assume that the layer of lubricant is composed of two primary films the plane of slip being between them. Each CH_2 group which is added to the molecule lengthens the carbon chain and therefore increases the plane of slip from the solid faces. Normally the compounds considered might form a zig-zag or flat spiral, but in this case the molecules suffer rearrangement under the attraction field of the solid.'

Although the force field of the solid surface will not extend past this adsorbed layer the orientation of the adsorbed film will affect the behaviour of the liquid next to it and the surface effect will be spread out to some degree in the liquid. Burnishing a lubricant film presumably helps adsorbed molecules with low mobility to orientate themselves so that only the non-polar groups are outermost; this high degree of order is probably destroyed by thermal agitation in the films prepared from liquids.

It has been shown (see Bowden and Tabor, 1956) that fatty acid molecules tend to be chemisorbed to oxidized metal surfaces by forming metallic soaps and fatty acid molecules may therefore be bound to glass oxides by stronger bonds than polar forces alone.

5. ADSORPTION AND PROPERTIES OF FATTY ACID FILMS

ORIENTATION OF MONO AND MULTI-LAYERS

Langmuir (1920) found that a monomolecular oil film could be deposited on a solid surface by dipping the solid beneath a water surface covered with a monomolecular film and withdrawing the solid slowly. After evaporation of the water the molecules in the film retained the orientation they had in the water. Blodgett (1934) used this technique for depositing on glass mono and multi-molecular layers of fatty acids with the general formula $CH_3(CH_2)_{n-2}COOH$, where n is the number of carbon atoms in a molecule.

To apply a film oriented with the CH_3-groups outermost the fatty acid is spread on acidified water and then compressed. The glass slide is rinsed in alkaline solution and the edges of the slide touched against the oil film which spreads instantly over the wet slide to form an adherent film.

Stearic acid may be deposited in successive layers, the layers of odd number being oriented with the CH_3-groups away from the glass and the layers of even numbers with them towards the glass thus:

| glass surface | —— | polar – non-polar | —— | non-polar – polar | . . . |

The former occurs when glass is raised through an oil film spread on alkaline water and the latter when glass coated with an adherent layer is lowered through a similar film. Blodgett observes that as the initially coated glass is again lowered into the water the liquid makes a contact angle of about 90° to the hydrophobic surface and the film is turned upside down as the slide carries it into the water.

Oriented films with CH_3-groups outermost cannot be wet by pure mineral oil or benzene although stearic acid is soluble in these liquids. Water droplets roll about on layers of 3 or 5 molecules deep. Films oriented in the opposite direction with the $COOH$-groups outermost are completely wet by clean water.

EFFECT OF SURFACE ADSORPTION DENSITY

Izmailova and Deryagin (1952) have studied the coefficient of static friction of glass on glass which had been treated with a mixture of stearic acid in Vaseline. The stearic acid was strongly adsorbed to clean glass as shown in Table 7.8 and was not removed

Table 7.8

Coefficient of static friction of clean and unclean glass coated with stearic acid

(*After Izmailova and Deryagin, 1952*)

Friction surfaces	Surface condition	μ_s clean surface	μ_s contaminated surface
Glass on glass	Untreated	1·027	0·614
	Thin layer of stearic acid solution	0·102	0·310
	Washing in benzene—1st	0·249	0·381
	2nd	0·251	0·614
	3rd	0·289	—
	4th	0·322	—
Glass on silica	Untreated	0·873	0·423
	Thin layer of stearic acid solution	0·138	0·261
	Washing in benzene—1st	0·278	0·300
	2nd	0·323	0·346
	3rd	0·344	0·423
	4th	0·352	—

by washing with benzene. When a poorly cleaned glass was treated with the mixture the original value of μ_s was obtained by cleaning showing that the stearic acid was not strongly adsorbed. The friction was dependent on the concentration of the fatty acid mixtures (Fig. 7.4).

Change in friction with time. Several workers have detected a slow change in the coefficient of friction with time when the glass is coated with adsorbed organic layers, *e.g.* Hardy and Doubleday (1922). Izmailova and Deryagin found that a clean glass surface gave a constant value of μ_s within a few minutes of treatment and they believed that the time lag in a surface reaching a constant value of μ_s was due to surface contaminants being slowly desorbed.

FRICTION AND MOLECULAR SIZE

Shafrin (1958) has measured the dependence of μ_k on the number of the carbon atoms in fatty acid molecules adsorbed to glass. Friction was measured between an elastically restrained steel ball ($\frac{1}{2}$ in.

dia.) and a treated glass specimen sliding at slow speeds. When the number n of carbon atoms reached 14 the friction had fallen to a constant value of $\mu_k \simeq 0.05$. The behaviour of the acid films when repeatedly traversed by the steel ball was interesting. Thus, using a 5000 g load acid films with $n \leqslant 12$ failed on the first traverse, while films having $n = 13$ and 14 did not begin to fail until the fifteenth traverse and films having $n \geqslant 16$ survived twenty traverses without

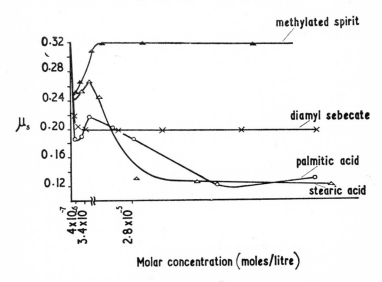

Fig. 7.4 Dependence of static friction coefficient of glass on glass upon concentration of surface active compounds in vaseline grease at 26°c (*After Izmailova and Deryagin*, 1952)

μ_k rising measurably. It was concluded that fatty acid monolayers adsorbed on glass behave as liquids when $n \leqslant 12$, as plastics when $13 \leqslant n \leqslant 15$, and as solids when $n \geqslant 16$.

EFFECT OF HALOGEN SUBSTITUTION

Shafrin (1958) has studied the effect of replacing the methyl group in adsorbed stearic acid films by a trifluoromethyl group $(CF_3(CH_2)_{n-2}COOH)$ and found a slight increase in the friction for both glass and steel. When halogen substitution was almost or fully complete, as in acids of the type $HCF_2(CF_2)_{n-2}COOH$ and $CF_3(CF_2)_{n-2}COOH$, there was a decrease in wettability which was greatest for the fully fluorinated derivatives. The lowest value of μ_k achieved with the trifluoromethyl acids was double that for the paraffinic derivatives. The van der Waals' forces between adjacent perfluoromethylene chains are considerably smaller than those between hydrocarbon chains and it was concluded that the higher friction of the fully fluorinated derivatives arose from their low packing density rather than the nature of the methyl terminal.

6. CHEMISORBED SILICONE LAYERS

It has been shown in the previous section that the coefficient of friction of glass can be greatly reduced by the adsorption of certain organic compounds, and also, that the lowering of the surface attractive forces results in the treated glass surface becoming hydrophobic. It is therefore natural that for practical purposes considerable attention should have been given to methods of producing stable hydrophobic and low friction layers on glass.

It was noted during the early preparation of the methychlorosilanes as stages in the production of silicone polymers that glass surfaces coming into contact with their vapours were rendered strongly water repellent. Such a process for water-proofing glass has been described by Patnode (1940). A reaction occurs between methylchlorosilane vapour and the water or OH⁻groups adsorbed to the glass surface which produces hydrochloric acid and permits the silicon atoms in the adsorbed molecule to link up with the free oxygen. This reaction, shown in Fig. 7.5, results in the formation of a silicone polymer which is strongly attached to the glass surface with the water repellent CH_3-groups outermost. Normally a glass surface will have a high water content and the methylchlorosilane will react to form a film several layers thick on the glass. Thus Vandervort and Willard (1948) found that the film produced by vapour reaction is at least 10–30 molecules thick, but rubbing the film reduces it to a monolayer. The monolayer must be chemically bonded to the glass because it can only be removed with destructive reagents such as hydrofluoric acid.

If a glass has been outgassed by heating in vacuum its surface cannot be water-proofed with the chloride compounds indicating the essential nature of the water reaction for the silicone to be formed. However, if a glass is dipped in a solution of dimethylpolysiloxane in a solvent such as carbon tetrachloride and heated to about 300°c then the surface becomes covered with a strongly

25

adherent and water repellent film. Rochow (1951) attributes the reaction to partial oxidation of the methyl groups but the glass surface must also be exposed by desorption of the bound water permitting the chemisorption of the silicone film. Wessel (1957) has shown that water emulsions of silicone oil give the highest contact angle when the glass is heated to 250–300°c. Dimethylpolysiloxane is a polymer formed from a repeating unit $[(CH_3)_2SiO]_n$ in which

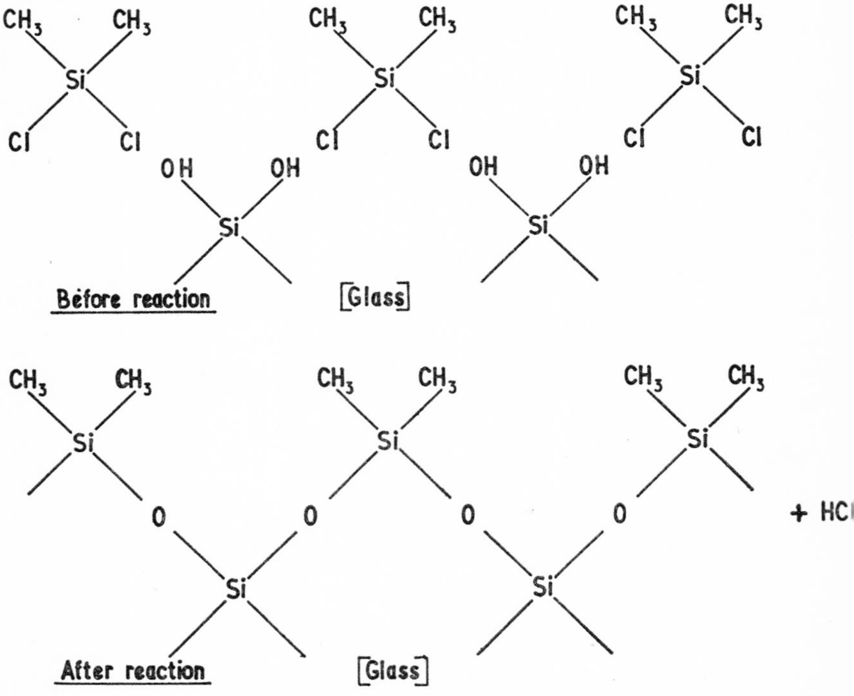

FIG. 7.5 PROBABLE ORIENTATION OF SILICONE FILM PRODUCED BY REACTION BETWEEN DIMETHYLCHLOROSILANE AND ADSORBED OH^-GROUPS

the structure is based on chains, or cycles, of —Si—O—Si— atoms. This is also the type of polymer film formed after methylchlorosilane reacts with OH^- groups as shown in Fig. 7.5.

The writer (1958) has noted that a fresh surface of silica prepared by evaporation of silicon monoxide in vacuum becomes strongly water repellent if exposed to the vapour emitted by silicone oils used in diffusion pumps. If the fresh silica surface is first exposed to water vapour and becomes covered with OH⁻ groups then the silicone molecules are not chemisorbed to the silica. The writer has also observed that glasses heated to 300°c in a vacuum containing small amounts of silicone vapour develop a high contact angle for water. These aspects are discussed at length in Chapter 5.

Method of treatment. Some of the methods of applying the water repellent film to glass will now be discussed. Norton † (1944) treated glass specimens in a desiccator connected to two or three bottles of methylchlorosilane. Dry air was bubbled through the methylchlorosilane (which has a vapour pressure of about 200 torr at room temperature) and into the desiccator for a few minutes. The specimens were then exposed to evaporate the hydrochloric acid which was completely volatilized in 2 hours. The chlorosilane vapours will burn and must be kept away from the skin because of the production of hydrochloric acid.

Hunter *et al.* consider that it is more desirable to apply the long chain alkyltrichlorosilanes in a solvent such as benzene because of their lower vapour pressure. When using chloride-free organosiloxane polymers a solvent may be used but the glass must be heat treated at about 300°c to fix the film to the glass.

CONTACT ANGLE AND FRICTION

A thorough study of the properties of polyorganosiloxane films on glass has been made by Hunter *et al.* (1947) who measured the contact angle of water and coefficient of static friction of the treated surfaces. The friction was measured with a borosilicate rider supported at three points on spherical beads, which were polished with a clean cloth. The tests were made in an atmosphere of 50% R.H. Soda-lime glasses were immersed for 30 min in redistilled benzene containing 0·02% of various organosilicon compounds and heat treated at different temperatures. Values are given in Fig. 7.6(*a*),

---

† Silicone preparations manufactured for use on glass are 'Repelcote' (Hopkins and Williams Ltd., London) and 'Dri-Film' (General Electrical Company, U.S.A.). Midland Silicones Ltd., London and Dow Corning Corporation, U.S.A. produce silicone preparations which can be applied as a fine mist to glassware passing through a lehr.

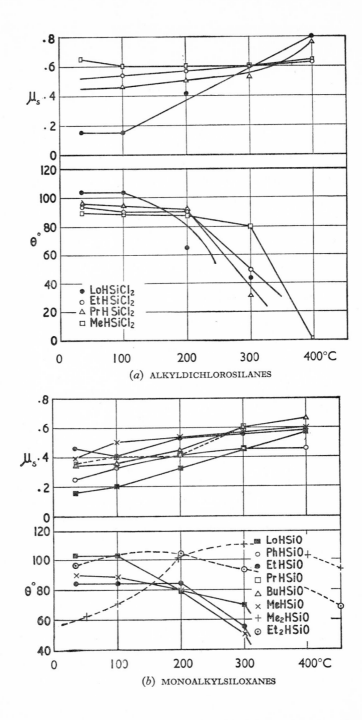

(a) ALKYLDICHLOROSILANES

(b) MONOALKYLSILOXANES

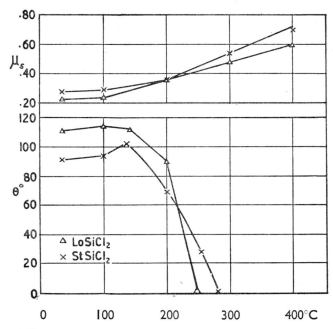

(c) LOROL SILICON TRICHLORIDE AND STEARYL SILICON TRICHLORIDE

FIG. 7.6   COEFFICIENT OF FRICTION AND CONTACT ANGLE OF WATER ON SOFT
GLASS TREATED AT DIFFERENT TEMPERATURES AFTER DIPPING IN 0.02% SILICONE/
BENZENE SOLUTIONS
(*After Hunter et al.,* 1947)

(*b*) and (*c*) of θ and μ_s as a function of the heat treatment temperature. The slides were initially cleaned in a mixture of chromic and sulphuric acids and before silicone formation $\theta = 0°$ and $\mu_s = 1·43$ (the latter figure is much higher than that normally measured for clean glass).

Fig. 7.6(*a*) shows that as the length of the alkyl group in the dichlorosilane used increased the contact angle rose and the friction decreased. These properties did not persist at high temperature because of oxidation of the alkyl group. The methyl derivative was the most stable, showing a fall in θ above 300°c. The second series

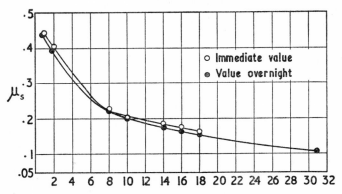

Fig. 7.7 Coefficient of friction of pyrex treated with 0·1 m solutions of alkyltrichlorosilanes ($C_nH_{2n+1}SiCl_3$) with different alkyl chain lengths (*After Hunter et al.*, 1947)

shown in Fig. 7.6(*b*) are for glasses treated with monoalkylsiloxanes and the results were erratic because there was no chloride for reaction with the hydroxyl groups on the glass. The third group in Fig. 7.6(*c*) is based on Lorol† and stearyl silicone trichloride. With this group the layers showed persistent or improved properties up to 150°c presumably because of the presence of chloride in the reacting coating.

Shown in Fig. 7.7 is the dependence of μ_s on the alkyl chain length when borosilicate slides were treated with alkytrichlorosilanes. The value of μ_s for the untreated glass was 0·45 because it was only polished with rouge and water. However, the friction

---

† Lorol chloride is a technical grade of lauryl chloride produced by Du Pont.

shows a steady decrease with chain length reaching a limiting value when treated with a compound corresponding to $C_{31}H_{63}SiCl_3$. It is shown in the previous section that Hardy and Doubleday found a similar relation between μ_s and chain length when working with the paraffins, etc. In their results μ_s did not reach an asymptotic

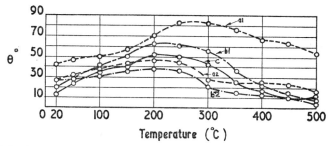

FIG. 7.8 DEPENDENCE OF THE CONTACT ANGLE FOR SILICONE TREATED BK7 GLASS ON THE HEAT TREATMENT TEMPERATURE AFTER CLEANING WITH DIFFERENT SOLUTIONS (*After Wessel*, 1958). (*a*1) CHROMIC/SULPHURIC ACID 30 min; (*a*2) WASHED IN DIST. WATER 2 h 30 min; (*b*1) TRICHLORETHYLENE AND CLOTH; (*b*2) TRICHLORETHYLENE WITHOUT CLOTH; (*c*) CARBON TETRACHLORIDE

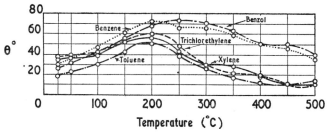

FIG. 7.9 TREATMENT OF 'TEMPAX' GLASS WITH DIFFERENT ORGANIC SOLVENT/ SILICONE SOLUTIONS. GLASS FIRST CLEANED WITH DETERGENT AND THEN HEAT TREATED AT 500°C FOR 60 min BEFORE DIPPING IN SOLUTION AND BAKING AT TEMPERATURES FROM 25 TO 500°C FOR 30 min (*After Wessel*, 1958)

value, but the compounds investigated did not cover such a large range of chain lengths.

Hunter *et al.* note that glass treated with chloride free dimethylsiloxane polymer shows a low contact angle which is only slightly raised by heating to 100°C. When the film is cured for 15 min at 300°C a maximum contact angle for water of 100° is realized; the high temperature is necessary for formation of the silicone film.

Rochow (1951) has given a value of $\theta = 103°$ for water on a dimethy-siloxane film and his figure is probably the correct one as it is more in agreement with that for paraffin wax, $\theta = 105°$, whose surface is usually supposed to contain CH_3-groups.

INFLUENCE OF CLEANING TECHNIQUES AND SOLVENTS ON BAKED LAYERS

Wessel (1958) has studied the influence of surface cleaning processes on the contact angle of water obtained when glass is silicone coated by heat treatment. Glasses were cleaned with a range of solutions as shown in Fig. 7.8 and then treated with a water emulsion of silicone oil. A treated specimen was baked up to 500°c in steps and held at the plotted temperature values for 30 min periods. Cleaning in a chromic/sulphuric acid solution produced the highest contact angle after silicone coating. It is evident from the curves that traces of the organic solvents used for cleaning have remained behind and influenced the subsequently attained contact angle. In a similar way the organic solvents used with the silicone oil influence the nature and behaviour of the hydrophobic film as shown in Fig. 7.9. Both sets of curves show that the hydrophobic coating is formed at about 200–300°c and at higher temperatures the contact angle falls as the organic material in the film is oxidized.

The silicone treatment has many applications *e.g.* glass bottles which have been silicone-coated are less easily fractured by abrasion. Ramsaur (1955) observed that water does not readily condense on silicone treated glass when it is cooled. Glass rendered hydrophobic by silicone polymers has a low electrical conductivity in humid atmospheres due to the discontinuity of the condensed water layer, as shown in Chapter 9. The discontinuity of a condensed water layer tends to make silicone-treated glass unsuitable for optical applications, because the discrete water droplets scatter incident light. Thus Ramsaur found that rain water droplets on silicone-treated automobile wind-screens badly obscured night viewing.

References

Belser, R. B., 1953, October, *Ceramic Age.*
Bikerman, J. J., and Rideal, E. K., 1939, *Phil. Mag.*, **27**, 687.
Blodgett, K. B., 1934, *J. Proc. Amer. chem. Soc.*, **56**, 495.
Bourdillon, J., 1957, *Nature, Lond.*, **180**, 1475.
Bowden, F. P., and Tabor, D., 1956, *Theory of Boundary Lubrication,* Methuen, London.

Ghering, L. G., Turnbull, J. C., 1940, *Bull. Amer. ceram. Soc.*, **19**, 290.

Hardy, W. B., 1925, *J. chem. Soc.*, **127**, 1222.

Hardy, W. B., and Doubleday, I., 1922, *Proc. roy. soc.*, **A**, **100**, 550.

Hardy, W. B., and Hardy, J. K., 1919, *Phil. Mag.*, **38**, 32.

Holland, L., 1958, *Brit. J. appl. Phys.*, **9**, 410.

Holland, L., 1960, 7th Nat. Symp. *American Vacuum Society*, p. 168, Pergamon Press.

Hunter, M. J., Gordon, M. S., Barry, A. J., Hyde, J. F., and Heidenreich, R. D., 1947, *Ind. engng. Chem.*, **39**, 1389.

Izmailova, B. I., and Deryagin, B. V., 1952, *Dokl. Akad. Nauk. SSSR*, **87**, 85.

Kinosita, K., 1953, *J. phys. Soc. Japan*, **8**, 782.

Langmuir, I., 1920 June, *Trans. Farad. Soc.*, **15**, 62.

Langmuir, I., 1934, *Frank. Inst. J.*, **218**, 143.

Norton, F. J., 1944, *Gen. Elec. Rev.*, **47**, No. 8, 6.

Patnode, W. I., 1940, U.S. Patent 2, 306, 222.

Putner, T., 1959, *Brit. J. appl. Phys.*, **10**, 332.

Ramsaur, R., 1955, *Glastech. Ber.*, **28**, 451.

Rochow, E. G., 1951, *An Introduction to the Chemistry of the Silicones*, 2nd Ed., Chapman and Hall Ltd., London.

Shafrin, E. G., 1958 July, 'The Lubricating Properties of Monomolecular Films Adsorbed on Solid Surfaces', Rep. U.S. Nav. Res. Lab. Progress.

Shaw, P. E., 1927, *J. sci. Instrum.*, **4**, 222.

Shaw, P. E., and Leavey, E. W. L., 1930, *Phil. Mag.*, **10**, 809.

Southwick, R. D., 1957 *The Strength of Abraded Glass*, Part VII, Preston Lab. Rep. No. 57–077.

Southwick, R. D., 1958, *Friction and Surface Damage in a Sliding Metal to Glass Contact*, Preston Lab. Rep. No. 58–035.

Tomlinson, G. A., 1929, June, *Phil. Mag. Suppl.*, 905.

Vandervort, G. L., and Willard, J. E., 1948, *J. Amer. chem. Soc.*, **70**, 3148.

Wessel, H., 1957, *Die Pharmazie*, **12**, 109.

Wessel, H., 1958, *Silikattechnik*, **9**, 201.

Weyl, W. A., 1949, *J. Soc. Glass Technol.*, **33**, 220.

Wooster, W. A., and Mcdonald, G. L., 1946, *Nature, Lond.*, **160**, 260.

Chapter 8

Adhesion of Metals and Polymers to Glass

1. INTRODUCTION

We have discussed in the previous two chapters the wetting and frictional properties of glass, *i.e.* phenomena arising from the attractive forces of unshielded atoms in the glass surface. In this chapter we are concerned with the nature and properties of the adhesion between glass and other solid substances. Glass is joined to solid materials for many purposes. It is used as an electrical insulator in metal lead-in electrodes; with organic resins in laminated or reinforced plastics; and as a substrate for thin solid films of metals and dielectrics widely applied for their optical and electrical properties.

When a solid material is joined by chemical forces to glass the adhesive strength is exceptionally high. Chemical bonding can arise from unshielded atoms in the surfaces of the contacting solids reacting to produce a compound at the boundary in a manner akin to the chemisorption of gases to solids. If the reactive components can diffuse across the interface then a transition layer will be produced between the solids. For the bulk materials to adhere the chemical compound formed at the interface must act as a coupling agent for both substances. The types of interfacial reaction which occur when metals and dielectrics are bonded to glass can be summarized as follows:

(*i*) *Ion exchange.* Metal ions replace sodium ions in the glass surface. Process believed to occur in the chemical precipitation of silver mirror films on glass.

(*ii*) *Metal oxide cementing layers.* Oxide layers on metal enhance the adhesion of glass to metals. Most metal oxide layers can be partially dissolved in glass when metal and glass are heated to a high temperature. Also even when solution is not promoted by high temperature treatment oxide films deposited from say the vapour phase have a high interfacial adhesion to glass.

(*iii*) *Polar or unsaturated groups in organic polymers.* Organic polymers adhere to glass if they contain polar or unsaturated groups which can orientate themselves on the glass surface. Orientation can occur when a monomer in contact with glass is polymerized.

(*iv*) *Metallic-organic compounds.* The [SiO]-groups in organo–silicon polymers continue the glass structure at the interface thereby bonding the polymer to the surface. Coupling agents may be used to bond non-polar polymers to glass, *e.g.* silicone compounds with unsaturated hydrocarbon terminals for bonding to a plastic. A chromium–organic complex has also been used for this purpose.

All of the above types of bond are discussed in detail in the ensuing chapter with the exception of item (*i*) which is considered in Chapter 3.

Weyl (1945) has classified another group of materials which adhere to glass, viz. substances which have a compatible ionic or compatible random arranged structure which adhere because similar forces exist in both media, *e.g.* anti-reflection films of fluoride compounds on glass. Vacuum evaporated films of calcium fluoride and magnesium fluoride are highly adherent to clean glass whereas cryolite films are easily rubbed off. The latter substance is a soft material and its degree of adhesion to glass is uncertain. It is not definite that fluoride films adhere to glass because of a compatibility of ionic structure. Thus, when such films are vacuum evaporated, they can react with oxygen in the vacuum system or with water on the glass surface to produce an oxide transition layer. Both the oxides of magnesium and calcium are common components of silicate glasses, whereas their fluorides are used in glass as opacifying agents because they form micro-crystals in the glass matrix. Volf (1961) states that the crystallization of fluorides in silicate glass depends on the crystalline form of the substance. Thus substances in the cubic system, *e.g.* CaF_2, crystallize in silicate glass, whereas AlF_3 (trigonal), ZnF_2 (monoclinic) and PbF_2 (rhombic) will not crystallize and act as opacifying agents. Evaporated films of these fluorides on amorphous substrates are usually composed of micro-crystals. The crystallites, observable by electron microscopy, tend to grow with a net plane parallel to the substrate, *e.g.* (111) for

CaF$_2$, but with other planes in random orientation. The tendency for the 'one-degree' orientation of the crystallites has been attributed to growth from a tightly packed net plane developing from a packed monolayer at onset of condensation. Growth of this kind can therefore occur where the forces between the base and condensate are merely physical. On the other hand, CaF$_2$ and MgF$_2$ films can be so firmly bonded to glass that they can only be removed by grinding. It is obvious that an investigation is required of depositing fluoride films on to fresh glass surfaces (or evaporated silica films) to determine the nature of the interfacial bond free from the effects of gas sorption.

It might appear surprising that the bond between glass and organic substances as described in item (*iii*) can be of a chemical nature. However, Deryagin (1955) and his co-workers have found that when polymer films were rapidly peeled from glass the separated bodies had opposing electrical charges on their surfaces, which caused sparking during stripping. Further, the work required to peel polymer films from surfaces exceeded by several orders of magnitude the surface energy of dielectric and metal substrates. Thus it is impossible to attribute adhesion between glass and certain organic substances to molecular forces such as are involved in surface tension effects and adhesion must arise from chemical bonding. For example, when a polymer containing polar groups such as [COOH] is in contact with glass a chemical bond could form by the hydrogen ion replacing a sodium ion in the glass surface. Equally sodium ions in the glass surface may replace the hydrogen ion in the polar group.

2. ADHESION OF METALS TO GLASS— GENERAL CHARACTERISTICS

ROLE OF OXIDE LAYER

It has already been shown in the previous chapter that most base metals leave a metal trace on glass when they are rubbed on a glass surface because the oxide film on the metal adheres to the glass, tearing metal from the abrader. Mercury appears to be a notable exception in that it wets glass only when completely free from oxygen. Other low melting point metals such as tin, indium and gallium only stick to glass via an oxide deposit. Indium, as observed by Rose (1944) and Belser (1954), readily sticks to glass if melted on the surface with a soldering iron, but a flux must not be used otherwise this removes the oxide cementing layer.

The writer and his colleagues have found that aluminium can be used for joining glass to metals by compressing an aluminium gasket so that it flows and frictionally adheres to the mating surfaces (Holden *et al.* (1959)). Seals of this kind made with a compression force of about 5000 lb/in. of 22 SWG aluminium wire can be heated repeatedly to about 200°c without failure. However, when the seal is heated to about 400°c the aluminium gasket undergoes appreciable flow and adheres firmly to the glass. It appears that the aluminium or its oxide adheres strongly to the glass in those regions where the aluminium on initially flowing removes surface contaminants from the surface. The aluminium/glass bond is stronger than the glass. Thus a circular glass plate sealed by aluminium to an annular steel flange underwent thickness shear on cooling due to differential thermal expansion.

The metal components in lead-in electrodes also adhere to glass because of the formation of a cementing metal oxide film between the metal and the glass. Partridge (1949) has discussed fully the theory of glass to metal sealing and the influence of metal oxide inter-layers on bond strength and stability. He states that the oxide layer is desirable for two reasons. First it prevents direct contact between molten glass and metal and secondly stops numerous gas bubbles liberated from the metal or the glass forming at the glass/metal boundary. (It follows from the discussion in Chapter 6 that gas bubbles will more easily form at an interface of high surface tension.) It is not the purpose of this work to discuss the preparation of glass to metal seals, this is adequately covered in Partridge's treatise, but we shall consider the knowledge obtained in this field of the nature of the bond between metal and glass.

Hull and Burger (1934) found that molten glass would not spread over a clean metal surface in an atmosphere of hydrogen, pure nitrogen or carbon dioxide. However, when the metal had been oxidized, the glass wetted and adhered to the metal surface in a nitrogen or carbon dioxide atmosphere. When the metal was heated in the reducing atmosphere of a hydrogen furnace wetting did not occur. The glass spread rapidly on an oxidized surface and the affinity was so strong that molten glass climbed the surface of a vertical metal plate.

Partridge (1949) found that iron was slightly oxidized when heated in the presence of molten enamel under a low gas pressure of 10^{-3} torr of carbon dioxide or nitrogen. A slight visible film of oxide was sufficient to promote glass adhesion and a reducing atmosphere, *e.g.* a nitrogen atmosphere with 10% hydrogen, was necessary to prevent this. However, when iron is covered with glass enamels an adherent coating is only produced when the metal base is corroded by the electrolytic action of the enamel. It appears that the resulting bond is *mechanical* in nature (Dietzel, 1935).

Obviously, adhesion of a glass to a metal is not the only requirement for the production of a stable lead-in electrode or glass enamel coating. The strain produced by the differential thermal expansion must not exceed the strength of the glass. Glass fails more easily in tension than in compression and enamel coatings on iron are usually compressed by the base contracting more than the enamel during cooling. Stable glass to metal electrode seals were prepared by Housekeeper (1923) by using thin-section copper electrodes which yielded under stress, reducing the stress to a safe value. Alternatively, one may combine metals and glasses whose expansion coefficients are reasonably matched.

Compact oxide films on oxidized metals are brittle and develop compressional stresses during growth. Such films may crack when reaching an optimum thickness or flake from a heated substrate due to a difference in their thermal expansion. Thus the strength of a metal-to-glass bond is critically dependent on the properties of the oxide cementing layer, which is normally kept thin to reduce shear stresses. Some metals, such as molybdenum, oxidize rapidly in air, producing thick non-adherent oxide coatings. Molybdenum can, however, be sealed to glass providing oxygen flow to the metal surface is only sufficient for the growth of a thin oxide layer.

Solution or interfacial bond. It has been suggested above that the oxide layer in glass to metal seals is soluble in both metal and glass and serves as a cement. Adhesion between a metal oxide layer and glass can be extremely high without solution occurring. Thus, metal oxide films deposited on glass by evaporation *in vacuo*, reactive sputtering or gas reaction techniques are highly adherent. Metal oxide films deposited on glass can be used to enhance the adhesion of subsequently deposited noble metal films; for an account of this see Holland (1956).

Platinum and noble metals. Hull and Berger believed that a metal oxide cementing layer was the easiest means of obtaining adherence between glass and metal but was not the only way. They considered the possibility of matching the metal lattice and the molecular dimensions of a glass and believed that platinum may or may not be an example of adherence without oxide, since it is known to be covered with an exceptionally stable layer of oxide. More recently, Dietzel and Coenen (1959) have attributed the adhesion of glass joined to platinum and silver to the diffusion of oxygen into the metal lattice forming a transition zone of bridging ions. Glass can be joined to copper even when a metal oxide film is not visible on the copper surface. Dietzel (1951) attributes the adhesion to oxygen ions diffusing into the copper, as with platinum and silver.

From studies of the adhesion of platinum films deposited on glass by vacuum evaporation the writer has concluded that a platinum oxide interlayer is essential for adhesion. Pure platinum films evaporated *in vacuo* do not adhere to glass, whereas platinum cathodically sputtered on to glass in a glow discharge containing oxygen does (Holland, 1956). The sputtered films contain oxide formed by a reaction between platinum and active oxygen. Koenig *et al.* (1955) have noted that platinum films sputtered in hydrogen on to different kinds of glass are partially oxidized by water vapour desorbed from the glass into the glow discharge. The platinum films became more metallic as the substrate was changed in the following order: soda-lime glass; 'Tempax' glass ('Pyrex' type); flint glass; this is also the order of decreasing water adsorption.

When base metals are vacuum evaporated on to glass the resultant films are usually highly adherent. The writer has attributed their adhesion to a metal oxide layer forming on the glass surface at the start of the evaporation. Such cementing layers can arise from reaction with oxidizing gases in the vacuum vessel or water adsorbed to the glass. Vacuum evaporated films of gold and silver are not adherent to glass. The adhesion of gold can be greatly enhanced by depositing it on a cementing oxide layer, *e.g.* bismuth oxide, previously applied to the glass. The adhesion of a silver coating can be enhanced by a similar technique or by deliberately contaminating the silver film with oxygen during its initial growth.

Alloy seals based on Fe, Ni, Co *and* Cr. Lead-in wires and metal connections to glass are usually made from alloys based on iron, nickel and chromium. By adjusting the composition of such alloys it is possible to match their thermal expansion to that of various glasses (Hull and Berger 1934).

Pure nickel has been used for lead-in electrodes in electric lamps but tends to collect bubbles. One type of lead-in electrode used in electric lamps is a 48% Ni 52% Fe alloy with a coefficient of thermal expansion about that of a soft-glass of the soda-lime or lead types. Nickel–iron alloys oxidize readily in a flame but the oxide film does not adhere firmly to the metal. Nickel–iron lead-in wires, coated with copper, have been used. The addition of a small amount of chromium to iron or nickel–iron alloys makes them resistant to the growth of thick oxide layers. The surface oxide is rich in green chromium oxide which tenaciously adheres to the base metal. When about 5–6% of chromium is added to a 42% nickel–iron basic alloy the coefficient of thermal expansion of the alloy is increased. Such an alloy is used in the radio industry for contact pins in moulded bases of soft glass of the lead silicate type. Metals sealed to the hard borosilicate glasses must have a low coefficient of expansion. Several alloys have been commercially developed for this purpose known as 'Kovar', 'Fernico', 'Therlo', they contain iron, nickel and cobalt and have a composition in the range 54–60% Fe; 24–31% Ni; 14–15% Co. The addition of cobalt lowers the expansion coefficient of nickel–iron alloys.

Volatile oxide layers. There is some uncertainty about the nature of the boundary surface between tungsten and glass seals formed at high temperature. Thus at temperatures above 2000°c the oxides formed on tungsten readily evaporate and if the metal is coated with alkali-free glass under these conditions an apparently 'oxide-free' seal with a bright metallic appearance is formed. However, low temperature seals can be made to tungsten with the oxide present so that the existence of an oxide film does not prevent a seal from forming.

Partridge was unable to break a high temperature tungsten/glass seal at the boundary zone, the break always occurred in the glass. Satisfactory boundary surfaces could not be prepared for analysis by X-rays and electron diffraction and it was not certain that an oxide did not exist on the tungsten surface.

Interfacial reactions. Chemical reactions may obviously occur when a metal is heated to a high temperature in contact with glass. For example, when silica is heated on tungsten filaments *in vacuo* the metal heater reacts with the silica during melting forming a tungsten oxide and lower silicon oxide, *e.g.* silicon monoxide. Other refractory metals such as tantalum and molybdenum react with silica when it is heated to its melting point *in vacuo*. Molybdenum oxidizes rapidly in air forming a loosely adhering layer and molybdenum seals are often made under reduced pressure.

Mitoff (1957) has observed a reaction between tantalum and sodium silicate glass (33 mol % Na_2O) when heated to 1000°c *in vacuo*. X-ray diffraction analysis showed that the interfacial compound was sodium metatantalate ($Na_2Ta_2O_6$). The interfacial compound was brittle and the glass readily sheared from the tantalum when cold. (A sodium tungstate would probably form if soda-lime glass was melted in contact with tungsten.)

Tests in the writer's laboratory showed that when soda-lime glass is melted and degassed on molybdenum *in vacuo* at a temperature as high as 1400°c the glass (unlike pure silica) is not reduced because it remains optically non-absorbing. Some of the soda must evaporate but a part may enter into a reaction with the molybdenum. The glass is not adherent but flakes away from the metal.

A reaction may also occur between the soda in an alkaline glass and iron leading to the formation of iron oxide and free sodium vapour; the reaction is rapid at temperatures of about 1000°c.

Holland *et al.* (1957) have observed a reaction between an evaporated titanium film and soda-lime glass when the titanium was oxidized by heating to 400°c in air to form titanium dioxide in the rutile modification. It was believed that the titanium formed a compound with the glass components. The reaction could be prevented by evaporating a base-layer of aluminium oxide or magnesium fluoride on to the glass, as shown in Plate 28.

Summary. It would appear from the foregoing observations that glass is generally sealed to base metals by the cementing action of an intermediate oxide film. The oxide layer may be prepared by oxidizing the metal before bringing it into contact with the glass or by making the seal in an oxidizing atmosphere. Other oxidizing processes which could promote wetting are the desorption of oxygen from the glass or metal member and the reaction of the oxides in the glass with the metal at high temperature. In the enamelling of iron the source of adhesion appears to be mechanical and depends on the surface roughness. It is uncertain whether platinum is sealed to glass by a surface layer of oxide or by oxygen diffusing into the metal lattice. It also appears possible that copper may be sealed to

26

glass either by an oxide cementing layer or by diffusion of oxygen ions into the metal. There is ample evidence that intermediate metal oxide layers help to produce adherent films of evaporated metals on glass.

Undoubtedly much of the glass to metal seal industry has developed as an art and many of the explanations of the foregoing observations are subject to conjecture. The processes by which glasses are bonded to metals can only be explained as the result of experimental investigations in which due attention is given to measuring the interfacial binding energies as discussed below.

3. THE WORK OF ADHESION OF METALS TO GLASS

Several workers have studied the wetting of metals by molten glass and measured the contact angle θ to find the degree of affinity between the materials. Wetting studies have a direct practical bearing on the handling of molten glass with metal tools, *e.g.* the drawing of glass fibres through platinum or platinum alloy bushings and the melting of glass in platinum vessels. When preparing metal/glass joints one must of course consider factors other than wetting alone, *e.g.* the effect on bond strength of metal oxide scaling and stresses arising from differential thermal expansion.

If one determines θ then the work of adhesion per unit area can be found from the equation

$$W_{\mathrm{SL}} = \gamma_{\mathrm{LV}}(1 + \cos \theta) \tag{i}$$

where γ_{LV} is the surface tension of a liquid in the presence of its vapour. The foregoing relation is derived in Section 2 of Chapter 6, where surface tension and contact angle are discussed.

When θ is made zero in the above equation then $W_{\mathrm{SL}} = 2\gamma_{\mathrm{LV}}$ which is the work necessary to overcome the cohesion of the liquid. As θ can only equal or exceed zero, it cannot give information on the work of adhesion at the interface if this exceeds the work of cohesion in the liquid as could occur for a chemical bond.

It is shown in Chapter 6 that the surface tensions of the solid and liquid are modified by the vapour emitted from the liquid. With glass only certain constituents are appreciably volatile, *e.g.* sodium, and these may not be adsorbed to a metal base at high temperature. However, as stated above, reaction between the surface of the metal base and oxygen in the atmosphere strongly influences the wetting of metals by molten glass. Adsorption of oxygen by a metal will reduce its surface energy or tension γ_{MO}. Thus, if the contact angle of a glass is lower on a metal when oxidized and the glass surface tension γ_{LO} is unaffected by the atmosphere, then the surface energy or tension γ_{ML} at the interface must be reduced by the oxide layer because $\gamma_{MO} = \gamma_{ML} + \gamma_{LO} \cos \theta$. This is the opposite effect to that of vapour adsorption which, if orientation of the adsorbed molecules does not occur, leaves γ_{SL} unchanged but raises θ and lowers γ_{SV} and γ_{LV} (p. 350).

Discussion of the surface energies of oxide covered and clean metals is outside of the scope of this work but Pask (1963) has reviewed the literature pertinent to metal/glass bonding. Reported values for the surface energies of metals such as Au, Ag and Cu are in the region of 1000–1500 ergs/cm^2, but these values are most certainly for metals which are covered with adsorbed gas molecules (probably oxygen), or which contain dissolved gas. The surface energies of silicate glasses at 1000°c are about 200–300 ergs/cm^2. The surface energy of an alkali glass may be reduced by sodium ions migrating to the surface. Thus the surface energy of a glass fracture surface should be higher than that of a melted solid. Parikh (1958) measured the surface tension of various glasses in the transformation-temperature range using the elongated fibre method described below. He found that water vapour reacted with the glass, lowering the surface tension, but other gases had no significant effect.

Before discussing the contact angles of specific glass/metal systems we shall consider methods of determining the surface tension of glass. Given a value of γ_{LV} for a particular glass and θ for a specific glass/metal system then W_A the work of adhesion can be found from equation (i).

MEASUREMENT OF SURFACE TENSION OF MOLTEN GLASS

Excellent reviews of methods of determining the surface tension of liquids have been published by Davies and Rideal (1961) and Mitchell *et al.* (1952); the latter deal specifically with glass. We shall consider briefly methods which can or have been applied to molten glass.

Ring-breaking method. If a metal ring connected to the arm of a balance makes contact to a liquid (Fig. 8.1(*a*)), for which the contact angle is zero, then the force required to detach the ring is given by

$$F = 4\pi r \gamma_{LV} \tag{ii}$$

where r is the mean radius of the ring. The total length over which the surface tension acts is twice the circumference of the metal ring ($2\pi r$), because the liquid forms a hollow cylinder. The surface tension does not act completely vertical as does the force due to the balance. Thus depending on the dimensions of the ring the true breaking force is always less than the breaking force applied vertically.

Dipping plate or cylinder method. If a very thin plate is suspended from the arm of a balance (Fig. 8.1(b)) there is an additional pull on the plate if it is wetted when it is partially immersed in a liquid (Wilhelmy, 1863). The excess pull is equal to the weight of the liquid lifted above the mean level of the liquid surface and is equal to the product of the perimeter and surface tension providing the contact angle is zero. A correction must be made for buoyancy. Thus the excess pull due to surface tension will be equal to the measured increase ΔF plus the up-thrust due to buoyancy. If the plate is replaced by a thin walled cylinder we have

$$\gamma_{LV} 2\pi(r_1 + r_2) = \Delta F + h\rho g 2\pi(r_1^2 - r_2^2) \tag{iii}$$

where h is the depth of immersion of the cylinder, r_1 and r_2 the outer and inner radius, ρ the density of the liquid and g the gravitational constant.

If the meniscus takes the form in Fig. 8.2(b) with a contact angle θ then the excess pull will not be γ_{LV} per unit perimeter but $\gamma_{LV} \cos \theta$. If one knows θ then γ_{LV} can be found. Babcock (1940) used the dipping cylinder method for measuring the surface tension of a range of glasses. After ensuring that the glass had wetted the end of the cylinder he found that the pull reached a maximum value when the cylinder was raised above the liquid surface. He used the relation $\gamma_{LV} = \Delta F / 4\pi r$ where r was the mean radius of the cylinder.

If an immersed plate is withdrawn from a liquid for a distance l the plate will be de-wetted and the work done will be $l\gamma_{LV} \cos \theta$. Work will not be expended in forming a liquid surface, *i.e.* $l\gamma_{LV}$. The *work of adhesion* per unit area is given by $W_{SL} = \gamma_{LV}(1 + \cos \theta)$, where γ_{LV} represents the work required to form unit area of liquid surface and $\gamma_{LV} \cos \theta$ is the work required to de-wet unit area of the plate. Thus $\gamma_{LV} \cos \theta$ has been referred to as the *work of wetting*.

Drop-weight method. The weight or volume V of a drop which falls from the tip of a tube (Fig. 8(c)) is mainly determined by the surface

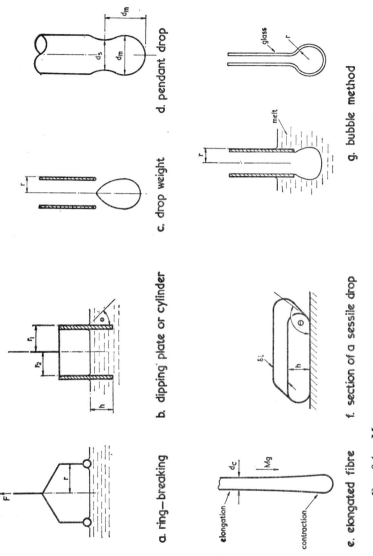

a. ring—breaking   b. dipping plate or cylinder   c. drop weight   d. pendant drop

e. elongated fibre   f. section of a sessile drop   g. bubble method

FIG. 8.1.   METHODS USED FOR DETERMINING THE SURFACE TENSION OF GLASS

tension of the liquid and the radius of the tube. Tate (1864) observed that 'the weight of a drop of liquid is proportional to the diameter of the tube in which it is formed'. Assuming that the drops form slowly then they detach themselves from the tip when the gravitational pull minus the force due to buoyancy in the surrounding medium equals the restraining force of the surface tension

$$\Delta\rho V g = 2\pi r \gamma_{LV} \qquad \text{(iv)}$$

where $\Delta\rho$ is the difference in density between the drop and the surrounding medium, g the gravitational constant and r the radius of the tube. This relation requires correction because some of the liquid forming the drop remains on the tube end when the liquid falls. Also, the surface tension does not act exactly vertically as assumed. The above relation can be applied to a molten drop falling from the end of a glass rod.

Various workers have investigated the drop-weight method and modified the relation to account for the foregoing effects (see, for example, Rayleigh (1874)). Tillotson (1911) and Lecrenier (1924) have used a modified relation for determining the surface tension of molten glass. Harkins and Brown (1919) give a correction factor which is a function of r and V.

The accuracy of the drop-weight method is usually uncertain but it is considered a simple method of determining the relative surface tensions of glass samples.

Pendant drop. A molten drop can be formed on the end of a glass rod as in Fig. 8.1(*d*) and its dimensions used for determining surface tension. The measurements can be made after cooling (Davis and Bartell 1948) or from a photograph of the molten drop. The surface tension is given by

$$\gamma_{LV} = \Delta\rho g d_m (1/H) \qquad \text{(v)}$$

where d_m is the equatorial diameter of the drop and $1/H$ is a function of the ratio of the diameters d_s/d_m. An empirical evaluation of $1/H$ is given by Andreas, Hauser and Tucker (1938).

Elongated fibre method. If the temperature of a glass fibre (Fig. 8.1(*e*)) is progressively raised the fibre first lengthens as it thermally expands and then contracts under the action of surface tension. When the gravitational force exceeds the surface tension the fibre lengthens and the fibre diameter is a maximum just before yield occurs. Equating the forces of surface tension and gravity we have

$$Mg = \pi d_c \gamma_{LV} \qquad \text{(vi)}$$

where M is the mass of the fibre resulting in the onset of elongation at a point d_c. Tammann and Rabe (1927) and Tammann and Tampke (1927) measured the surface tension of glass fibres using the above relation. Keppeler (1937) determined the diameter of a fibre at a point d_c where during heating neither contraction nor elongation had occurred. This method gave a value of γ_{LV} about half of that measured by the bubble method. Keppeler could not explain the reason for this but the matter is discussed further in the next section.

Sessile drop method (negative values of cos θ*).* A drop of liquid resting on a horizontal surface which it does not wet ($\theta > 90°$) draws itself into a circular patch. The shape of a vertical section through the drop depends upon the amount of liquid present. The upper surface of a small drop of liquid tends to be spherical in shape, but as the volume of a droplet is increased the outer surface becomes plane and the depth h constant (Fig. 8.1(f)). Consider a section of width δl through a circular liquid patch as in Fig. 8.1(f). When the drop is stationary the forces acting on the liquid patch are in equilibrium. The hydrostatic force tending to make the droplet expand is balanced by the horizontal components of the surface tension. The hydrostatic force acting over the area δl by h is equal to the mean pressure ($\frac{1}{2} h \rho g$) times the area $\delta l h$, *i.e.* $\frac{1}{2} \rho g h^2 \, \delta l$. This will be in equilibrium with the horizontal components of the surface tension γ_{LV} and $\gamma_{LV} \cos \theta$ when $\theta > 90°$ these components must be added and we have

$$\tfrac{1}{2} \rho g h^2 \, \delta l = \gamma_{LV}(1 - \cos \theta) \qquad \text{(vii)}$$

since values of cos θ above $90°$ are negative.

More complex relations have been developed to determine γ_{LV} from the shape of a sessile drop with a curved upper surface but we shall not consider them here.

Maximum bubble pressure. If a spherical bubble is formed in a liquid the work done in enlarging its interior surface of area A is $\gamma_{LV} \, dA$ and as dA arises from an increase dr in the bubble radius r we have

$$\gamma_{LV} \, dA = \gamma_{LV} 8 \pi r \, dr$$

The gas pressure in the bubble must be equal to the hydrostatic pressure plus an excess pressure P_e balancing the surface tension. The work done in increasing the bubble area is

$$P_e \, \Delta V = \gamma_{LV} \, dA$$

where ΔV is the change of volume so that

$$P_e 4\pi r^2 \, dr = \gamma_{LV} 8\pi r \, dr$$

$$P_e = \frac{2\gamma_{LV}}{r} \qquad \text{(viii)}$$

If a gas bubble is slowly formed at the end of a tube immersed in a liquid the radius of curvature of the bubble first decreases to a minimum and then rises again. Thus P_e passes through a maximum. As the bore of a capillary tube is decreased then its radius approaches that of the hemispherical base of the bubble at the point of maximum pressure. If the liquid does not wet the tube then equation (viii) is still applicable but the capillary radius cannot be taken as equal to r, because the bubble is distorted in shape by the liquid displaced from the outer wall of the tube. Apart from an uncertainty in determining r a further error may arise when measuring the depth of the bubble which must be known for calculating the hydrostatic pressure.

The maximum bubble pressure method has been used for determining the surface tension of glass by Jaeger (1917), Parmelee and Harman (1937), Parmelee and Lyon (1937), Badger *et al.* (1937) and Keppeler (1937). Dorsey (1928) has derived a relation which allows for the hydrostatic flattening of large bubbles.

If one blows a glass bubble (Fig. 8.1(*g*)) at the end of a tube then the pressure inside the bubble when maintained in the molten state is

$$P_e = \frac{4\gamma_{LV}}{r} \qquad \text{(ix)}$$

i.e. the excess pressure is twice that of equation (viii) because the surface area has been doubled.

Pietenpol (1936) placed a glass bubble under a known gas pressure and determined surface tension by measuring the bubble diameter at the onset of melting. The pressure required to maintain a given size bubble will be different when the weight of the bubble acts downwards to that required when the weight of the bubble is supported from below. For a bubble hanging downwards we have

$$\gamma_{LV} = \frac{P_e r}{4} + \frac{W}{2\pi r}$$

where W is half the weight of the bubble and for a supported bubble

$$\gamma_{LV} = \frac{P_e r}{4} - \frac{W}{2\pi r}$$

Care must be taken with the bubble method to ensure that a given bubble is in equilibrium with the measured excess pressure. For a given surface tension value P_e is higher for low values of r. If the glass melt has a high viscosity then r will slowly reach the equilibrium value. Thus the tendency is to obtain higher values of γ_{LV} when the bubble is growing and lower values when shrinking.

RESULTS OF SURFACE TENSION MEASUREMENT

Mitchell *et al.* (1952) have collated published values for the surface tension of glass. They found that surface tension values determined before about 1936 were in poor agreement and varied with the measuring techniques used as shown in Table 8.1. Keppeler (1937)

Table 8.1
Surface tension of glass† determined in different ways
(*Compiled by Mitchell et al., 1952*)

Author	Date	Method	Order of magnitude of surface tension (dynes/cm)
Tillotson	1911	Drop weight from filter	150
Griffith	1920	Drop shape (Quincke)	430
Lecrenier	1924	Drop weight from crucible	450
Washburn, Shelton and Libman	1924	Dipping cylinder	150
Tammann and Rabe	1927	Elongated fibre	170
Keppeler	1937	Elongated fibre	160
Keppeler	1937	Max. bubble pressure	320

† Predominantly soda-lime silica.

observed that the measured surface tension values tended to fall into two groups as can be seen in Table 8.1. Keppeler himself found that the elongated fibre method gave surface tension values for soda-lime glasses and pure boric oxide which were about one-half of those obtained from the maximum bubble pressure method; he could not explain the reasons for this. It is apparent, however that whilst the temperature of the glass was known to be 1400°c

Table 8.2

Surface tension values of different glasses

SiO₂	Na₂O	K₂O	CaO	MgO	Al₂O₃	ZnO	B₂O₃	As₂O₃	PbO	BaO	Temp. range (°C)	γ_LV (dynes/cm)	References
Sodium silicates													
74·87	16·0	—	9·4	—	—	—	—	—	—	—	1100→1400	270→256	Dip. cyl. method Vickers (1937)
73·18	16·02	—	7·77	3·02	—	—	—	—	—	—	1226→1400	309→303	Max. bubble pressure Parmelee and Harman (1937)
67·75	14·84	—	7·20	2·80	7·41	—	—	—	—	—	1220→1396	339→333	Max. bubble pressure Parmelee and Harman (1937)
72·5	17·4	—	10·1	—	—	—	—	—	—	—	1200→1350	304→302	Max. bubble pressure Badger, Parmelee and Williams (1937)
80	20	—	—	—	—	—	—	—	—	—	1100→1400	276→273	Max. pull dip. cyl. Shartsis and Spinner (1951)
50	50	—	—	—	—	—	—	—	—	—	1100→1400	300→284	Max. pull dip. cyl. Shartsis and Spinner (1951)
72·9†	11·0	—	11·7	0·2	4·1	—	—	—	—	—	1250→1400	333→330	Max. pull dip. cyl. Babcock (1940)
75·98‡	13·84	—	8·93	—	—	—	—	—	—	—	1400	321	Max. bubble pressure Keppeler (1937)
Lead borates													
—	—	—	—	—	—	—	100	—	—	—	800→900	76→80	Max. pull dip. Pt-cyl. Shartsis et al. (1948)
—	—	—	—	—	—	—	89·9	—	10·1	—	800→900	76→78	Max. pull dip. Pt-cyl. Shartsis et al. (1948)
—	—	—	—	—	—	—	50·9	—	49·1	—	800→900	89→92	Max. pull dip. Pt-cyl. Shartsis et al. (1948)
—	—	—	—	—	—	—	24·5	—	75·5	—	800→900	163→160	Max. pull dip. Pt-cyl. Shartsis et al. (1948)
—	—	—	—	—	—	—	—	—	100	—	900→1000	132→135	Max. pull dip. Pt-cyl. Shartsis et al. (1948)

Glass										Temperature (°C)	Surface tension	Method / Reference
Lead silicates												
3:2	—	—	—	—	—	—	—	96·8	—	1000→1300	142→158	Max. pull dip. Pt-cyl. Shartsis et al. (1948)
9·36	—	—	—	—	—	—	—	90·64	—	1000→1300	177→183	Max. pull dip. cyl. Shartsis et al. (1948)
24·3	—	—	—	—	—	—	—	75·7	—	1000→1300	219→223	Max. pull dip. cyl. Shartsis et al. (1948)
34·91	—	—	—	—	—	—	—	65·09	—	1000→1300	233→235	Max. pull dip. cyl. Shartsis et al. (1948)
31·2	—	2·3	—	—	—	—	0·3	66·2	—	1000→1300	219	Max. pull dip. cyl. Shartsis and Smock (1947)
Zinc borates												
	—	—	—	—	—	100	—	—	—	1000→1300	83→94	Max. pull dip. cyl. Shartsis and Canga (1949)
	—	—	—	—	10	90	—	—	—	1000→1300	82→95	Max. pull dip. cyl. Shartsis and Canga (1949)
	—	—	—	—	55	45	—	—	—	1000→1300	137→154	Max. pull dip. cyl. Shartsis and Canga (1949)
	—	—	—	—	60·8	39·2	—	—	—	1000→1300	201→207	Max. pull dip. cyl. Shartsis and Canga (1949)
	—	—	—	—	70·6	29·4	—	—	—	1000→1300	279→288	Max. pull dip. cyl. Shartsis and Canga (1949)
Barium crown 58·8§	3·2	10·3	—	—	4·1	3·4	0·3	—	19·9	1000→1300	264→265	Max. pull dip. Pt-cyl. Shartsis and Smock (1947)
Barium flint 45·7	—	8·9	—	—	8·1	—	0·4	23·3	13·6	1100→1300	239→246	Max. pull dip. cyl. Shartsis and Smock (1947)
Borosilicate crown 65·88§	13·84	—	8·93	—	—	—	10·0	—	—	1400	278	Max. bubble pressure Keppeler (1937)
68·8	7·8	14·7	—	—	—	8·5	0·2	—	—	1000→1300	244→231	Shartsis and Smock (1947)

† +0·3% SO₃.　　‡ +1·35% R₂O₃.　　§ +1·35% R₂O₃.

with the bubble method with the fibre it was not known accurately. It is probable that the divergency in the results arises from the glass viscosity delaying equilibrium from being attained with the elongated fibre.

Mitchell *et al.* state that recent workers have obtained surface tension values agreeing to within one percent using different methods of measurement. Among the procedures successfully used are the maximum bubble pressure, the dipping cylinder and the pendant drop. The values of surface tension fall between 250–350 dynes/cm, depending upon the glass composition and temperature.

In their review Mitchell *et al.* have collected together nineteen tables giving the surface tension of glasses of differing compositions and temperatures. Surface tension values for glass have been selected from the results of several workers and are presented in Table 8.2.

Dependence on temperature. As the temperature of molten glass is raised its surface tension usually falls. Pietenpol (1936) using blown glass bubbles has measured the surface tension of several glasses and found that γ_{LV} appeared to fall sharply at between 600°–750°C. He noted that this was really a region of softening where the viscosity was decreasing and surface tensions determined in this zone were *apparent* values. Using a soda potash glass he measured a temperature coefficient of surface tension of -0.4 dyne/cm degC. Parmelee and Lyon (1937) found that the surface tension and density of a sodium borosilicate glass decreased almost linearly with temperature between 1000°–1350°C. Babcock (1940) found that the temperature coefficient for a range of glasses was -0.02 dyne/cm degC. The temperature coefficient of the zinc borates may be negative or positive (Shartsis and Canga, 1949). Shartsis and Smock (1947) reported that a group of optical glasses of the flint and barium crown type had a positive temperature coefficient of surface tension; borosilicate crowns containing potash had a negative coefficient.

Composition. Attempts have been made to calculate the effect of an oxide component on the surface tension. Tillotson (1912) used the relation $\gamma = a_1 p_1 + a_2 p_2 + \ldots$ where a is an empirical factor and p the percentage concentration of a component. Surface tension values measured by Tillotson do not agree with recent work and thus his derived values for a cannot be used. Babcock has shown the effect on the surface tension of a glass of substituting one oxide component for another. Lyon (1944) has correlated the surface tension values reported by seven workers for glasses in which the ratio $SiO_2 : Na_2O$ exceeded 3·25. From this he found the effect on γ_{LV} of adding 1% of various oxides as shown in Table 8.3. Lyon concluded that surface tension may be treated as an additive function of composition giving a result within about 4 dynes/cm at 1200°–1400°c.

Table 8.3

Effect of 1% oxide on the surface tension of glass in which
the ratio $SiO_2 : Na_2O$ exceeds 3·25
(*After Lyon, 1944*)

Oxide	Surface tension increase (dynes/cm)	
	1200°c	1400°c
SiO_2	3·25	3·24
Fe_2O_3	(4·5)†	(4·4)
Al_2O_3	5·98	5·85
B_2O_3	0·23	0·23
CaO	4·92	4·92
MgO	5·77	5·49
BaO	(3·7)	(3·8)
Na_2O	1·27	1·27
K_2O	(0·00)	(−0·75)

† Values in parentheses indicate order of magnitude only; they are present in significant amounts in very few of the glasses treated.

CONTACT ANGLES OF GLASSES ON METALS

Measuring methods. Weiss has measured the contact angle θ of glass specimens on platinum, molybdenum and tungsten using the apparatus shown in Fig. 8.2. The metal substrate and glass droplet were arranged inside a platinum tubular heater in a vacuum vessel. The system was initially evacuated with a mercury diffusion pump and liquid nitrogen trap and then the desired reducing or oxidizing atmosphere admitted to the vessel. The velocity with which a droplet of glass attains the equilibrium angle θ depends on the glass viscosity. Weiss raised the temperature of his system to 1300°c, allowing from $\frac{1}{2}$ to 10 hours for obtaining equilibrium. Contact angles were measured by the projection method to within about ± 3°.

Pask and his collaborators † have made a systematic measurement of the contact angle of molten silicate glass on Cu, Ag, Au, Pd, Pt and Ni at various temperatures in vacuum and in atmospheres of different gases. They used an Alundum cylindrical furnace with a platinum winding (Zackay *et al.*, 1953). A glazed porcelain tube with Pyrex ball joints sealed to its ends was mounted inside the

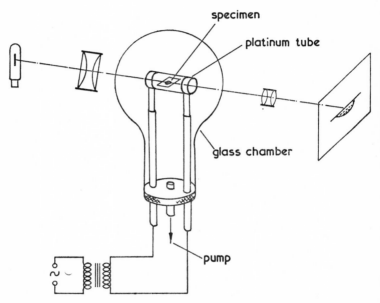

FIG. 8.2 APPARATUS FOR MEASURING THE CONTACT ANGLE OF A GLASS DROP-LET ON A METAL SURFACE (*After Weiss*, 1956)

furnace tube. An optical window and a vacuum/gas line were connected to the Pyrex joints. Vacuum was obtained with a mercury diffusion pump and the pressure measured with a McLeod gauge ($p > 10^{-4}$ torr). The metal specimen was supported by a quartz member. The temperature measured by a thermocouple showed about 1 degree variation over a 2 in. length at about 1400°c. Fulrath *et al.* (1957) have placed the glass and metal specimen inside a tungsten filament furnace with cylindrical radiation shields of molybdenum. The apparatus was mounted inside a metal vessel exhausted by an oil diffusion pump with the pressure measured

† Ceramic Laboratories, University of California.

with an ionization gauge ($p < 10^{-5}$ torr). The glass specimen could be dropped on to the metal after it had been thermally degassed. Cline *et al.* (1961) have described an apparatus in which a molten droplet could be formed on the end of a glass rod and allowed to drop on to a degassed metal surface inside a silica tube. In this apparatus a vacuum pressure of 10^{-5}–10^{-6} torr was obtained.

Given in Table 8.4 are values of θ for several glass/metal combinations as reported by different workers. The temperature of the glass/metal system and gas atmosphere used are included in the table.

PLATINUM AND ITS ALLOYS

Alloy composition. Platinum and its alloys are practically the only metals which are not corroded by continuous contact with molten glass in an oxidizing atmosphere. Platinum crucibles are used in the preparation of optical glasses and platinum bushings are used in the continuous manufacture of glass fibres. In both applications it is desirable that the glass does not wet the metal because in the former case the glass melt is conserved and in the latter the filament formation is improved. An alloy of platinum and rhodium is often used for crucibles and bushings because glasses wet it less than platinum. However, when lead oxide glasses are melted in platinum or Pt–Rh alloy crucibles reduction of the lead oxide must be avoided, otherwise metallic lead will contaminate the platinum. Melting must therefore occur under oxidising conditions which tend to promote wetting. Moore (1958) has prepared an interesting survey of the uses of platinum in the glass industry.

Cherniak and Naidus (1957) have studied the wetting of a number of platinum alloys, silica and alumina by two types of glass heated in a furnace in air. The composition of the glasses and the platinum alloys are given in Fig. 8.3, together with the contact angle of each type of glass as a function of temperature when on the different base materials. To avoid gravitational forces distorting the spherical shape of a droplet the weight of each specimen was kept to 0·1 g. The contact angles were determined by raising the specimen to a given temperature then cooling rapidly and measuring θ at normal temperature. The surface tension of glass varies with temperature and an experiment was made to find the difference between the high and normal temperature value of θ. Using glass II specimens on a platinum–rhodium support θ was 1·5°–2·5° less than when measured

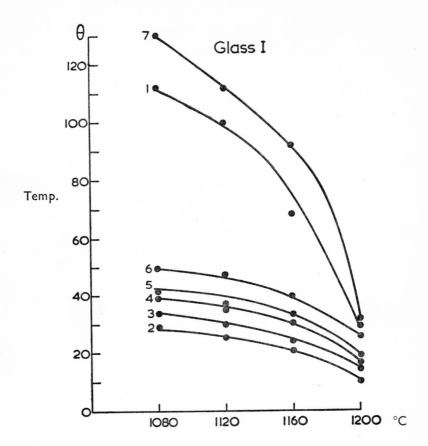

Fig. 8.3   Contact angle of two types of glass on different platinum

Glass	SiO₂	B₂O₃	Al₂O₃	C
I	54·49	10·83	11·4	1$
II	74·27	—	1·36	$

directly at between 950°–1100°c. The contact angle values plotted in Fig. 8.3 show that, of the metal supports, palladium was the most wettable and the least was a 7% rhodium–platinum alloy. A 1% chromium–platinum alloy had the same wettability as pure platinum and a 5% nickel–platinum alloy; the latter was readily oxidized at the temperature studied.

Dietzel and Coenen (1959) have measured the contact angle of two soda-lime glasses on Pt–Rh alloys in air and nitrogen. Their results plotted in Fig. 8.4 show that in air the contact angle reaches

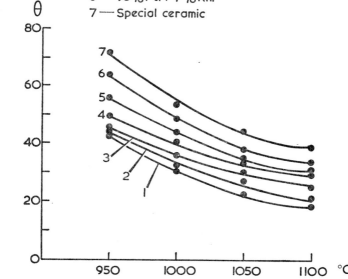

Glass II

1 — Fused quartz
2 — 100% Pd.
3 — 75% Pd. + 25% Pt.
4 — 75% Pt. + 25% Pd.
5 — 100% Pt.
6 — 93% Pt. + 7% Rh.
7 — Special ceramic

ALLOYS, SILICA AND ALUMINA (*After Cherniak and Naidus,* 1957)

ercentage			
gO	$Fe_2O_3 + TiO_2$	Na_2O	SO_3
38	0·21	1·73	—
9	0·15	15·7	0·62

a maximum for alloys with 20–40% Rh by weight. Dietzel and Coenen concluded that the Pt–Rh alloys could not absorb oxygen in their lattices to the same extent as pure platinum or rhodium and that oxygen absorption was essential to form a transition zone for wetting to occur.

Gas atmosphere. Shown in Table 8.4 are the results of the contact angle measurements made by Pask and his collaborators for soda type glasses on platinum in vacuum and in various gases. The results are difficult to interpret because there is wide disagreement

27

in the values for θ in similar atmospheres. However, it appears that θ is lowest in oxygen or vacuum (< 0.01 torr) and highest in nitrogen, water vapour and helium. It is of interest that θ is similar in oxygen and high vacuum. However, it should be appreciated that platinum is normally covered with a tenacious monoatomic layer

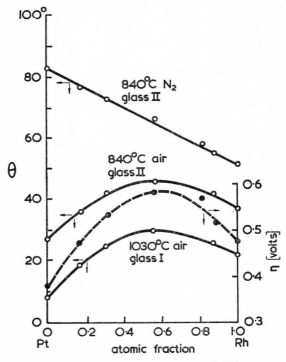

FIG. 8.4   CONTACT ANGLE OF SODA-LIME GLASS ON Pt/Rh-ALLOYS AND OVER-POTENTIAL OF Pt/Rh-ALLOYS AT 23°C (*After Dietzel and Coenen*, 1959)

Glass	SiO_2	Na_2O	CaO	BaO	R_2O_3
I	67	25	8	—	—
II	69	17	5·8	1·7	2·3

of oxygen forming a chemisorbed layer of PtO. In fact platinum evaporates faster in oxygen than in an inert gas because of the formation of a volatile oxide. Thus, in vacuum at a pressure of 10^{-6} torr there may still be sufficient oxygen present to form a chemisorbed layer even at high temperatures where evaporation may occur.

Fulrath *et al.* (1957) observed that the contact angle of sodium disilicate glass was less in a vacuum at a pressure of 10^{-5} torr ($\theta = 15°$) than in an isolated vessel at 10^{-3} torr ($\theta = 60°$). Further raising the pressure with oxygen made the contact angle decrease again. Volpe *et al.* (1959) state that the rise in the contact angle with vacuum pressure probably arose from the presence of water vapour in the vacuum atmosphere. As a vacuum vessel is isolated from its pumping system the gas pressure rises because desorbed gases are not being removed from the vessel. Water vapour is usually the principal component of vacuum atmospheres in unbaked metal systems. It would appear worth-while to investigate the contact angle of glasses on platinum under conditions where sorption of oxygen or water vapour by metal and glass could be reduced to a negligible amount, *i.e.* in ultra-high vacuum. Care would be required to avoid oxygen liberation by glass oxide dissociation.

Effect of glass composition. Weiss has measured the contact angle of a range of silicate glasses on platinum in oxidizing and reducing atmospheres. His results show that the addition of Na_2O, CaO and BaO to a borosilicate glass lowers the contact angle in both atmospheres. When 5 mol % of CaO or BaO was included in a borosilicate glass (65 mol % SiO_2; 18 mol % B_2O_3; 2 mol % Al_2O_3; 10 mol % Na_2O) the contact angle was reduced from 25° to zero in an oxidizing atmosphere. Weyl (1945) has stated that a glass melt of good solvent power for platinum is prepared with caesium as a major constituent. Adams and Pask (1961) found that adding up to 44 mol% Fe as iron oxide to sodium disilicate did not affect either the adherence or the contact angle on platinum measured at 1000°c in vacuum (< 0.01 torr).

GOLD, SILVER AND COPPER

The contact angle of sodium disilicate on gold at a temperature of 1000°c has been found to be about 60° and almost unaffected whether measured in vacuum, inert or active atmospheres (see Table 8.4). On the other hand the contact angle of soda-glass on copper and silver decreases from about 60° to zero in an oxidizing atmosphere.

Wetting can be considered as the first stage in a reaction between a molten substance and a solid. Thus wetting is often a prelude to chemical attack, solution or diffusion. It is interesting therefore to consider the conditions necessary for gold, copper and silver to be incorporated in glass. Just as an oxidizing atmosphere is necessary

Table 8.4

Contact angles of various glasses on different metal substrates

Metal substrate	Type of silicate glass	Atm. and pressure (torr)	Temp. °C	θ	Reference
Iron	$Na_2O.2SiO_2$	vac. (10^{-3})	1000	55	Fulrath et al. (1957)
	$Na_2O.2SiO_2$	vac. (10^{-5})	1000	30	Fulrath et al. (1957)
iron (Armco)	$Na_2O.2SiO_2$	vac. ($<10^{-5}$)	900–1000	55±2	Cline et al. (1961)
iron (Armco)	$Na_2O.2SiO_2$	vac. (5.10^{-5})	940–1000	react.→FeO + Na(g)	Hagan and Ravitz (1961)
magnetite (Fe_3O_4)	$Na_2O.2SiO_2$	vac. ($<10^{-5}$)	900–1000	2±1 (react.)	Cline et al. (1961)
iron (99-98%)	$Na_2.2SiO_2 + 10$ mol % Fe	vac. ($<10^{-5}$)	1000	32 (react.)	Adams and Pask (1961)
	$Na_2.2SiO_2 + 30$ mol % Fe	vac. ($<10^{-5}$)	1000	21 (react.)	Adams and Pask (1961)
	$Na_2.2SiO_2 + 45$ mol % Fe	vac. ($<10^{-5}$)	1000	21 (react.)	Adams and Pask (1961)
Nickel	soda	He	900	55	Zackay et al (1953)
	soda	H_2	900	60	Zackay et al. (1953)
	soda	air, O_2	900	0	Zackay et al. (1953)
Titanium	$Na_2O.2SiO_2$	vac. (10^{-5})	1000	135→80 (react.)	Fulrath et al. (1957)
Zirconium	$Na_2O.2SiO_2$	vac. (10^{-5})	1000	135→80 (react.)	Fulrath et al. (1957)
Molybdenum	$Na_2O.2SiO_2$	vac. (10^{-5})	1000	wetted	Fulrath et al. (1957)
	80 mol % (SiO_2+Na_2O)+ 18 mol % B_2O_3+ 2 mol % Al_2O_3	N_2 (750) O_2 (0·2)	1300	100(5 mol % Na_2O) 0(25mol % Na_2O)	Weiss (1956)
		N_2 (740) H_2 (20)	1300	100(5 mol % Na_2O) 0(30 mol % Na_2O)	Weiss (1956)
	boro- (20 mol % B_2O_3)	N_2 (750) O_2 (0·2)	1300	40	Weiss (1956)
	boro- (20 mol % B_2O_3)	N_2 (740) H_2 (20)	1300	60	Weiss (1956)

	Glass	Atmosphere	Temp. (°C)	Value	Reference
Palladium	soda-lime-	air	950–1100	42–20	Cherniak and Naidus (1957)
	boro-alumino-	air	1080–1200	30–10	Cherniak and Naidus (1957)
	soda	He	900	60	Zackay *et al.* (1953)
	soda	H$_2$	900	43	Zackay *et al.* (1953)
	soda	air	900	25	Zackay *et al.* (1953)
	soda	O$_2$	900	20	Zackay *et al.* (1953)
Platinum	soda-lime-	air	950–1100	66–31	Cherniak and Naidus (1957)
	soda-lime-	air	840–1030	27–8	Dietzel and Coenen (1959)
	boro-alumino-	air	1080–1200	40–20	Cherniak and Naidus (1957)
	soda-lime-	N$_2$	840	82	Dietzel and Coenen (1959)
	boro- (20 mol % B$_2$O$_3$)	N$_2$ (740) H$_2$ (20)	1300	70	Weiss (1956)
	boro- (20 mol % B$_2$O$_3$)	N$_2$ (730) O$_2$ (20)	1300	30	Weiss (1956)
	Na$_2$O.2SiO$_2$	vac. (10^{-3})†	800→1100	130→35$\}\overline{60}$	Fulrath *et al.* (1957)
	Na$_2$O.2SiO$_2$	vac. (10^{-3})†	1100→800	35→85$\}$	Fulrath *et al.* (1957)
	Na$_2$O.2SiO$_2$	vac. (10^{-5})	900→1300	15	Fulrath *et al.* (1957)
	Na$_2$O.2SiO$_2$	vac. (10^{-5})	1000	22±3	Volpe *et al.* (1959)
	soda	He (atmos.)	900	60	Zackay *et al.* (1953)
	soda	H$_2$	900	43	Zackay *et al.* (1953)
	soda	air, O$_2$	900	0	Zackay *et al.* (1953)
	Na$_2$O.2SiO$_2$	O$_2$ (10–1000)	1000	15–10	Volpe *et al.* (1959)
	Na$_2$O.2SiO$_2$	N$_2$ (10–1000)	1000	22–32	Volpe *et al.* (1959)
	Na$_2$O.2SiO$_2$	CO$_2$ (10–1000)	1000	20–29	Volpe *et al.* (1959)
	Na$_2$O.2SiO$_2$	A (10–1000)	1000	17–22	Volpe *et al.* (1959)
	Na$_2$O.2SiO$_2$	He (1000)	1000	24	Volpe *et al.* (1959)
	Na$_2$O.2SiO$_2$	CO (10–1000)	1000	40–66	Volpe *et al.* (1959)
	Na$_2$O.2SiO$_2$	H$_2$ (10–1000)	1000	56–49	Volpe *et al.* (1959)
	Na$_2$O.2SiO$_2$	H$_2$O (10–100)	1000	58–63	Volpe *et al.* (1959)
	Na$_2$O.2SiO$_2$	20% H$_2$O 80% O$_2$ (v.p. H$_2$O=0·05)	1000	15	Volpe *et al.* (1959)
	Na$_2$O.2SiO$_2$	20% H$_2$O 80% N$_2$ (v.p. H$_2$O=0·05)	1000	60	Volpe *et al.* (1959)

Table 8.4 (continued)

Metal substrate	Type of silicate glass	Atm. and pressure (torr)	Temp. °C	θ	Reference
Platinum (continued)	80 mol % (SiO₂ + Na₂O) +	N₂ (730) O₂ (20)	1300	53 (5 mol % Na₂A) 0 (20 mol % Na₂O)	Weiss (1956)
	18 mol % B₂O₃ + 2 mol % Al₂O₃	N₂ (740) H₂ (20)	1300	95 (5 mol % Na₂O)	Weiss (1956)
	Na₂O.2SiO₂ + 2–44 mol % Fe	vac. (<10⁻⁵)	1000	22 (30 mol %Na₂O) 12–17	Adams and Pask (1961)
Gold‡	SiO₂	vac. (10⁻³) →air atmos.	1100	138 →136, 115	Moore and Thornton (1959)
	Na₂O.2SiO₂	vac. (10⁻³ – 10⁻⁵)	900–1040	60	Fulrath et al. (1957)
	Na₂O.2SiO₂	vac. (10⁻⁵)	1000	65 ± 2	Volpe et al. (1959)
single and polycrystalline	soda	He (≅ atmos.)	900	60	Zackay et al. (1953)
single and polycrystalline	soda	H₂ (≅ atmos.)	900	45–50	Zackay et al. (1953)
single and polycrystalline	soda	air (≅ atmos.)	900	55	Zackay et al. (1953)
single and polycrystalline	soda	O₂ (≅ atmos.)	900	53–4	Zackay et al. (1953)
	Na₂O.2SiO₂	O₂ (10–1000)	1000	65–64	Volpe et al. (1959)
	Na₂O.2SiO₂	CO₂ (10–1000)	1000	61–60	Volpe et al. (1959)
	Na₂O.2SiO₂	N₂ (10–1000)	1000	58–62	Volpe et al. (1959)
	Na₂O.2SiO₂	H₂O (10–1000)	1000	66–65	Volpe et al. (1959)
	Na₂O.2SiO₂	He (10–1000)	1000	62–63	Volpe et al. (1959)
	Na₂O.2SiO₂	H₂ (10–1000)	1000	64–66	Volpe et al. (1959)
	Na₂O.2SiO₂	A (10–1000)	1000	62	Volpe et al. (1959)
Tungsten	Na₂O.2SiO₂	vac. (10⁻⁵)	1000	wetted	Fulrath et al. (1957)
	80 mol % (SiO₂ + Na₂O) +	N₂ (750) O₂ (0–2)	1300	60 (5 mol % Na₂O) 22 (40 mol % Na₂O)	Weiss (1956)
	18 mol % B₂O₃ + 2 mol % Al₂O₃	N₂ (740) H₂ (20)	1300	115 (5 mol % Na₂O) 0 (30 mol % Na₂O)	Weiss (1956)
	boro- (20 mol % B₂O₃)	N₂ (750) O₂ (0–2)	1300	60	Weiss (1956)
		N₂ (740) H₂ (20)	1300	50	Weiss (1956)
Tantalum	Na₂O.2SiO₂	vac. (10⁻³)	1000	80 (react.)	Fulrath et al. (1957)
	Na₂O.2SiO₂	vac. (10⁻⁵)	1000	80 (react.)	Mitoff (1957)

Table 8.4 (continued)

Silver				
(single and polycrystalline)	soda	He	900	70–4	Zackay et al. (1953)
(single and polycrystalline)	soda	H_2	900	72–8	Zackay et al. (1953)
(single and polycrystalline)	soda	air, O_2	900	0	Zackay et al. (1953)
65% Ag 35% Pd	soda	He, H_2	900	66	Zackay et al. (1953)
	soda	air	900	0	Zackay et al. (1953)
35% Ag 65% Pd	soda	He	900	63	Zackay et al. (1953)
	soda	H_2	900	51	Zackay et al. (1953)
	soda	air	900	0	Zackay et al. (1953)
Copper	soda	He, H_2	900	60	Zackay et al. (1953)
	soda	air, O_2	900	0	Zackay et al. (1953)

atmos.—atmospheric pressure; react.—reaction between glass and metal; vac.—vacuum; wetted—glass spread over surface.

† Probably water vapour.   ‡ Gold may wet in oxidizing atmospheres glasses containing lead or bismuth oxides.

for soda glass to wet copper and silver so also is an oxidizing atmosphere essential for these metals to be dissolved atomically by glass. Gold behaves similarly to copper and silver in requiring oxidizing conditions for incorporation in glass. Thus it has been observed that gold diffuses into vitreous silica in oxygen but not *in vacuo*.

Moore and Thornton (1959) melted gold pellets on polished fused silica for 15 min at 1100°c in vacuum at a pressure of 3×10^{-5} torr and in dry oxygen. The force required at room temperature *to shear* the solidified pellets from the silica surface was found to vary from zero for gold melted *in vacuo* to 725 lb/in² for gold melted under oxygen at a pressure of 150 torr. Whenever a bond developed fracture occurred in the silica rather than at the gold-silica interface. Silica plates with gold pellets bonded to them were not under strain when viewed in a polarograph, suggesting that the gold had yielded on cooling. Tests using Au^{198} as a tracer showed that gold diffused into the silica lattice when heated in oxygen at a high pressure but not in vacuum.

An interesting feature of this work was that the contact angles of the gold on the silica hardly differed after melting in vacuum or oxygen. Thus gold melted at 1100°c under a reduced pressure of 10^{-3} torr had a value of θ equal to 138°, decreasing to 136° when air was admitted to the vacuum system. Moore and Thornton stated that the wide variation in the bond strength without appreciable change in the contact angle indicated that bond strengths could not be correlated with calculated values for the work of adhesion.

As diffusion was known to occur one immediately considers whether the diffusion zone extended to the edge of the droplet. (In fact the conditions could resemble those which are responsible for the advancing edge of a moving droplet having a higher contact angle than the receding edge which moves over the previously wetted surface.) Moore and Thornton found that if a gold pellet which had been melted on silica in air was reduced in volume *in situ* then on remelting the remaining gold the smaller droplet formed had a lower contact angle (from the photograph shown $\theta \simeq 115°$). This experiment indicated that under normal conditions gold diffusion did not extend completely to the edges of a droplet. Prolonged heating at 1100°c to promote overall diffusion was not possible because the silica was devitrified.

Gold appears to have a low affinity for soda-lime glass even under oxidizing conditions and fired gold coatings used for gilding are not very adherent to soda-lime glass. In the manufacture of silver yellow and gold or copper ruby glasses the glass base must have some solvent power for the metal. If heavy lead oxide glasses are used no solvent difficulties are encountered but with soda-lime glass metallic gold is soluble only if small quantities of tin oxide, bismuth oxide or ceria are added to the glass (Weyl, 1945; Tress, 1962).

The affinity of the nobler metals for glass can be observed on a micro-scale when thin gold or silver films ($\simeq 100$ Å thick) are evaporated on to glass surfaces *in vacuo*. Such films deposited on crown glass have a structure which is composed of almost isolated crystallites which grow larger at the expense of the smaller crystallites when the films are heated. On the other hand, if a gold or silver film is partially deposited and exposed to oxygen the aggregation of the subsequent metal deposit is reduced. Likewise, aggregation of gold films on a soda-lime glass is reduced if calcium oxide is first deposited on the glass by polishing with chalk. The greatest reduction in the aggregation of a film is obtained by depositing the metal on to certain metal oxide base coatings, *e.g.* gold on bismuth oxide films and silver on zinc oxide films (for a review of this, see Holland, 1956). Gold films deposited on freshly evaporated silica coatings in vacuum are highly aggregated.

It may be inferred from the foregoing that *whereas sodium disilicate glass does not wet gold under oxidizing conditions there may be several glass compositions which would wet gold.*

WORK OF ADHESION OF GLASSES TO THE NOBLER METALS

Bond strength. Weiss (1956) has measured the surface tension and contact angle on platinum of the range of glasses shown in Table 8.5. The contact angle θ was measured in an atmosphere of 730 torr $N_2 + 20$ torr O_2 at 1300°c and the surface tension γ_m at 900°–1100°c in air using the elongated fibre method. From these results Weiss calculated the work of adhesion $\gamma_m(1 + \cos \theta)$.

The bond strength of a glass was measured after melting a fixed charge of glass inside a platinum tube of 3·4 mm inner dia. 0·2 mm wall thickness and 9 mm length. The end of the platinum tube containing the glass was rested on a platinum plate and fired in a furnace so that the glass became fused to the plate. A breaking force was then applied at right angles to the plane of the glass/platinum junction; the force was raised at a rate of 4 kg/min.

Shown in Table 8.5 and Fig. 8.5(*a*) are values of the bond strength B as a function of the work of adhesion. From these

Table 8.5

The relation between the contact angle, surface tension and bond strength of various glasses on platinum (*After Weiss, 1956*)

Glass No.	Glass composition [Wt %]										γ 900°c calculated [dynes/cm]	γ_m 900°c measured [dynes/cm]	θ 1300°c	$\gamma_m[1+\cos\theta]$ [ergs/cm²]	Bond strength [kg/cm²]
	SiO₂	B₂O₃	Al₂O₃	MgO	CaO	BaO	PbO	Li₂O	Na₂O	K₂O					
1	48·0	2·0	3·0	—	5·0	38·0	—	4·0	—	—	363	345±5	17	675	108±8
2	71·0	0·2	2·3	—	5·5	3·6	—	—	15·3	2·1	318	300±4	18	585	90±20
3	54·0	—	10·0	10·0	8·0	10·0	—	8·0	—	—	426	363±6	47	610	87±13
4	77·0	—	3·0	—	5·0	2·0	—	3·0	10·0	—	341	311±3	32	575	64±6
5	79·7	—	2·0	1·0	—	3·0	—	0·5	13·8	—	324	295±5	16	578	55±11
6	64·5	15·0	3·0	—	—	—	—	—	4·5	13·0	255	269±4	25	513	35±3
7	53·4	20·4	4·5	—	—	—	—	—	—	21·7	244	255±8	33	469	29±8
8	49·7	26·3	4·5	—	—	—	—	—	—	20·5	220	220±6	21	425	27±5
9	58·7	—	0·4	—	2·2	—	28·2	—	4·0	8·6	242	237±3	14	404	20±3
10	49·2	—	—	—	—	—	37·0	—	1·2	10·4	241	228±3	50	375	9±2

curves Weiss obtained the relation $B^{1/4} \simeq \gamma_m(1 + \cos \theta)$. Weiss also calculated the surface tension of his different glasses from data prepared by Dietzel (1942). In Fig. 8.5(*b*) values of the bond strength are plotted as a function of the adhesion energy using the calculated values of γ. The latter curves are in good agreement with those in Fig. 8.5(*a*).

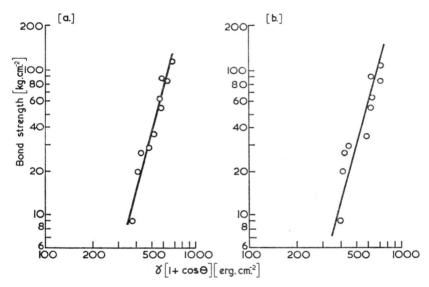

FIG. 8.5 BOND STRENGTH BETWEEN PLATINUM AND DIFFERENT GLASSES AT ROOM TEMPERATURE AS A FUNCTION OF THE WORK OF ADHESION $\gamma(1 + \cos \theta)$ (*After Weiss*, 1956). (*a*) GLASS SURFACE TENSION γ_m MEASURED BETWEEN 900–1100°C, (*b*) GLASS SURFACE TENSION CALCULATED AFTER DIETZEL FOR ABOUT 900°C

It follows from the relation between the work of adhesion and bond strength that the bond strength will be raised when γ is increased or θ is decreased. Thus it does not follow that θ will have to tend to zero to obtain a high bond strength if γ is high. This can be seen in Table 8.5 where glass number 3, having the greatest value of θ, has a high bond strength because of its high value of γ.

Electrochemical effect. Dietzel and Coenen (1959) have measured the surface tension of two types of soda-lime glass and their contact angles on platinum, rhodium, gold and Pt–Rh alloys. (The values of θ for Pt–Rh alloys are shown in Fig. 8.4.) Dietzel and Coenen also determined the electro-chemical 'over-potential' η of the different metal surfaces. η was determined by an electrolytic method and corresponded to the potential required at an anode surface for the dissociation of oxygen molecules. Anodes were made of the various metals used in the contact angle studies with a cathode

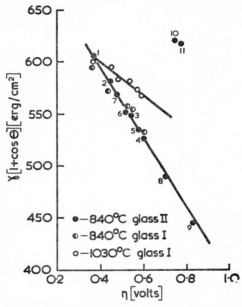

(1) 100% Pt, (2) 90% Pt/Rh, (3) 80% Pt/Rh, (4) 60% Pt/Rh, (5) 30% Pt/Rh, (6) 20% Pt/Rh, (7) 100% Rh, (8) 95% Pt/Au, (9) 100% Au, (10) (11) Pt/Be.

Fig. 8.6 The work of adhesion of soda-lime glasses to metal alloys as a function of the 'over-potential' (*After Dietzel and Coenen*, 1959). The compositions of Glasses I and II are given in Fig. 8.4.

made of platinum immersed in a 1N H_2SO_4 electrolyte. The applied voltage was raised slowly and measurements were made of the reversible decomposition potential E_Z for H_2O and the applied potential E_A at which the current in the electrolyte rose sharply. The 'over-potential' η was taken as $E_A - E_Z$ and is plotted in Fig. 8.4 for different Pt–Rh alloys. It can be seen that the curve resembles that for the contact angle measured in air.

Dietzel and Coenen believed that the higher the value of η the lower was the diffusion coefficient of oxygen atoms in a particular alloy. From this it was deduced that adhesion of glass to noble metals arises from the diffusions of oxygen atoms into the metal lattice.

Values of the adhesion energy for several alloys are given in Fig. 8.6 as a function of η. It is of interest to observe that the Pt–Be alloys do not obey the same relation as that for the Pt–Rh and Pt–Au alloys. This is attributed to the wetting mechanism being the formation of BeO at the metal surface and not oxygen diffusion.

Fulrath (1957) calculated that the interfacial energy ($\gamma_{SL} = \gamma_{SV} - \gamma_{LV} \cos \theta$) of sodium disilicate glass on gold at about 1000°c was 1230 dynes/cm using the values $\theta = 60°$, $\gamma_{AU} = 1370$ dynes/cm and $\gamma(Na_2O \cdot 2SiO_2) = 286$ dynes/cm. The work of adhesion can be calculated from $\gamma_{LV}(1 + \cos \theta)$ as 430 ergs/cm^2.

Nature of interfacial forces. There is no accepted single theory for the influence of certain glass components and atmospheric oxygen on the wetting (or dissolving) of noble metals by glass. An obvious question is in what form are the noble metals dissolved by the glass, *i.e.* as neutral atoms or in combination with oxygen?

Weyl (1945) contends that the polarizability of the glass components is an important factor in the foregoing phenomena. Thus glasses are normally formed of noble gas ions such as O^{2-}, Si^{4+}, Na^+, Ca^{2+} whose polarizability is low and can be neglected for practical purposes. However, this is not true for glasses containing large cations (Cs^+, Ba^{2+}) or ions of non-noble gas character (Pb^{2+}, Cd^{2+}, Zn^{2+}). To produce a glass with solvent power or high adhesion to a metal one has to introduce polarizable ions, preferably cations with incomplete outer shells.

Weyl considers that gold is soluble in soda-lime glass only at the highest temperature where its vapour pressure reaches noticeable values. Platinum, with its much lower vapour pressure, is practically insoluble. On cooling the glass melt the gold precipitates in globules and relatively large crystals because the solvent forces are insufficient to overcome the forces which hold the gold in the metallic phase. The addition of 0·5–2·0% SnO_2 to a soda-lime glass increases its low temperature solubility appreciably. Weyl believes that the tin ions in the glass have an affinity for both the glass and the gold atoms and terms this property 'metallophilic'. Tin oxide has a similar solvent effect on copper and silver in soda-lime glass.

Tress (1962) has discussed the source of adhesion between atoms of the nobler metals and glass. He observes that compounds of the nobler metals when heated to redness frequently decompose, yielding metal, whereas with glasses containing copper, silver or gold the reverse occurs as metal precipitates on cooling. This has given rise to what he terms the 'solvent theory', whereby the molten base glass is a solvent for metal, giving a solution in which the dissolved metal remains in a nilvalent state. Chilling of the glass yields an undercooled solution. When metal is precipitated from the oversaturated solution the colloidal metal or crystallites † colour the glass, an effect which is termed 'striking'.

Tress contends that there is both oxidized metal as well as nilvalent metal in a glass containing the nobler metals. He states that the ratio of the oxidized metal to the reduced metal depends on the oxidizing power of the glass and this can be expressed by a factor μ_{O_2}, known as the chemical potential of oxygen in glass. As evidence for oxidation of the nobler metals in glass he notes that bulk copper, silver and gold needed oxidizing conditions to be incorporated appreciably into base glasses. Also, if attempts are made to incorporate more than about 0·1% by weight of gold into an ordinary leadless glass, the chemical potential of oxygen is not high enough to prevent excess gold from being precipitated. When ceria is added to the batch this allows more gold to be incorporated. Ceria also retards the striking of the gold and silver colours; whilst an atmosphere of hydrogen aids the striking of copper ruby and to a slight extent ceria-gold colours. Striking of a gold colour in a ceria-free glass was not noticeably affected by an hydrogen atmosphere, indicating that Au^0 was present and that easily reducible Au^3 was absent.

Tress concludes that copper, silver and gold when incorporated in glass take up a definite ratio R^1/R^0 of onevalent to nilvalent metal depending on the chemical potential of the oxygen in the glass.

It has been shown above that Dietzel and Coenen attribute the adhesion of glass to the nobler metals to the diffusion of oxygen into the metal lattice. With copper, adhesion may arise from a superficial copper oxide film which partially dissolves in the glass or in the absence of a visible oxide layer by oxygen diffusing into the copper lattice (Dietzel, 1951).

Glasses vary in composition so drastically that there is no reason to suppose that a single mechanism will explain the binding of a glass to the nobler metals. However, it would appear at present that the soda-lime glasses are bound to the nobler metals by oxygen which diffuses into the metal lattice. With glasses containing solvent oxides adhesion could also arise from the atoms in the nobler

---

† Electron microscopy has shown that gold ruby glass contains cubic crystals of gold.

metal having an affinity for oxygen molecules less firmly bound in the glass structure. In fact not only should this promote wetting but also dissolution of the nobler metal. The diffusion of silver ions in place of sodium ions in silicate glasses has been observed. Also, gold atoms diffuse into silica in the presence of oxygen.

CONTACT ANGLES OF GLASSES ON IRON

Iron and steel components are often finished with glass enamels so that there has been extensive technical interest in the mechanism by which the glass wets the metal.

Iron is easily oxidized in the atmosphere and molten glass readily wets iron oxide. Molten glasses in prolonged contact with iron usually react with the metal and corrode its surface. Cooke (1924) fired a cobalt bearing enamel on iron in nitrogen and obtained a poorly adherent coating. Dietzel and Meures (1933) observed that a glass enamel would not wet a steel plate if melted in vacuum or in a reducing atmosphere.

Cline *et al.* (1961) observed that sodium disilicate on Armco iron in vacuum at 900°–1000°c had a contact angle of about 55° and poor adherence. Some reaction occurred between the glass and the iron because the glass became tinted green-blue. Molten sodium disilicate on magnetite (Fe_3O_4) had a contact angle of 2° and the adhesion was high. The glass became darker as it dissolved iron oxide but it possessed no crystalline phases.

Sodium disilicate dropped in vacuum on to iron which had been previously oxidized in air (FeO-film 5 μ thick) spread outwards with a contact angle of 24° at 900°c, retracting to about 55° on solution of the oxide. The adherence was poor and the glass at the metal interface was tinted blue-green. When the temperature of the system was raised to 1000°c the glass was able to spread and dissolve more iron or iron oxides. After some 3 hours the iron surface became covered with green crystalline prisms identified as fayalite ($FeSiO_4$). The glass droplets had corroded the iron to a depth of 14 μ. When the sodium disilicate continuously dissolved iron oxide it finally developed excellent adhesion.

Hagan and Ravitz (1961) showed that at high temperatures iron reacts with sodium disilicate to form iron oxide and volatile sodium. Using powdered iron and glass they found the reaction was slow at 935°c but rapid at 995°c.

Adams and Pask (1961) found that adding iron oxide to sodium disilicate lowered its contact angle on iron in vacuum at 1000°c from 55° to 21° at 30 mol % Fe. The contact angle decreased exponentially with the iron content. Adherence was poor without iron in the glass and it increased as the iron content and reaction at the interface increased. Fayalite crystals appeared in the glass at the interface and the iron base appeared to be attacked along the grain boundaries.

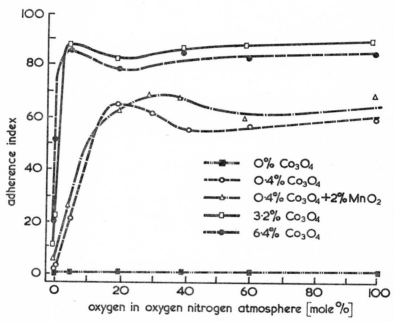

FIG. 8.7 ADHERENCE INDEX OF GLASS ENAMELS CONTAINING COBALT OXIDE AS A FUNCTION OF THE OXYGEN CONTENT OF THE FIRING ATMOSPHERE; TOTAL GAS PRESSURE $= 3 \cdot 75$ torr (*After Eubanks and Moore*, 1955)

ADHESION OF ENAMEL TO IRON

Dietzel (1935) proposed that the adhesion of an enamel to iron could arise from roughening of the iron surface by galvanic corrosion. Thus an enamel containing cobalt oxide could give rise to the reaction $CoO + Fe \rightarrow FeO + Co$. Harrison *et al.* (1952), using radioactive cobalt in a porcelain enamel, confirmed that cobalt was liberated from the molten enamel and deposited during the early stages of firing, presumably on to electronegative areas. Richmond *et al.* (1953) showed that a correlation existed between the roughness of an iron interface and the adherence of a porcelain enamel.

Eubanks and Moore (1955) tested the adherence of porcelain enamels containing different amounts of cobalt oxide when fired on iron in various oxygen–nitrogen atmospheres. The basic enamel frit contained by weight 51% SiO_2; 16·1% B_2O_3; 5·7% Al_2O_3; 15·4 Na_2O; 3·5% K_2O; 8·3% CaF_2. One hundred parts of the frit were mixed with six parts of enamelling clay and one part of borax. The ground-coat was applied in water to iron specimens by dipping and had a dry thickness of about 0·007 in. The enamel was fired at 843°c for $3\frac{3}{4}$ min after taking $2\frac{1}{4}$ min to reach temperature. Gas was admitted to the surface up to a pressure of 3·75 torr after first evacuating it with a rotary pump to 0·5 torr. The gases in the furnace were analysed either chemically or by mass spectrometry, and it was found that the oxygen content of a given sample did not vary more than five parts in one thousand from that calculated. The adherence of each specimen was evaluated by the Porcelain Enamel Institute adherence meter.† This instrument establishes the fraction of a test area over which a coating continued to adhere after a specimen has been deformed in a prescribed manner.

The adherence index of the enamels as a function of the oxygen concentration is given in Fig. 8.7. The curves have been measured for enamels with different weight percentages of Co_3O_4 added to the basic frit. The results show that firing in almost a pure oxygen atmosphere did not produce an adherent coating when cobalt oxide was absent from the enamel. (Although an oxide film would have formed on the iron it is not possible to say whether the glass would have dissolved this faster than it was formed under an oxygen pressure of 3·75 torr.) When cobalt oxide was added to the enamel the adherence of the coating rose reaching a maximum at a lower partial pressure of oxygen the higher the Co_3O_4 content.

Microscopic examination of the enamel–iron interface showed that the highest adherence obtained corresponded with the maximum roughening of the iron surface. Thus specimens fired with 0·4% Co_3O_4 in the ground-coat showed increasing roughness as the oxygen in the atmosphere was increased up to 20 mol %, which is roughly the oxygen content of air. Above 20 mol % O_2 neither the roughness nor adherence increased further. Tests with low concentrations of oxygen in the firing atmosphere (0·02 mol % O_2)

---

† 'Test for Adherence of Porcelain Enamel to Sheet Metal, a Tentative Standard Test of the Porcelain Enamel Institute', Bulletin T-17, 1951. Porcelain Enamel Institute, Washington D.C.

showed that the iron could be roughened by raising the cobalt oxide content of the enamel. When 2% MnO_2 was added to an enamel containing 0·4% Co_3O_4 the adherence of the enamel was enhanced. This was attributed to the manganese dioxide functioning as an oxidizing agent and supplying oxygen to the interface.

CONCLUSIONS

From the foregoing we know that:

(*i*) Glass wets and is well bonded to iron oxide.

(*ii*) Some or all of the oxide formed on iron during firing under oxidizing conditions is dissolved by molten glass. Wetting and adherence is obtained if the dissolved iron oxide in the glass reaches some critical amount.

(*iii*) Soda in molten glass can react with iron to form iron oxide and free sodium.

(*iv*) Glass enamels are only adherent to iron when the substrate becomes roughened by a galvanic effect requiring a combination of cobalt oxide in the glass and an oxidising atmosphere.

(*v*) It is not clear to what extent an iron oxide film is still necessary on the roughened surface to act as a cementing layer. Dietzel (1951) states that iron only sorbs oxygen to a limited degree so that glass cannot be bound to iron by a diffusion zone of oxygen ions as proposed for the nobler metals.

4. ADHESION OF SYNTHETIC RESINS TO GLASS

INTRODUCTION

Glass is combined with polymeric adhesives and plastics materials for a variety of purposes. For example, safety glass made from laminated plate may be bonded with an adhesive film such as polyvinyl butyral, glass components may be joined together with vinyl phenolic adhesives and glass fibres may be used to reinforce polyester or epoxy resin components.

It has been generally found from a study of adhesives that polar molecules bond best to polar molecules and non-polar to non-polar. In fact it has been claimed that similar polarities are esential for good adhesion. The surface of clean glass contains cations which are electrically unbalanced and glass is a markedly polar substance. Thus when bonding glass to glass by means of polymers it has been found that polar materials with functional groups such as —OH, —COOH, —C=O, and —COOCH₃ produce adherent bonds. Polymeric substances with such chemical groups in their structure are the epoxies, butyrals, polyvinyl acetate, copolymer vinyl chloride–acetate–alcohols and polyacrylates. According to Moser (1956*a*) various combinations of these resins with either phenolic or butadiene–acrylonitrile polymers are used most commonly in glass adhesives.

Many plastics material are non-polar and the polymer molecules in their surfaces are saturated. Thus, a polar adhesive used for bonding glass to glass may be unsuitable for bonding glass to polymers with saturated surface molecules. To overcome this an intermediate coupling agent is used with different reactive groups at its boundaries which will bind both the glass and desired resin together as follows:

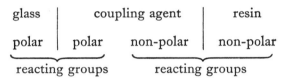

Silicate glasses generally have a great affinity for water and the bond strength at a resin-glass interface may be greatly weakened under wet conditions. Coupling agents may be used to raise the strength of the interface bond and this is discussed below in the section on glass reinforced plastics.

EFFECT OF GLASS TREATMENT ON STRENGTH OF RESIN ADHESIVES

Moser (1956*b*) considers that the contact angle of water on glass and plastics materials indicates the strength of the surface forces and whether a strong bond between the substances is likely to result. Shown in Table 8.6 is the contact angle of water on glass specimens which have been cleaned in different ways and exposed to various compounds. The bond strength of polymers joined to the clean glass surface was 1900 lb/in² for a polar Vinylite adhesive ($\theta \simeq 45°$) and 1100 lb/in² for the slightly less polar epoxy resin ($\theta \simeq 50°$). The bond strength may be influenced by surface films on the glass. Thus when the glass was coated with a hydrophobic layer

Table 8.6

The influence of the glass pre-treatment on the
bond strength of polymer adhesives
(*After Moser, 1956b*)

Treatment	Air-water system $\theta°$	Bond strength (lb/sq in.)†			
		Copolymer Vinylite		Epon adhesives	
		Room temp.	After H_2O	Room temp	After H_2O
Fire polished	0	1100	600	1100	600
Chromic acid	0	1900	1400	1000	500
Trichlorosilane	90–95	No adhesion		No adhesion	
Organo-silicate primer	41–43	1100	1000	400	300
AlCl$_3$	42–44	2100	1000	1200	800
SnCl$_3$	28–30	1900	900	1200	800
Molybdic acid	43–44	1300	1000	800	800

† Cross-lap tensile method ASTM D1344-54T.

of dimethyl silicone the resins were non-adherent. On the other hand, treatment of the glass with aluminium chloride or stannous chloride, which probably left a film of metal oxide on the surface, improved the bond strength. It can be seen in Table 8.6 that exposure of the resin coatings to moisture decreases their adhesion to glass. The zero contact angle of the glass surface after chromic acid cleaning is responsible for the poor wet strength of the epon adhesive, *i.e.* the glass surface prefers to adsorb moisture rather than the less polar organic material.

Moser's use of comparative contact angles for indicating glass/polymer adhesion can only be taken as a rough guide, because, as shown in Table 8.6, a glass cleaned with chromic acid has a high bond strength but a low contact angle compared with that of the polymer adhesives (Table 8.7). When an adhesive is cured in contact with a glass surface the molecules may orientate themselves so that the composition of the polymer at the glass interface is different from that of the polymer cured in air. Thus the contact angle of water on the latter would have no relation to its adhesion properties. Finally, if the surface energy of one of the contacting surfaces was high, this would enhance the bond strength even though the surfaces manifested different affinities for water.

CONTACT ANGLES OF WATER ON RESIN COATINGS AND
ADHESIVE STRENGTHS

Moser has measured the contact angle of water on coatings of synthetic resists on glass and other substrates. He states that providing a resin film is thin one may observe the degree to which the coating is orientated on the support. For example, when a resin-coated material gives a low contact angle with respect to water this indicates that the resin surface is polar. From this Moser infers that the polymer coating has been well bonded to the glass support and will in turn bond well to a second glass surface, as is required when laminating glass.

Table 8.7

Contact angle of water on polymer coatings
together with bond strengths
(*After Moser, 1956a*)

Polymers	*Bond strength under tensile load* lb/in^2	*Type of bond failure*	$\theta°$
Polyvinyl acetate (AYAF)	550	Adhesion	25–28
Polyvinyl acetate-dibutyl phthalate	1200	Adhesion	18–20
Polyvinyl chloride-acetate (VMCH)	400	Adhesion	65–67
Polyvinyl chloride-acetate (VYHH)	100	Contact and adhesion	60–62
Polyvinyl chloride-acetate alcohol	1200	Largely glass	24–26
Polyvinyl butyral-dibutyl phthalate (XYHL)	1200	Adhesion	18–20
Methyl methacrylate	0–100	Very little if any adhesion	62–64
N-propyl methacrylate	200	Adhesion	63–65
Polyvinyl alcohol	400	Adhesion	14–15
Polyvinyl chloride	0–100	No adhesion	66–68
Cellulose nitrate	200	Adhesion and contact	36–37
Ethyl cellulose	0–50	No appreciable adhesion	60–61
Phenolic (Durez 12987)	500	Adhesion	22–24
Phenolic (Br 17620)	300	Adhesion	38–40
Substituted phenol-aldehyde (BV-1112)	100	Adhesive too brittle	43–44
Aryl sulfonamide-formaldehyde (MS-80)	100	Cohesive	33–35
Styrene-butadiene (Pliolite S-5)	0–100	No appreciable adhesion	70–72
Cyclized rubber (Pliolite S-50)	100	Little adhesion	37–40
Neoprene Type GN-A	0–100	Adhesive	35–38
Butadiene-acrylonitrile (Hycar OR-15)	200	Cohesive	35–36
Epoxy: Epon 1062	500	Adhesion	20–23
Epon 824	200	Adhesion	50–52
Epon 1001	400	Adhesion	60–62

A bipolar resin film suitable for bonding glass to glass is not suitable for bonding glass to a non-polar solid. Thus a coupling agent is required for overcoming the dissimilarity between the attractive forces of a glass adhesive and a non-polar polymer. For example, glass which has been coated with certain types of polyvinyl butyral still has a low contact angle for water, whereas cast phenolic resin has a contact angle of about 43°. A 'bifunctional adhesive' must be used with a non-polar group for attaching to the phenolic resin and a polar group extending into space for attachment to the polyvinyl butyral.

Shown in Table 8.7 is the contact angle of water on a range of polymer formulations applied to glass, together with the bond strengths of a number of glass/adhesive/glass laminates as measured by Moser (1956a). The heat-curing adhesives were bonded to the glass by initially air-drying the resin coatings for 1 hour followed by heating for 10 min at 120°c. The glass specimens were then laminated together to form a crosslap under 200 lb/in² pressure and cured for 45 min at 135°c. Adhesive bonds made with catalyzed epoxy resins were allowed to age for seven days at room temperature before testing. The contact angles given in Table 8.7 should be treated as qualitative because the thickness of the resin film was not specified. Also, the orientation of a resin film may be influenced by the type of solvent used for casting the layer.

The bond strength of the polymers listed in Table 8.7 can be greatly improved by combining them with other resins or by the addition of plasticizers. Thus some grades of polyvinyl butyral on glass give high contact angles to water, *i.e.* $\theta = 40$–$60°$, but when plasticized with dibutyl phthalate the contact angle is reduced to 18–20°. The bond strength is also raised by the plasticizer from 600 lb/in² to over 1000 lb/in².

ELECTRICAL NATURE OF ADHESION AND RADIATION EMISSION

It has been mentioned in the introduction to this chapter that adhesion between solids can arise from chemical bonding in which charge transfer occurs producing an electrical double-layer. Evidence that the bonding of certain organic polymers to glass is of a chemical nature and can be ionic in character has been obtained by Karasev *et al.* (1953), and Deryagin (1955). They observed that when polymers coatings were stripped rapidly from a glass base electrical effects occurred such as charging of the separated surfaces, sparking and luminescence. It appeared that an electrical double layer had formed at the polymer/glass interface and during rapid stripping of the polymer the double layer was separated. Karasev *et al.* found that when coatings of various polymers were stripped from glass at a low gas pressure (0·1–1 torr), then at a certain threshold speed of stripping the gas glowed brightly due to an electrical discharge. When the gas pressure was further reduced the glass luminesced under the action of electrons pulled out of the polymer by the strong electric fields in the gap between the polymer and glass. The electron energies ranged from 10^3 to 10^4 eV.

Williams (1957) has investigated the nature of the light emitted during adhesive breaks between polymers and glass. The polymers (polyvinyltoluene and polystyrene) were prepared in flat bottomed Pyrex vials and on cooling to about 90°c they broke away from the glass with an accompanying emission of light. The light was emitted in flashes of 1–4 μsec duration and of diminishing magnitude. Williams found that the radiation consisted of light of two bands occurring at wavelengths between 5200–5600 Å and 5750–6400 Å. Adhesive breaks seemed to occur over large contact areas when a given critical stress was exceeded and not as a result of a continuous stripping action. The electrons pulled out of the polymer by the high electric field created by the adhesive break made the glass luminesce. Williams states that electrical effects may arise from cohesive breaks in either the polymer or the glass and he observed weak light emission when glass was broken in the dark.

GLASS REINFORCED PLASTICS

Bonding materials. When glass is free from surface imperfections it has an exceptional high strength but this cannot in practice be realized because of the ease with which the surface is marred and the low average stress at which cracks develop from the damaged surface. When glass fibres are bonded with a polymer a two-phase material is obtained which can be readily shaped by moulding or machining and which has a high resistance to the growth of cracks. The glass fibres may be in the form of rovings, chopped strand mat or woven fabrics. Soda-lime glass is often used for the fibres because of its ease of drawing but for electrical purposes a low alkali glass is required. Also the high water adsorption of soda-lime glass influences the wet strength of the bonded material, and for high mechanical strength low alkali glasses are used (see Brossy *et al.*, 1957). The bonding materials are usually polyesters or epoxides which have good mechanical properties up to 150°c. Silicone bonded materials may be used up to 250°c.

The polyester and epoxide resins are prepared as linear polymers forming viscous liquids. The polymers are then cross-linked at normal temperature using a monomer, such as styrene or dicyandiamide, with a catalyst. During polymerization a small amount of condensation product is produced.

Strength of polyester-glass sheet. The form of the glass cloth greatly influences the strength of the resin bonded material. Case (1956) found that polyester impregnated cloth prepared from an array of parallel fibres had twice the flexural strength and three times the elastic limit compared with that of a woven cloth. These advantages were obtained in the direction of the fibres which were stressed in either tension or compression. Two-dimensional strength could be obtained by laminating parallel fibre mats with the fibres at right angles.

Typical data on the strength of polyester-glass sheet have been collected by Gurney (1959) and are shown in Table 8.8. The glass

Table 8.8
Strength of polyester-glass sheet
(*After Gurney, 1959*)

Reinforcement	Bidirectional glass fabric	Unidirectional glass fabric	Glass mat
Percentage glass by weight	60–65	62–67	30–45
Tensile strength $(lb/in^2 \times 10^{-3})$	40–50	78–86	10–24
Young's modulus $(lb/in^2 \times 10^{-6})$	1·0–2·8	4·0–5·0	1·0–2·0

fibres contribute to the strength and stiffness only in the direction of their length and it has been calculated that a two-dimensional mat of fibres should have a strength and stiffness only one-third of the longitudinal strength of a parallel array of fibres.

The high resistance to propagation of cracks in glass reinforced plastic is shown by cyclic loading tests on notched test pieces. For a given notch and nominal stress cycle the number of cycles for failure may be higher for the plastic than, for example, an aluminium alloy.

Cyclic loading. Bulk glass withstands a cyclic loading for about the same time as it withstands a steady load equal to the maximum experienced during cycling. The *delayed* fracture arises from atmospheric attack of the glass surface. Glass reinforced plastics fail under cyclic loading in a shorter period than that necessary for failure under static loading of the same intensity. Thus they exhibit a *fatigue* effect as well as *delayed* fracture. The explanation for this is that failure of the glass-polymer bond permits atmospheric attack of the glass, especially if the polymer is crazed. Deterioration under cyclic loading may also arise from damage to the glass surface when it rubs against other fibres or slides in the polymer matrix.

WATER ADSORPTION AND SURFACE TREATMENT

The strength of the two-phase system depends amongst other things on the bond strength at the glass-polymer interface. Moisture adsorption at the glass surface may locally inhibit polymerization during curing, or subsequent adsorption of water may lower the flexural strength of the bonded material. Thus when a resin-bonded glass cloth is exposed to high humidity or water immersion it tends to lose flexural strength.

Coupling agents or primers have been developed to improve the wet strength of the bonded glass cloth and these are discussed below. Gurney (1959) states that the treatment of glass fibres with coupling agents yields a more durable plastic under wet conditions, but there is insufficient experience for assessing long-term properties. Further, it has been reported that unstressed polyester-glass specimens showed no deterioration in strength after exposure to English weather for two and a half years and that static water tanks made of this material have been in use for the same period. Test pieces loaded to high stresses and subjected to wetting and drying and variations in temperature showed a deterioration in properties. Epoxides are usually superior to polyester under such conditions.

Case and Robinson (1955) state that parallel glass fibre laminates with polyester resins have flexural strengths of 82 000 lb/in² wet and 123 000 lb/in² dry.

Water reacting coupling agents. Certain coupling agents used for treating glass fibres reduce the loss in strength of resin-impregnated

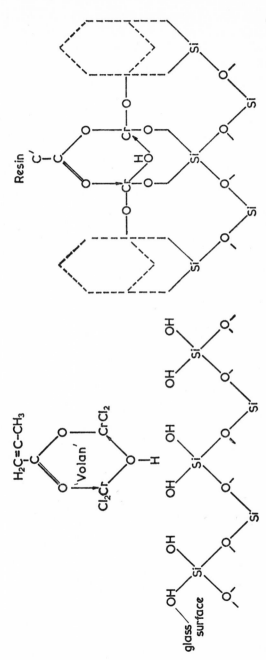

FIG. 8.8   REACTION BETWEEN 'VOLAN' AND ADSORBED WATER ON A GLASS SURFACE TO FORM A CHEMISORBED LAYER WITH UNSATURATED ORGANIC GROUPS FOR KEYING TO A RESIN

glass cloths when wet. The two principal coupling agents available are 'Volan'† which is methacrylic acid co-ordinated with chromium to form a reactive complex, and vinyl silicone or vinyl silane, depending on the mode of application.

The chromium atom in Volan is linked with chlorine ($CrCl_2$) which reacts with water adsorbed to the glass liberating hydrochloric acid. The surface reaction permits the chromium-oxygen terminals of the Volan to continue the glass structure and the unsaturated organic groups to be available for keying to a resin, as in Fig. 8.8. Torrey (1952) claims that flexural strengths of 66 000–68 000 lb/in² and wet flexural strengths of 56 000–58 000 lb/in² after 3 hours in boiling water have been obtained with Volan treated fabric. These values refer to woven-spun cloths. Thus their flexural strengths are less than those of the parallel array fibres discussed above.

Bjorksten and Yaeger (1952) have treated glass fabric with vinylchlorsilane to form a vinyl silicone polymer on the glass. The silicon atom in the coupling agent becomes chemically linked to the glass as the chlorine removes adsorbed water by forming hydrochloric acid (a full discussion of the silicone treatment will be found in Chapters 3 and 7). The unsaturated vinyl group is then free to react with unsaturated groups in the laminating resin. Clark (1952) found that the vinyl silicone finish resulted in higher dry and wet strengths for resin-laminated glass fibres than Volan 114. According to Rochow (1951) O. K. Johannson‡ experimented in 1938 with treating glass with organochlorosilanes with the object of improving the adhesion of lacquers to glass.

Heat-cleaning. Usually glass fibres are coated with an organic size to lubricate them when the yarn is twisted and woven. This size must be removed before treatment with a coupling agent or lamination. Hoffman (1952) states that cleaning the fibres by heating is the most satisfactory method of preparing glass cloth to be used in silicone resin laminates. The vinyl-chlorosilane treatment, which is effective with polyester resin laminates, did not give any improvement over heat-treated cloth when used with silicone resins.

Heat-treating silicone films. Silicones free from chlorine can be made

---

† Du Pont de Nemours and Co. Inc.

‡ Rochow refers to testimony for interference 81 077 before U.S. Patent Office.

to form chemisorbed layers on glass by heat treatment which removes the surface water. Thus Jellinek (1952) treated glass fibres with a vinyl silicone in a solvent. The coating was heat-cured at 275°c for 5 min. He states that if alkali is present on the surface the adhesion is impaired and it must be removed from the glass fibres by washing. Glass fibres treated as described and laminated with bakelite resin (BRSQ-147) retained over 90% of their flexural strength when wet, whereas the same fibres treated with Volan 114 only retained 60% when wet.

Case and Robinson (1955) state that silicones dissolved in solvents are less effective than silicone emulsions for applying to glass fibre.

Gate (1956) has described an organo–silicon compound dissolved in methyl cellosolve known as D9132† which can be diluted with de-ionized water and applied to glass cloth. As it does not liberate hydrochloric acid in the presence of moisture and must be heated to about 150°c for a few minutes it probably resembles the vinyl silicone polymer used by Jellinek. Shown in Fig. 8.9 are the flexural strengths of heat-cleaned cloths and cloths treated with vinyltrichlorosilane and D9132 when impregnated by different resins. The

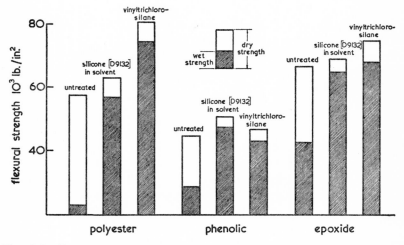

FIG. 8.9 FLEXURAL STRENGTH OF GLASSCLOTH LAMINATED WITH DIFFERENT RESINS AND TREATED WITH CHLOROSILANE AND SILICONE COUPLING AGENTS (*After Gate*, 1956)

† Midland Silicones Ltd.

non-toxic nature of D9132 permits it to be easily applied to the glass cloth.

Metal-coated fibres. Resins used for bonding fibre glass structures usually have a high adhesion to metals. Thus there is the possibility of using a metal-coated fibre glass to obtain a high bonding strength. Callinan and Lucas and Brossy *et al.* (1958) have described a method for copper coating glass fibre by reducing a glass containing copper oxide. However, no work appears to have been done on bonding metallized glass fibres with resins.

Metal films produced on glass by reduction of oxides are unlikely to be completely continuous because of the tendency of the free metal atoms to aggregate during heat treatment. Brossy *et al.* observed that the copper on their reduced fibres was in the form of microscopic plates like fish scale. More continuous metal films can be formed by evaporation of metals in vacuum but this would require costly equipment for metallizing fibres. The writer has observed that epoxy coating applied to aluminium films on glass may shear the aluminium from the glass when the resin coating shrinks on curing.

References

Adams, R. B., and Pask, J. A., 1961, *J. Amer. ceram. Soc.*, **44**, 430.

Andreas, J. M., Hauser, E. A., and Tucker, W. B., 1938, *J. phys. Chem.*, **42**, 1001.

Babcock, C. L., 1940, *J. Amer. ceram. Soc.*, **23**, 12.

Badger, A. E., Parmelee, C. W., and Williams, A. E., 1937, *J. Amer. ceram. Soc.*, **20**, 301.

Belser, R. B., 1954, *Rev. sci. Instrum.*, **25**, 180.

Brossy, J. F., Case, J. W., Houze, A. L., and Lasday, A. H., 1957, *Soc. Plastics Industry*, 12th Annual Mtg., *Section 16-A*.

Brossy, J. F., Case, J. W., Houze, A. L., and Lasday, A. H., 1958, *Soc. Plastics Industry*, 13th Annual Mtg., *Section 2-C*.

Callinan, T. D., and Lucas, R. T., 'The Electrical Properties of Glass Fiber Paper—II', Naval Research Lab. Rep. No. 4042.

Case, J. W., 1956, *Material and Methods*, September, **44**, 115.

Case, J. W., and Robinson, J. D., 1955, March, *Modern Plastics*, **32**, 151.

Cherniak, M. G., and Naidus, G. G., 1957, *J. tech. Phys.*, *Acad. Sci. U.S.S.R.*, **27**, 2268.

Clark, G. A., 1952, Nov., *Modern Plastics*, **30**, 142.

Cline, R. W., Fulrath, R. M., and Pask, J. A., 1961, *J. Amer. ceram. Soc.*, **44**, 423.

Cooke, R. D., 1924, *J. Amer. ceram. Soc.*, **7**, 277.

446   The Properties of Glass Surfaces

Davies, J. T., and Rideal, E. J., 1961, *Interfacial Phenomena*, Academic Press Inc. (New York, London).

Davis, J. K., and Bartell, F. E., 1948, *Analyt. Chem.*, **20**, 1182.

Deryagin, B. V., 1955, *Research*, **8**, 70.

Dietzel, A., 1935, *Sprechsaal*, **68**, 3, 20, 34, 53, 67, 84.

Dietzel, A., 1942, *Sprechsaal*, **75**, 82.

Dietzel, A., 1951, *Glastechn. Ber.*, **24**, 263.

Dietzel, A., and Coenen, M., 1959, *Glastechn. Ber.*, **32**, 357.

Dietzel, A. and Meures, K., 1933, *Sprechsaal*, **66**, 647.

Dorsey, N. E., 1928, *J. Washington Acad. Sci.*, **18**, 505.

Eubanks, A. G., and Moore, D. G., 1955, *J. Amer. ceram. Soc.*, **38**, 226.

Fulrath, R. M., Mitoff, S. P., and Pask, J. A., 1957, *J. Amer. ceram. Soc.*, **40**, 269.

Gate, P. A. J., 1956, *The Rubber and Plastics Age*, **37** (9).

Gurney, C., 1959, *Nature*, **183**, 24.

Hagan, L. G., and Ravitz, S. F., 1961, *J. Amer. ceram. Soc.*, **44**, 428.

Harkins, W. D., and Brown, F. E., 1919, *J. Amer. chem. Soc.*, **41**, 499.

Harrison, W. N., Richmond, J. C., Pitts, J. W., and Benner, S. G., 1952, *J. Amer. ceram. Soc.*, **35**, 113.

Hoffman, K. R., 1952, Nov., *Modern Plastics*, **30**, 146.

Holden, J., Holland, L., and Laurenson, L., 1959, *J. Sci. Instrum.*, **36**, 281.

Holland, L., 1956, *Vacuum Deposition of Thin Films*, Chapman and Hall Ltd., London.

Holland, L., Putner, T., and Bateman, S. K., 1957, *J. opt. Soc. Amer.*, **47**, 668.

Housekeeper, W. G., 1923, *J. Amer. I.E.E.*, **42**, 954.

Hull, A. W., and Burger, E. E., 1934, *Physics*, **5**, 384.

Jaeger, F. M., 1917, *Z. anorg. allgem. Chem.*, **101**, 1.

Bjorksten, J., and Yaeger, L. L., 1952 July, *Modern Plastic*, **29**, 124.

Jellinek, M. H., 1952 Nov., *Modern Plastics*, **30**, 150.

Karasev, E. B., Krotova, H. A., and Deryagin, B. V., 1953, *Dokl. Akad. Nauk SSSR*, **88**, 77.

Keppeler, G., 1937, *J. Soc. Glass Technol.*, **21**, 53(T).

Koenig, H., Loeffler, H. J., and Lappe, F., 1955, *Glastechn. Ber.*, **28**, 131.

Lecrenier, A., 1924, *Bull. Soc. Chem., Belg.*, **33**, 119.

Lyon, K. C., 1944, *J. Amer. ceram. Soc.*, **27**, 186.

Mitchell, D. W., Mitoff, S. P., Zackay, V. F., and Pask, J. A., 1952, *Glass Industry*, **33**, 453; **3**, 515.

Mitoff, S. P., 1957, *J. Amer. ceram. Soc.*, **40**, 118.

Moore, H., 1958, *Platinum in the Glass Industry*, Mond Nickel Co. Ltd., London.

Moore, D. G., and Thornton, H. R., 1959, *J. Res. Nat. Bur. Stand.*, **62**, 127.

Moser, F., 1956a, Dec., *Plastics Technol.*

Moser, F., 1956b, April, *The Glass Industry*.

Parikh, N. M., 1958, *J. Amer. ceram. Soc.*, **41**, 18.

Parmelee, G. W., and Lyon, K. C., 1937, *J. Soc. Glass Technol.*, **21**, 44T.

Parmelee, C. W. and Harman, C. G., 1937, *J. Amer. ceram. Soc.*, **20**, 224.

Partridge, J. H., 1949, *Glass to Metal Seals*, Soc. Glass Technol., Sheffield.

Pask, J. A., 1963, *Glass-metal Interfaces and Bonding*, UCRL-10611, Lawrence Radiation Lab., Berkeley, California.
Pask, J. A., and Fulrath, R. M., 1960, Fundamentals of Glass-to-Metal Bonding: X—Nature of Wetting and Adherence, University of Calif., Ceramic Lab. Xth Tech. Rep., Series 48, No. 10.
Pietenpol, W. B., 1936, *Physics*, **7**, 26.
Rayleigh, Lord, 1874, *Phil. Mag.*, **48**, 321.
Richmond, J. C., Moore, D. G., Kirkpatrick, H. B., and Harrison, W. N., 1953, *J. Amer. ceram. Soc.*, **36**, 410.
Rochow, E. G., 1951, *An Introduction to the Chemistry of Silicones*, 2nd Ed., Chapman and Hall Ltd., London.
Rose, K., 1944, *Scientific American*, **170**, 154.
Shartsis, L., and Canga, R., 1949, *J. Res. Nat. Bur. St.*, **43**, 221.
Shartsis, L., and Spinner, S., 1951, *J. Res. Nat. Bur. St.*, **46**, 385.
Shartsis, L., and Smock, A. W., 1947, *J. Res. Nat. Bur. St.*, **38**, 241.
Shartsis, L., Spinner, S., and Smock, A. W., 1948, *J. Res. Nat. Bur. St.*, **40**, 61.
Tammann, G., and Rabe, H., 1927, *Z. anorg. allgem. Chem.*, **162**, 17.
Tammann, G., and Tampke, R., 1927, *Z. anorg. allgem. Chem.*, **162**, 1.
Tate, T., 1864, *Phil. Mag.*, **27**, 48.
Tillotson, E. W., 1911, *J. Ind. Eng. Chem.*, **3**, 631.
Tillotson, E. W., 1912, *J. Ind. Eng. Chem.*, **4**, 651.
Torrey, J. V. P., 1952 November, *Modern Plastics*, **30**, 154.
Tress, H. J., 1962, *Glass Technol.*, **3**, 95.
Vickers, A. E. J., 1937, *J. Soc. Glass Technol.*, **21**, 60T.
Volf, M. B., 1961, *Technical Glasses*, Sir Isaac Pitman & Sons Ltd., London.
Volpe, M. L., Fulrath, R. M., and Pask, J. A., 1959, *J. Amer. ceram. Soc.*, **42**, 102.
Washburn, E. W., Shelton, G. R., and Libman, E. E., 1924, *Univ. Ill. Eng. Exp. Sta. Bull.*, **140**, 53.
Weiss, W., 1956, *Glastechn. Ber.*, **29**, 386.
Weyl, W. A., 1945, *Glass Industry*, **26**, 557.
Wilhelmy, L., 1863, *Ann. Phys.*, **119**, 177.
Williams, R. C., 1957, *J. appl. Phys.*, **28**, 1043.
Zackay, V. F., Mitchell, D. W., Mitoff, S. P. and Pask, J. A., 1953, *J. Amer. ceram. Soc.*, **36**, 84.

CHAPTER 9

Electrical Properties of Glass Surfaces and Thin Layers

1. INTRODUCTION

Apart from their theoretical interest the electrical properties of glass surfaces are of great practical importance. Glass is widely used for making electrical insulators and the vacuum envelopes of thermionic and photo-electric devices. The surface electrical properties of the glass employed will determine whether there is an accumulation or leakage of surface charges, which is usually important in the operation of such devices.

Chemically reduced glasses and enamels have semi-conducting properties and may be used for high resistance elements or resistance thermometers with a large negative coefficient.

Glass is commonly employed as a substrate for electrically conducting films. Thus transparent semi-conducting films of metal oxides are prepared on glass as resistance heating elements for demisting observation windows and for removing electro-static charges; transparent metal films deposited *in vacuo* are used for similar purposes. Precision resistors made from thin films of Nichrome on glass are beginning to replace the resistance elements of more traditional manufacture. Capacitors prepared from vacuum evaporated films of silica or glass sandwiched between metal films have also appeared in recent years. The advent of the transistor with its low operating potential has greatly reduced the degree to which associated electronic components need be stressed making it possible to use thin film resistors and capacitors. Such elements are usually prepared in miniature circuits by vacuum evaporation through masks on to glass substrates. The smooth finish of the glass base ensures structural continuity in the super-imposed coatings.

It is not intended to enter here into a discussion of the electrical properties of films deposited on glass, but rather to deal with the electrical properties of the glass surface. Readers who are interested in the electrical properties of thin films deposited on glass should consult the writer's earlier work (Holland, 1956). Some attention is however, given in this chapter to the properties of thin film capacitors made from glass and silica and thin film resistors prepared from reduced glasses.

The electrical properties of glass were first reviewed by Littleton and Morey (1933) in a work which was later incorporated in a book by Morey (1954); Stevels (1957) and Sutton (1960) have also reviewed this field. The foregoing deal with the electrical properties of the surface but it is not their prime topic as it is here.

2. CONDUCTION PROCESSES

SYMBOLS AND MEASUREMENTS

Symbols. The symbols used in this chapter mainly refer to measurements made with electrodes arranged parallel on the same surface and are as follows :

χ_v Volume conductivity of surface layer (Ω^{-1} cm^{-1}).

ρ_v Volume resistivity of surface layer (Ω cm).

χ_B, ρ_B Volume conductivity and resistivity of the base material.

χ_s Surface conductivity (Ω^{-1}/square).

ρ_s Surface resistivity (Ω/square).

χ_T, ρ_T Total surface conductivity or resistivity including a contribution to the leakage from the base material.

C_v Volume capacity of surface layer F cm^{-1}.

C_s Surface capacity (F/square).

C_T Total surface capacity including contribution from the base material.

It should be noted that the surface electrical values for capacity or conductivity refer to parallel electrodes of equal length on the opposite sides of a square area of surface. Surface values can be converted to volume ratings when the thickness of the conducting surface layer is known and defined. Thus the volume resistivity is given by

$$\rho_v = \frac{Rwt}{l}$$

where R is the resistance of a specimen of thickness t, specimen/ electrode width w and length l. If $l = w$ then we have $R = \rho_s$ and $\rho_v = \rho_s t$.

The foregoing assumes the existence of a conducting layer on an insulating substrate, whereas in practice the substrate may also be partially conducting. Curtis (1915) has calculated that for electrodes of infinite length spaced 1 cm apart on a test piece 1 cm thick, the contribution of the volume of the material to the leakage resistance is 2·7 times its volume resistivity. As the leakage of electricity through the volume and over the surface are in parallel we have for the total resistivity

$$\frac{1}{\rho_T} = \frac{1}{\rho_s} + \frac{1}{2 \cdot 7 \rho_B}$$

When the electrodes are of 1 cm width and 1 cm apart on a base of infinite thickness the contribution of the base to the leakage resistance is $1 \cdot 3 \rho_B$.

CONDUCTION IN SOLIDS

Before discussing the electrical properties of the glass surface in detail we shall first consider electrical conduction in general and summarize the electrical properties of bulk glass. A substance may be classified in terms of its electrical conductivity as a metallic, semi or ionic conductor †. Metallic conductors have a volume conductivity (χ) greater than about $10^2 \ \Omega^{-1} \ cm^{-1}$ at normal temperature and a temperature coefficient of conductivity $d\chi/dT$ that is negative. The conductivity of semiconductors is mainly electronic (electrons, positive holes or both) and ranges from 10^{-10} to $10^2 \ \Omega^{-1} \ cm^{-1}$ at normal temperature and $d\chi/dT$ is positive. In the simplest cases the conductivity is related to the temperature as follows:

$$\chi = \chi_0 \exp\left(-E/RT\right) \tag{1}$$

where E is an activation energy.

Ionic conductors have low conductivities even at high temperature and at normal temperature χ may be as low as $10^{-16} \ \Omega^{-1} \ cm^{-1}$. They have a positive temperature coefficient and the above equation

---

† Readers interested in a detailed discussion of conduction processes in metal oxides and ionic crystals should consult Kubaschewski and Hopkins 1953) and Mott and Gurney (1948).

must be modified to include exponential terms arising from the respective conductivities of the anion and cation.

There are many intermediate types between the three kinds of conductors described and the conduction mechanism of a given compound may change more or less continuously as its composition or temperature is changed. Semiconductors are usually metallic compounds which have an excess or deficit of the metal component and conduction arises from flow of electrons or positive holes respectively. Semiconduction may be promoted by foreign cations which replace some of the metal atoms in the lattice or exist interstically in the lattice structure. Thus, a semiconducting compound is either impure or its composition is not exactly stoichiometric, whereas that of an ionic conductor must be stoichiometric, *i.e.* the number of cations and anions are equal. The electronic conduction of semiconductors invariably gives rise to some absorption for visible light whilst ionic conductors are transparent.

VOLUME CONDUCTION IN GLASSES

Pure silica has a low volume conductivity of less than 10^{-18} Ω^{-1} cm^{-1} and the addition of other oxides enhances the conductivity. Thus the presence of alkali greatly raises the conductivity and χ_B for soda-lime silicate glass is about 10^{-10} Ω^{-1} cm^{-1} and for lead silicate about 10^{-12} Ω^{-1} cm^{-1}. Electrical conduction is normally ionic and arises from the flow of alkali ions. It has been found that the alkali ions are more easily transported than those of the alkaline earths and that the mobility decreases as the effective ionic radius increases. Conduction in nominally pure lead silicate has been attributed to migration of Pb^{++} ions.

It is shown in Chapter 3 that Na^+ ions are the most mobile components of glass whereas the O^{2-} ions with which they are associated in the SiO_2 random network are not mobile at normal temperatures. Thus if electrical conduction by alkali ions occurs it will gradually cease as alkali ions migrate in the glass and a negative space charge grows at the anode and a Na^+ space charge grows at the cathode.

Effect of temperature. The electrical conductivity of glass increases as the temperature is raised because of the greater ease with which the ions can move when thermal agitation has weakened the forces binding them to the silica network of the glass structure. Curtis

(1915) found that the volume conductivity of several glasses rose by a factor of 3–4 when their temperature was raised from 20° to 30°c. Most workers have found that the conductivity of glass varies with temperature as given by equation (1) above; a relation between the thermal diffusion of ions and their transport under an electric field is given in Chapter 3.

If alkali–silicate glasses are melted then electrolysis occurs according to Faraday's laws of electrochemistry. Faraday (1839) himself observed the electrolysis of a flint glass but failed to observe conduction in green bottle glass heated with an oxy-hydrogen flame; it is most likely that the soda content was volatilized from the surface at the high temperature used.

DEPENDENCE OF RESISTIVITY ON FIELD STRENGTH

Poole (1921) has reported that the bulk conductivity of microscope cover glass rises with increase in the electric field E across the specimen. His results follow the relation $\log \chi_b = aE + b$, where b is a constant and a is a coefficient dependent on temperature. Working at field strengths up to 0.7 Mv cm^{-1} Poole found that a decreased from 1.5 at 15°c to 0.91 at 74°c. Conductivity measurements made at normal temperatures showed a slightly lower bulk conductivity when the field was being reduced than when it was being increased. Poole attributed this to the influence of polarization. No information is given on the time interval over which measurements were made and the influence on the results of dielectric absorption or true conduction are not known. Moon and Norcross (1930) have confirmed Poole's relation between conductivity and field strength for several glasses. They used mercury and chemically deposited silver electrodes with direct current at room temperature, taking measurements some five or ten minutes after commencement of current flow when equilibrium had apparently been obtained.

Bush and Connell (1922) found that the volume conductivity of Corning glass G-702, silica and porcelain were almost independent of field strength but that their conductivity increased with rise in field strength after degassing at 350°c in vacuum. The field dependence partly persisted when the materials were exposed to atmosphere for long periods. The volume resistivity of 'Pyrex' was dependent on the electric field before and after degassing *in vacuo*. The loss of gas and water from the heated glasses raised their volume resistivity, *i.e.* six times for Corning G-702 and three times for 'Pyrex'. Undoubtedly hydrogen ions in the glass structure participated in the conduction at normal temperature and they would be removed at high temperature partly with the less mobile oxygen ions.

Joffé *et al.* (1927) observed that the electrical conductivity of thin glass foils followed a relation similar to that given by Poole when the field strength was high but Ohm's law was obeyed at low field strengths. The observed departure at high field strengths was attributed to ions being sufficiently accelerated by the field to produce more ions by impact. The theory of this is discussed at length on p. 513. Joffé *et al.* also found that the initial application of a high field strength raised the conductivity when measured at low field strengths.

As conduction in normal glasses is ionic it is possible to produce an excess of ions at one electrode and a depletion of ions at the other as the current flows. Such an effect will influence the distribution of the applied potential across the glass and complicate measurement unless non-polarizing electrodes are used. Unfortunately none of the work reported above was done under these conditions.

Forrest (1947) has reported that semiconducting glazes, containing reduced iron oxide and silica, exhibit a rise in conductivity with field strength. The glazes were excess electron conductors and polarization was not likely to occur. Forrest noted that the voltage dependence of the conductivity was highest when measurements were made with a small gap between the surface electrodes. It was established that temperature changes arising from variations in current flow were not responsible for the effect. It appeared therefore that the phenomenon arose from contact resistance, which was a greater part of the total resistance when the electrode separation was small. The contact resistance was found to be proportional to $V^{-0.8}$ and the current flowing when the contact resistance predominated was proportional to $V^{1.8}$. A non-ohmic relation may be obtained when a metal electrode is in contact with a semiconductor or insulator. Mott and Gurney have shown that at low field strengths the current flowing through a crystalline insulator will be proportional to V^2.

INFLUENCE OF SORBED GAS

Experiments by Bush and Connel (1922) suggested that sorbed gases were primarily responsible for conduction at room temperature. This was investigated by Rebbeck and Ferguson (1924) who used tubes made of soda-lime silicate filled with mercury and immersed in a liquid electrolyte. When a potential was applied across the tube wall with the mercury as cathode a coating of bubbles containing oxygen and hydrogen formed between the mercury and the glass wall. Drying the mercury and the glass and filling by distillation in vacuum did not prevent bubble formation but when the tubes were annealed or baked in vacuum at 350°c practically no gas subsequently developed. When the gas had formed it could be made to disappear by reversing the potential.

A possible explanation of the effect was that an adsorbed water film had undergone electrolysis but a sample of the gas showed it contained 18% by volume of oxygen and the remainder hydrogen. Sodium was found to diffuse to the cathode surface and form an amalgam with the mercury electrode and the gas could have partly been created by the sodium reacting with adsorbed water, *i.e.* $Na + H_2O \rightarrow NaOH + \frac{1}{2}H_2$.

Further tests showed that an annealed glass immersed in water liberated more gas the longer it was in contact with the water. However, when a glass was annealed its conductivity decreased and did not rise to the original figure even after the tube had contained water for a prolonged period.

The most likely explanation of this effect is that when the water contacted the annealed glass hydrogen ions diffused into the glass replacing those of sodium. The ion-exchange process would leave the electrical conductivity almost unchanged but result in gas being liberated during current flow. Rebbeck and Ferguson appreciated the possible effect of hydrogen diffusion (if not ion-exchange). Thus when the inside of the glass tube was in contact with acid before distilling in the mercury cathode then the gas subsequently liberated was twice that obtained by water treatment. If a voltage was applied to the tube whilst it contained acid with the acid connected as anode then even greater volumes of gas were subsequently released with the mercury cathode. These results strongly suggested that hydrogen had diffused into the glass.

Another interesting feature was that gas bubbles appeared at the mercury cathode when the applied voltage was raised to the small value of 1·3 V. Such a low voltage for ion mobility indicated that the gas ions were not firmly held in the glass.

Milnes and Isard (1962) found that the volume resistivity of lead silicate glasses (38–64 mol% PbO), nominally alkali free, decreased as their water content increased. Thus ρ_v for a 50mol%PbO 50mol% SiO_2 glass at 100°c was about 10^{13} Ω cm after melting *in vacuo*, falling to 10^{12} Ω cm after melting in oxygen and steam. Conduction was attributed to migration of Pb^{++} ions. The water was assumed to consist of OH^-groups in the glass which raised the mobility of the lead ion by hydrogen bonding to the oxygen atoms surrounding the lead ions. It is of interest that the glasses absorbed less water than that given by the square root law ($\sqrt{P_{H_2O}}$) when the partial pressure of the water vapour above the melt was raised.

Influence of composition. Introduction of lead oxide, boron oxide or alkaline earth oxides into sodium silicate glass decreases its volume conductivity at normal temperature. This has been attributed to the metal ions of the foregoing oxides being firmly bound in the glass structure and obstructing the passage of the more mobile alkali ions. It is now known that certain types of glasses, (*e.g.* extra dense flint and sodium borosilicate) have a two- or three-phase structure and the foregoing explanation cannot be considered complete. In a glass containing a large amount of lead oxide the sodium would have to migrate from islands of silicate through a lead oxide matrix, as shown in Plate 1. Thus the production of a two-phase structure may be the reason for the lead oxide reducing the mobility of Na^+ ions. Undoubtedly a thorough study of electrical conduction in such glasses would be valuable.

Glass systems exist where reduction apparently occurs in the glass forming network. Thus Bayton *et al.* (1956) have described the properties of tungstate and molybdate glasses which are black, have a high volume conductivity and do not show d.c. polarization, indicating that conduction is by electrons. Reduction may also occur in the network modifiers of silicate glass so that it contains free metal atoms, *e.g.* Pb, Sb or Bi, which act as electron donors and this is discussed later.

DIELECTRIC ABSORPTION AND IONIC CONDUCTION

If a voltage is applied to glass at normal temperature then the initial current will exceed the true conduction current and gradually fall to the conduction value with time. The excess current initially flowing arises from an effect known as *dielectric absorption* and is a general characteristic of both inorganic and organic substances of very high resistivity. Thus the current flowing at any instant after application of the voltage is determined not only by the instantaneous voltage and temperature but is a function of the time elapsed from the application of the voltage.

The dielectric in an *ideal* capacitor would be a perfect insulator and no direct current could flow through it. Also upon application of an electric field, if the current density was sufficiently high, the ideal capacitor would be charged almost instantaneously and on short-circuit would release the charge over the same short time interval.

In practice solid dielectrics deviate from the ideal because there are considerable forces between the constituent atoms or molecules. When a potential is applied to a dielectric the following may occur:

(*i*) the electrons are displaced with respect to their atomic nuclei,

(*ii*) the atoms are displaced with respect to each other within the molecule,

(*iii*) molecules with permanent dipole moments are orientated in the applied field,

(*iv*) free ions move through the dielectric.

Processes (*i*) and (*ii*) are believed to occur instantaneously and according to Cohn and Guest (1944), who have surveyed this field, item (*iii*) is generally considered to be unimportant in solid dielectrics because the bonds between neighbouring molecules restrict dipole rotation more strongly than viscous flow. Water, however, in or on a dielectric, will show some dipole orientation.

From the foregoing it could be concluded that when a potential is applied to a dielectric the movement of the electrons relative to their nuclei constitutes a true displacement current which is reversible, whereas the movement of the less mobile ions, producing an ionic current, will occur over a longer period and be only partly reversible. Thus when the applied voltage is removed the electron displacement charge will quickly disappear, but only some of the ions will be able to move slowly back to their initial positions under the internal field produced by their displacement. Presumably those ions which are able to move through the solid without final obstruction produce the true conduction current.

As true conduction in glass arises from movement of alkali ions or ions of absorbed hydrogen atoms the conductance will decrease as the anode surface becomes denuded of such ions. If the glass temperature is raised above about 100°c the mobility of the ions rises considerably and the conductance may decrease rapidly. Buff (1895) observed that the conductance of glass decreased with time and attributed this to polarization. It was Warburg (1884, 1913), however, who showed that the decay arose from depletion of Na^+ ions and could be prevented by using a non-polarizing electrode of, for example, mercury amalgam.

At ambient temperature dielectric absorption produces a superposed transient current many times greater than the true conduction current by which it is finally succeeded. Guyer (1933, 1949) has investigated dielectric absorption. He showed that if one plots the *charge* current and *discharge* current as a function of time and subtracts the discharge ordinates from those of the charge curve the difference in the current at any time is roughly constant and equal to the true conduction current *i.e.* the ionic current in normal glasses.

The rate at which the total current (*i.e.* absorption and conduction components) falls to the conduction value depends on the conductivity of the glass. Thus, if the conductivity of the glass is higher than 10^{-13} Ω^{-1} cm^{-1}, the absorption current is normally not greater than 10% of the conduction current after 1 min. However, if the conductivity is less than 10^{-13} Ω^{-1} cm^{-1}, the absorption current may take a considerable time to decrease to a negligible value. Raising the temperature of a glass will raise its conductivity and the absorption current will decrease more rapidly.

Muray (1962) identifies a third conducting region of steady conduction reached when ion migration has formed negative (O^-) and positive (Na^+) space charges at the electrodes. He contends that the space charges opposing the applied field are responsible for a reduced but constant conductivity. Electron flow occurs at the cathode/glass interface by electrons combining with non-bridging oxygen atoms in the surface producing O^- ions. Na^+ ions in the positive space charge combine with the O^- ions and increase the field across the interface permitting further creation of O^- ions. Current flow is balanced at the anode by the O^- space charge field exceeding the applied field, because the electron donation from the metal to the non-bridging oxygen atoms causes Na^+ diffusion.

It has often not been made clear in the literature but the reader must take care to differentiate between the current decay due to dielectric absorption and decay due to *free* ion migration. We shall now briefly consider some practical examples of *apparent*

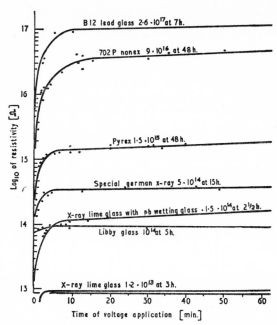

FIG. 9.1 EFFECT OF DIELECTRIC ABSORPTION CURRENT ON THE APPARENT RESISTIVITY OF DRY GLASS AS A FUNCTION OF THE TIME AFTER APPLYING VOLTAGE (*After Bronson, see Hull*, 1932)

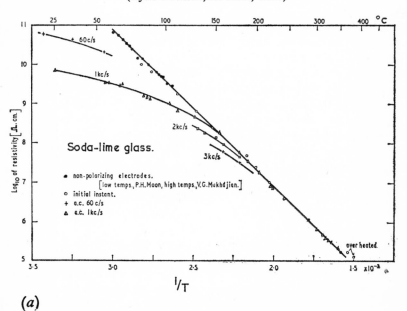

(*a*)

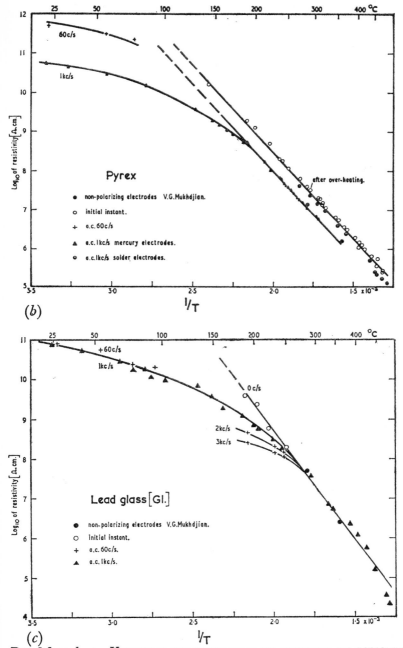

FIG. 9.2 *a, b, c,* VOLUME RESISTIVITIES OF GLASS MEASURED BY DIFFERENT METHODS UNDER CONDITIONS WHERE DIELECTRIC ABSORPTION IS NEGLIGIBLE
(*After Robinson,* 1932)

conduction in the region of dielectric absorption and *true* conduction arising from free ion transport.

The volume electrical resistivities of a series of dry glasses have been determined as a function of time by Bronson (see Hull, 1932) and are shown in Fig. 9.1. When d.c. measurements are made the resistivity is *apparently* low initially and rises with time to an almost constant value as shown in Fig. 9.1. It is evident from the figure that applying a voltage to an insulator sometime before use will subsequently provide a higher leakage resistance.

A.C. and d.c. conductivity. When the glass temperature is above 100°c the absorption current vanishes quickly but the conduction current may also fall off as sodium (or hydrogen) ions are removed from the anode. Robinson (1932) used baths of fused sodium salts as non-polarizing electrodes which supplied sodium to the glass and prevented the formation of a high resistance layer. The slow rate of current decay obtained with this method made it possible to apply the voltage for a known time interval ($\frac{1}{5}$ sec) and measure with a ballistic galvanometer the quantity of electricity passed by the sample. Robinson also determined the resistivity from the initial (instantaneous) current and made measurements using alternating currents of various frequencies. His results for three different glasses are shown in Figs. 9.2(*a*), (*b*) and (*c*). Robinson has included in these graphs the results of Moon who used sodium thiosulphate electrodes with soda-lime glass and those of Mukhdjian and Keely (see Schönborn, 1924) who used electrodes of sodium nitrite with all three glasses.

The d.c. measurements show that the resistivity of the four glasses has a temperature dependence which follows equation (1) on p. 450. The writer has calculated the activation energies from Robinson's curves and the results for E in terms of kcal g mol^{-1} are as follows: soda-lime glass – 18·4; Pyrex – 20·2; lead glass G1 – 24·8; fused quartz – 27·6. The value for the soda-lime glass agrees quite well with those given in Chapter 3 derived from the electrical conductivity and diffusion rates of Na$^+$ ions, *i.e.* 17·8 and 18·3 kcal g mol^{-1} respectively. The high activation energy for silica agrees with the known difficulty Na$^+$ ions have in diffusing through its structure.

Resistivities measured with a.c. become progressively less than the d.c. values as the temperature of the glass is lowered and the frequency is raised. The decrease in the resistivity arises from the dielectric absorption current becoming predominant over the conduction current when the time of current flow between field reversals is much shorter than that of the transient absorption current.

3. SURFACE CONDUCTIVITY OF GLASS IN HUMID ATMOSPHERES

The electrical conductivity of glass exposed to the atmosphere is usually much higher at the surface than in depth and the surface conductivity rises with the relative humidity. From this and other observations it was inferred by Faraday (1830) that the surface conductivity of glass was due to adsorbed water which could form an electrolyte with alkali dissolved from the glass.

The sorption of water by glass is fully dealt with in Chapter 4. Briefly, the amount of water adsorbed per unit area by a glass surface depends in a complex manner on the degree to which the surface has been roughened by chemical treatment or weathering, the composition of the surface layers, the temperatures of the glass and atmosphere, and the relative humidity. Weathered glass may have had alkali removed from the surface by leaching or alkaline salts left on the glass. A silica layer on aged glass may be porous but if the glass has been heat treated and the silica film sintered then the surface will have a reduced moisture content and alkali ions will diffuse more slowly to the surface.

Geddes (1936) has studied the conductivity of freshly broken glass surfaces and found that in dry air or clean water vapour there was no appreciable surface leakage. Nor was there appreciable leakage when clean water vapour was admitted to a vacuum chamber containing freshly fractured glass! In ordinary air the surface resistance was initially low, then increased rapidly and finally fell again to a value slightly higher than that of the newly exposed surface. Geddes believed that atmospheric contaminants were responsible for conduction. However, such changes in the surface resistivity suggest that the glass surface layers were being chemically and structurally altered.

It is shown in Chapter 4 that water vapour is not physically adsorbed to silica unless chemisorbed OH^- groups have already formed on the surface. If the silica has been exposed to saturated water vapour then chemisorption can occur from a condensed water layer. However, if the water vapour is unsaturated and the adsorbent a fresh surface it may take a long time for the impinging molecules to find the reactive surface sites. Such an effect has been observed by the writer for adsorption of water on a fracture surface of soda-lime glass at low pressure, see page 336. There is need to study the conductivity of fresh glass surfaces under conditions of known temperature and water vapour pressure.

Kuznetsov (1953) has studied the effect of humidity on the surface conductivity of a number of glasses and silica. He considers that the conductivity of water absorbed by porous layers of pure silica is enhanced by the presence of a double electrical layer of ions at the liquid/solid boundary. Further that porous silica layers on glass contain water which dissolves components of the glass forming an electrolyte of high conductivity.

Kuznetsov prepared porous silica films on a silica substrate and baked them at 700°c to remove water and organic material. He found that the surface conductivity of 5000 Å thick layers in dry air was 10^{-17} Ω^{-1}/square, which was close to that of unfilmed silica. When exposed to water vapour the surface conductivity rose by 15–20 times over a relative humidity range of 33–98%. Maximum increase occurred between R.H. = 33–60%. Knowing the thickness of the films the specific conductivity χ_v of the layer could be found. This was about 10^{-5} Ω^{-1} cm^{-1} for a film exposed to 98% R.H. The films were believed to have pores of about 150 Å dia. and occupy 20% of the film volume. If the pores were completely filled with moisture at 98% relative humidity and the water was responsible for conduction then the volume conductivity of the water would have been about 5×10^{-5} Ω^{-1} cm^{-1}. The latter value is $8 - 10$ times the conductivity of distilled water and Kuznetsov believed that this was due to conduction in an adsorbed layer of ions at the interface. It is equally possible that adsorption of OH^- ions by the silica dissociated the water and released H^+ ions in the solution. Thus Lindenthal (1952) has found that adding quartz powder to distilled water raises the electrical conductivity of the water.

Also, it is known that quartz grains render water acid out of proportion to the low solubility of quartz, which is further evidence for the release of H^+ ions by chemisorption of OH^- ions.

When the surfaces of silicate glasses are leached by acids or weathering the surface layer is not necessarily pure silica neither does the layer prevent completely the leaching of alkali from the underlying material. Kuznetsov leached a glass (TK-5) in an acetic acid solution. The pores formed in the silica surface layer were believed to have a radius of 15–20 Å and occupy a volume of 12–15% of the total volume of the film. The surface conductivity of a leached layer of 1300 Å thickness at R.H. = 98% was 5×10^{-10} Ω^{-1}/square giving a volume conductivity for the film of about 3×10^{-5} Ω^{-1} cm^{-1} and a volume conductivity of the solution in the pores of 2×10^{-4} Ω^{-1} cm^{-1}. The solution values varied between 40–160 times the conductivity of distilled water indicating the presence of hydrolysis products in the films.

As final evidence of the above theories Kuznetsov found that the temperature coefficient of electrical conductivity $[\Delta\chi/(\chi \Delta T) \times 100\%]$ at 20° indicated the presence of water on silica and electrolytes on glass. Thus the temperature coefficient for bulk glasses was between 19–25% degc^{-1} Ω^{-1}, whereas the value for the surface layers at 98% R.H. was 1·9–2·1, which agrees with 2·0 for electrolyte solutions. Similarly, the temperature coefficient for bulk silica was 25% degc^{-1} Ω^{-1} compared with a value of 2·4 for surface films, which was the same as that of water.

There is a similarity between curves of surface resistivity of glass as a function of the humidity and adsorption isotherms for water on glass (Fig. 9.3 and Fig. 4.11). Thus the rapid rise in surface leakage occurs at a relative humidity of about 50% coinciding with the adsorption of an *effective* monomolecular layer of water. However, the actual area for adsorption will depend on the degree to which the surface has been eroded and this would be limited for a freshly fractured surface. At high humidities a weathered or leached surface would presumably contain electrolyte in the surface pores.

Direct Current Measurement of Surface Leakage

Effect of relative humidity. Curtis (1915) has measured with direct current the surface leakage of a number of substances including silica, window plate and German glass (a soft glass tubing). He found, as shown in Fig. 9.3, that as the relative humidity reached values between 30–60% the surface resistivities fell rapidly. When the silica specimen was cleaned in chromic acid and distilled water its surface resistivity was much greater at high humidities. Clean silica can only adsorb a monomolecular layer of water on its surface and there is no alkali to form an electrolyte. Thus the 'unclean' specimens were probably contaminated with hygroscopic compounds condensed from the atmosphere which absorbed moisture

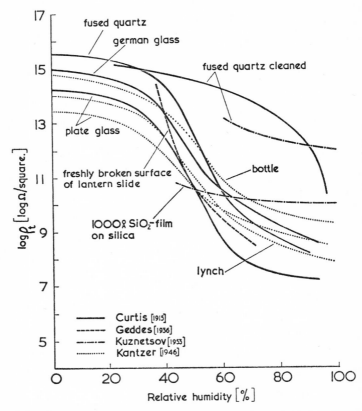

FIG. 9.3 SURFACE RESISTIVITY OF DIFFERENT MATERIALS AS A FUNCTION OF RELATIVE HUMIDITY AT 20–25°C

and these were removed by the cleaning. Silica insulators must be kept very clean and not handled if a high resistivity is to be obtained.

Kuznetsov (1953) investigated the effect of humidity on the surface resistivity of silica after chemical cleaning and baking at 700°c to remove contaminants. His results are plotted in the chain dotted curve in Fig. 9.3 and roughly agree with those of Curtis.

Also shown in Fig. 9.3 are the values of ρ_T measured by Geddes (1936) for a freshly broken surface of soda-lime glass exposed to water vapour in the atmosphere.

Effect of glass composition. One of the most thorough studies of the effect of humidity on the surface resistivity of different glasses was that of Fulda (1927). Glasses of different composition were

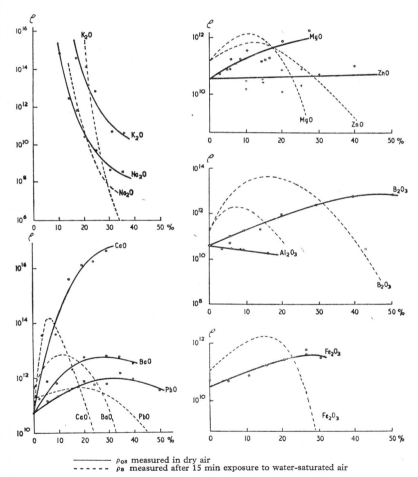

——— ρ_{os} measured in dry air
- - - - - ρ_S measured after 15 min exposure to water-saturated air

FIG. 9.4   RESISTIVITIES OF SODIUM SILICATE (18% Na_2O 82% SiO_2) GLASS AT 25°C AS A FUNCTION OF THE PERCENTAGE WEIGHT OF DIFFERENT OXIDES REPLACING THE SILICA (*After Fulda*, 1927)

prepared by replacing silica with different oxides in a sodium silicate glass containing by weight 18% Na_2O; 82% SiO_2. The glasses were heated at 300°–400°c and after cooling to 25°c the resistivities determined. Water-saturated air was then passed over the surface for 15 min and the resistivity remeasured. If in the first measurement the effect of surface conductance can be ignored then the surface resistivity is given by $1/\rho_s = 1/\rho_T - 1/\rho_{os}$. It has been contended that the time for which the glasses were exposed to moist air before measurement was too short for equilibrium to be reached. However, as shown further on, 15 min would be ample for condensed moisture to dissolve alkaline material on the glass surface and for leaching of the alkali in the interior to commence.

The results obtained by Fulda for ρ_{os} (full line) and ρ_s (dashed line) are given in Fig. 9.4 and show that with the exception of the alkaline oxides all other oxides added to the glass have an optimum concentration at which the surface resistivity reaches a maximum. Morey, when reviewing the above work, correctly cautions the reader that Fulda's results do not necessarily apply to sodium silicates of different binary composition or to glasses of more complex composition. However, it will be generally observed from the work reviewed in this chapter that for most commercially prepared glasses the presence of the alkaline oxides lowers the surface resistivity of glass whereas the inclusion of basic oxides or boron oxide increase the resistivity.

Surface electrolysis. It is well known that alkali is removed from glass by water. Thus Le Clerc (1954) has shown that the surface conductivity of glass increases rapidly during the first two to three hours exposure to humid conditions and attributed this to alkali ions migrating from the glass into the moist layer. As early as 1894 Kohlrausch and Heydweiller found that the conductivity of successive samples of water left in contact with a glass surface decreased and finally approached a constant low value. From this it can be deduced that leaching of alkali from glass by water should ultimately raise its surface resistivity in a humid atmosphere.

As the adsorbed water contains ions dissolved from the glass it will function as an electrolyte and measurement of the surface conductivity may greatly change the concentration of the ions in the solution near the electrodes. Thus if the rate of transport exceeds the rate of discharge concentration polarization will result and the conductivity will fall during measurement. Should the glass resist attack then the rate of electrolysis by a continuous d.c. current at room temperature may exceed the dissolution rate of ions from the glass. The measured surface conductivity will then decrease with time to a value limited by the rate of ion diffusion from the glass interior to the surface.

In exceptional cases the passage of a small d.c. current through the surface layers of a glass can accelerate leaching. Edge and Old-field (1960) give the following graphic example of the disintegration of a G.E.C. borosilicate glass SBN 124 containing by weight 66·0% SiO_2; 2·0% Al_2O_3; 4·0% Na_2O; 3·0% K_2O; 24% B_2O_3; 1% minor constituents. A glass tube of 0·5 mm thickness had electrodes sealed into each end giving a 5 mm conducting path-length. When a potential difference of 55 V was applied to the electrodes under tropical conditions at 55°c the glass completely broke down. Without the applied potential the glass survived the same conditions with only partial surface leaching.

Edge and Oldfield have measured the surface conductivity of a G.E.C. high thermal expansion glass (C.S.G.3) containing 29·4 mol % of alkali oxides which is used for sealing copper lead-in electrodes. Measurements were made on a glass button into which were sealed two copper electrodes about 1·23 mm apart. The specimens were exposed to static and flowing humid air in a test chamber held at 18°–20°c. The relative humidity of the moist air stream was about 90%. Resistances were measured at a voltage of 85 V d.c. using a 20 million megohmmeter.† To avoid polarization effects the test voltage was applied for 10 sec for each measurement and the polarity reversed during measurement. The minimum resistance value reached during the 10 sec test was recorded. When the polarization effect was studied the 85 V d.c. were applied continuously.

The variation in surface conductivity with time of exposure is shown in Figs. 9.5(*a*)–(*g*). Curves marked *A* are for static air and curves marked *B* for streaming moist air. Curves marked *C* show the behaviour in streaming moist air when the test voltage is continuously applied. The first set of curves (*a*) cover a 20 min exposure in the humidity box. The specimens were then transferred to a dry box for 5 min and then replaced in moist air for remeasurement as in Fig. 9.5(*b*). This procedure was repeated and the results are plotted in Fig. 9.5(*c*). The curves show that the act of exposing the

---

† Made by Electronic Instruments, Ltd.

glass to moist air permanently affects the surface so that after it has been dried it rapidly reabsorbs moisture in humid air.

The results in Figs. 9.5(d)–(g) are for specimens which were alternately exposed to streaming moist air (B) and static air (A) with an intermediate 5 min drying period.

Edge and Oldfield analyse the curves in Fig. 9.5 for short periods of exposure to a humid atmosphere as follows:

(*i*) There is an initial rapid increase in the surface conductivity during which the sorption of an aqueous layer is tending towards completion and the partial pressure of water vapour in the air is approaching its saturation value.

(*ii*) This is followed by a more gradual increase due to attack of the glass surface layers by the aqueous adsorbate.

The time taken for (*i*) to reach equilibrium is about 5 min in static air and 1–1½ min for streaming air. After this stage process (*ii*) is dominant and the conductivity increases linearly with time. The slope of this part of the curve is a measure of the initial rate at which the adsorbate attacks the glass. Extrapolation of the linear part of the curve to zero time gives an intercept p on the conductivity axis which is roughly a measure of the amount of 'free' alkali initially present on the glass in the form of alkali hydroxide or carbonate due to weathering or processing. Similar behaviour to the foregoing is shown by the variation in the electrical conductivity of water in which alkali glasses are immersed as shown in Chapter 3.

The variation of the electrical conductivity of a glass surface in a humid atmosphere may now be defined in terms of χ_{s0} the initial conductivity and $d\chi_s/dt$ the rate of change of conductivity occurring during process (*ii*) above. Shown in Table 9.1 are values of the foregoing terms calculated by Edge and Oldfield from the curves in Fig. 9.5. The table shows that χ_{s0} progressively increases as the specimens are exposed to water and dried leaving the leached alkali on the surface to rapidly absorb water vapour on re-exposure. The consequence of this behaviour is that $d\chi_s/dt$ decreases with increasing time of previous exposure.

It is obvious from curve C in Fig. 9.5 that polarization due to migration of the leached ions to the electrodes has masked the rise in conductivity which should result from the adsorption of water and leaching of ions.

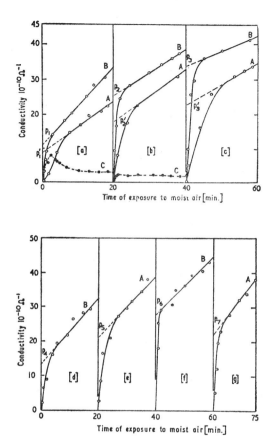

A—static air; B—humid air stream; C—test volts applied continuously. Curves [d] and [f] were measured in moist air and after drying. Curves [e] and [g] in static air

FIG. 9.5   EFFECT OF SUCCESSIVE 20 min PERIODS OF MEASUREMENT OF SURFACE CONDUCTIVITY OF HIGH ALKALI SEALING GLASS (*After Edge and Oldfield*, 1960)

Effect of alkali leaching. Edge and Oldfield lowered the surface conductivity of a high alkali glass several hundred times by leaching the surface and baking the glass. Heat treatment of leached glass sinters the enriched surface layer of silica and lowers the rate of diffusion of alkali ions from the glass interior to the surface. With a high alkali glass prolonged leaching may result in the surface layer crazing on heat treatment because the thermal expansion of the glass interior and surface differ greatly. Crazed surfaces have a high conductivity because of their large surface area for adsorption and exposure of the ions in the glass interior. Edge and Oldfield found that the optimum conditions for producing an uncrazed surface coating was to treat the glass in water at 50°c for 2 hours and then heat it to 180°c for 20 min. During the baking alkali ions migrated to the surface but the initially low surface conductivity could be regained by washing in hot water. In fact once the sintered surface layer had been formed it could be further freed from alkali and compacted by again immersing the glass in boiling water and baking at 250°c for 20 min.

Table 9.1

Effect of exposure time on χ_{s0} and $d\chi_s/dt$ for partially leached samples of high alkali glass

(*After Edge and Oldfield, 1960*)

Intercept χ_{s0} $(10^{-10}\,\Omega^{-1})$		$d\chi_s/dt$ $(10^{-10}\,\Omega^{-1}\text{min}^{-1})$	*Method*	*Time of previous exposure* (min)
P_1	11	1·1	B	0
P_2	26	0·65	B	20
P_3	33	0·47	B	40
$P_{1'}$	10	0·75	A	0
$P_{2'}$	19	0·65	A	20
$P_{3'}$	23	0·62	A	40
P_4	14	1·0	B	0
P_5	21	0·92	A	20 method B
P_6	29	0·82	B	{20 method B {20 method A
P_7	22·5	0·77	A	{40 method B {20 method A

Note. Conductivity measured between copper electrodes 1·23 mm apart in a glass button.

Using the leaching technique Edge and Oldfield measured the values of χ_{s0} and $(d\chi_s/dt)$ for the range of sealing glasses given in Table 9.2. Their results indicate that the initial concentration of surface alkali and initial rate of attack decrease for the glasses tested in the order: high alkali; soda; lead; borosilicate. If the reader consults the section in Chapter 3 which deals with the estimation of the attack of glass by water in terms of the alkali dissolved he will see

Table 9.2

Summary of surface conductivity properties of a
range of sealing glasses

(*After Edge and Oldfield, 1960*)

Type of glass † and metal electrodes	Total alkali Mol % (Na_2O+K_2O)	Treatment of seals	χ_{so}		$d\chi_s/dt$
			t	$10^{-10}\,\Omega^{-1}$	$(10^{-10}\,\Omega^{-1}min^{-1})$
C.S.G.3. High alkali (pure copper)	29·4	None	—	800	1000
		Leached t min at 50°c, baked	5	—	0·4
		Boiled for 15 min	10	—	0·13
		and baked	30	—	0·09
		again	50	—	0·07
			70	—	0·05
			120	—	0·01
			150	—	0·0015
		Onset of surface	{180	—	0·13
		mosaic crazing	{230	—	> 300
X8 Soda (26% Cr; 74% Fe)	16·3	None	—	200	100
		Rinsed and dried	—	90	2·5
		Leached and baked	—	0·15	0·03
LI Lead oxide (copper clad 42% Ni; 58% Fe)	13·3	None	—	40	10
		Leached and baked	—	~0·05	0·01
SBN 124 Borosilicate (28% Ni; 16% Co; 56% Fe)	6·4	None	—	1·0	0·1
		Rinsed and dried	—	0·5	0·005
		Leached and baked	—	0·025	~0·001

† Made by G.E.C. Ltd.

that the attack and surface conductivity are roughly in similar order
to the alkali contents of the glasses.

Powdered glass. Using powdered glass with large surface area Pike
and Hubbard (1957) have found that at high relative humidities the
resistance of a compressed powder may fall to an equilibrium value
whereas the water sorbed continues to rise. The glass powder
(-30, $+50$ U.S. Standard Sieve), was clamped in a polystyrene
tube between end terminals of copper turnings and humid air was
blown through the tube. The effects of polarization during resistance measurement were reduced by using a special ohmmeter.
Shown in Fig. 9.6 are the resistance and water sorption values of
several glasses as a function of the time of exposure at 98% R.H.
The curves show that the resistivity is not solely dependent on the
amount of water sorbed but must also be influenced by the amount
of material dissolved from the glass. There are several possible

explanations for the resistivity reaching a constant value as will be shown by consulting Chapter 3. Powdered glass initially releases its alkali into solution more rapidly than bulk material because of its large surface area. Thus the resistivity could fall to a constant value, although water sorption continues, because the leaching rate

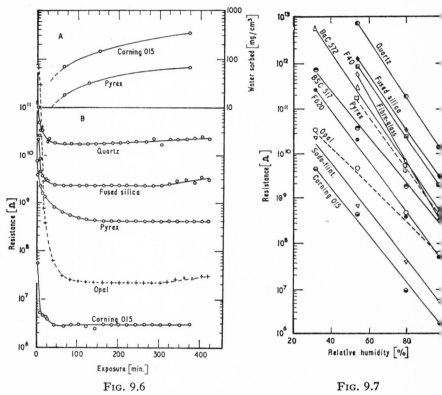

FIG. 9.6   FIG. 9.7

ELECTRICAL RESISTANCE AND WATER SORPTION OF SEVERAL AGGREGATES
(*After Pike and Hubbard*, 1957)

A—typical curves illustrating continued sorption of water with time; B—surface resistivity of five aggregates measured at 98% R.H.

rapidly falls to zero. Alternatively the silica dissolved by the alkaline adsorbate may reduce the rate of attack and the release of alkali as shown in Fig. 3.8. It is also by no means conclusive that polarization did not occur.

Shown in Fig. 9.7 are the resistivities of a range of glass powders as a function of humidity. These results roughly agree with the water sorption values for the same powders shown in Fig. 4.9. The compositions of some of the glasses used in the above tests are given in Table 3.8 and those of the remaining glasses by weight are as follows: Corning 015 – 22% Na_2O; 6% CaO; 72% SiO_2; F40 glass – 30% BaO; 20% TiO_2; 50% SiO_2; soda-flint – 20% Na_2O; 20% PbO; 60% SiO_2. The opal (hydrous silica) used contained 93% SiO_2.

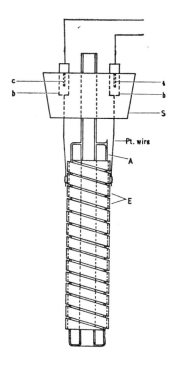

FIG. 9.8   PYREX TEST GLASS
AND ELECTRODES USED BY
YAGER AND MORGAN (1931)

ALTERNATING CURRENT SURFACE LEAKAGE

The alternating current surface leakage of E.J. Pyrex† glass was

---

† Chemically resistant glass.

determined by Yager and Morgan (1931) at different temperatures and relative humidities. Measurements were made using a Pyrex tube, $1\frac{3}{8}$ in. dia by 8 in. long, on which was deposited two adjacent metal spirals, each $\frac{1}{2}$ in. wide. The metal electrodes were 100 cm long and separated by an uncoated glass surface of 0·25 mm width. The surface leakage apparatus is shown in Fig. 9.8. The metal spirals were initially formed by silvering and thickened by copper and gold electro-plating. Connections were made to the metal spirals by platinum wires sealed in the glass. The inner wall of the tube was sealed off at A to prevent electrical conduction over its surface. The projection of the inner tube was used for holding the test apparatus in a hard rubber stopper S which fitted into the humidity chamber. The exhaust vapours passed out of the apparatus through the inner tube.

With the conductance head described a change in conductivity as small as 5×10^{-14} Ω^{-1} could be measured which corresponded to the calculated conductance of a monomolecular layer of water.

Measurements were made of the electrical conductance and capacitance at 25 and $50°\text{c} \pm 0·05°$ at 1, 3, 10, 30, 50, 75, 100 kc/sec and at different relative humidities from 0 to 96%. The electrical conductance of the Pyrex test head measured at zero humidity before and after exposure at different relative humidities was repeatable. From this it could be inferred that the change in volume conductivity with relative humidity was insignificant compared to the large change which occurred in the conductance of the surface.

The surface conductivity χ_s and the surface capacitance C_s were obtained by subtracting the volume quantities χ_{os} and C_{os} measured at zero humidity from the total measured quantities χ_T and C_T.

Surface conductivity. Initial tests were made to find the time taken for a surface to come into equilibrium at a given relative humidity. At high humidities several hours were required even for approaching an equilibrium condition but a really stable state could never be attained. Shown in Fig. 9.9 is a curve of the total surface conductivity as a function of time measured at 25°c, 95% R.H. and 30 kc/sec; it took about half an hour for a constant humidity to be reached in the test chamber.

Surface conductivity values derived from the measured values of χ_{os} and χ_T have been plotted in Figs. 9.10 and 9.11 as a function of the relative humidity and frequency respectively.

The d.c. surface resistivity curves in Fig. 9.3 reported by Curtis differ from those in Fig. 9.10 because they tend to approach a constant resistivity at high humidities whereas the a.c. measurements show a continuous fall in the resistivity. The d.c. values are almost certainly limited by polarization.

Effect of glass temperature. The surface conductivity for a given humidity is greater at 50° than at 25°c. Yager and Morgan attribute this to the greater conductivity of the adsorbed layer at 50°c because they state that the amount of water sorbed at the higher temperature can be expected to be less than at 25°c.† Raising the

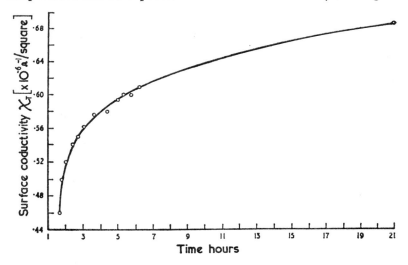

FIG. 9.9 CHANGE OF TOTAL SURFACE CONDUCTIVITY OF PYREX GLASS WITH TIME MEASURED AT 30 kc/sec AND 96% RELATIVE HUMIDITY AT 25°C (*After Yager and Morgan*, 1931)

temperature would increase the rate at which alkali diffused from the glass. Edge and Oldfield (1958) have found that increasing the temperature from 20° to 90°c for a glass with an alkali oxide content of 30% mol % raised the initial d.c. resistivity in humid air to almost that of a dry sample. The influence of temperature on surface conductivity is complex. Thus Bronson (see Hull, 1932) found that

---

† It was not clear from the paper whether the relative humidity referred to a saturated vapour pressure at one temperature (25°) when the sample temperature was changed from 25° to 50°c. From these remarks the latter appears confirmed.

the resistivity of silica rose a hundred times as the temperature was increased only 12°C, but the resistivity of Pyrex rose to a maximum at about 10°C above ambient and then decreased with further rise in temperature.

Influence of frequency. The curves in Fig. 9.11 show a dependence of the surface conductivity on frequency whilst the conductivity of

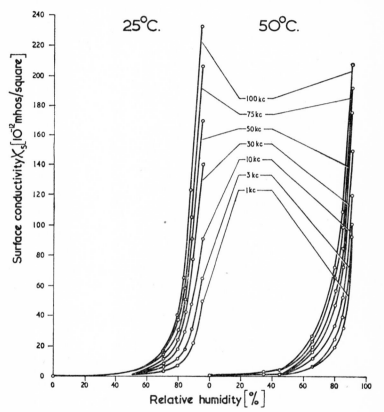

FIG. 9.10 SURFACE CONDUCTIVITY OF PYREX GLASS AT 25 AND 50°C FOR VARIOUS FREQUENCIES AS A FUNCTION OF RELATIVE HUMIDITY (*After Yager and Morgan,* 1931)

water and dilute solutions is independent of frequency over the range 1 to 100 kc/sec. Yager and Morgan proposed two possible mechanisms for the observed frequency dependence; these were (*i*) the water molecules in the adsorbed film were orientated by surface forces and hence might show a change in conductivity with frequency due to different relaxation times and (*ii*) electrode polarization might have occurred due either to chemical reactions

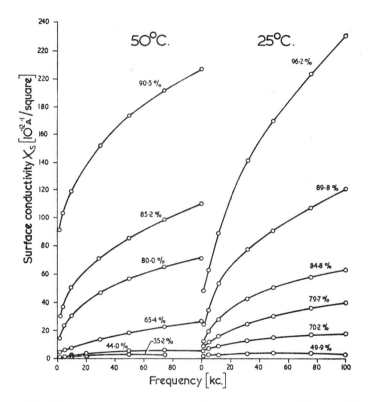

FIG. 9.11 SURFACE CONDUCTIVITY OF PYREX GLASS AT 25 AND 50°C FOR VARIOUS RELATIVE HUMIDITIES AS A FUNCTION OF FREQUENCY (*After Yager and Morgan*, 1931)

at the electrodes or to the rate of transport of ions to the electrodes being much higher than their rate of discharge.

The voltage gradient used in the above experiments was 200 V/cm. Tests were made of the volume conductance and capacitance of *water* in a gold-plated condenser operated at 80 V/cm and these showed an increase of conductance and a decrease in capacitance with increasing frequency which was undoubtedly due to electrode polarization. The latter results indicate that the surface conductivity of glass, as determined from the dimensions of the test gap, is not an absolute value.

Surface capacity. The surface capacity values measured at different relative humidities at 25°c are shown in Fig. 9.12. The curves have

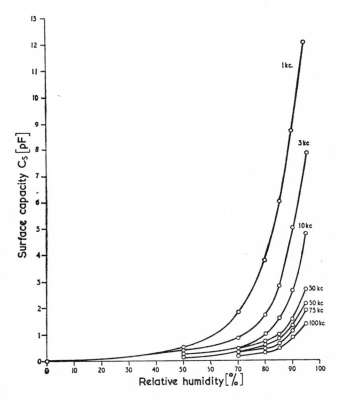

FIG. 9.12 SURFACE CAPACITY VALUES OF PYREX MEASURED AT 25°C FOR VARIOUS FREQUENCIES AS A FUNCTION OF RELATIVE HUMIDITY (*After Yager and Morgan*, 1931)

the same general form as the corresponding conductivity curves but the effect of frequency is reversed. It should be noted that both χ_s and C_s directly depend on the thickness of the adsorbed film.

The total power factor, *i.e.* of glass plus adsorbed water, was found from the relation

$$\cos \theta_T = \frac{\chi_T}{\sqrt{\chi_T^2 + \omega^2 C_T^2}}$$

and is plotted in Fig. 9.13 as a function of the relative humidity at 25°c. The power factor at a given humidity is lowest at the highest

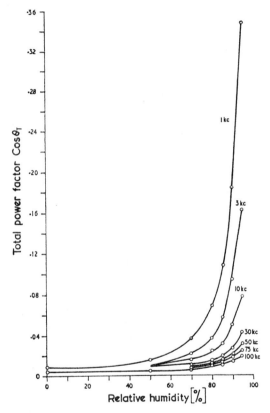

FIG. 9.13 TOTAL POWER FACTOR OF PYREX MEASURED AT 25°C FOR VARIOUS FREQUENCIES AS A FUNCTION OF RELATIVE HUMIDITY (*After Yager and Morgan*, 1931)

frequencies. The ratio of the total power factor to that of the Pyrex glass alone is given in Table 9.3 and it can be seen that the adsorbed water greatly increases the power factor at low frequencies and high humidities.

Table 9.3

Ratio of total power factor to power factor of dry Pyrex

(After Yager and Morgan, 1931)

Frequency (kc/sec)	% Relative humidity						
	25°C				50°C		
	50	80	90	96	44	80	90
1	1·43	8·03	21·82	41·73	1·21	12·51	49·40
30	1·07	2·18	4·57	7·46	1·08	2·76	6·55
100	1·01	1·58	2·76	4·35	1·07	1·92	3·54

4. PREVENTION OF SURFACE LEAKAGE BY SURFACE TREATMENT

WAX TREATMENT

One method of lowering the surface conductivity of glass is to coat the surface with a water repellent material which will prevent the formation of a continuous water layer. Waxes have been used for this purpose (Cohn and Guest, 1944). Thus Ceresin has a total surface resistivity ρ_T of about 8×10^{16} Ω/square which remains constant at relative humidities between 30–90%. Paraffin wax has a value of ρ_T equal to 10^{15} Ω/square at R.H. $= 30\%$ which falls to 5×10^{14} Ω/square at R.H. $= 90\%$. Hou (1938) found that the surface conductivity of fused quartz was *raised* by a hundred times at all values of relative humidity after it had been dipped in ceresin wax. The difference in the coefficient of expansion of the wax and the silica may have resulted in the wax cracking on cooling producing microscopic surface flaws which held water molecules. Meakins (1950) has used quaternary ammonium compounds such as alkyltrimethylammonium bromide on glass in place of paraffin wax, because the hydrophobic layer is held to the glass by a polar terminal. These coatings are less effective than the silicones discussed below but they may be of value where it is desirable to avoid acid conditions during film formation.

SILICONE TREATMENT

It has been shown in Chapters 3 and 7 that glass can be rendered water repellent by the application of silicone compounds, which form chemisorbed layers on the glass. The SiO-groups of the silicone adhere to the glass surface and continue the glass structure whilst the non-polar and hydrophobic CH$_3$-groups extend outwards from the adsorbed layer. The silicone layer may be applied in one of two principal ways. Thus one may use organosilicon chlorides which react with water adsorbed to the glass, thereby releasing hydrochloric acid and exposing the surface atoms which chemisorb a silicone layer. Alternatively one may treat the glass with a silicone fluid and remove the adsorbed water by heating the glass.†

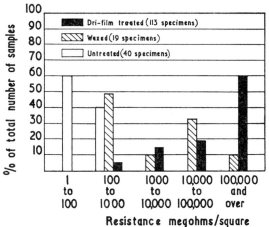

FIG. 9.14 SURFACE RESISTIVITY OF UNGLAZED STEATITE COIL FORMERS WHEN TREATED WITH WAX AND SILICONES AND EXPOSED IN SATURATED WATER VAPOUR (*After Norton*, 1944)

Norton (1944) treated steatite coil formers with methylchlorosilane and found that the resultant surface resistivity in a saturated atmosphere of water was higher than that attained by waxing the surface as shown in Fig. 9.14. Norton also observed, as shown in Fig. 9.15, that the resistivity of a silicone treated steatite former rose more rapidly when the relative humidity was decreased from 100 to 50%. Water condensed on silicone treated surfaces is in the form of small discrete droplets, which have a large area to volume ratio, and evaporate faster than a continuous film.

---

† Midland Silicones Ltd. (London) and Dow Corning Corporation (Michigan) have prepared technical reports on the silicone treatment of glass for electrical purposes.

31

Johannsen and Torok (1946) have treated Pyrex chemical resistant glass by dipping in a dilute solution of dimethylsilicone in a non-flammable solvent and afterwards baking to fix a film of silicone on the surface. The glasses were cleaned by boiling in distilled water and heating at 450°c. They were then dipped in a 2% solution of a liquid silicone (DC200) in carbon tetrachloride or perchloroethylene with a viscosity of 1000 centistokes. After

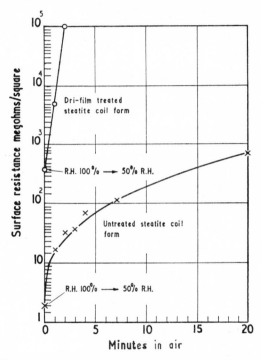

FIG. 9.15 TIME TAKEN FOR STEATITE TO REACH EQUILIBRIUM SURFACE RESISTIVITY AS CONDENSED MIXTURE EVAPORATES (*After Norton*, 1944)

evaporation of the solvent at 100°c for 30 min the specimens were baked at an optimum temperature of 300°c for 30 min. Specimens prepared in this way had a resistivity above 10^{12} Ω after 11 days in salt water, whereas waxed samples dropped in resistivity immediately they were immersed. The power factor of specimens exposed to water was improved by silicone treatment.

Hunter *et al.* (1947) have studied the effect on the surface resistivity of treating glass with different silicone compounds and stearic acid and afterwards heating the glass for 15 min at different temperatures. Measurements were made on microscope slides of 2 cm width with silver electrodes 1·5 cm apart. The applied potential was 500 V and the relative humidity 50%. The resistivity of the untreated glass was 10^8–10^9 Ω and the values obtained after treatment at different temperatures are shown in Fig. 9.16; to obtain values in terms of ρ_s the resistivities should be multiplied by 2/1·5.

Hunter *et al.* found that when the contact angle θ for water on glass fell below 50°–60° the surface resistivity was reduced by a

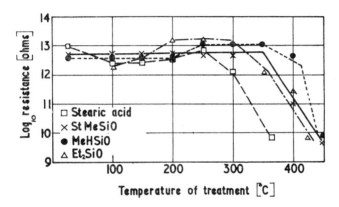

FIG. 9.16 RESISTIVITY OF MICROSCOPE SLIDES AFTER TREATMENT WITH VARIOUS ORGANO-SILICA COMPOUNDS AT DIFFERENT TEMPERATURES (*After Hunter et al.*, 1947)

factor of 10^4. There did not appear to be any correlation between θ and ρ_s for $\theta > 60°$; the resistivities were much the same whether $\theta = 70°$ or 110°. Using equation (4) in Chapter 6 it can be shown that a contact angle of 50°–60° should correspond to a surface coverage of about 75% of a monomolecular layer of water when R.H. = 100% and this is apparently sufficient to greatly decrease ρ_s. It is improbable that a silicone treated glass surface would be free from flaws and adsorbed water molecules may be densely packed in certain regions. As shown in the next section, the presence of alkali ions in the glass surface is ultimately responsible for the breakdown of silicone films in humid atmospheres and the adsorbed water molecules would tend to migrate where the alkali concentration is highest.

Meakins *et al.* (1950) found that silicone layers formed by heating glass for one hour at 250°C in contact with silicone compounds produced the most stable insulating layers when the glass had been initially cleaned with chromic acid. If the silicone compound was reactive, *e.g.* ethyl or methylchlorosilane, vigorous cleaning was not essential.

When silicones are applied to alkali glasses the alkali ions are still able to diffuse through the silicone film, but a continuous layer

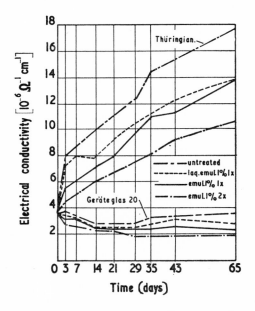

FIG. 9.17   CONDUCTIVITY AS A FUNCTION OF TIME OF DOUBLE DISTILLED WATER IN SILICONE TREATED FLASKS OF THÜRINGIAN AND GERÄTEGLAS 20. THE FLASKS WERE HEAT TREATED AFTER COATING WITH WATER EMULSIONS OF SILICONE OIL AND SILICONE LACQUER (*After Wessel*, 1958)

of electrolyte is unable to form on the silicone film in a humid atmosphere. If, however, a silicone treated specimen is immersed in water then the electrical conductivity of the water will rise as the alkali is leached from the glass.

Wessel (1958) silicone treated 250 ml flasks of Thüringian glass (soda-lime silicate with $\simeq 4\%$ Al_2O_3) and Jenaer Geräteglas 20 (sodium borosilicate with $\simeq 11\%$ ZnO and 4% Al_2O_3). The flasks were filled with double distilled water and the electrical conductivity of the water measured after different times at room temperature is given in Fig. 9.17. The results for the Thüringian flask show that the rate of change of the conductivity of the water is the same for the treated and untreated glass after about three days. Presumably the silicone film inhibits the rapid dissolution of the alkali ions on or near to the glass surface but does not decrease their diffusion.

The conductivity of the water in contact with treated and untreated Geräteglas first decreases and then very slowly rises. It is shown in Chapter 3 that dissolution of boron oxide from sodium borosilicate glass tends to neutralize the alkaline solution formed from leached alkali and this protects the silica network from attack.

The silicone treatment of glasses used for sealing metal lead-in electrodes has been studied by Edge and Oldfield (1958). They found that a high expansion glass (G.E.C. C.S.G.3 used with copper electrodes) containing about 30 mol % of mixed alkali oxides had a low surface resistivity in humid atmospheres. The glass surface was treated with sulphur dioxide at 150°–250°c to lower its alkali content as described in Chapter 3 and the samples leached in boiling water and baked at 150°–250°c. Unfortunately, the sulphur dioxide reacted with the copper lead-in electrodes and ρ_s was not reproducible.

Edge and Oldfield silicone treated the sealing glass, using various methods of application. They found that films prepared by heat curing silicone fluids in non-flammable solvents or from hydrolized methyl-chlorosilanes rapidly broke down under tropical conditions. Films prepared from low temperature curing fluids dissolved in methyl ethyl ketone or emulsified in water and from a water soluble salt of a silicone withstood 100 hours in a tropical test before breakdown.

To improve the performance of the silicone treated surfaces the alkali was leached from the glass in warm water care being taken, as discussed on p. 469, to see that surface crazing did not subsequently occur when the glass was heated during silicone treatment.

When the sealing glass was leached and baked and then treated with a 2% solution of a methylchlorosilane in carbon tetrachloride it maintained a low surface leakage after 1000 hours under tropical test. The tropical test consisted of exposing the glass to 95% R.H. at 55°c for 12 hours then cooling to room temperature and staying there without the humidity source for 12 hours giving a 24-hour total cycle.

In a later paper Edge and Oldfield (1960) showed that silicone films on the sealing glasses soda (X8) and lead (LI) (listed in Table 9.2) were more stable under tropical test if the alkali was leached as described above. Silicone films were most stable on a borosilicate sealing glass (SBN 124) when the glass was unleached or at most washed in cold water and dried at 80°c. Attempts to leach the surface in hot water had a deleterious effect on the tropical life of a subsequently desposited silicone film.

The initial surface resistivities of all of the four types of sealing glass after silicone treatment under optimum conditions was $> 2 \times 10^{12}$ Ω. After the glasses had been tropical tested for 2000 hours their resistivities had fallen as follows: high alkali $- 10^9 - 10^{10}$ Ω; soda $- 10^8 - 10^9$ Ω; lead $10^{10} - 10^{11}$ Ω; borosilicate $- 10^{11} - 10^{12}$ Ω. For most practical purposes the life of the silicone film can be taken as 2000 hours before failure.

5. CONDUCTION IN REDUCED SURFACE LAYERS

HYDROGEN TREATMENT

When silicate glasses are heated in hydrogen certain metal oxides may be reduced producing a dark surface film. The oxides of lead, bismuth and antimony, if present in glass, are readily reduced (see, for example, Randall and Leeds, 1929). Green and Blodgett (1948) studied the effect of heat treating in hydrogen glasses containing the above oxides for the purpose of producing electrical conduction in a thin surface layer. We shall now consider their work.

The samples were melted in an oxidizing atmosphere and nitrates were used in all batches to ensure oxidation. The glasses were poured into preheated graphite moulds, placed in an annealing furnace at 600°c, and cooled slowly for 12 hours. Bismuth oxide glasses which had been melted under highly oxidizing conditions were brownish when cooled but partial reduction could be avoided by adding 1.0% As_2O_3 to the glass. Each glass sample was cut into pieces 1 in. $\times$ 1 in. $\times \frac{1}{4}$ in. and lightly sandblasted because this surface finish gave the lowest and most consistent surface resistivities after hydrogen reduction. The samples were placed in an asbestos boat and exposed overnight to the reducing atmosphere of hydrogen in an electric furnace. One end of the boat was about 100°c hotter than the other.

Samples that had been treated at 330°–430°c ranged from almost no blackening at the lower temperature end to a very dense black coating at the high temperature end. Electrical conduction occurred in the reduced surface layer which was less than 0·001 in. thick and was enhanced with the rise in the content of the reducible oxide. Surface resistance values of 10^9–10^{10} Ω/square were obtained for reduced lead oxide glasses whereas resistances as low as 10^2–10^3 Ω/square were obtained for reduced lead oxide glasses containing bismuth oxide.

Effect of composition on conductivity

With lead oxide glasses a small conductivity was developed by hydrogen treatment when the lead oxide content was 30 mol % and the conductivity rose as the lead oxide was further increased. Reduced glasses containing only PbO and SiO_2 had a surface resistivity which could be roughly represented by the formula

$$\log \rho_s = 0·097C + 12·84$$

where C was the mol % of PbO. Substituting 8·3 mol % B_2O_3 for SiO_2 did not affect the above relation but 34·8 mol % of B_2O_3 greatly increased ρ_s. A lead borate glass with 88% by weight of lead oxide likewise gave no measurable conduction when reduced. Introduction of 5·8 mol % Al_2O_3 produced a glass with non-ohmic behaviour.

Replacement of silica by bismuth oxide in a simple SiO_2:PbO glass greatly reduced the resistance. Thus a silicate glass with a PbO content of about 30 mol % had a value of $\rho_s = 10^{10}$ Ω/square which fell to about 10^4 Ω/square when SiO_2 was replaced by 7 mol % of Bi_2O_3. Addition of bismuth oxide also resulted in glasses with the smallest variation in resistivity after reduction and permitted conduction in a much greater variety of compositions.

Lead-antimony oxide glasses also possessed low values of ρ_s after reduction. Thus a glass containing 30·9 mol % PbO; 11·8 mol % Sb_2O_3; 57·3 mol % SiO_2 had a surface resistivity of 10^6 Ω/square and when the Sb_2O_3 content was raised to about 27 mol % and the PbO content proportionally lowered ρ_s fell to only 20 Ω/square after reduction at 310°c.

Effect of heat treatment temperature

Most of the foregoing glass samples which developed high surface conductivities after hydrogen reduction exhibited optimum heat treatment temperatures for which the surface resistivity was lowest. Inspection of the tabular data shows that in the treatment range 250°–400°c the optimum temperature was roughly 300°–350°c.

If reduced specimens of lead oxide glasses were given a second treatment in hydrogen at high temperature for short periods many of the test glasses showed considerable reduction in resistivity. This

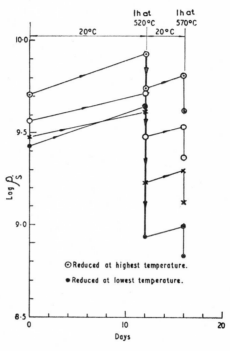

FIG. 9.18   EFFECT OF AGEING AND REHEATING TREATMENT ON RESISTIVITIES OF LEAD OXIDE GLASS (*After Green and Blodgett,* 1948)

effect was studied using a glass containing 32·5 mol % PbO; 61.3 mol % SiO_2; 6·2 mol % BaO. Samples of the glass were reduced at various temperatures for 18 hours and ρ_s measured on cooling and after standing at room temperature for 12 days. The samples were then reduced again at 520°c for 1 hour and after 4 days again heated to 570°c for 1 hour in hydrogen. The changes in the surface resistivities with age and subsequent reduction are presented in Fig. 9.18.

Shown in Fig. 9.19 are values of ρ_s of a lead silicate glass obtained after heat treatment under various conditions. This figure, which is discussed in detail in a later section, also shows an optimum heat treatment temperature.

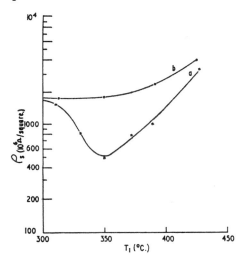

Curve a   samples treated in hydrogen at various temperatures T_1 for 16 h and then slowly raised to 520°c.
Curve b   samples heated to T_1 in nitrogen and from T_1 to 520°c in hydrogen
FIG. 9.19   SURFACE RESISTANCES OF LEAD SILICATE GLASS AFTER HYDROGEN REDUCTION (*After Blodgett*, 1951)

THEORY OF CONDUCTION IN REDUCED LAYER

Green and Blodgett advance the following theory for electrical conduction in the reduced glasses. When the reducible oxides of lead, antimony or bismuth react with hydrogen then free metal atoms are released in the glass and the hydrogen is removed as water. As the temperature of the glass is raised the chemical reduction of the oxide is increased but at the same time the mobility of the free metal atoms in the glass increases. Thus at high temperature the metal atoms liberated in the glass structure will be able to coalesce into droplets which are a more stable configuration than a uniform dispersal of metal atoms unassociated with the random SiO_2-network. Such a process explains the optimum temperatures at which lowest surface resistivities were obtained after prolonged heating and accounts for the rise in conductivity when lead oxide glasses were given additional heat treatment for short periods at very high temperature.

It is known that gold and copper atoms in glass are not strongly bound by the oxygen in the silica network and coalesce under surface tension forces to form droplets whose size depends upon the heat treatment. Also an oxygen active metal deposited as a thin layer on glass *in vacuo* will form discrete crystallites when heat treated if an interfacial oxide film of the metal is not present to bind it to the glass. Thus films of lead, bismuth and antimony on glass readily become discontinuous when heated. Armi (1943) found that the conductivities of Pb-films evaporated on glass held at liquid nitrogen temperature decreased as their temperature was raised above a critical value. The lead atoms were originally frozen into random positions and coalesced into isolated particles as their thermal mobility rose.

Before aggregation occurs the conductivity of a metal film on glass may initially rise as the temperature is raised because lattice defects produced during condensation are removed. Such an effect does not apparently occur with a reduced metallic layer because even before aggregation the metal atoms do not form a coherent metal sheet but are dispersed in the glass.

One may roughly calculate the distance between conducting ions using the following expressions:

$$\text{Molecular volume of glass} = \frac{\text{mol wt glass}}{\text{density}}$$

where the molecular weight of the glass is given by the sum of the mol fractions of the components times their molecular weights. The number of molecules of a given oxide in the molecular volume of the glass will be given by its molecular fraction times Avogadro's number. Thus, if the free atoms responsible for conduction were uniformly dispersed in the glass and occupied the same positions as in the untreated glass, the volume per ion for say a lead glass would be in cubic ångström units

$$\text{vol/Pb ion} = \frac{\text{mol vol of glass} \times 10^{24} \text{ Å}^3}{\text{mol fraction PbO} \times 6 \cdot 023 \times 10^{23}}$$

The distance between Pb ions will then equal the cube root of the volume they each occupy. Using the above expressions, Green and Blodgett calculated the interatomic distances for Pb ions in a range of lead silicate compositions. Their values are given in Table 9.4, together with the minimum resistance values obtained after reduction. Obviously if the lead oxide glass possessed a two-phase

Table 9.4

Calculated distances of lead atoms in lead silicate glass
and related conductivity of reduced glasses
(*After Green and Blodgett, 1948*)

Mol % PbO	Pb–Pb (Å)	ρ_s ($\Omega/square$)
24·9	5·48	10^{11}
33·3	4·98	10^{10}
44·7	4·51	$10^8 - 10^9$

structure, as suggested by Plate 9.1, then the interatomic distances given in the table would be average values.

Further evidence for electronic conduction in the reduced glasses is the fact that introduction of Na_2O into lead–antimony silicate glasses increases ρ_s for the reduced material, which is the opposite to what would be expected if the conduction was ionic. It is believed that the Na^+ ions act as traps for the electrons in their jumps between free metal atoms.

CONDUCTING LAYERS FOR RESISTORS AND SURFACE LEAKAGE

Electrically conducting glasses have been used for preparing high ohmic resistors and anti-static coatings on insulators. The conducting layer may be produced by reducing the surface of bulk glass or by using a frit of the required material spread over a surface. Odarenko (1946) reported that the Rosenthal Porcelain Company in Germany produced during the last war a glass resistance coating by mixing graphite in various proportions with a ground glass of special composition and low melting point. The mixture was sprayed on to porcelain and fused at about 800°–900°c. The resistors covered a range of 50–100 Ω/square to 150–200 10^6 Ω/square. It was believed that the graphite particles in the glass made multi-contacts in the same way as addition of graphite to a plastics resin produces a conducting coating. One cannot neglect a possible reaction between certain oxides in the glass and the graphite which releases gas and free metal.

Forrest (1947) has made resistance thermometers with a large temperature coefficient from semiconducting glazes developed by Vose (1943). The glazes were made by Taylor Tunnicliffe from 40% Fe_2O_3 with other ceramic materials. It is of interest to note here that the writer has vacuum evaporated semiconducting films of partially reduced Fe_2O_3 films on to glass for anti-static coatings; unlike thin metal films they resist complete oxidation and loss of conduction in the atmosphere. Also, whilst it may be necessary to heat treat a glass in hydrogen to produce free metal atoms for conduction, it is usually possible to vacuum evaporate a mixture of metal oxides and silica and by control of the vacuum conditions produce a reduced layer directly.

Blodgett (1951) has studied the hydrogen treatment of an X-ray shield glass containing by weight 61% PbO; 8% BaO; 31% SiO_2. The glass was either used in plate form or ground in a ball mill and sprayed in a suspension of alcohol and water on to other bodies. Coatings of the lead oxide glass were usable on the inner walls of high voltage electronic devices, such as X-ray tubes, for grading the potential and leaking away electrical charges. The coatings of the reduced lead silicate glass had a surface resistivity of about 10^9–10^{10} Ω/square and withstood in vacuum voltages of 150 kV across 1·5 in.

PREPARATION OF REDUCED LEAD OXIDE GLASS

Silica film. Blodgett found that the highest conductivities were obtained when the X-ray glass had a ground surface and that the reduced layer penetrated the glass to a depth of about one micron. If a thin film of silica was developed on the glass by leaching out the lead oxide with acid then the subsequently reduced layer which formed under the silica film was more stable. Blodgett states that:

'silica served the following four purposes:

(1) It was found by experiment that the conductivities developed by hydrogen treatment were more reproducible when the glass had a silica film than when the film was lacking. This was attributed mainly to the fact that with a silica film the layer of glass that was treated in hydrogen was situated underneath the film and was, therefore, an integral part of the bulk of the glass. In the case of plates which had no silica film the surface was always somewhat modified by the mechanical processes of grinding and polishing; also, it was possible for particles of Carborundum from the grinding wheel to become lodged in the surface.

(2) The acid which formed the silica film by leaching lead oxide out of the surface also served to leach out any foreign substances soluble in dilute acid which were ground into the surface.

(3) A silica film affords good protection to the conducting layer. The layer developed by hydrogen treatment is very thin, and if there is no silica film, lies immediately at the surface of the glass, where it may easily be injured. Also if there is no silica film the conducting layer is readily attacked by damp air, especially if the air is hot. With a silica film on the surface, hot hydrogen penetrates the film readily and develops conductivity in the glass underneath, but water vapour subsequently is hindered from reaching the conducting layer, especially if the silica is hardened by being taken to a high temperature at the end of the hydrogen treatment.

(4) The film minimizes the evaporation of reduced lead from the glass. All the hydrogen treatments are carried out at temperatures above the melting point of lead.'

The silica film was about 1000 Å thick, *i.e.* it reduced the reflection of the glass for red light. The film was produced by soaking the glass in a dilute acid solution (1% HCl) at 35°c for 3 min. The acid treated glass was then heated in an oven to sinter the silica; heat treatment at 100°c for 10 min was sufficient to compact the film and prevent further acid attack.

ELECTRICAL PROPERTIES

The silica surface layer did not raise the contact resistance when the resistance of the underlying reduced layer was measured. Apart from the high value of resistivity to be measured the silica film undoubtedly contained holes and adsorbed water which raised its conductivity. (Silica films of comparable thickness $\simeq 1000$ Å prepared by evaporating silicon monoxide in vacuum will withstand a stress of about 12 V if free of pinholes.)

PROPERTIES OF REDUCED LEAD SILICATE GLASS

Blodgett (1951) found that to develop conductivity in the lead silicate glass the glass had to be treated in hydrogen first at a low temperature and then at a high temperature. When low temperature treatment was omitted by heating the glass in oxygen to a high temperature before admitting hydrogen, the reduced plate did not become conducting and a subsequent treatment could not be found which would render it conducting. This result agrees with the theory advanced earlier that at high temperatures the metal atoms freed by the reduction coalesce into isolated droplets. Given in

Fig. 9.19 are two curves for glasses reduced in one and two stages. Curve (a) is for samples treated in hydrogen at various initial temperatures T_1 for 16 hours and then slowly raised to 520°c, and curve (b) for samples heated to T_1 in nitrogen and from T_1 to 520°c in hydrogen.

The curves show that the most favourable conditions for promoting conductivity was to treat the glass in hydrogen for some 16 hours at 350°c. This was also the lowest reducing temperature at which the surface layers of the glass became optically absorbing giving an optical transmission of 40% through one specimen surface. At this stage the glass was almost non-conducting. In the second stage the plate was slowly heated in hydrogen to 520°c, giving an ultimate resistance of about 480×10^6 Ω/square.

The reduced layers discussed above were all protected by optical interference films of silica. Blodgett determined the thickness of the conducting layer by dissolving away the silica coating with hydrofluoric acid making the assumption that the dissolution rate of the reduced layer would be equal to that of the silica network. A sintered layer dissolved at a rate of 10 Å/min at 25°c in a solution of one part of HF. in 1000 parts of water.

If one plots the change in the conductivity χ_s of the reduced film as a function of the time of acid erosion then the slope $d\chi_s/dt$ would be a negative constant providing the volume conductivity is constant throughout the layer. If, however, χ_v varies within the layer, then its value at a given depth can be found by combining the relations for the rates of change of conductivity and thickness, *i.e.*

$$\frac{d\chi_s}{dt} \cdot \frac{dt}{dl} = \frac{d\chi_s}{dl}$$

which corresponds to the decrease in the conductivity for a small decrease in thickness. It can be seen from the relations on p. 449 that $d\chi_s/dl$ is equal to the volume conductivity χ_v at a given depth in the reduced layer. By this method Blodgett found that the volume conductivity of the best conducting layer was $1 \cdot 2 \times 10^{-3}$ Ω^{-1} cm^{-1} (or $\rho_v = 830$ Ω cm).

The volume conductivity is given by the equation

$$\chi_v = nev$$

where n is the number of conducting electrons per cubic centimetre, e the charge on the electron ($1 \cdot 6 \times 10^{-19}$ coulomb), and v the mobility of an electron estimated by Blodgett to be about 1 cm^2 sec^{-1} V^{-1}. From the foregoing it was estimated that $n = 10^{16}$ electrons/cm^3. The number of lead atoms in the unreduced glass was about $8 \cdot 3 \times 10^{21}$ atoms/c.c. If each reduced lead atom could contribute an electron to the semiconduction then only about one millionth of all the lead atoms participated in the conduction. The remaining lead atoms coalesced and formed droplets which made the glass appear black but did not add to the conduction.

Temperature variation of resistance. The reduced lead silicate glass is a semiconductor and it follows from equation (1) on p. 450 that a plot of log ρ as a function of $1/T$ should produce a straight curve with a slope

$$\frac{\mathrm{d} \ln \rho}{\mathrm{d}\,(1/T)} = \frac{Q}{k}$$

Blodgett found that Q the activation energy was not constant having values of 0·065 eV in the range 25°–100°c and 0·11 eV in the range 335°–440°c. Forrest (1947) has studied the temperature variation of resistance of the semiconducting glazes containing about 40% Fe$_2$O$_3$ and 60% ceramic materials. He obtained a linear relation between log ρ and $1/T$ in the range 0°–150°c with $Q \simeq 0 \cdot 25$ eV.

The thermal e.m.f. of a conducting sample of lead silicate glass was 10 μV/°c and the direction of the current flow showed that it was an n-type conductor.

The ratio of the hot-to-cold resistance of the reduced lead silicate glass remained constant when determined over a range of cold resistivities. Presented in Table 9.5 are values of ρ_s for a

Table 9.5

Measurements of the ratio of hot-to-cold resistance
of reduced lead silicate glass
(*After Blodgett, 1951*)

ρ_s at 25°c (10^6 Ω/*square*)	ρ_s at 280°c (10^6 Ω/*square*)	*Ratio*
800	193	0·241
1545	372·5	0·241
2480	600	0·242
6850	1732	0·253

reduced plate measured at 25° and 280°c. The resistivity of the plate at ambient temperature was raised after each test by reoxidizing the reduced lead by heating the glass in hot water or damp air.

The table shows that the resistance ratio remained constant when the cold resistance was increased 8·6 times from 800 to 6850 $M\Omega$/square. Thus the activation energy for electronic conduction must be independent of the number of atoms donating electrons. This is a property of semiconductors whose concentration of conduction sites is insufficient for the electron centres to react with each other.

6. SURFACE EFFECTS ARISING FROM BOMBARD-MENT AND IRRADIATION

We are concerned here with effects arising from the bombardment of glass by electrons and positive ions and from irradiation with u.v. light. Many of the phenomena discussed are characteristic of dielectric materials generally and not specific to glass alone. For this reason most attention has been given to practical data resulting from investigations using silicate glasses.

Symbols. For easy reference the symbols to be used are set out below although for convenience they have also been defined in their related sections

i_p Primary electron current incident on a specimen.

i_t Electron current transmitted through a specimen.

i_s Secondary electron current emitted from a specimen.

$\delta = i_s/i_p$ Secondary electron emission coefficient.

eV_p Primary electron energy in electron volts.

V_a Anode potential of primary electron source.

V_s Potential of target specimen.

V_c Potential of secondary electron collector with respect to target, see fig. 9.20.

V_1 First crossover potential $\delta = 1$.

V_2 Second crossover potential $\delta = 1$.

V_{max} Value of V_s corresponding to δ_{max}.

i_i Initial photo-electric current.

i_{sat} Saturated photo-electric current passed after initial current decays.

γ_p Quantum coefficient of the photo-electric effect, *i.e.* number of electrons emitted per incident photon.

V_g Electrical breakdown voltage in the gas space between two metal electrodes covered with insulating material.

SECONDARY ELECTRON EMISSION

General. Information on the secondary electron emission characteristics of glass is limited and often indefinite as the reader will find
if he consults the comprehensive work by Bruining (1954) on
secondary electron properties of materials. Stevels (1957) has commented that in view of the large amount of electronic apparatus
using glass envelopes and insulators it is surprising that so little

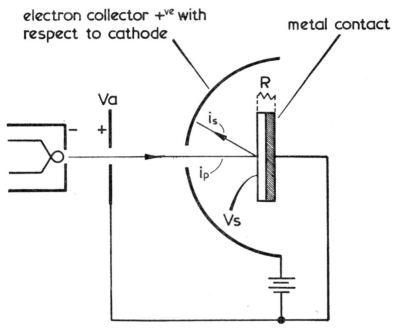

FIG. 9.20   SCHEMATIC ARRANGEMENT OF SIMPLE ELECTRON SOURCE AND
TARGET FOR SECONDARY ELECTRON EMISSION STUDIES

work has been done in determining their secondary electron emission characteristics. Also so casual have many physicists become
in referring to glass as if the chemical composition was not important that the writer had great difficulty when preparing this section
in ascertaining the types of glass that had been studied!

Most insulators when bombarded with electrons release secondary electrons and the ratio δ of the number of secondary electrons
emitted to the number of incident electrons rises to a maximum
and then decreases as the energy of the primary electrons is

32

increased as shown in Fig. 9.21. It should be noted that δ refers here to all of the secondary electrons emitted from a plane within a solid angle 2π, *i.e.* δ is an integrated value. With most materials δ and Vmax rise as the incident angle of the primaries increases because for a given penetration of the primary electrons the secondaries are liberated nearer to the surface. δ does not appear to have been measured for glass as an angular function of either the incident or secondary electrons.† The applied potentials at which the energy of the primary electrons coincide with $\delta = 1$ are known as the first and second *crossover potentials*, *i.e.* V_1 and V_2 respectively. These quantities are of importance in electronics because they determine the potential assumed by glass insulators and envelopes.

To understand how a dielectric target attains a potential depending on the bombardment conditions we shall consider the simple system shown in Fig. 9.20 with the potential of the secondary electron collector V_c equal to that of the accelerating anode V_a. The incident electrons are accelerated by an anode and reach an energy eV_a. Due to leakage a resistance will exist between the target and the anode designated R. Obviously if $R = 0$ then the target is at the anode potential, *i.e.* $V_a = V_s$. If R has a high value or tends to infinity and V_a is between the first and second crossover potentials then V_s will rise until the retarding field $V_s - V_a$ is sufficient to prevent the low energy secondaries from escaping, under these conditions $V_a < V_s < V_2$. When $V_1 < V_a < V_2$ and $R \to \infty$ and the retarding field $V_s - V_a$ is small then V_s approaches V_2. Likewise if the potential of the secondary collector is biased positive with respect to the target contact V_a then this will oppose the retarding potential $V_s - V_a$ and $V_s \nrightarrow V_2$.

When $V_a > V_2$ and $R = \infty$ then V_s will stick at the second crossover potential.

Thus we can say that for electron energies above the first or second crossover potentials the target cannot attain a potential above V_2 and when R is a finite amount the target potential will tend to stick near to V_a, providing $V_a < V_2$.

When the energy of the incident electrons eV_a is below that of the first crossover value and $R = \infty$ then the specimen will accumu-

---

† Since this was written the writer has found that Matskevich (1957) has reported that the fraction of a primary electron beam *directly* reflected from fused silica is about 0·32 for primary energies of 0 to 5 kV when the incidence beam is normal to the surface. Raising the incidence to 70° gradually increases the *reflection* factor to about 0·45.

late a negative charge until it reaches the cathode potential and electron bombardment ceases.

Second crossover potential. The physical meaning of the second crossover potential is not clear. The theory has been advanced that

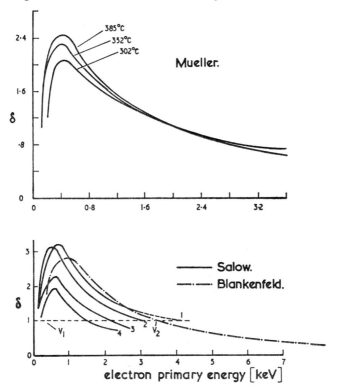

1. 'Gundelachglas' blown from molten glass, 5μ thick.
3. Hard glass blown from molten glass, 15μ thick.

2. 'Gundelachglas' cleaned with HF. acid and distilled water, 30μ thick.
4. Cover glass cleaned with HF acid and distilled water, 150μ thick.

FIG. 9.21 SECONDARY ELECTRON EMISSION OF DIFFERENT GLASSES AT ROOM TEMPERATURE (*After Salow, 1940, Mueller, 1945, and Blankenfeld, 1951*)

the secondary electron emission rises with the electron energy until the incident electrons penetrate so deeply that the slow secondary electrons cannot escape. However, as already shown if $\delta > 1$ and the leakage resistance to the bombarded surface is high, then the insulator will develop a charge which sets up a retarding field and this limits the secondary current so that it almost equals that of the incident electrons. A problem arising in the measurement of δ as a function of the incident electron energy for insulators such as glass is ensuring that the bombarded insulator does not become charged. This necessitates the use of thin insulating layers mounted on conducting electrodes to ensure charge leakage. Obviously, if the insulator is too thin then there is a risk that the incident electrons will sufficiently penetrate the insulator to strike the backing layer. One may also measure δ with very small incident currents so that when $i_p \rightarrow 0$ δ approaches its true value. Holland and Laurenson (1963) have found that δ-curves for 1000 Å thick films of silicon monoxide evaporated on titanium film electrodes showed hysterisis due to surface charging when V_a was raised and lowered from 0 to 2 kV with a primary current of $\simeq 100\mu A/cm^2$.

Obviously if δ was determined under conditions where the specimen became charged and $V_c = V_a$ then this could give an apparent crossover potential. Thus, if V_a was between the two crossover values and $R \rightarrow \infty$ then $V_a < V_s < V_2$, as described above, but V_a could be erroneously taken as the second crossover potential.

McFarlane (1957) has shown that the position of the second crossover potential can be varied. He found that magnesium oxide coated luminescent screens and screens containing a large quantity of potassium silicate had high second crossover potentials (> 18 kV). There was no reason why these screens should prevent electron penetration or permit more secondaries to escape and he concluded that some other effect was occurring, such as a variation in the potential of the second crossover with the applied electric field strength, *i.e.* the potential difference between V_a and V_s. Thus there is evidence that δ itself is strongly field dependent and this effect could be influenced in turn by the structure of the target surface.

Measurement. Salow (1940) measured the secondary electron emission of glass and silica and noted that the cleaning of the glass and preparation of the surface had an important effect on the measured value of δ. Shown in Fig. 9.21 are characteristic curves of δ as a function of the energy of the incident electrons for different glasses and surface treatments. Salow prevented the specimen from becoming charged by bombarding it with low velocity electrons so that it was kept at cathode potential V_c. A second electron source was used for measurement of secondary emission and the primary electrode had a potential $V_a - V_c$. The second source of electrons was modulated to distinguish between the two secondary currents.

Blankenfeld (1951) has also measured δ as a function of the energy of incident electrons over a wide range of values and his results are plotted in Fig. 9.21. Blankenfeld used as a target glass foil cut from a bubble blown at the end of a heated glass tube. The glass foil was coated with 'Aquadag' so that good contact was made with a metal backing electrode. When thick glass foils were used the surface of the glass sometimes became charged affecting the measurements. The surface charge was leaked to the backing plate with thin foils but equally care was required to ensure that electrons were not reflected by the backing electrode due to penetration of primary electrons. Shown in Table 9.6 are values for the

Table 9.6
Secondary electron characteristics of silica and glass
(*After Salow, 1940*)

Material	V_1 $\delta = 1$	V_2 $\delta = 1$	V_{max}	δ_{max}	Surface preparation
Silica	30	2300	400	2·1	HF-acid and distilled water
Silica	< 50	3800	440	2·9	Heated to 1200°c in air
Cover glass	< 60	1700	330	1·9	HF-acid and distilled water
'Gundelach' glass	—	4000†	440	3·1	Blown from molten glass
'Gundelach' glass	—	3500	400	3·15	HF-acid and distilled water
Hard glass	< 40	2300	340	2·3	Blown from molten glass
Mica	30	3200	380	2·3	Cleavage
Mica	30	3500†	380	2·5	Cleavage

† Extrapolated.

first and second crossover potentials and the maximum value of δ together with the corresponding potential V_{max} as measured by Salow. It is apparent that the mode of surface preparation is as important as the glass composition in determining the emission characteristics.

Mueller (1945) has measured δ as a function of the energy of the primary electrons for 'Chemical Pyrex'. The glass was heated to raise the conductivity and remove the surface charge. His results are plotted in Fig. 9.21. For primary accelerating voltages above 3 kV δ fell from 0·82 to 0·41 at 10 kV. The variations between the curves in Fig. 9.21 are attributed to changes in the glass resistivity and not to temperature dependence of the yield.

Dependence on Temperature. Blankenfeld has measured the secondary electron emission coefficient as a function of temperature of foils blown from glass tube. His results are given in Fig. 9.22 and show that until a temperature above 450°c is reached δ for a given electron energy is almost constant. The fact that δ was not found to be temperature dependent indicates that the glass did not develop a surface charge. Otherwise heating the glass would have increased the leakage conductance thereby altering the surface potential and

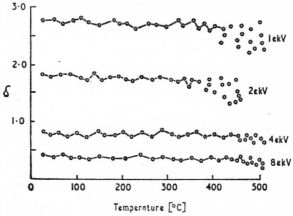

FIG. 9.22 SECONDARY ELECTRON EMISSION OF GLASS AS A FUNCTION OF TEMPERATURE (*After Blankenfeld*, 1940)

the energy of the impinging electrons. Observation of the photoelectric effect using thick glass specimens shows that borosilicate glass develops a surface charge at room temperature whereas similar specimens of soda-lime glass may remain uncharged because of their higher volume conductivity. One would therefore expect that δ would show less dependence on temperature for soda-lime glass because of its higher conductivity at normal temperature. The actual glass used by Blankenfeld is unknown. Mueller found that the secondary yield of chemical Pyrex measured with $V_p = 400$ V was $2 \cdot 3 \pm 1\%$ when measured over a temperature range 240°–420°c.

Surface finish. Gentry *et al.* (1955) have reported that the glass envelopes of electronic valves may have a secondary emission coefficient which exceeds unity at electron energies above 100 eV, so that a bombarded surface acquires a positive charge. They claim that if the glass surface is roughened by sand blasting the secondary electron emission can be made less than unity and that δ is a function of the surface roughness rather than of the chemical composition of the glass, *i.e.* at least for all the glasses commonly used in the manufacture of electron discharge devices. Usually soda-lime silicate glasses are used in these applications.

Secondary electrons released from smooth metal surfaces are emitted at angles substantially independent of the incidence angle of the electron beam and the emission approximately follows a cosine law. (See, for example, Jonker (1957) who used polycrystalline and single crystal metal targets and found that secondary electrons emitted with different energies, from 1·5 to 100 eV, all had an approximate cosine distribution.)

If the emission characteristics of glass are similar to those of metals then the surface roughening would result in a large fraction of the secondary electrons striking the glass surface. If, as would be expected, a large proportion of the secondary electrons striking the glass had energies corresponding to $\delta < 1$, then roughening would result in a decrease in the net emission and the surface would become negative.

The glass envelopes of Bayard–Alpert ionization gauges used for measuring gas pressure in the *ultra*-high vacuum range $10^{-7} - 10^{-10}$ torr become negative when exposed to electron bombardment and attract positive gas-ions. An ionization gauge can therefore be used as an ion-pump (see Alpert 1953). Such gauges are usually made of borosilicate (Pyrex type) glass and are operated with anode voltages of about 140 V. Leck and Carter (1958) have found that Bayard–Alpert gauges exhibit two different sensitivies (*i.e.* ratio of ion current to gas pressure at constant electron current) and attributed this to the glass envelope assuming either a positive or negative potential. When the envelope was positive sorption of positive ions could not occur and the high secondary electron emission coefficient resulted in an electron current flowing to the anode electrode which could not be separated from the electron ionizing current.

Leck and Carter believed that the glass initially had a value of $\delta > 1$ and this was reduced to $\delta < 1$ when the glass had been used for several hours or repeatedly baked *in vacuo*. Thus the wall potential changed from being initially positive, *i.e.* $V_s \simeq V_a$, to zero with respect to the cathode. Leck and Carter suggest that baking the glass at 500°c *in vacuo* produces a clean surface with a low value of δ. It is just as possible that the heat treatment altered the concentration of alkali atoms in the glass surface as these are a liberal source of secondary electrons. Also some of the work was done with oil diffusion pumps and decomposed hydrocarbon layers could have formed on the glass surface. Redhead † has stated that he has found that the potential of the envelope of Bayard–Alpert gauge may vary but is always negative with respect to the anode electron collector.

Obviously much more detailed work is required in measuring δ for different glasses with and without surface films of, for example, material evaporated from the cathode electrode or adsorbed from the vacuum atmosphere.

ELECTRON TRANSMISSION BY THIN GLASS FILMS

A current may flow in a dielectric many times greater than that of a primary electron beam. Pensak (1949) observed currents in silica films a hundred times larger than the primary beam current and proportional to the energy absorbed from the primary beam. He believed primary electrons liberated electrons in proportion to their energy. Conduction in the film occurs by holes or electrons depending on the sign of the potential applied to the surface electrodes.

The transmission of electrons by thin films of Pyrex glass and other substances has been studied by Spear (1955). The glass films were about 1 μ thick and taken from blown bulbs. The glass films were sandwiched between evaporated aluminium electrodes of about 30 Å thickness and as the electron energy range of the specimens were about 10 keV the error in determining the transmitted current due to absorption in the electrodes was negligible. In the experiments discussed below the two aluminium electrodes were at the same potential so that the penetrating electrons entered a field free space.

We shall term here the incident electron current i_p and the transmitted current i_t and the current flowing through the first and

---

† Reported during a discussion at the American Vacuum Society Symposium, 1960.

second aluminium electrodes i_T and i_B respectively. Thus we have the following arrangement

$$
\begin{array}{ccc}
i_T & & i_B \\
\uparrow & & \uparrow \\
i_p \rightarrow |\,\text{Al}\,| \quad \text{Pyrex} & |\,\text{Al}\,| \rightarrow i_t
\end{array}
$$

Spear found that the loss of velocity by electrons in their passage through thin Pyrex films approximately followed the Thomson–Whiddington law. This relation in terms of the incident electron energy† V_p and the energy V_x which electrons have at a depth x in the film is

$$V_p^2 - V_x^2 = b\rho x$$

where ρ is the density. By plotting i_t/i_p as a function of V_p and extrapolating the linear part of the curve to $i_t/i_p = 0$ it was possible to obtain a value $V_p = V_0$. Some electrons pass through the foil for energies below V_0, but V_0 was defined as the most probable threshold energy above which incident electrons pass through the film. When $V_p = V_0$ then $V_x = 0$ if $x = d$ the film thickness and thus $b = V_0^2/m$, where m is a mass per unit area of the film.

Given in Table 9.7 are values of V_0 and b taken from Spear's

Table 9.7

Equation constants for Thomson–Whiddington law
applied to Pyrex films
(*After Spear, 1955*)

m (mg cm^{-2})	V_0 (keV)	V_0' (keV)	b† (V^2 g^{-1} cm^2)	$V_0'^2/m$ (V^2 g^{-1} cm^2)	x'/d
0·815	22·5	15·9	$6·2 \times 10^{11}$	$3·1 \times 10^{11}$	0·50
0·15	9·65	6·75	$6·2 \times 10^{11}$	$3·1 \times 10^{11}$	0·50
0·18	10·5	7·56	$6·1 \times 10^{11}$	$3·2 \times 10^{11}$	0·52

† For metals $b \simeq 4 \times 10^{11} V^2$ g^{-1} cm^2.
V_0 probable threshold energy for direct transmission of incident electrons through a film of thickness d.
V_0' threshold energy for secondary current flow to outer electrode when incident electrons penetrate distance x'.

results for Pyrex films of different thickness. If one plots i_B/i_p against V_p and extrapolates the linear part of the curve to $i_B/i_p = 0$

† V_p and V_x are used here to imply electron volts, *i.e.* energy terms.

then the corresponding electron energy V_0' is lower than that of V_0 which shows that current begins to flow to the second electrode before complete penetration has taken place. If we set $V_0' = V_p$, *i.e.* the bombarding electron energy in the Thomson–Whiddington relation, then the primary electrons at some depth x' will have zero energy, *i.e.* $V_x' = 0$ so that $V_0'^2/b\rho = x'$. We know, however, that $V_p = V_0$ is the most probable energy for the onset of direct transmission of electrons through the film. If the film has a thickness d then we have $V_0^2/d = b\rho$ so that $x'/d = (V_0'/V_0)^2$. From measurement of the electron energies V_0' and V_0 for current to flow to the second electrode and be transmitted respectively, one can find the corresponding x'/d values. These have been determined by Spear and are given in Table 9.7. The results show that a steady current of slow electrons flows in a bombarded dielectric film if the primary beam has penetrated to about half the depth of the specimen.

Rohatgi (1957) has bombarded borosilicate glass with electrons and measured the current flow as a function of the potential across the glass. A characteristic space charge relation was obtained from which an electron mobility of about 5×10^{-5} $cm^2V^{-1}sec^{-1}$ was estimated.

PHOTOELECTRIC EFFECT

The photoemission of electrons from borosilicate and soda-lime silicate glasses has been studied by Rohatgi (1957). The glass samples were exposed in vacuum to u.v. light from a quartz mercury lamp and with light from glow discharges in argon and neon. The test glasses were 10 cm^2 in area and 0·35 cm thick. They were chemically cleaned and a gold film was vacuum evaporated on to one surface in which a platinum electrode had previously been embedded. The metallic coating was covered with a second glass and the platinum wire led out of the vessel through a glass tube. This ensured that scattered photons could not reach the metal surfaces.

Borosilicate specimens. The borosilicate (Pyrex) specimens were mounted in a silvered glass tube with a quartz window as shown in Fig. 9.23. The specimens were baked at 250°c *in vacuo* to free them from adsorbed films. Using a mercury diffusion pump and liquid nitrogen trap the vacuum pressure was reduced to 10^{-6} torr.

When the u.v. light striking the glass specimen was filtered by passing it through a glass slide the photoelectric current was reduced to zero. Since the glass slide only transmitted u.v. light above about 3300 Å it was clear that a wavelength of 2537 Å for silica was photoelectrically active whereas 3300 Å was not.

Shown in Fig. 9.24 are characteristic curves of the photoelectric current as a function of time with constant u.v. light intensity and different potentials applied to the electron collector. It can be seen that on irradiation of the specimen the current rises rapidly and then more slowly to a maximum value (termed here initial current i_i). The current then drops exponentially to a value i_{sat},

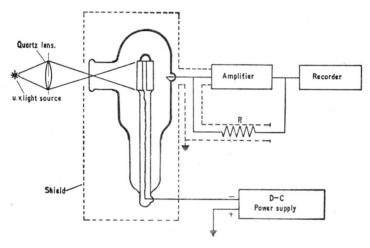

FIG. 9.23 PHOTOELECTRIC CURRENT MEASURING APPARATUS USED BY ROHATGI (1957)

the magnitude of which increases as the applied potential on the collector increases, whereas i_i is almost independent of the potential. This is clearly shown in Fig. 9.25 relating i_i and i_{sat} to the collector potential.

Rohatgi has explained the curves in Figs. 9.24 and 9.25 as follows. Pyrex glass contains some 10^{13} Na atoms per cm^2 in a glass surface layer 10 Å deep and these atoms undergo photoelectric ionization on irradiation by u.v. light of $\lambda = 2437$ Å. The energy of the photons corresponds to 4·9 V which is just below the ionization potential 5·1 V of isolated Na atoms and obviously exceeds that of the same atoms in the glass. The liberated electrons are removed by the collector leaving conducting Na^+ ions in the glass. As the photoelectron current i_1 flows across the vacuum space the electrical resistivity of the glass impedes its flow and the glass attains a positive potential almost equal to that applied to the collector.

The current flow of Na$^+$ ions in the glass rises with increase of the potential across the glass. (According to Kraus and Darby (1922) the mobilities of alkali ions in glass is about 10^{-7} cm^2 V^{-1}sec^{-1} and the drift velocity even at 1000 V/cm is quite low.) Rohatgi found that the Na$^+$ ions apparently did not leave the glass and enter the gold backing film. He presumed that they accumulated at the cathode interface building up a space charge

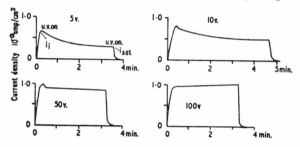

FIG. 9.24 VARIATION IN PHOTOELECTRIC CURRENT WITH TIME OF U.V. IRRADIATION. SPECIMEN MADE OF PYREX GLASS. THE ELECTRON COLLECTOR VOLTAGE IS GIVEN ON EACH CURVE (*After Rohatgi*, 1957)

which could finally reduce the field within the glass to zero thereby terminating current flow.

As the curves in Figs. 9.24 and 9.25 show, the saturated current, depending on the light intensity, is lower than the initial current for collector potentials below a critical value. The limitation of the saturation current by space charge (or polarization) due to Na$^+$ ion accumulation did not ultimately terminate the current flow. It was believed that the Na$^+$ion space charge was partly neutralized by donation of electrons to the glass from the gold negative electrode. It is shown in the previous section that electrons pass through glass with a mobility several hundred times higher than that of Na$^+$ ions. Polarization due to low ion mobility could be prevented by heating the glass. Thus, at 200°c, the value of i_1 was the same as at room temperature but it did not decay with time.

Photocurrent and light intensity. The initial current which is independent of space charge increases linearly with the intensity of the u.v. light, but the saturation current is not linear at low applied potentials as shown in Fig. 9.26.

It will be appreciated from the previous discussion that the saturation current represents a continuous current flow which is linked by photocurrents from the glass, positive ions in the glass and electrons transferred from the gold electrode to the glass. Rohatgi contends that when the applied field is raised so that the

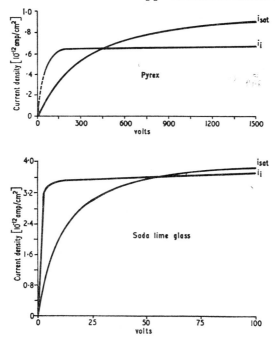

FIG. 9.25 RELATION BETWEEN APPLIED VOLTAGE AND INITIAL AND SATURATED PHOTOELECTRIC CURRENTS FROM PYREX AND SODA-LIME GLASSES WITH CONSTANT U.V. LIGHT INTENSITY (*After Rohatgi*, 1956)

field across the glass increases, the drift velocities of the ions and the electron flow from the gold electrode also increase. Thus when the potential across the glass reaches a certain value the space charge disappears and the saturation current becomes linearly related to the light intensity.

Several experiments were made which established that the dependence of i_{sat} on the light intensity did not arise from optical absorption of radiation with a wavelength above 3300 Å producing internal photoconductivity. Similarly that such transmitted radiation did not release electrons from the Au/glass cathode interface. It was also found that the temperature rise of the specimen due to

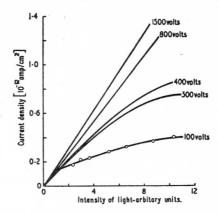

FIG. 9.26 DEPENDENCE OF THE SATURATED PHOTOELECTRIC CURRENT i_{sat} FROM PYREX GLASS ON THE U.V. LIGHT INTENSITY AT DIFFERENT CONSTANT VALUES OF COLLECTOR VOLTAGE (*After Rohatgi*, 1957)

absorption of radiation was sufficiently small to have negligible effect on the ionic conductivity.

Soda-lime glass. If the photoelectric current arises from the superficial alkali atoms then soda-lime glass with about six times the density of sodium atoms of Pyrex glass should give proportionally larger currents. Rohatgi did in fact find that at the same light intensity the current for soda glass was some six times that from Pyrex. His results for soda glass are given in Fig. 9.25.

Quantum efficiency. The quantum efficiency of the photoelectric effect for photons with a wavelength of 2537 Å was determined from measurements of electrons released from the glass surface. The quantum efficiency γ_p is then equal to the number of electrons emitted by an incident photon. The value of γ_p for a clean Pyrex surface *in vacuo* was about $1·06 \times 10^{-4}$ and for soda glass about 6×10^{-4}.

In conclusion, Rohatgi measured values of γ_p for glass exposed to radiation from glow discharges in argon and neon. In these experiments the glass was in the same vessel as that used for the glow discharge. Using Pyrex specimens γ_p was equal to 10^{-3} for the light from the glow discharge ($\lambda \ll 1200$ Å) and γ_p was reduced to 10^{-4} when the radiation passed through a quartz filter. Thus at $\lambda > 2300$ Å $\gamma_p = 10^{-4}$ which agrees with the value given above for Pyrex irradiated by light from a mercury quartz lamp. Rohatgi states that this indicates that the glass specimen was free from adsorbed water at the high gas pressure required for the glow discharge.

PLASMA AUGMENTATION OF SURFACE CONDUCTIVITY

When highly ionized gases are in contact with glass, superficial conductivity over the insulator surface appears to occur. This effect was first reported by Fowler and Sakuntala (1957) who observed that the magnitude of the superficial conductivity appeared to be a function of the ion (presumably electron) concentration in the plasma.

When a flowing hydrogen plasma was passed down a glass tube through a transverse magnetic field the plasma resistances observed using probes was about 1000 Ω but when the probes touched the glass walls the resistance (infinite in the absence of the plasma) was very small. Thus at a plasma concentration of 10^{16} to 10^{17} ions/c.c. the glass resistance was less than 1 Ω. 'Pyrex' showed the effect strongly and 'Vycor' to a less degree.

Fowler and Sakuntala suggest that the induced surface conductivity may explain the leakage of charges of both signs from the walls of normal electrical discharge tubes. They advance the theories that surface conduction is either electron mobility in an adsorbed layer or the filling of the conduction bands of the surface layers with electrons from the plasma as donor.

Muray (1962) bombarded Pyrex (7440) with a high-intensity electron beam and found that the surface became charged without surface conduction by free electrons. He stated that the heat energy released by ions in a plasma recombining on a glass surface could raise the glass conductivity. Also, it would be difficult to distinguish current flowing in a plasma sheath from that on a surface, when using surface electrodes.

ELECTRICAL BREAKDOWN OF GAS SPACE WITH GLASS INSULATORS

Devins (1955) has studied the electrical breakdown in pure nitrogen between two metal electrodes covered with soda-lime glass plates 0·221 cm thick. The breakdown potential V_g of a gas depends on the number of gas atoms encountered by an electron traversing a gap and this in turn is a function of the product of the gas pressure p at constant temperature and the electrode spacing d, *i.e.* $V_g = f(pd)$. Devins found that the breakdown voltage for glass-covered electrodes agreed with that for metal electrodes if allowance was made for the fraction of the applied potential which appeared across the glass insulators due to their electrical capacity. Fig. 9.27 shows the true breakdown voltage V_g calculated from the known capacitive division with the dielectric constant of the glass taken as 8·0. The h.t. supply had a frequency of 60 cycles/sec. The onset of corona

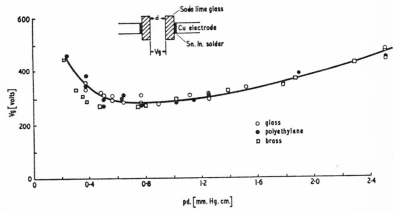

FIG. 9.27   BREAKDOWN VOLTAGE OF GLASS AND OTHER MATERIALS IN NITROGEN AS A FUNCTION OF Pd, WHERE V_g IS THE TRUE BREAKDOWN VOLTAGE CORRECTED FOR CAPACITANCE EFFECT OF INSULATING MATERIALS (*After Devins*, 1955)

was observed by the appearance of short voltage pulses across a 50 000 Ω resistor in series with the test electrodes.

7. DIELECTRIC PROPERTIES OF FOILS AND FILMS

Glass is widely used as an electrical insulator and has been employed on a limited scale as a dielectric in capacitors. We are concerned here with the properties of glass surfaces and thin layers, and we shall consider the effects on the dielectric properties of working with thin films and foils. Thin glass layers prepared by glass blowing can be made down to a few tenths of a micron thick. Vacuum evaporated films of silica and glass can be produced ranging in thickness from a few ångström units up to several microns. The blown films are usually free from defects over a large area, whereas the evaporated films may be slightly porous and contain pinholes. For these reasons the dielectric properties of vacuum evaporated layers can rarely be assumed to be those of thin sections of bulk material.

BREAKDOWN STRENGTH OF GLASS FOILS

Electrical breakdown of silicate glass arises as shown by Joffé *et al.* (1927) from three principal causes which depend on the thickness and temperature of the insulator as follows:

(1) At high temperature where the ions are mobile breakdown is due to a continued growth in the ion current as the passage of current produces heat. Such a failure depending on the Na^+ ion content occurs at temperatures above about 150°c with field strengths of 10^4–10^5 V/cm and is termed here *thermal* breakdown.

(2) At low temperature, *i.e.* about ambient, ionization by impact produces breakdown when the maximum velocity v_0 of an ion satisfies the condition $\frac{1}{2}mv_0^2 = ep$, where p is the ionizing potential. The field strength for dielectric failure is almost 10^6 V/cm and the region is termed *disruptive* breakdown.

(3) When the insulator is so thin that the number of ionizations are too small for an avalanche to develop then breakdown occurs probably by the field pulling out ions. This region is reached with glass films less than 0·2 μ thick with breakdown occurring at about 10^8 V/cm. We shall term this region *field* breakdown.

It is possible to develop a layer on a glass surface which is depleted of ions, *e.g.* due to chemical corrosion and nearly all of the applied potential may be dropped across this zone. The field reached in this layer may be hundreds of times greater than that existing in the more conducting and homogeneous material.

Moon and Norcross (1930) have found that there is a temperature region between that of the disruptive and thermal zones, which is a transition region termed by them *intermediate*.

Thermal, intermediate and disruptive breakdown. An extensive study has been made of the dielectric strength of glass by Moon and

33

Norcross (1930). To avoid edge effects, such as surface conduction and corona, facilitating breakdown, the specimens were either made in the form of spheres with mercury or acidulated water electrodes or in the form of plates immersed in a semiconducting bath. Breakdown was measured with a d.c. supply and it was found that the temperature determined both the magnitude and nature of the dielectric failure. Shown in Fig. 9.28(a) and (b) are the breakdown voltages V for Corning G-1 lead glass (20% PbO) as a function of film thickness d and temperature T respectively. These curves show that the breakdown voltage follows a relation of the type $V = K_1 d$

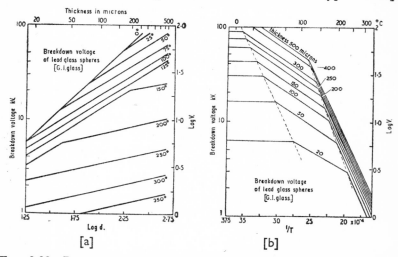

FIG. 9.28   BREAKDOWN STRENGTH OF LEAD OXIDE 'G-1' GLASS SPHERES. (a) AS A FUNCTION OF THICKNESS AND (b) AS A FUNCTION OF RECIPROCAL TEMPERATURE (*After Moon and Norcross*, 1930)

for low temperatures, changing to $V = K_2 d^{2/3}$ at $T > 125°$c and to $V = K_3 d^{0.25}$ at $T > 200°$c.

Thus there are three distinct ranges of breakdown determined by temperature. The first breakdown zone at low temperature is the *disruptive* one, where the glass fails due to electrical overstress without evidence of overheating. At high temperatures the *thermal* breakdown arises from resistance heating due to the ion current. Between these regions is the *intermediate* or transition zone.

The breakdown characteristics of other glasses and of silica were found by Moon and Norcross to be similar to that of the lead glass discussed above. One can specify the performances of the materials tested by the equation

$$V = K_r d^{n_r} (10)^{b_r/T}$$

where T is the absolute temperature, K, n and b are constants determined experimentally and the suffix r denotes the breakdown region 1 – disruptive, 2 – intermediate, 3 – thermal. Listed in Table 9.8 are values of n and b for the three breakdown regions for a range of materials.

Table 9.8

Constants for the electrical breakdown equation applied to three regions of failure
(*After Moon and Norcross, 1930*)

Material	Effect of thickness				Effect of temperature		
	K_1	n_1	n_2	n_3	b_1	b_2	b_3
Fused quartz (non-polar. electrodes)	5000	1·00	0·63	0·50	0	330	2250
Pyrex	4800	1·00	0·70	—	0	715	—
Cover glass	—	—	—	—	—	687	1500
G-1 glass	3100	1·00	0·66	0·25	0	470	1540
Lime glass	4500	1·00	0·63	0·815	0	735	1910
Lime glass (non-polar. electrodes)	4500	1·00	0·63	0·45	0	735	1530
Celluloid	2500	1·00	—	—	0	705	3300
Mica	10 600	1·00	—	—	0	—	—

It should be noted that when the normal electrodes were replaced by non-polarizing electrodes the breakdown strength was reduced in the thermal region. Thus polarization due to Na^+ ion accumulation or depletion at the electrode surfaces reduces the ion-current and raises the dielectric strength.

Given in Table 9.9 are the breakdown voltages and transition temperatures for a range of materials. In the thermal region there is correlation between the alkali content and the breakdown of glass but at normal temperature the soda-lime glass with the highest alkali content has a higher disruptive strength than lead oxide glass. This may be connected with the tendency for semiconduction in lead oxide glasses to arise from excess electrons as discussed on p. 486.

Guyer (1944) has stated that at high temperature when the breakdown of glass is largely of the thermal type dielectric heating becomes cumulative as losses raise the temperature which, in turn,

Table 9.9

Chemical composition and breakdown strength of glass and other materials

(After Moon and Norcross, 1930)

Material	% SiO$_2$	% Na$_2$O +% K$_2$O +% CaO	log ρ$_{25}$	Kilovolts per cm			Transition temperature (°C)	
				Disruptive	Intermediate †	Thermal ‡	T$_1$	T$_2$
Fused quartz	99·8	trace	19·0	5 000	1815	560 §	− 31	270 ‡
Pyrex	80·8	4·5	13·8	4 800	1050	200	− 20	140
G-1 glass (lead glass)	66	13·8	14·9	3 100	1200	102	+ 22	150
Cover glass	—	—	12·7	—	730	60	+ 20	165
Lime glass	69·7	21·0	11·5	4 500	355	32	− 33	217
Celluloid (125 μ)	—	—	—	2 500	420	—	− 10	140
India mica	—	—	16·3	10 600	—	—	+100	—

Note. ρ$_{25}$ is the resistivity at room temperature.
† For 200 μ and 100 degc.
‡ For 200 μ and 300 degc.
§ With non-polarizing electrodes. Ordinary electrodes would probably give a higher breakdown gradient in the thermal region and a greater T$_2$.

increases the dielectric loss. Thus in the thermal region *the breakdown strength of glass decreases as the frequency of the applied voltage rises.*

Electrical breakdown in thin foils. Joffé *et al.* (1927) have made a study of the breakdown mechanism in thin glass foils ranging from 0·02 to 20 μ in thickness. (The nature of the glass was not specified.) Shown in Fig. 9.29 are the electrical field strengths for failure

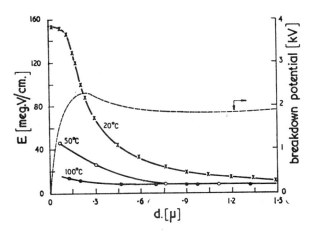

FIG. 9.29   BREAKDOWN STRENGTHS OF THIN GLASS FOILS (*After Joffé et al.,* 1927)

plotted as a function of foil thickness at different constant temperatures. Joffé *et al.* found that for thin foils between 0·3–5 μ the *breakdown potential* was independent of the thickness, but below about 0·2 μ the *field strength* for failure became almost independent of thickness. Thus three zones of breakdown exist as the glass thickness is increased; the first two regions are shown in Fig. 9.29 and the third region in Fig. 9.28.

Theory of disruptive breakdown. Joffé *et al.* have explained the dependence of the breakdown on thickness as follows. Consider an ion traversing the dielectric then its '. . . final velocity v_0 is proportional to the field E, because of Ohm's law,

$$I = nev_0 = neuE \tag{1}$$

n being the number of ions per cm³, I the current per cm², and u the mobility of the ion. The final value of the velocity v_0 is reached in a short distance λ_0 that we may call the *starting distance* of the ion. Some considerations taken from the study of conductivity of dielectrics lead us to the assumption that λ_0, which is small, is large compared with the lattice constant and lies between 10^{-6}–10^{-5} cm.

We now assume that the field E has a value such that v_0 reaches a value v_k satisfying the equation

$$\tfrac{1}{2} m v_k^2 = eP \tag{2}$$

P being the ionization potential of the lattice for which ionization by impact takes place and a new ion is formed. The next ionization at a distance λ_0 gives two new ions and so on. Let us suppose the thickness of the dielectric is $d = z_0 \lambda_0$, then the number of new ions appearing is $2^{z_0} = 2^{d/\lambda_0}$. We suppose now n_0 primary ions per cm³ of the dielectric. Then the number of ions in the whole dielectric is

$$N = n_0 \int_0^d 2^{x/\lambda_0} \, dx = \frac{n_0 \lambda_0}{\log 2} \left(2^{d/\lambda_0} - 1 \right) \tag{3}$$

The average density of electrons n becomes

$$n = \frac{N}{d} = \frac{n_0}{\log 2} \frac{\lambda_0}{d} \left(2^{d/\lambda_0} - 1 \right) \tag{4}$$

If d/λ_0 is large the number of free ions and the current increase in such a way that a breakdown is inevitable. The sufficient condition for a breakdown is expressed by equation (2). The corresponding field E_b (such that $v_0 = v_k$) is given by

$$E_b = \frac{v_k}{u} = \frac{1}{u} \sqrt{\frac{2eP}{m}} \tag{5}$$

(since from equation (1) $E_b = v_k/u$).

In fact a definite potential gradient, taking into account space charges, is the condition for a breakdown independent of the thickness and of the shape of the electrodes.

The case is different if the thickness d of the dielectric is not very great in comparison with λ_0, as, for instance, if $d/\lambda_0 = 10$; $2^{10} \simeq 1000$.

In this case ionization by impact increases the number of ions about a hundredfold and the current increases in the same proportion, but this does not produce important results, for, instead of a current of 10^{-11} amp, we have 10^{-9} amp, which is far too low to produce a breakdown. What are now the conditions for breakdown in thin sheets of dielectrics? We may suppose that this is fixed by a definite current I, and therefore a definite number of ions n is necessary in order to produce a discharge. The condition becomes

$$n_0 \lambda 2^{d/\lambda} = \text{const} \tag{6}$$

or to a sufficient approximation

$$\frac{\log n_0}{\log 2} + \frac{d}{\lambda} = \text{const} \tag{7}$$

The λ in these formulas is not identical with the λ_0 in the preceding ones, where λ_0 is the starting distance necessary to reach the equilibrium velocity v_0. Here λ is the distance required to reach the velocity v_k; λ_0 is therefore the maximum value of λ for the case that $v_0 \leqslant v_k$. . . . in strong fields the value v_k is reached in a distance λ smaller than λ_0.

To a first order of approximation we neglect the loss of energy during the acceleration of the ions. Then the energy of an ion is given by the difference of potential along the distance travelled by the ion. The ionization energy is reached as soon as the corresponding ionizing potential P is passed,

$$\lambda = \frac{P}{E} = \frac{Pd}{V}$$

The condition (7) becomes

$$\frac{\log n_0}{\log 2} + \frac{d}{\lambda} = \frac{\log n_0}{\log 2} + \frac{V}{P} = \text{const} \tag{7}$$

Therefore, for a given n, at constant temperature,

$$V = \text{const}; \qquad Ed = \text{const} \tag{8}$$

Formulas (5) and (8) represent two limiting cases of the general relation between the discharge potential V_b (or the discharge field E_b) and the thickness of the insulator. Formula (5) should hold for thick dielectrics with V_b proportional to d, *i.e.* E_b should be independent of the thickness. This is in keeping with the results of

Moon and Norcross for glass foils of 20–500 μ thick tested at below 125°c. For very thin insulating layers equation (8) indicates that the breakdown potential is independent of thickness whilst E_b is inversely proportional to thickness, which is in agreement with the results of Joffé *et al.* for foils between 0·2–5 μ.

Further evidence for exponential increase in the number of ions by ionization in strong fields was obtained by Joffé *et al.* who measured the current through the dielectric as a function of the field strength. Care was taken to avoid Joule heating of the foils and the current was measured after a short time of applying the potential. The results obtained showed that as the field strength was increased the current first increased linearly, in keeping with Ohm's law, and then finally at high field strengths rose exponentially.

The ionization theory did not explain the breakdown in foils below 0·2 μ thick. Breakdown in this case was attributed to ions being extracted from the dielectric by the field.

More recent work by Keller (1948, 1951, 1952) and Vermeer (1954, 1956) shows that the above treatment neglects the influence of the measurement conditions on the breakdown strength. Keller demonstrated that foils of soda-lime glass of optical interference thickness lost their Joule heat to the electrodes more easily than thick specimens. He also found that the breakdown strength was reduced by the conduction current flowing during application of the pre-breakdown field. Using impulse testing, a higher and linear relation was found between breakdown voltage and thickness. The latter suggests that breakdown was affected by resistance heating of the glass by the pre-breakdown field.

When the glass temperature was varied, the breakdown strength measured at a given field rise time τ remained constant at about 9×10^6 V/cm up to a critical temperature, and then decreased. The critical temperature was lowered by prolonging τ. Thus, for $\tau = 6 \times 10^{-6}$ sec, the field strength began to decrease at 0°c and for $\tau = 10^{-3}$ sec at −100°c. These results show that temperature is not the only factor responsible for lowering breakdown strength. It is possible that pre-breakdown conduction in a glass, if prolonged, drastically alters the field distribution in the glass due to ion migration.

Vermeer investigated borosilicate glass and showed that more consistent breakdown results were obtained after specimens had been etched with hydrofluoric acid or cleaned with hot chromic acid. When the heating of the dielectric by field application was negligible, because of the short duration of the impulse, the breakdown strength was not influenced by the nature of the electrode, *i.e.* metal film or electrolyte. The breakdown strength of the borosilicate glass showed a similar dependence on τ as described above for soda-lime silicate, having a breakdown strength of $9\cdot2 \times 10^6$ V/cm in the constant region *i.e.* up to $100°$c at $\tau = 10^{-5}$ sec.

DIELECTRIC CONSTANTS AND POWER FACTORS OF THIN LAYERS

Before discussing the dielectric constants and power factors of thin glass layers we shall briefly consider the properties of bulk materials. More complete information on the dielectric properties of a range of silicate glasses will be found in the work by Morey (1954).

The *dielectric constant* ϵ of a material is defined by the relation $\epsilon = C/C_v$, where C is the capacitance of a capacitor using the specified material and C_v is the capacitance when the dielectric is vacuum; $\epsilon = 1\cdot0006$ for air at low voltages. The capacity of a conductor can be defined as the ratio of the charge Q placed on the conductor to the potential V arising from the charge, *i.e.* $C = Q/V$.

When an alternating current I flows into a capacitor and charges it to a potential V part of the energy is absorbed by the dielectric. Thus the displacement current of a practical capacitor is not exactly $90°$ out of phase with the e.m.f. and the difference between the current and voltage components is termed *the phase difference*. The component of the current in phase with the e.m.f. is then $I \cos\theta$ and the power loss is $VI \cos\theta$.

Dielectric loss in glass due to electrical conduction losses can be found from the relation for the *power factor*

$$\cos\theta = \frac{\chi_v}{\sqrt{\chi_v^2 + \omega^2\epsilon^2}}$$

where χ_v is the conductivity and $\omega = 2\pi f$ the angular velocity of the alternating field. When $\theta \to 90°$ we may take the power factor as equal to $\tan\delta$ where $\delta = \frac{\pi}{2} - \theta$ is termed the *loss angle*.

When the conductivity arises from ion transport then the conduction losses will decrease as the temperature decreases or the frequency increases. However, it has already been stated at the beginning of this chapter that absorption currents flow in glass as internal changes occur under the electric stress. When the glass is exposed to an alternating field the absorption current is invariably greater than the conduction current because the time of current flow between field reversals is shorter than the duration of the

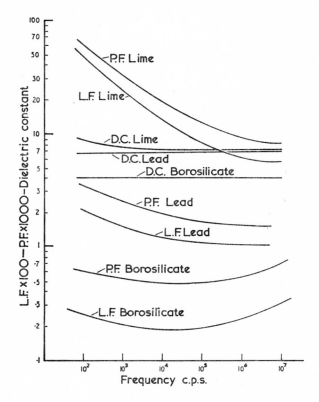

FIG. 9.30 POWER FACTOR (PF), LOSS FACTOR (LF) $\epsilon \tan \delta$ AND DIELECTRIC CONSTANT (DC) AS A FUNCTION OF FREQUENCY OF BOROSILICATE GLASS (CORNING 707), LEAD-OXIDE GLASS (CORNING 001) AND SODA-LIME GLASS (CORNING 008) (*After Guyer*, 1944)

transient absorption current. Thus, to obtain a correct value for the power factor χ_v must be determined over the frequency range used.

The dielectric constant of most glasses decreases as the frequency of the applied field increases, the variation being greatest for high-loss glass and smallest for low-loss glass. Increasing the temperature raises the dielectric constant but the rate of increase is less at high frequencies. Shown in Fig. 9.30 is the power factor and dielectric constant as a function of frequency for three different glasses. Also included in the figure is the *loss factor* which is equal to ϵ tan δ.

Drawn foils. Thin glass foils have been used as the dielectric in capacitors and a review of the work in this field will be found in Shand (1958). Glasses containing large amounts of lead oxide have dielectric constants as high as those of mica. Thus, according to Shand a special Corning glass (8871) has a dielectric constant at 1 Mc/sec and room temperature of 8·4 compared with 7·1 for Muscovite mica. The breakdown strength of the glass is about half that of mica. Shand states that the Corning glass can be drawn down to a thickness of a thousandth of an inch in widths up to two inches. The glass ribbon and thin metal electrodes are stacked alternately and the capacitor formed into a single unit by application of pressure and heat.

Vitreous enamel. Bradford *et al.* (1947) have described a capacitor developed during the last war which used a layer of vitreous enamel in place of mica. The capacitors were prepared by spraying layers of vitreous enamel alternating with layers of conductive silver paste deposited by the silk screen process. The dielectric enamel had a composition in the range 15–25 mol % silica, 3–11 mol % alkali oxides, 5–11 mol % alkali fluorides, 15–25 mol % lead oxide, and 11–30 mol % of other bivalent metal oxides. The coatings were applied to steel conveyor plates which had been precoated with a dilute solution of ethyl cellulose in methanol. After drying, the capacitors were baked to remove some of the organic matter and to free the enamel-silver structure from the steel plate.

The enamel capacitors produced were rated at 500 V and had a capacitance of about 0·01 μF per in^3. Thus, a typical capacitor of size 0·3 in. × 0·3 in. × 0·05 in. had a capacitance of 50 pF. The temperature coefficient of the enamel capacitors had a uniform positive value of about 105 parts per million per degc. The capacitors were usable at temperatures up to 125°c. Leakage resistance was between 10^{10}–10^{12} Ω for capacitances up to a few thousand pF. Capacitor networks were produced on a common base by printing silver conductors in special patterns.

EVAPORATED FILMS

Silicon monoxide. The evaporation of metals and dielectrics under vacuum to condense thin layers on substrates has proved a useful way of preparing films for optical and electrical purposes. It is natural, therefore, that attention should have been given to the evaporation of dielectrics for use in thin film capacitors. It is practical to evaporate films of some inorganic compounds, *e.g.* the halides and certain sulphides, but it is difficult to evaporate most metal oxides (except the rare earth oxides such as cerium dioxide) because they enter into a reaction with the refractory support or dissociate at the low gas pressure used. Silica is difficult to evaporate without dissociation, but fortunately Hass (1950) has shown that films with almost the composition of SiO_2 can be prepared by evaporating a lower oxide of silicon (SiO) which is volatile and sublimates without reacting with a tungsten heating element. For this reason it has become general to use thin SiO-films as the dielectric layers in miniature electronic circuits.

The characteristics of silicon monoxide when vacuum evaporated will be found in the work by Holland (1956), and we shall only briefly consider the subject here. If silicon monoxide is slowly evaporated at a gas pressure of 10^{-4} torr so that oxygen is absorbed by the condensing film then the deposit tends to have the composition of silica. If the evaporation temperature is too high and deposition too rapid then the silicon monoxide may dissociate in the crucible and the condensate inadequately absorb gas during deposition. Usually it takes some 10 min to condense a 1000 Å thick film which resembles silica in its properties. SiO-films† generally have a small absorption in the u.v. region, indicating incomplete oxidation; impurities such as iron in the silicon monoxide will also produce optical absorption.

Evaporated silicon monoxide films have been used for capacitors in layers of several micron thickness with deposition times of an hour or more. However, such thick films *must be annealed during growth*. Holland *et al.* (1960) have found that the SiO-films are under stress and must be annealed at 200°c or above otherwise they may peel from the support. The nature of the stress, *i.e.* compression or tension depends on the conditions of growth. SiO-films

---

† Although the coatings tend to have the composition of silica when slowly deposited we shall use the term silicon monoxide to identify the method of production.

rapidly deposited ($\simeq 10$ Å/sec) at a low pressure ($< 5 \times 10^{-5}$ torr) tend to be deficient in oxygen and are initially under tension which changes to compression as they absorb gas when exposed to the atmosphere. Coatings slowly deposited (2 Å/sec) at a high pressure (10^{-4} torr) are under a compressive stress due to sorption of gas during film growth. Stresses may also be imposed on the film by preferential expansion between the substrate and coating.

The properties of SiO-films in miniature capacitors have been studied by Hoeckelman *et al.* (1957) who termed their product the 'micronic' capacitor. Siddall (1959), working in the writer's laboratory, has made an extensive study of the dielectric properties of SiO-films and their relation to the deposition conditions. The SiO-films were deposited on aluminium electrodes evaporated on to 'Pyrex' glass.

The SiO-films were annealed at 250°c during growth and coated with evaporated aluminium top electrodes. Insulation faults could be removed from the thin film capacitors by operating the capacitor at a voltage above that required for normal working; a process termed 'self-healing'. The evaporated metal electrodes are either oxidized or volatilized in the breakdown region by arcing or resistance heating (Plate 29).

Siddall found that at a given gas pressure (10^{-4} torr) the rate of deposition had a significant effect on the electrical properties of silicon oxide films because, as already established, it influenced the silicon to oxygen ratio in the films. He stated that

'It is necessary to deposit the oxide at less than about 5 Å/sec in order to keep the value of loss angle tangent below 0·02 at 1 kc/sec and 200°c. The use of low deposition rates also increases the value of electric field strength at which repeated breakdown occurs. Breakdown becomes frequent at field strengths between 2×10^5 and 4×10^5 V/cm for films deposited at the rate of 10 Å/sec or above. These figures are improved by a factor of 2 for deposition rates of the order 2 Å/sec.

The dielectric constant of slowly deposited films (2 Å/sec) is less than that of bulk silica due to the lower density of the films. Higher values of dielectric constant at deposition rates of the order 20 Å/sec could be due to the presence of free silicon.

After heating (the capacitors) to 430°c in air for 30 min and cooling again to room temperature, a permanent decrease in capacitance of between 6% and 24% is observed. The values of loss angle tangent are also reduced from values lying between 0·01 and 0·04 to values less than 0·002 measured at 25°c and 1 kc/s.

A capacitance of 0·01 μF/cm^2 of film area can be obtained for dielectrics of thickness about 1400 Å, but such a capacitor will withstand a maximum applied voltage of 12 V d.c. It is necessary to increase the thickness by a factor of between 5 and 10 if a working voltage of 60 V d.c. is needed. The capacitance is then reduced to about 0·001 $\mu F/cm^2$.'

It is difficult to evaporate silicates from a single vapour source without preferential evaporation of the more volatile components. Haenlein and Guenther (1958) have continuously evaporated boro-silicate films for capacitors on to a moving aluminium strip *in vacuo*, using separate vapour sources for the SiO and B_2O_3 components. The loss angle of pure SiO-films was reduced by including B_2O_3 in the deposit and by annealing. At room temperature $\tan \delta = 10^{-2}$ for a pure SiO-film and 10^{-3} for a 75% SiO; B_2O_3-film.

Mixed oxide glass films have been prepared by reactively sputtering from metal cathodes in oxygen. Sinclair and Peters (1963) have prepared films of the lead oxide silicates by sputtering simultaneously from lead and silicon cathodes in oxygen. Williams *et al.* (1963) have prepared aluminosilicate films by reactively sputtering an Al/Si-alloy.

References

Alpert, D., 1953, *J. appl. Phys.*, **24**, 860.

Armi, E. L., 1943, *Phys. Rev.*, **63**, 451.

Bayton, P. L., Rawson, H., and Stanworth, J. E., 1956, *Nature*, **178**, 910.

Blankenfeld, G., 1951, *Ann. Physik*, **9**, 48.

Blodgett, K. B., 1951, *J. Amer. ceram. Soc.*, **34**, 14.

Bradford, C. I., Weller, B. L., and McNeight, S. A., 1947, *Electronics*, **20**, 106.

Bruining, H., 1954, *Physics and Applications of Secondary Electron Emission*, Pergamon Press Ltd., London.

Buff, H., 1859, *Lieb. Ann.*, **110**, 257.

Bush, V., and Connell, L. H., 1922, *J. Franklin Inst.*, **194**, 231.

Le Clerc, P., 1954, *Silicates Industr.*, **19**, 237.

Cohn, E. M., and Guest, P. G., 1944, *U.S. Bur. Mines Inform. Circular*, I.C. 7286.

Curtis, H. L., 1915, *Bull. Bur. Stand.*, **11**, 359.

Devins, J. C., 1955, 'The Second Townsend Coefficient for Insulating Surfaces', Gen. Elect. Res. Rep., 55-RL-1437.

Edge, J., and Oldfield, L. F., 1958, *J. Soc. Glass Technol.*, **42**, 227T.

Edge, J., and Oldfield, L. F., 1960, *Glass Technol.*, **1**, 69.

Faraday, M., 1830, *Phil. Trans.*, part 1, 49.

Faraday, M., 1839-55, 'Experimental Researches in Electricity' (p. 38 of The Everyman Library, J. M. Dent and Co., London).

Forrest, J. S., 1947, *J. sci. Instrum.*, **24**, 211.

Forrest, J. S., 1949, *J. sci. Instrum.*, **26**, 254.

Fowler, R. G., and Sakuntala, M., 1957, *J. chem. Phys.*, **27**, 824.

Fulda, M., 1927, *Sprechsaal.*, **60**, 769, 789, 810, 831 and 853.

Geddes, S., 1936, *J. roy. tech. College*, Glasgow, **3**, 551.

Gentry, C. H. R., Oldfield, R. C., and Horsfall, J. P., Brit. Pat. No. 813, 904.

Green, R. L., and Blodgett, K. B., 1948, *J. Amer. ceram. Soc.*, **31**, 89.

Guyer, E. M., 1933, *J. Amer. ceram. Soc.*, **16**, 607.

Guyer, E. M., 1944, *Proc. Inst. Rad. Eng.*, **32**, 743.

Haenlein, W., and Guenther, K. G., 1958, *Advances in Vacuum Science and Technology, Proc. 1st Inter. Congr. Vac. Tech.*, **2**, 727, Pergamon Press, London.

Hass, G., 1950, *J. Amer. ceram. Soc.*, **33**, 353.

Hoeckelman, R. F., Hoornstra, C. W., and Yang, M., 1957, 'Micronic Capacitor', Wright Air Devel. Center, Tech. Rep. 57–22.

Holland, L., 1956, *The Vacuum Deposition of Thin Films*, Chapman and Hall Ltd., London.

Holland, L., and Laurenson, L., 1963, *2nd Inter. Sympos. on Residual Gases in Electron Tubes and Related High Vacuum Systems.* Milan.

Holland, L., Putner, T., Ball, R., 1960, *Brit. J. appl. Phys.*, **11**, 167.

Hou, C. H., 1938, *Rev. sci. Instrum.*, **9**, 90.

Hull, A. W., 1932, *Physics*, **2**, 409.

Hunter, M. J., Gordon, M. S., Barry, A. J., Hyde, J. F., and Heidenreich, R. D., 1947, *Ind. Engng, Chem.*, **39**, 1389.

Joffé, A., Kurchatov, T., and Sinelinkov, K., 1927, *J. Math. Phys. Mass. Inst. Tech.*, **6**, 133.

Johansson, O. K., and Torok, J. J., 1946, *Proc. Inst. Radio Eng.*, **34**, 296.

Jonker, J. L. H., 1957, *Philips Res. Rep.*, **12**, 249.

Keller, K. J., 1948, *Physica*, **14**, 475.

Keller, K. J., 1951, *Physica*, **17**, 511

Keller, K. J., 1952, *Phys. Rev.*, **86**, 804.

Kohlrausch, F., Heydweiller, Ad., 1894, *Ann. Physik Chem.*, **53**, 209.

Kouznetzov, A. Ya., 1953, *J. Chim. Phys.*, *U.S.S.R.*, **27**, 657.

Kraus, C. A., and Darby, E. H., 1922, *J. Amer. chem. Soc.*, **44**, 2783.

Kubaschewski, O., and Hopkins, B. E., 1953, *Oxidation of Metals and Alloys*, 1st edn., Butterworths Scientific Publications, London.

Leck, J. H., and Carter, G., 1958, Proc. 1st Intern. Congr. Vacuum Techniques, vol. **1**, p. 463, Pergamon Press, London, 1960.

Lindenthal, J. W., 1952, 'On the Application of the Polarization Theory to Ceramic Problems,' Division of Ceramics, Pennsylvania State College (ONR Tech. Rep. 51).

Littleton, J. T., and Morey, G. W., 1933, *The Electrical Properties of Glass*, J. Wiley and Sons, Inc., New York.

McFarlane, A. B., 1957, *Brit. J. appl. Phys.*, **8**, 248.

Matskevich, T. L., 1957, *J. tech. Phys. U.S.S.R.*, **27**, 289 (English transl., *Soviet Phys. Tech. Phys.*, **2**, 255).

Meakins, R. J., 1950, *Austral. J. appl. Sci.*, **1**, 120.

Meakins, R. J., Mulley, J. W., and Churchward, V. R., 1950, *Austral. J. appl. Sci.*, **1**, 113.

Milnes, G. C., and Isard, J. O., 1962, *Phys. Chem. Glasses*, **3**, 157.

Moon, P. H., and Norcross, A. S., 1930, *Elect. Eng.*, **49**, 762.

Morey, G. W., 1954, *The Properties of Glass*, 2nd edn., Reinhold Publishing Corp., New York.

Mott, N. F., and Gurney, R. W., 1948, *Electronic Processes in Ionic Crystals*, Clarendon Press, Oxford.

Mueller, C. W., 1945, *J. appl. Phys.*, **16**, 453; 1946, **17**, 62.

Muray, J. J., 1962, *J. appl. Phys.*, **33**, 1525.

Norton, F. J., 1944, *Gen. Elect. Rev.*, **47**, 6.

Odarenko, T. M., 1946, 'German Developments in Semi-conducting Materials', Rept. C-71.

Pensak, L., 1949, *Phys. Rev.* **75**, 472.

Pike, R. G., and Hubbard, D., 1957, *J. Res. Nat. Bur. Stand.*, **59**, 127.

Poole, H. H., 1921, *Phil. Mag.*, **42**, 488.

Randall, J. T., and Leeds, R. E., 1929, *J. Soc. Glass Techn.*, **13**, 16T.

Rebbeck, J. W., and Ferguson, J. B., 1924, *J. Amer. chem. Soc.*, **46**, 1991.

Robinson, D. M., 1932, *Physics*, **2**, 52.

Rohatgi, V. K., 1957, *J. appl. Phys.*, **28**, 951.

Salow, H., 1940, *Z. techn. Phys.*, **21**, 8.

Schoenborn, H., 1924, *Zeit. Physik*, **22**, 305.

Shand, E. B., 1958, *Glass Engineering Handbook*, p. 341, 2nd edn., McGraw-Hill Book Co. Inc., London.

Siddall, G., 1959, *Vacuum*, **9**, 274.

Sinclair, W. R., and Peters, F. G., 1963, *J. Amer. ceram. Soc.*, **46**, 20.

Spear, W. E., 1955, *Proc. phys. Soc.*, **B, 68**, 991.

Stevels, J. M., 1957, *Handbuch der Physik*, **20**, p. 350.

Sutton, P. M., 1960, 'The Dielectric Properties of Glass', *Progress in Dielectrics*, General Editor J. B. Birks, p. 113, Heywood & Co. Ltd., London.

Vermeer, J., 1954, *Physica*, **20**, 313.

Vermeer, J., 1956, *Physica*, **22**, 1247, 1257, 1269.

Vose, W., 1943, Brit. Pat. No. 577,748.

Warburg, E., 1884, *Wied. Ann.*, **21**, 622.

Warburg, E., 1913, *Ann. d. Physik*, **40**, 327.

Wessel, H., 1958, *Silikattechnik*, **9**, 201.

Williams, J. C., Sinclair, W. R., and Koonce, S. E., 1963, *J. Amer. ceram. Soc.*, **46**, 161.

Author Index

34+

Subject Index